Ring-tailed Lemur
Lemur
Pp.358–375

Pp.376–449

Ruffed Lemurs
Varecia
Pp.450–479

Woolly Lemurs
Avahi
Pp.481–513

Indri, Babakoto
Indri
Pp.578–595

Sifakas, Simponas
Propithecus
Pp.514–577

Aye-aye
Daubentonia
Pp.596–611

Cheirogaleidae

Lepilemuridae

Lemuridae

Indriidae

Daubentoniidae

CONSERVATION INTERNATIONAL
TROPICAL FIELD GUIDE SERIES

LEMURS
of Madagascar
Third Edition

Russell A. Mittermeier, Edward E. Louis Jr.,
Matthew Richardson, Christoph Schwitzer,
Olivier Langrand, Anthony B. Rylands,
Frank Hawkins, Serge Rajaobelina,
Jonah Ratsimbazafy, Rodin Rasoloarison,
Christian Roos, Peter M. Kappeler
& James Mackinnon

Illustrated by
Stephen D. Nash

Photo Editing & Layout by
Paula K. Rylands

CONSERVATION
INTERNATIONAL

2010

Inquiries to the publisher should be directed to the following address:

Russell A. Mittermeier
Editor, CI Tropical Field Guide Series
Conservation International
2011 Crystal Drive, Suite 500
Arlington, VA 22202
USA

ISBN 978-1-934151-23-5

Printed and bound by Panamericana Formas e Impresos S.A., Bogotá, Colombia

10 9 8 7 6 5 4 3 2 1

This book is dedicated
to

**Doris Swanson
(1928–2010)**

of Spokane, Washington and Hayden Lake, Idaho

in recognition of her long-term devotion to
species conservation around the world, and in
particular her very generous support
of lemur conservation projects in Madagascar.

CONTRIBUTORS

As in the previous two editions, this field guide draws extensively on the knowledge of dozens of dedicated primatologists, including many with advanced degrees and others whose personal experience in the field often exceeds that of those formally trained. Many of these experts are active participants in the IUCN/SSC Primate Specialist Group and were involved in the IUCN Red List assessment process for lemurs.

The authors are especially grateful to the following contributors for sharing their special knowledge of lemurs:

Michel Andriambololona
Nicole Volasoa Andriaholinirina
Matthew Banks
Frederick Boltz
Maarten de Wit
Rainer Dolch
Joanna Durbin
Anna T. C. Feistner
Rollande Finoana
Jörg U. Ganzhorn
Nick Garbutt
Fabian Génin
Martine Girard-Lanchec
Laurie Godfrey
Christopher Golden
Steven M. Goodman
Linn Fenna Groeneveld
Colin P. Groves
Andreas Hapke
Michael Hoffman
Steig E. Johnson
Alison Jolly
William L. Jungers
William R. Konstant
David W. Krause
Richard Lewis
Robert D. Martin
Roderic B. Mast
Mireya Mayor
David Meyers
Erik Patel
James Patterson
Ingrid J. Porton
Joyce Powzyk
Clément Joseph Rabarivola
Julien Rabesoa
Ute Radespiel
Olivier Rahanitriniaina
Marlène Rakotomalala

Noro Raminosoa
Fabi Randrianarisoa
Hanta Rasamimanana
Aimé Rasamison
Tovo Rasolofoharivelo
Rabarison Rasolonirina
Felix Ratelolahy
Besoa Ratsisakanana
Gisèle Raveloarinoro
Angelin Razafimanantsoa
Marie Razafindrasolo
Yves Rumpler
Derek Schuurman
Takayo Soma
Viviana Sorrentino
Eleanor Sterling
Ian Tattersall
Urs Thalmann
Astrid Vargas
Nathalie Vasey
Lynne Villers
Lucienne Wilmé
Sébastien Wohlhauser
Patricia C. Wright
John R. Zaonarivelo

Russell A. Mittermeier

Russell Mittermeier has been President of Conservation International (CI) since 1989, is currently a Vice-President of the International Union for Conservation of Nature (IUCN), and has served as Chairman of IUCN's Species Survival Commission (IUCN/SSC) Primate Specialist Group since 1977. Prior to joining CI, he was Vice-President for Science at World Wildlife Fund-US. A primatologist and herpetologist by training, Dr. Mittermeier's publications include 20 books and over 570 articles, and he has conducted fieldwork on three continents and in more than 20 countries. He received his PhD in Biological Anthropology from Harvard University in 1977.

Edward E. Louis Jr.

Ed Louis has been the Director of the Conservation Genetics Department for Omaha's Henry Doorly Zoo Grewcock Center for Conservation and Research for the past 14 years. He has carried out extensive fieldwork in Madagascar since 1998, developing baseline molecular, distribution, and census data on its lemurs, boas, tortoises, geckos, amphibians, and orchids. He received his DVM and PhD in Genetics from Texas A&M University in 1994 and 1996, respectively.

Matthew Richardson

Matt Richardson is a freelance author, historian and primatologist from Toronto, Canada. A member of the IUCN/SSC Primate Specialist Group, he works closely with scientists and conservation NGOs the world over on academic publications and research.

Christoph Schwitzer

Christoph Schwitzer received his PhD in Zoology from the University of Cologne, where he studied the nutritional ecology of lemurs. He was part of the primatological research group at Cologne Zoo before becoming Programme Coordinator for the *Association Européenne pour l'Etude et la Conservation des Lémuriens* (AEECL) in Madagascar, where he established a field research and conservation programme. He has been Head of Research at Bristol Zoo Gardens since 2006, and Executive Secretary of AEECL since 2007.

Olivier Langrand

Olivier Langrand is Senior Vice President for International Government Relations at Conservation International. He holds a Master of Science in Zoology from the University of Natal, South Africa, and has 25 years of experience in the design and implementation of field research and tropical forest conservation programs. He is also an expert on the birds of the southwestern Indian Ocean islands, and the author of more than 80 scientific papers and four books on the biodiversity of the Africa/Madagascar region. Olivier lived in Madagascar for 12 years, and was awarded the Order of National Merit in 1997 by the President of Madagascar for his outstanding contributions to biodiversity conservation.

Anthony B. Rylands

Anthony Rylands began his career in 1976 studying primates at the National Institute for Amazon Research (INPA), Manaus, Brazil. He received his PhD from the University of Cambridge in 1982, and from 1986 to 2005 was Professor of Vertebrate Zoology at the Federal University of Minas Gerais in Brazil. Rylands is a member of the Brazilian Academy of Sciences, and Deputy Chair of the IUCN/SSC Primate Specialist Group. He has authored and edited more than 220 articles, books and reports on primate ecology, behavior, taxonomy, biogeography and conservation. He is currently a Senior Research Scientist at Conservation International.

Frank Hawkins

Frank Hawkins is Vice-President for the Africa/ Madagascar program at Conservation International. He lived in Madagascar for nearly 20 years, working on conservation projects and researching birds, primates, and carnivores. He completed a PhD on the conservation of western Malagasy birds in 1994.

Serge Rajaobelina

Serge Rajaobelina is the President of Fanamby, a Malagasy non-governmental environmental organization that he founded in 1997. Prior to that, he served as Assistant Program Officer for the World Wildlife Fund-US Madagascar Program from 1988-89, and then as Conservation International's Program Officer for Madagascar (1989–1994) and its Madagascar Program Director (1995–1996).

Rodin Rasoloarison

Rodin Rasoloarison obtained his PhD from the University of Antananarivo in 2000 for his taxonomic revision of Madagascar's mouse lemurs (*Microcebus*). He has since continued to study the taxonomy and biogeography of cheirogaleids in the field and in museum collections around the world. He is a research coordinator for the German Primate Center (DPZ).

Christian Roos

Christian Roos is a geneticist at the German Primate Center (DPZ) and Deputy Regional Coordinator of the Southeast Asian section of the IUCN/SSC Primate Specialist Group. He studies the phylogeny, phylogeography and population genetic structure of various primate groups. Although working mainly on Asian primates, he has performed several molecular studies on Malagasy lemurs, including indriids, cheirogaleids and lepilemurids. He received his PhD in Biology from the Technical University of Munich in 2003.

Peter Kappeler

Peter Kappeler is Professor of Sociobiology and Anthropology at the University of Göttingen, Germany and Director of the Kirindy Forest Research Station of the German Primate Center (DPZ), where he has been studying lemur behavior and ecology since 1988. He has served as President of the German Primate Society and the European Federation for Primatology, and as Vice President for Research of the International Primatological Society. He received his PhD in Zoology from Duke University in 1992.

Jonah Ratsimbazafy

Jonah Ratsimbazafy received his PhD in Physical Anthropology from the State University of New York at Stony Brook in 2002, with a study of black-and-white ruffed lemurs in Madagascar's Manombo forests. He is presently the Training and Conservation Coordinator for the Durrell Madagascar Programme, and an Adjunct Associate Professor in the Department of Paleontology and Anthropology at the University of Antananarivo.

James MacKinnon

James MacKinnon is Senior Technical Director of Conservation International in Madagascar. He has lived in Madagascar for 11 years working on conservation and conducting field research on fruit-bats. He spent 6 years as an advisor to Madagascar National Parks and has been closely involved in the efforts to expand the country's protected area network. He received his PhD in Zoology from the University of Aberdeen in 1998.

Stephen D. Nash

A native of Great Britain and a graduate of the Natural History Illustration Department of the Royal College of Art in London, Stephen Nash has been Scientific Illustrator for Conservation International since 1989, producing images for conservation education and biological publications. Prior to this, he was part of the World Wildlife Fund-US Primate Program. Based at the State University of New York at Stony Brook, he is a Visiting Research Associate in the Department of Anatomical Sciences and an Adjunct Associate Professor in the Department of Art.

Paula K. Rylands

Paula K. Rylands is the Photo and Graphic Design Coordinator for the President's Office of Conservation International. She has a BA in Social and Cultural Anthropology from the University of Maryland and has studied art and design in England. Originally from Brazil, she has done fieldwork on African diaspora in the rural areas of Minas Gerais, is an amateur photographer, and works with video production.

ACKNOWLEDGMENTS

We are especially grateful to the late Doris Swanson and to Shawn Concannon, whose generous support and long-term commitment to species conservation has helped to underwrite much of the research behind this book, as well as the publication itself.

We are also grateful to the Margot Marsh Biodiversity Foundation, which has supported dozens of lemur research and conservation projects since 1996, providing a considerable portion of the information found in this book.

Thanks are also due to the following photographers, who kindly donated the use of images that greatly enhance the text: Rambinintsoa Andriantompohavana, Marina B. Blanco, Greg Davies, Claudia Fichtel, Christopher Golden, Colin P. Groves, Andreas Hapke, David Haring, Mitchell T. Irwin, Jukka Jernvall, William R. Konstant, Susan M. McGuire, Bernhard Meier, Jean Freddy Ranaivoarisoa, Hery Nirina Theophile Randriahaingo, Pete Oxford (<www.peteoxford.com>), Richard Randrianampionona, Iñaki Relanzón, Melanie Seiler, Viviana Sorrentino, and John R. Zoanarivelo, and Luci Betti Nash for her illustration of a fossil crocodilian.

William L. Jungers and Laurie R. Godfrey were most helpful and patient in giving us their time and expert advice in putting together illustrations of the extinct lemurs (Figs. 3.3 and 3.4), and to William L. Jungers and David W. Krause for their detailed input to chapter 1.

The authors would also like to acknowledge the major contributions of Jörg U. Ganzhorn, Ian Tattersall, David M. Meyers, William R. Konstant, and Roderic B. Mast to the two earlier editions of this book.

Finally, we thank the staff at Conservation International who helped in the preparation of this field guide, notably Ella Outlaw, Jill Lucena, and Doan Nguyen, all from the President's office.

TABLE OF CONTENTS

INTRODUCTION

It gives us great pleasure to present this revised and expanded third edition of *Lemurs of Madagascar*, which updates the first edition, published in 1994, and the second, published in 2006. Madagascar is without a doubt the world's highest primate conservation priority, with very high species diversity and unmatched endemism at the species, genus, and family levels. It is the second country on the world list for primate species diversity (in spite of being less than 7% the size of Brazil, the world leader in primate diversity, and roughly one-third the size of Indonesia, third on the list), and its 97 species (and 101 taxa when you include subspecies) are all endemic.[1] This diversity is even more striking at the generic and family levels—fully five families and 15 genera are found nowhere else. Compare this to Brazil, the richest country on Earth in terms of primate species and subspecies, with 135 (78 or 58% of which are endemic); only four of its 18 genera are endemic, and none of its five families.

Furthermore, the 2008 IUCN Red List classifies 41% of the lemurs as threatened with extinction; eight of these Critically Endangered[2], 18 Endangered, and another 15 as Vulnerable. As high as this percentage is, it is certainly an underestimate of the extinction risk faced by lemurs, since 42 of the species and subspecies are currently listed as Data Deficient. Indeed, fully 24 lemur species were described *after* the Mammal Red List Workshop was held in Madagascar in April, 2005. Many of these will doubtless move into one of the threatened categories when more detailed assessments have been conducted.

Looking at Madagascar's primate diversity in yet another way, although it is only one of 91 countries to have wild primate populations, it alone is home to 15% (101 of 668) of all primate species and subspecies, 20% (15 of 73) of all primate genera, and 36% (5 of 16) of all primate families—a great responsibility for one single nation.

Madagascar also demonstrates clearly that primate extinctions are a very real phenomenon and not just a figment of the conservationist's imagination. Fully eight genera and at least 17 species of lemur have already gone extinct on this island since the arrival of our own species there roughly 2,000 years ago. As indicated in the pages that follow, many others could disappear within the next few decades if action is not taken. Today, the major threats to lemurs include deforestation due to slash-and-burn agriculture (known as *tavy* in Madagascar), logging, firewood collection, charcoal production, seasonal burning of dry forests to create cattle pasture, and live capture of lemurs as pets. Sadly, the hunting of lemurs as a source of food, a threat that we used to consider less severe than in other parts of the world, is now emerging as a major problem in many areas, and requires special attention.

What is more, Madagascar is currently undergoing a period of political turmoil. The coup that took place in early 2009 has yet to be resolved as we finalize this new edition. Although many conservation activities continue in spite of the political problems, the breakdown of law and order in certain parts of the country has had serious impacts. This has especially been the case in parks and reserves with valuable timber such as Marojejy National Park and Masoala National Park in the northeastern part of the country. Almost immediately following

---

1. Two species, *Eulemur fulvus* and *Eulemur mongoz*, also live on the nearby Comoros Islands, but they were almost certainly introduced there by our own species.

2. The blue-eyed black lemur, *Eulemur flavifrons*, is here considered to be Critically Endangered rather than Endangered as listed by IUCN (2008).

the onset of the crisis, illegal loggers moved into both of these protected areas. Organized hunting of lemurs for commercial purposes sprung up in that region as well, but now appears to be under control—at least for the time-being—as a result of a concerted international press campaign that brought the issue to the attention of the Malagasy authorities. To further exacerbate the problem, most international donor agencies suspended their support to Madagascar, excepting only assistance for the most dire humanitarian situations. This suspension has included support for conservation programs from bilateral agencies, the World Bank, and others, none of which has been reactivated as of late 2009. This places a great deal of responsibility on the international and national non-governmental organizations active in Madagascar, which alone have continued to operate throughout this crisis.

Conservation International and the Primate Specialist Group of the International Union for Conservation of Nature's Species Survival Commission (IUCN/SSC), along with numerous other organizations, have long recognized Madagascar as one of their top priorities. This third edition of *Lemurs of Madagascar* will facilitate the identification of lemurs in the field. What is more, by summarizing available data on their ecology, distribution and conservation status, it is hoped that it will also stimulate further interest in the survival of these animals in their natural habitats. In spite of several centuries of observation and collection and five decades of research, we are still discovering new species, we are not clear as to the limits of the distributions of many of the known species, and we have at best only anecdotal information on the conservation status and population numbers for the majority of them.

Increased field and laboratory research is showing us how little we knew of these animals as recently as a decade ago. Indeed, a total of 48 lemur species and subspecies previously unknown to science have been described since the first edition of this guide was published in 1994, and 34 of them since the second edition in 2006. A further six old names have been resurrected from the literature (*Cheirogaleus crossleyi, Cheirogaleus minusculus, Cheirogaleus sibreei, Eulemur rufifrons, Varecia variegata editorum* and *Varecia variegata subcincta*) since 1994, based on a re-evaluation of the diversity of each genus[3]. Much of this work has been conducted by several of the authors of this volume. As we go to press with this third edition, we know of still more species that await formal description, along with a number of others that *may* be new to science but which need further investigation. All these additions will bring the total lemur list for Madagascar to well over 110 and perhaps as many as 125, an amazing number for an island of its size and with so little habitat remaining. Madagascar is sometimes referred to as the "Eighth Continent," and for primates this is certainly the case. Indeed, the primate fauna of Madagascar is comparable in every way to that of Africa, South and Middle America, and Asia.

In addition to the description of previously unknown taxa, field research continues to fill the gaps in our knowledge of species once believed to be extremely rare and endangered. Two good examples are the hairy-eared dwarf lemur (*Allocebus trichotis*) and the aye-aye (*Daubentonia madagascariensis*). Both were once believed to be nearly extinct, but they continue to be found at new (though still widely dispersed) sites in different parts of the country. Neither is ever found in large numbers nor at high densities, so we cannot consider their populations to be secure, but their situation is certainly better than had been believed as recently as 15–20 years ago.

---

3. These species and subspecies had already been formally described but were subsequently synony-mized with other forms.

On the other hand, with the description of so many new species (splitting up what were once considered wide-ranging forms), the conservation challenge increases dramatically. Many of the new taxa are known only from their type localities, and quite a few have tiny ranges in areas of extreme habitat fragmentation. Surely, as knowledge increases, a number of these new forms are likely to enter the ranks of the Endangered and even the Critically Endangered.

Given the amazing diversity of Madagascar's lemur fauna and its great global importance, it is sobering to reflect on the extent of the degradation and loss of their forest habitats. By the 1950's, only 27% of Madagascar was forested[4] and this had further declined to an estimated 16% by 2005 (Harper *et al.*, 2007; MEFT, USAID and CI, 2009). Subsequently, about 50,000 ha of forest was destroyed each year between 2000 and 2005 (MEFT, USAID and CI, 2009). This equates to a current cover of about 94,000 km² of spiny, dry and humid forests (MEFT, USAID and CI, 2009)—an area roughly equivalent to the American state of Indiana. However, it should be remembered that the fragmentation and isolation of the forest fragments is extreme. Harper *et al.* (2007) calculated that the area of what they termed "core forest" (forest more than 1 km from a forest edge) decreased from more than 90,000 km² in the 1950s to less than 20,000 km² in 2000. Furthermore, the area in patches of 100 km² or more decreased by more than half in that period.

In terms of protected areas, in 2003 only about 3% of Madagascar's land area was protected. This corresponds to around 17,000 km² (1.7 million ha), or slightly more than the size of Connecticut, and only a small portion of that was effectively managed. In light of this, it was particularly encouraging when, in 2003, the Government of Madagascar committed to tripling the country's protected area coverage in five years (subsequently revised to be by the end of 2012). This pledge was announced by President Marc Ravalomanana in September 2003, at the 5th World Parks Congress in Durban, South Africa. This historic declaration served as a rallying point for everyone concerned for the biodiversity in Madagascar. Subsequently named "The Durban Vision," this commitment attracted major international attention and funding. What is more, the government has made good progress towards this goal, creating 29 new protected areas covering 30,000 km², with the creation of a further 40 additional reserves covering 11,000 km² still underway. By January 2010, there were 4.7 million ha of protected areas in Madagascar, and the government, NGOs, and community groups were actively working to create a further 1 million ha.

What is more, the international community pledged more than $50 million to a trust fund to cover some of the recurrent costs of the country's parks and reserves, a figure that was achieved by March, 2008. During the political upheaval of 2009, the transitional government continued to support the creation of new protected areas; however, the long term success of the Durban Vision will require resolution of Madagascar's current political problems, as well as a substantial increase in support from Madagascar's future leaders and from the international community. What direction this will take remains quite uncertain as of early 2010.

In any case, it is hoped that this third edition of *Lemurs of Madagascar* will once again make a contribution by compiling the latest information on lemur ecology, distribution, and conservation status in one handy publication. In so doing, we hope to encourage further research, add to our knowledge of lemur biology in general, and stimulate the growth of ecotourism in Madagascar. This industry, which had been growing steadily and was fully espoused and supported by the government and by private enterprise, should continue as

---

4. Humbert and Cours Darne (1965) indicated that 90% of the island was forested before humans arrived.

a major foreign exchange earner for the country, providing a strong economic justification for the maintenance and protection of parks, reserves and natural habitats. Although ecotourism fell dramatically since the political problems began in early 2009, we have high hopes that it will come back quickly once the situation stabilizes. (Indeed, in spite of the problems, some tourism still took place, with about 190,000 people visiting the country in 2009, a major drop from the all-time high of 380,000 the previous year but still encouraging.) Since lemurs are the most attractive, conspicuous, and best known component of Madagascar's wildlife, they are ideally suited to stimulate the growth of ecotourism. What is more, they really are Madagascar's wildlife ambassadors to the world, a position they have long occupied and will hopefully continue to occupy for a long time to come.

Russell A. Mittermeier
President, Conservation International
Chairman IUCN/SSC Primate Specialist Group

HOW TO USE THIS FIELD GUIDE

This third edition of *Lemurs of Madagascar* has been designed for easy use and to be an indispensable companion for the ecotourist, and especially for the primate-watcher. The 101 lemur species and subspecies currently recognized are illustrated and described in detail, and information is provided on the distribution, ecology, and behavior of each, accompanied by an array of photos, illustrations, and maps. The information presented in the pages that follow will not only help the reader identify what species he or she has just seen, but can also be used in advance of a visit to Madagascar to plan field trips based on a "must see" list of lemurs.

Quick Visual Reference

On the inside front cover we provide a color-coded Quick Visual Reference to the five families of living lemurs: Cheirogaleidae (mouse lemurs, giant mouse lemurs, dwarf lemurs, and fork-marked lemurs), Lepilemuridae (sportive lemurs), Lemuridae (bamboo lemurs, the ring-tailed lemur, true lemurs, and ruffed lemurs), Indriidae (woolly lemurs, sifakas, and the indri), and Daubentoniidae (aye-aye). Representative illustrations of the genera in each family are depicted to the left of a colored bar that appears later in the field guide on pages pertaining to species within that taxonomic grouping. Thus, all the reader need do, after spotting a lemur in the field, is open the cover, check the representative illustrations to determine the basic type of animal that has been observed, and flip to the section of the book bearing the same color code and a set of illustrations that should help confirm the identification.

Introductory Chapters

Chapter 1, *Madagascar's Ancient Geological History*, gives an overview of the geological history of the island, while Chapter 2, *Origin of the Lemurs*, briefly presents theories of how lemurs may have arrived there. Chapter 3, *The Extinct Lemurs*, describes eight genera and 17 species that have gone extinct since humans reached the island roughly 2,000 years ago. Chapter 4, *Discovery and Study of the Living Lemurs*, provides an historical account of exploration and field research that has led to this documentation of the present day lemur fauna. In Chapter 5, *Conservation of Lemurs*, we discuss threats to the extant species, as well as actions taken to safeguard them. Finally, in Chapter 6, *The Living Lemurs*, and Chapter 7 to 11, which make up the bulk of this book, we present detailed accounts of the 101 species and subspecies.

The Living Lemurs

The core of this book is devoted to descriptions of these animals, arranged according to their family and genus. Each of the five families is introduced by a brief text covering biological affinities and distinctive traits, as well as a series of representative photographs. The description of each genus consists of a brief statement regarding its distinguishing characteristics and other information pertinent to its taxonomy, along with explanations of the taxonomic framework used in this field guide. This is augmented by illustrations depicting basic morphology, unique field markings, and characteristic postures that can be used to distinguish one species from another, by photographs of the animals in the wild and in captivity, and by maps that can be used to verify whether a sighting has taken place within the known or presumed range of the species.

Each lemur is introduced by its Latin name, the name of the author(s) who described it, the most commonly used English name, other English names, and then French, German and Malagasy names. The description is presented in five sections: *Identification*, *Geographic Range*, *Natural History*, *Conservation Status* and *Where To See It*. Primary sources of information are referenced in the text, and a complete list of these references is presented at the end of the book.

Identification: This section includes information needed to identify the species based upon what can be seen and, in some cases, heard in the field. Body size and weights are given, where available, followed by a description of distinctive color patterns and characteristics of the head, body, and tail. We also mention other sympatric lemurs with which a given species or subspecies might be confused (if any), and suggest how to distinguish among them.

Geographic Range: This section provides a description of the animal's geographic range, and should be used in conjunction with the map depicting the overall range for the genus in question. When trying to identify species, your location in Madagascar is often the best clue. Be aware, however, that maps and descriptions simply give range limits; nowadays a given lemur will not necessarily be found in all forests within its former range. Also remember that Madagascar is imperfectly known zoologically; if you wander off the beaten path, it is possible that you will make a new scientific discovery or at least an addition to our knowledge of the geographic distributions of the species. If you are confident that you have observed a particular lemur outside the range we have specified, please let us know. Photographs and geographic coordinates are essential in helping us confirm identifications and range extensions.

Natural History: In this section we summarize what is known about the ecology and behavior of each species and subspecies. This information will probably not be needed for identification, but will enhance the reader's appreciation of these animals and sometimes provide clues as to where they are most likely to be found. Bear in mind that some species are better known than others, and that no lemur has been studied in all parts of its range or in all the habitats that it occupies. In some cases, virtually nothing may be known about an animal's natural history. Again, new observations are valuable. Remember to record species or subspecies, map locations or GPS coordinates, time of the year, and any other information pertinent to your sightings, including forest type, prominent plant species nearby, and plant (or animal) parts eaten or otherwise used.

Conservation Status: Virtually all lemurs are under threat from various human activities. This section summarizes how severely a particular species or subspecies is threatened and what human activities are most significant. Remember that all lemurs are protected under Malagasy law and by international treaties, so it is essential that you do not disturb these animals in any way, and certainly that you *not* try to take lemurs (living or dead) or lemur body parts of any kind out of the country. In this section, we also provide a list of all the protected areas in which each lemur is known to occur, as well as its conservation status according to the *IUCN Red List of Threatened Species*. Categories of Threat, in order of increasing severity, are Least Concern, Vulnerable, Endangered and Critically Endangered, and some species are so poorly known that they are either in a Data Deficient category, or indeed not yet assessed at all. Lastly, we make note of areas that may warrant further investigation for each species, as part of the overall effort to establish new parks and reserves in Madagascar.

Where To See It: Since the primary purpose of this field guide is to stimulate lemur tourism and to help travelers identify animals observed in the wild, we offer recommendations as to the best sites for viewing particular species in their natural habitats. This is not meant to be a comprehensive list since sightings are possible throughout a species' range, both in protected and unprotected forests. Indeed, we encourage visitors to explore other less known sites, especially on their second or third trip to Madagascar, after they have learned a bit more about the country and its people. The *Where To See It* section is primarily for the visitor who has only a short time in Madagascar and wants to see as many lemurs in the wild as possible. Note that in some cases, especially for some of the new species described over the past few years, we cannot yet recommend any readily accessible viewing sites.

Appendices

Following the accounts for each family (Chapters 7 to 11), we present three appendices to further aid the reader. Appendix A is a series of national maps that depict the island's topography, major cities and towns, rivers, and protected areas. Appendix B, *Biogeographic Regions and Floristic Domains of Madagascar*, provides descriptions and representative photos of Madagascar's principal terrestrial habitats, and this is followed by Appendix C, *Key Lemur-watching Sites in Madagascar*, which describes around 64 promising locations at which visitors to Madagascar are likely to encounter lemurs in their natural habitats. This portion of the field guide is drawn from the *Where to See It* sections that are provided for each lemur species, allowing the reader to see at a glance the range of taxa that might be viewed at a particular site.

Primate-watching / Primate-listing
Starting Your Lemur Life-List

This section (Appendix D) is intended to help launch "lemur-watching" and "lemur life-listing" as a new hobby or sport, based on the extraordinary global success of birdwatching as a pastime and as a force in tourism over the past century. Indeed, what is planned for Madagascar is part of a larger worldwide effort to stimulate primate-watching and primate life-listing in a major way, and to make this new activity a significant contributor to conservation in general. A checklist of all living lemurs can be filled in by readers as they travel from one destination to another, and will hopefully encourage return visits to this amazing country. Furthermore, given that no publication of this kind is ever truly complete, we invite readers to use the final section of the field guide to report new information, e.g., unusual color forms, the presence of species in areas from which they have not been reported, and potential new species. The opportunity to contribute to our growing knowledge of lemurs is open to all who visit Madagascar.

References

Information from over 1,100 scientific papers, books, chapters, dissertations, and reports has been used to produce this field guide, much of it coming from results of recent and ongoing research. Citations throughout the text enable the reader to track down original sources for much of the data that we present.

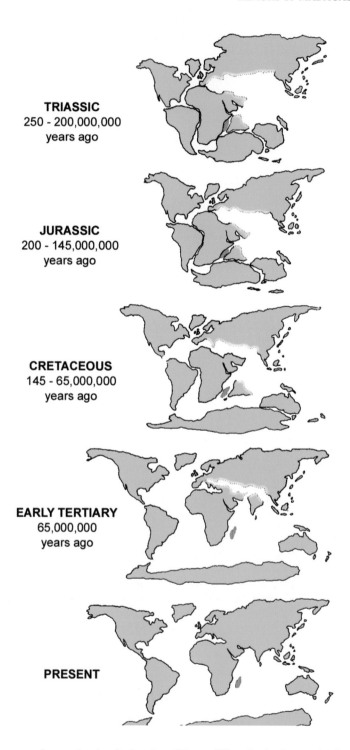

TRIASSIC
250 - 200,000,000
years ago

JURASSIC
200 - 145,000,000
years ago

CRETACEOUS
145 - 65,000,000
years ago

EARLY TERTIARY
65,000,000
years ago

PRESENT

Fig. 1.1: Sequence of maps showing the location of the world's major landmasses in the past,
with Madagascar in red.

CHAPTER 1

MADAGASCAR'S ANCIENT GEOLOGICAL HISTORY

Maarten de Wit
University of Cape Town

Introduction

Madagascar has a long history of geological and biological co-evolution with parts of other continents. Until relatively recently, it occupied the heartland of the supercontinent Gondwana. Before the formation of the latter, parts of northeastern Madagascar originated together with Precambrian rocks of the Indian Dharwar Craton more than 3 billion years ago, while other parts have African roots that go back more than 2.5 billion years, likely linked to the Tanzanian Craton. These disparate continental fragments amalgamated between 600 and 650 million years ago during the birth of Gondwana. But it took another 500 million years before Madagascar emerged from its Gondwana stem, breaking off its African connections between 160 and 180 million years ago, breaking its direct link with Antarctica 60 million years later, and then finally severing its ties with India and the Seychelles 10 million years after that, i.e., roughly 90 million years ago. Madagascar has since carved out a new geological chapter for itself as an independent micro-continent with a unique paleontological record, history of local climate change, volcanism, and high-plateau formation. Today, the island is seismically active and is experiencing regional east/west extension and tectonic uplift that, together, induce high rates of natural erosion, similar to that seen along the East African Rift.

The sea around Madagascar is deep beyond the narrow bank on which it sits. To the east, the water depth increases rapidly to near 5 km, and is floored by Cretaceous oceanic crust. To the west, the island is separated from Africa by the Mozambique Channel, at depths of 2.0 to 3.5 km. The Davie Ridge, 500–1,000 m below sea level, runs down the middle of the channel. This ridge demarcates an extinct fault along which Madagascar was displaced, more than 1,000 km southward away from Africa, between 160 and 120 million years ago. Dredge samples from these shallows indicate that the Davie Ridge contains remnants of old continental rocks that were occasionally exposed above sea level and covered by volcanic rock during the Late Cretaceous and the Cenozoic (Eocene/Miocene), well before Madagascar reached its farthest separation from Africa.

A shallow marine platform links Madagascar in the northwest to the line of young (0–7 million years ago), active volcanic islands of the Comoros, and to similar volcanic rocks of the Nosy Be archipelago (7–10 million years ago). Along the south coast of Madagascar, a shallow plateau of volcanic rocks—the Madagascar Plateau—extends some 800 km into the Indian Ocean. This plateau formed when Madagascar separated from India and the Seychelles about 90 million years ago to herald the final severance from its terrestrial Gondwana roots.

Precambrian rocks are exposed in the eastern two-thirds of Madagascar. These were all extensively metamorphosed and melted during the Pan African events of 650 to 550 million years ago; processes that enriched Madagascar with a wide range of precious minerals. The western part of Madagascar is covered by extensive sedimentary basins that preserve a 350 million year-old record of evolution from Early Carboniferous to Recent times.

Malagasy Building Blocks: Archean (3.2–2.5 Billion Years Ago) Fragments of India and Africa

The rocks of north and central Madagascar offer unique windows into how our Earth worked when it was young. The Precambrian basement of Madagascar includes remnants of early Archean crust more than 3 billion years ago. In the northeast of Madagascar in a region known as the Antongil Block, including Nosy Sainte-Marie, granitic rocks are dated between 3.3 and 3.2 billion years ago. The Antongil Block was once part of a larger landmass that connected to similar rocks in India.

The continental crust that makes up central Madagascar is over 500 million years younger, and has links to African rocks in Tanzania and Somalia. This Antananarivo Block yields ages of 2.6 to 2.5 billion years ago, and includes ancient oceanic crust preserved in three greenstone belts of that age at Maevatanana, Beforona and Andriamena. The two ancient Malagasy blocks were welded together relatively recently (600 million years ago) along the Betsimisaraka suture zone.

A large area of quartzite and marble—the Itremo complex—covers the western edge of the Antananarivo Block. The marble preserves abundant stromatolites, and the quartzites retain excellent current structures and mudcracks that attest to deposition in a shallow water environment around 1.7 billion years ago. A younger one (the Molo sequence, about 650 million years old) overlies the Itremo complex, and likely once covered the entire Precambrian crust of Madagascar.

Southernmost Madagascar, south of the Ranatsoro lineament, is different again. Here the Archean and the younger rocks are all deformed together into a separate high-grade metamorphic block, intruded by massive 650 million year-old anorthosites. The latter are the source of Madagascar's iridescent labradorite gems. This southern block is cut by spectacular ductile faults, aged at around 600 million years, which can be traced over hundreds of kilometers and matched to collinear extensions now exposed in Tanzania, northern Mozambique, and southern India (at that time attached to Africa), providing ample scientific proof of an African heritage for southern Madagascar.

An Ancient "Andean-Like" Volcanic Mountain Chain Connected Madagascar to India 800–700 Million Years Ago

Central and northern Madagascar are riddled with 800 to 700 million year old granites intruded into the older rocks, and strung out along a 450-km-long belt that resembles the roots of an Andean-like volcanic mountain chain. In a Gondwana reconstruction, this belt was connected to similar rocks found on the Seychelles and northwestern India, part of a contiguous volcanic arc—a "ring of fire" along the western margin of a Pacific-like ocean known as the Mozambique Ocean that has since disappeared. At that time, however, the width of this ocean was at least 2,000 km.

The Closing of the Mozambique Ocean Causes "Himalaya-Style" Collision Tectonics in Madagascar

Around 650 million years ago, the Mozambique Ocean started contracting, and between 600 and 500 million years ago Madagascar's continental blocks became trapped during collision between two major continents—East Gondwana (India, Antarctica, Australia) and West Gondwana (South America, Africa). This amalgamation resulted

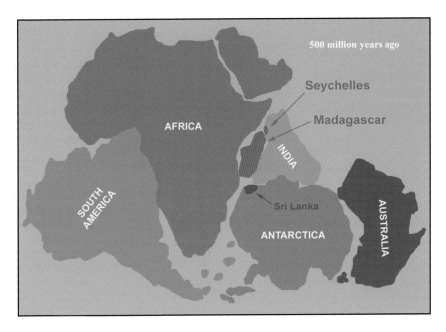

Fig. 1.2: A schematic representation of the position of Madagascar 500 million years ago (Late Cambrian/Early Ordovician) in relation to the landmasses that formed present-day South America, Africa, India, Antarctica, and Australia.

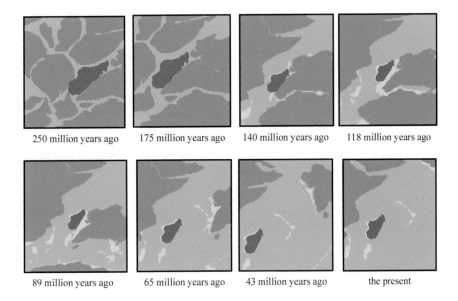

| 250 million years ago | 175 million years ago | 140 million years ago | 118 million years ago |

| 89 million years ago | 65 million years ago | 43 million years ago | the present |

Fig. 1.3: The gradual isolation and formation of the island of Madagascar, which began to split from eastern Gondwana and the present-day African coast 180-160 million years ago.

in the formation of mountain ranges of Alpine-Himalaya proportions, with proto-Madagascar welded into a central position within the supercontinent of Gondwana. The ancient mountain ranges were subsequently eroded away and, today, Madagascar is the world's best example of what lies below Mt. Everest and surrounding peaks, to be exposed when they eventually become exhumed. The roots of Madagascar's old mountain ranges mostly comprise high-grade metamorphic rocks with rare types like charnockites and enderbites (high-pressure equivalents of granites that form at depths of 30–45 km below the surface), and abundant gem-quality minerals such as sapphire and ruby.

From Ice Sheets to Deserts in Paleozoic to Mesozoic Times in Gondwana

Two hundred million years later, Madagascar came to be successively invaded by ice, rivers, shallow seas, and deserts. Mid-Carboniferous (350 million years ago) to mid-Jurassic (180 million years ago) sedimentary rocks that record these major climate changes are preserved in three basins that still cover about one-third of Madagascar along its western margin (the Ambilobe [or Diégo], Mahajanga [or Majunga], and Morondava basins). These rocks are Madagascar's equivalents of the classic Gondwana sequences of India and Africa.

First, as the old mountains of Madagascar eroded away, the landscape became covered by a 2–5 km-thick, continental ice sheet of Antarctic proportions that lasted up to 50 million years. Spectacular glacial deposits—tillites—are preserved in the southern Morondava Basin where they rest unconformably on the Precambrian basement. Massive tillites with Precambrian boulders of up to 2 m in diameter, polished surfaces, striated pavements and many other features indicative of glaciations are well preserved. The glacial series is abruptly overlain by coal-bearing sequences dominated by sandstones and plant-rich mudstones. Coal beds in places reach 10 m in thickness. Extensively mined in the mid-1900s, the coals have been re-excavated recently in small-scale operations, and are presently being further evaluated for larger-scale, open-pit mining. The rest of the sequence comprises sediments deposited in meandering rivers and cool temperate swamps covered with *Glossopteris* flora. A thin and discontinuous marine limestone caps the entire sequence (known as the Sakoa Group). This Lower Permian Vohitolia limestone provides the local signal of a major global sea level rise associated with the sudden melting of the Antarctic-like ice sheet that covered much of central Gondwana.

The Sakoa is overlain by a 2–4 km-thick delta sequence (Sakamena Group) with abundant plant and vertebrate fossils. The upper Sakamena has yielded a number of important aquatic and terrestrial reptiles and mammal-like reptiles (therapsids). The terrestrial therapsids are similar to those found in South Africa, but the aquatic reptile species are restricted to the Morondava Basin. As the local climate changed to drier conditions, the aquatic animals became increasingly endemic, whereas their terrestrial counterparts remained cosmopolitan.

The Permian-Triassic (P/T) transition around 251 million years ago, which records the greatest collapse and recovery of global biodiversity in Earth's history, is preserved with high resolution in the Morondava Basin. Contained here is a rich assemblage of distinctive, end-Permian pollen taxa that shows a sudden decline and replacement by lycopsid spores, which are replaced in turn by a characteristic Triassic pollen assemblage.

Overlying the Sakamena is the 1–6 km-thick Isalo Group of white sandstones with large-scale (1–10 m) cross-bedding, and red-bed sequences deposited during the desert

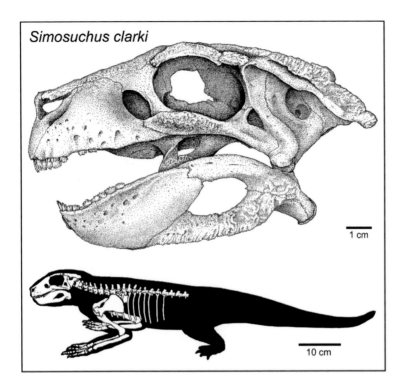

Fig. 1.4: The herbivorous pug-nosed crocodile, *Simosuchus clarki* Buckley *et al.*, 2000, a small-to medium-sized crocodyliform from the late Cretaceous of Madagascar (Illustration by Luci Betti Nash).

conditions of the Early Jurassic that had set in across much of the interior of Gondwana. Then, just after the onset of the Middle Jurassic (180 million years ago), marine conditions returned, and thereafter widespread fossiliferous limestones formed, such as the famous Mid-Jurassic Ankara and Kelifely limestones. This sudden flooding by shallow seas marks the end of a long period of terrestrial conditions that had lasted across central Gondwana some 120 million years ago, and heralded the start of the separation of Madagascar away from Africa.

The Birth of Madagascar and Clues to Its Present Biodiversity

Between 160 and 180 million years ago, Madagascar finally separated from Africa and Antarctica. It then moved southward relative to Africa along the Davie Fracture Zone for about 40 million years. The northwest coast of Madagascar repeatedly emerged and then submerged, giving rise to significant oil and gas reservoirs. The terrestrial deposits have yielded important discoveries of Mid-Jurassic dinosaurs and the world's earliest known tribosphenic[5] mammals (marsupials, placentals, and their extinct allies).

---

5. The three-cusped molar tooth design that is considered one of the most important characteristics of mammals.

By the onset of the Cretaceous some 145 million years ago, southern Madagascar cleared the point where it came close to northern Mozambique. From that time until the Neogene, marine conditions prevailed in all three Malagasy basins, with one exception. Vast volcanic eruptions accompanied the break away of Madagascar from India around 90 million years ago. Remnants of the early Late Cretaceous basalt and rhyolite sequences, dated between 84 and 92 million years ago, crop out across large sections of coastal Madagascar. These basalts might once have covered the entire island.

Above these basalts, terrestrial sandstones and shales were deposited in the Mahajanga Basin until the end-Cretaceous (65 million years ago) when marine conditions briefly returned. From the upper parts of this section of sandstones and shales (known as the Maevarano Formation), a very rich terrestrial and freshwater fauna has been recovered. The upper section contains an exceptionally diverse vertebrate assemblage that includes fishes, frogs (including a giant toad), turtles, snakes, lizards, crocodiles (seven species), numerous important dinosaurs, birds (including *Rahonavis ostromi*, a species that provides strong evidence for the dinosaurian origin of birds, and the sample from which by far the oldest proteinaceous components of claw material [keratin] have been recovered), a marsupial, and four species of other mammals.

Cosmopolitan Vertebrate Communities on an Isolated Micro-Continent

The terrestrial vertebrate communities of Late Cretaceous (100–65 million years ago) times are similar to those on other Gondwanan landmasses, especially those recovered from the end-Cretaceous Deccan Plateau in India (65 million years ago). Several dinosaur and other vertebrates found in Madagascar at the very end of the Cretaceous were remarkably cosmopolitan, with close relatives in not just India but also South America (Krause *et al.*, 2006). Yet this is a time when Madagascar was apparently well isolated, separated from the East African coast by some 400 km and even further from India/Seychelles, and Antarctica. Sets of "stepping-stones" between Madagascar and Africa via the Davie Ridge, and between Madagascar and India via the Maldives/Chacos/Reunion track have been proposed as possible routes, but there is no geologic evidence for direct land connections at the end of the Cretaceous. Similarly, a terrestrial Kerguelen land-bridge with Antarctica/South America has been proposed, but plate reconstructions show that such a connection had been severed long before the end of the Cretaceous.

Thus, while fossil evidence suggests that there may have been a land connection between Madagascar, Africa, India, and South America near the end-Cretaceous, there is no robust geological or geophysical data yet to support this. And between the end-Cretaceous and the Quaternary there are no terrestrial or freshwater vertebrate fossils yet discovered on Madagascar that might throw light on the details of Madagascar's further evolution and the origin of its present-day unique biodiversity. Linking Madagascar's inhabitants across this nearly 63-million-year gap, during which Cretaceous cosmopolitanism gave way to extreme isolationism, remains a first-order quest in paleontology and natural history.

Active Tectonism, Volcanism and the Sculpting of Madagascar's Recent Landscape

Relative to its size, Madagascar has an exceptional elevation that reaches to almost 3,000 m. The origin of these highlands is likely related to recent tectonic and volcanic activity. The island is seismically active and Neogene-Quaternary volcanism occurs in several localities, most notably in the Ankaratra Highlands (2,300–2,700 m) of central

Madagascar. The most tectonically active region (with up to 1,700 small earthquakes per year) occurs in the central region of the high plateau, some 15–28 km beneath the volcanic fields of Ankaratra and Itasy. Another highly active region occurs around the Alaotra and Ankay Rifts, a Neogene-Recent graben (rift) covered by Pliocene/Pleistocene sediments that strike into the volcanic zones of central Madagascar. This rift zone bears similarities to the East African rift system, and is presently extending in a similar east/west orientation.

Fault scarps with up to 10 m displacement occur along the inland margins of the Morandava and Mahajanga basins, and extensive scarps occur along large sections of the west coast. Seismic activity is also common along the faults of the Mahajanga Basin and farther south, near Ankililioaka, where lavas extruded around 9 million years ago along the Tulear fault.

In general, Madagascar supports a young landscape. The geomorphology across the Precambrian is dominated by granite inselbergs surrounded by steep escarpments and remnants of deeply weathered erosion surfaces with thick laterites cut by steep cliffs, erosion gullies (lavakas), and channels. Spectacular canyons dissect east-tilted Isalo sandstones in central-west Madagascar, and open karst features are sculpted into the large Jurassic limestone massifs of northern and western Madagascar. A number of distinct erosion surfaces exist across the island that range from near sea level to the grasslands at about 1,200–1,500 m. Some of the escarpments along the east coast date back to the time of the

Fig. 1.5: An example of severe erosion in the Sahamalaza region, in northwestern Madagascar, where the blue-eyed black lemur (*Eulemur flavifrons*) is found (photo by R. A. Mittermeier).

breakup of Gondwana. However, the deep young canyons that cut into Cenozoic sediments are testimony to a substantial uplift in the Neogene, and a significant rise in elevation over the past 10–15 million years across central and northern Madagascar. Recent work has shown a direct link between low-intensity/high-frequency earthquake activity in central Madagascar and formation of its distinct lavaka 'fields.' The tectonic uplift and extension probably triggered an increase in erosion rate and changes in local climates, both of which in turn likely triggered changes to the vegetation cover of the island, soil degradation and off-shore sedimentation. But these processes have yet to be quantified.

With this geological history as background, the following chapter explores the origins of the lemurs, a controversial subject on which there are a number of different opinions.

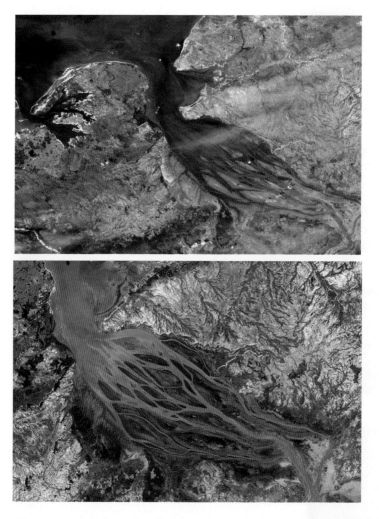

Fig. 1.6: The estuary of the Betsiboka (Madagascar's largest river) is one of the world's fast-changing coastlines. Logging has cleared the land, and erosion results in very high sediment loads after heavy rains (bottom photo). Astronauts describe this view of Madagascar as "bleeding into the ocean" (photo courtesy of NASA's Earth Observatory: < http://earthobservatory.nasa.gov/ IOTD/view.php?id=4388>).

Fig. 1.7: Severe erosion and burning to the west of the Makira forest in northeastern Madagascar (photo by R. A. Mittermeier).

Fig. 2.1: An ancestral lemur makes its way from continental Africa to Madagascar.

CHAPTER 2

ORIGIN OF THE LEMURS

As we have detailed in Chapter 1, the island of Madagascar once formed part of the great southern landmass of Gondwana. This enormous supercontinent began to break apart about 180 million years ago into the individual landmasses we know today as Africa, South America, Antarctica, Australia and the Indian subcontinent. Initially, Madagascar remained attached to Africa, but about 160 million years ago, together with the Indian subcontinent (in addition to Australia and Antarctica, which collectively formed "East Gondwana"), it began to break away from Africa (and South America, which collectively formed "West Gondwana") (see Scotese, 2000; Yoder and Nowak, 2006). East and West Gondwana fragmented further, but the Indian subcontinent and Madagascar remained joined together as "Indo-Madagascar" for another 70 million years before finally separating about 90 million years ago. By that time, Madagascar had assumed its present position relative to the east coast of Africa, separated by the Mozambique Channel. The channel is just over 400 km wide at its narrowest point.

This has interesting implications for the origin of lemurs. In the early days of the science of plate tectonics—the subdiscipline of geology that deals with continental drift—it seemed that we had found a simple explanation for Madagascar's biological uniqueness. The island, it was widely assumed, had merely parted from Africa with a sampling of that continent's fauna aboard. And while Africa's fauna saw a great deal of replacement of one group by another over the course of the epochs that followed, the fauna of isolated Madagascar did not.

The clarification of Madagascar's geological history has resulted in much rethinking of this scenario. If Madagascar has been essentially where it is now in relation to Africa for the past 90 million years or so, we cannot explain the presence of lemurs in Madagascar by an African "founder effect" (although this may explain the presence of some of the more ancient members of the island's biota). Primates comparable in evolutionary level to the lemurs (the so-called "primates of modern aspect" or euprimates) are not known in the fossil record until they appear abruptly in beginning of the Eocene epoch, some 55 million years ago (Martin *et al.,* 2007). These are distinct from the plesiadapiforms (so-called archaic primates) which have a fossil record dating back to 65 million years ago. They are not necessarily primates, and they are not the ancestors of the euprimates—the radiations are separate. Tavaré *et al.* (2002; see also Soligo and Martin, 2006; Martin *et al.,* 2007; Soligo *et al.,* 2007) argued that the origin of the primates dates back to the Cretaceous. Most of the Eocene euprimates are either Adapiformes or Omomyiformes and, while quite similar, some authors link the former to the strepsirrhine primates (prosimians—all but the tarsiers) and the latter to the haplorhines (tarsiers, monkeys and apes) (see Kay *et al.,* 1997; Fleagle 1999). The euprimates have, however, been documented by fossils very largely from North America and Europe, and the only fossil fragments from Africa are from Egypt and the Arabian peninsula (Yoder *et al.,* 1996). There is virtually no fossil record of terrestrial mammals in Africa for the first half of the Age of Mammals, and there is no known last common ancestor of the euprimates. The adapiform primates went extinct in the Early Oligocene (34 million years ago) and were a radiation of euprimates very largely restricted to the northern continents. Martin (1993) and Martin *et al.* (2007) proposed that the adapiform and omomyiform euprimates together represent a parallel northern continental radiation quite separate from the strepsirrhines and haplorhines, but already sharing derived primate-defining features in common with them. They argue that the last common ancestor of the euprimates would, therefore, be much older than is widely thought and would go back to the Cretaceous 85.9 million years ago (with the 95% confidence limits of 73.3–95.7 million years ago) (Tavaré *et al.*, 2002; Soligo *et al.*, 2007).

Divergence time estimates based on a number of studies have indicated the lemuroid dispersal to have occurred between 80 to more than 50 million years ago. A mean age was calculated by Masters *et al.* (2006b) from 10 studies as 60 million years (that is when lemuroids diverged from the African-Asian lorisoids). A more recent analysis by Horvath *et al.* (2008) indicated an earlier date for the split between the African lorises (and galagos) and the lemurs at 75 million years ago (with a 95% credibility interval of 66.9–84.4 million years ago).

Nevertheless, even if the ancestors of the primates were much older than was previously thought, and even that certain key events in mammalian evolution took place in Africa a little earlier than in the northern continents (for which relatively complete fossil records are available), it would still seem that the ancestors of today's lemurs most likely reached Madagascar by a sea crossing from Africa (Yoder *et al.*, 1996; Roos *et al.*, 2004). Large, matted clumps of floating vegetation are routinely washed down major rivers and out to sea, sometimes with unwilling mammals and other passengers aboard. There are numerous cases in which this is the only plausible mechanism for the dispersal of terrestrial mammals (and other terrestrial vertebrates, see below) to oceanic islands (Simpson, 1940). Despite the width of the Mozambique Channel, Madagascar's lemurs most likely represent one more such case.

There are a number of aspects, however, which need to be considered before accepting this as an explanation, not least among them whether sea currents and winds would favor, or even permit, a passage from the continent where the ancestors were presumed to have lived, and also whether the passage would be short enough for the survival of the unwilling passengers. This last aspect was discussed by Kappeler (2000), who indicated that torpor or month-long hibernation, a trait of *Microcebus* and *Cheirogaleus*, would have contributed to the likelihood of survival of a sea passage. This was based on the incorrect supposition of Purvis (1995) that the mouse and dwarf lemurs are the most ancestral of the living lemurs. They are in fact one of the more recent lineages (see below). The galagos are the mainland relatives of the lemurs and they do not show torpor or hibernation as an adaptation to stressful environments (Mzilikazi *et al.*, 2004) and Stankiewicz *et al.* (2005) also discounted the evidence for this. Stankiewicz *et al.* (2005) reviewed and investigated the likelihood of a sea crossing, taking into account even such fortuitous events as freak winds and tornados or trees on the floating vegetation which could act as a sail. Their unequivocal conclusion was that "current and wind trajectories [as they are today] show that the most likely fate for a raft emerging from an estuary on the east coast of Africa is to follow the Mozambique current and become beached back on the African coast."(p.1). That is, transport from Madagascar to Africa is very much more likely than the reverse. Even if the passage was possible, the time it would take would make survival of any mammals unlikely. They concluded that an alternative explanation was needed for the ancestral lemur's colonization of Madagascar.

Another possibility that has been raised is that islands or even a bridge was formed from peaks along the north-south running Davie Ridge in the Mozambique Channel at times when sea level was lower, which could have facilitated a crossing (e.g., Tattersall, 1982; McCall, 1997; Masters *et al.*, 2006a). This would have occurred during the second half of the Eocene and not the Oligocene, and the idea that it might have allowed for the lemur colonization of Madagascar by the ancestral lemur was suggested by McCall (1997) based on a divergence time for the lemuroids and lorisoids at about 40 million years ago. This, as discussed above, would be too recent (Martin, 2000). A land bridge has also been discounted for geological reasons (Rabinowitz and Woods, 2006). Even if there were small islands at some time during the Cenozoic, they still would have been separated by hundreds of kilometers of ocean (Ali and Huber 2010).

Krause *et al.* (1997) suggested that the currents in the Mozambique Channel may have been favorable for a crossing from Africa to Madagascar in the Late Cretaceous, about 65 million years ago, when Madagascar and Africa lay about 15° further south from where they are now. This possibility was strongly supported by Ali and Huber (2010) who, using paleo-oceanographic modeling, concluded that in the Eocene epoch strong currents in the Mozambique Channel certainly would have flowed eastward and that there were occasions when so-called "trajectories" starting in the region of northeast Mozambique and Tanzania would have fast, jet-like eddies with velocities indicating that crossings to Madagascar could have been possible in 25–30 days or even less. The region was also subject to tropical cyclones at that time. Transient storms and ocean current activity were consequently favorable to sea crossings; the cyclones providing not only the rafts (large, floating islands of vegetation) but also the drinking water. Ali and Huber (2010) concluded that favorable currents (from Mozambique and Tanzania to the north coast of Madagascar) would have persisted through the Oligocene, but that Madagascar, moving north, would have breached the margin of the subtropical and equatorial gyres by the early Miocene, and currents thereafter would have been perennially directed westwards, as they are today.

With the possible exception of a podocnemine turtle, the diverse record of Cretaceous terrestrial fossils on Madagascar, which includes representatives of several mammalian clades, has not (yet) revealed links to the extant Malagasy fauna. What is more, the few molecular-clock data that exist imply Cenozoic origination of the major vertebrate groups, from fishes to mammals, at a time when Madagascar was already isolated. For example, the closest relatives of Madagascar's indigenous freshwater fish (cichlids) are found in the East African great lakes, and present molecular estimates of divergence between major cichlid lineages considerably younger than the separation of Madagascar from East Africa. Similar patterns are seen for all of the terrestrial groups of Malagasy mammals, including lemurs. There is even evidence of Cenozoic origins of certain groups (e.g., chameleons) on Madagascar that then purportedly emigrated to other landmasses. The global chameleon fossil record goes back 20 million years, yet molecular phylogenies suggest a Malagasy origin with multiple "out of Madagascar" radiations to Africa and other Indian Ocean islands. If this interpretation of the chameleon radiation is correct, there was "two-way traffic" across the Mozambique Channel, and Madagascar provided a source for at least some biodiversity elsewhere, probably from sometime during the Oligocene.

However, difficult questions remain unanswered. Chameleons and small terrestrial mammals (e.g., tenrecs, rodents, carnivora, and lemurs) might have crossed significant sectors of the Indian Ocean on vegetation floats, but what about larger terrestrial mammals (e.g., the recently extinct pygmy hippos), frogs (which are relatively intolerant of marine conditions), and freshwater fish in the apparent absence of land bridges? Could the larger mammals have swum significant distances? Could the rafts of vegetation been large enough to harbor freshwater and its inhabitants? These questions, going back as far as the time of Alfred Russel Wallace and the birth of the science of biogeography, still loom large, and will not be answered until a better Cenozoic fossil record on Madagascar is brought to light.

The phylogenetic relationships among lemurs above the species level have been obscure for a long time. Several arrangements among lemur families—the main branches of this adaptive radiation—have been proposed based on analyses of various morphological traits (Tattersall and Schwartz, 1974; Tattersall, 1982). All subsequent genetic analyses have confirmed lemur monophyly, i.e., all lemurs are the descendants of a single successful colonization event (Yoder et al., 1996; Roos et al., 2004; Yoder and Yang, 2004; Karanth et al., 2005; Horvath et al., 2008). Supporting the findings of Roos et al. (2004) and Yoder and Yang (2004), Hovarth et al. (2008) concluded that the diversification of lemurs on Madagascar began with the separation of the lineage leading to the aye-aye (*Daubentonia*), about 66 million years ago (54.9–74.7 million years ago), extending as such across the Cretaceous/Tertiary boundary of 65 million years ago. Current evidence indicates that further splits of lemurs into families did not begin to occur until about 42 million years ago, more than 20 million years later in the middle Eocene, but the possibility remains that there were unrecorded lineage extinctions during this time (Yoder and Yang, 2004). The first major divergence in evidence today, following that of the separation of *Daubentonia*, was between the "true" lemurs (Lemuridae) and the ancestors of the Cheirogaleidae, Lepilemuridae and Indriidae. The indriids subsequently separated, and then the lepilemurids, all within a period of about 10 million years (Yoder and Yang, 2004).

Madagascar is the last place on Earth to have experienced the disappearance of diverse groups of large indigenous mammals (megafauna), and one of the last large habitable regions to be colonized by humans. Most of the documented extinctions occurred after the first arrival of humans on Madagascar, about 2,000 years ago (Burney et al., 2004). The earliest date for man's presence came from cut marks suggesting the removal of flesh from a radius bone of a sloth lemur (*Palaeopropithecus ingens*) dated at 2,325 ±43 years before present (Perez et al., 2003).

Elephant birds, relatives of the ostrich, the largest of which stood 3 m tall and at 450 kg, were probably the heaviest bird that ever lived, and were still present on the island near the end of the of the first millennium A.D., as were at least 17 species of large, now extinct lemurs. The stratigraphic resolution of this megafaunal "extinction window" is estimated to have been between 500 and 1,500 years ago. At least 48 species of large Malagasy mammals, birds, and reptiles became extinct, leaving the region with no indigenous terrestrial vertebrates of a body weight greater than 12 kg.

The list of extinct land vertebrate species includes two aardvark-like mammals of the genus *Plesiorycteropus* (Order Bibymalagasia), three dwarf hippopotami (Stuenes, 1989; Faure and Guérin, 1990), two species of giant tortoise (Gerlach and Canning, 1998), a giant fossa (*Cryptoprocta*) (Goodman et al., 1997, 2003a), a giant jumping rat (*Hypogeomys*) (Goodman and Rakotondravony, 1996), 21 birds, including three cuckoos (of an endemic genus *Coua*), a ground roller (of the endemic genus *Brachypteracias*), two shelducks (*Alopochen* and *Centrornis*), a mesite (*Monias*), a large gallinule (*Hovacrex*), a plover (*Vanellus*), a cormorant (*Phalacrocorax*), eight kinds of elephant birds (the endemic *Aepyornis* and *Mullerornis*), and three eagles (the very large *Stephanoaetus mahery* and two species of the genus *Aquila*), a huge crocodile (*Crocodylus robustus*), and 17 giant lemurs, some of which grew to be as large as a female gorilla (Goodman and Rakotondravony, 1996; Hawkins and Goodman, 2003; Goodman and Hawkins, 2008; Turvey, 2009).

In the next chapter we discuss in more detail the 17 large and remarkable lemurs that tragically are now extinct. Their loss emphasizes that the lemurs surviving today could face a similar fate if major conservation efforts currently underway are not effective.

a. *Mullerornis agilis*
b. *Aepyornis maximus*
c. *Aepyornis hildebrandti*
d. Ostrich

Fig. 2.2: An old postcard from the Musée de l' Académie Malgache, Antananarivo, Madagascar, showing the skeletons of three species of elephant birds along with that of an ostrich.

Fig. 2.3: A mural showing a pair of elephant birds guarding their nest, while a man to the right hides behind a tree waiting to steal their eggs. It is likely that humans caused to the extinction of these enormous, flightless birds (picture courtesy of the Berenty Museum).

Extinct Holocene vertebrates of Madagascar
(not included are 17 extinct lemurs, see chapter 3)

Mammalia
Order Bibymalagasia
  Family Plesiorycteropidae Patterson, 1975
    Plesiorycteropus madagascariensis Filhol, 1895
    Plesiorycteropus germainepetterae MacPhee, 1994
Order Artiodactyla
  Family Hippopotamidae Gray, 1821
    Hippopotamus lemerlei A.Grandidier in Milne-Edwards, 1868
    Hippopotamus laloumena Faure and Guérin, 1990
    Hippopatamus madagascariensis (Guldberg, 1883)
Order Carnivora
  Family Eupleridae Chenu, 1850
    Cryptoprocta spelea Grandidier, 1902
Order Rodentia
  Family Nesomyidae Forsyth-Major, 1897
    Hypogeomys australis G. Grandidier, 1903

Aves
Order Aepyornithiformes
  Family Aepyornithidae Bonaparte, 1853
    Aepyornis gracilis Monnier, 1913
    Aepyornis hildebrandti Burckhardt, 1893
    Aepyornis maximus I. Geoffroy St. Hilaire, 1851
    Aepyornis medius Milne-Edwards and A. Grandidier, 1866
    Mullerornis agilis Milne-Edwards and A. Grandidier, 1894
    Mullerornis betsilei Milne-Edwards and A. Grandidier, 1894
    Mullerornis grandis Lamberton, 1934
    Mullerornis rudis Milne-Edwards & A. Grandidier, 1894
Order Falconiformes
  Family Accipitridae Vieillot, 1816
    Stephanoaetus mahery Goodman, 1994
    Aquila sp. A
    Aquila sp. B
Order Anseriformes
  Family Anatidae Vigors, 1825
    Alopochen sirabensis (Andrews, 1897)
    Centrornis majori Andrews, 1897
Order Pelecaniformes
  Family Phalacrocoracidae Reichenbach, 1850
    Phalacrocorax sp.
Order Mesitornithiformes
  Family Mesitornithidae Wetmore, 1960
    Monias sp. (undescribed)
Order Gruiformes
  Family Rallidae Vigors, 1825
    Hovacrex roberti (Andrews, 1897)
Order Charadriiformes
  Family Charadriidae Vigors, 1825
    Vanellus madagascariensis Goodman, 1996

Order Cuculiformes
    Family Cuculidae Vigors, 1825
        Coua berthae Goodman and Ravoavy, 1993
        Coua delalandei (Temminck, 1827)
        Coua primaeva Milne-Edwards and A. Grandidier, 1895
Order Coraciiformes
    Family Brachypteraciidae Bonaparte, 1854
        Brachypteracias langrandi Goodman, 2000

Reptilia
Order Crocodylia
    Family Crocodylidae Cuvier, 1807
        Crocodylus robustus Vaillant and A. Grandidier, 1872
Order Testudines
    Family Testudinidae Batsch, 1788
        Aldabrachelys / Dipsochelys abrupta (A. Grandidier, 1868)
        Aldabrachelys / Dipsochelys grandidieri (Vaillant, 1885)

Fig. 3.1: A reconstruction of the extinct subfossil lemur *Megaladapis edwardsi* (courtesy of S. D. Nash).

CHAPTER 3

THE EXTINCT LEMURS

Remarkable as is the diversity of today's lemur fauna, it pales in comparison—both in number of species and in the variety of ecological adaptations—with what an early explorer would have found on the island as little as a thousand years ago. Since the arrival of humans on Madagascar, fully eight genera and at least 17 lemur species have gone extinct (Figs. 3.3 and 3.4). This represents 15% of all known species of lemurs (living and extinct) and over one-third (8/23) of all known genera, and it is noteworthy that all of the now extinct species were larger than those that survive today. There are 73 living primate genera and these eight extinct lemur genera represent as such a loss of 10% of the world's primates in historic times. This loss of lemurs in Madagascar in geologically very recent times is a dramatic example of the kind of extinction spasm that conservationists are constantly warning us about and, indeed, many of the surviving lemur species could fall victim to the same fate if conservationists are unsuccessful in their efforts. In the previous chapter we mentioned the existence of this subfossil lemur fauna of Madagascar. Here, we briefly describe this extinct fauna in order to convey some sense of the catastrophic loss of primate diversity that this unique island has already experienced, in the hope that it will make us redouble our efforts to save those that remain.

Discovery of the Subfossil Lemurs

A century ago, C. I. Forsyth Major (1894a) described the first subfossil remains of giant extinct lemurs recovered from marshes in the center and southwest of Madagascar. Not only were these remains clearly those of lemurs much larger than any which survive today, they were equally clearly of no great antiquity (hence the "subfossil" appellation). These discoveries kicked off a flurry of paleontological activity, and by the early years of the 20th century a host of recently extinct lemur genera and species had been described. In a review published as early as 1905, the paleontologist Guillaume Grandidier (son of the explorer Alfred) was able to show that many more names than necessary had been bestowed upon the large collection of subfossil lemur bones that had been amassed by that time. However, among those names were most of the extinct genera recognized today. Despite extensive excavations during the first half of the century, notably by Charles Lamberton (1934a, 1934b, 1936a, 1936b, 1938) of the Académie Malgache, no new extinct lemur genera were recovered between the first decade of the century and the late 1980s.

In 1986, a team led by Elwyn Simons of Duke University began work in karst caves on the Ankarana Massif in the far north of Madagascar. Besides discovering at least one new genus of extinct lemur (*Babakotia*), this team has made finds that have caused considerable rethinking of the adaptations of the extinct lemurs and the relationships among them. The team also made finds indicating that species that still survive today, among them *Prolemur simus* and *Indri indri*, once had much more extensive ranges.

The Subfossil Sites

Until the mid-20th century, subfossil lemurs were known almost exclusively from the center, south and southwest of Madagascar. Now, however, the only major biogeographic region of Madagascar where subrecent fauna remains unsampled is the eastern rain forest. Perhaps even more importantly, the recent era of fieldwork has allowed the collection of complete or relatively complete skeletons in which skulls and the various elements of the body skeleton are positively associated. This contrasts with earlier excavations in which bones tended to be dredged up one by one from swamps and muddy marsh bottoms. Given such circumstances of excavation, the association of postcranial bones with skulls and with each other tended to be a matter of guesswork and size-matching. As it turned out, this was not the most accurate procedure.

Most of currently known subfossil sites consist either of marsh deposits (dried to varying extents) or of deposits washed into limestone caves or fissures. Most such sites are rich in the bones of many other vertebrates besides primates (living as well as extinct). Common among such remains are those of pygmy hippopotami, giant tortoises and the famous elephant birds (*Aepyornis* and *Mullerornis*).

Of particular interest is the Ankilitelo pit cave in the karst landscape of the Mikoboka Plateau in southwestern Madagascar. It has a uniquely rich subfossil mammal fauna (34 species in all), which is very recent (around 500 years old), making it one of the most diverse Holocene assemblages in Madagascar (Simons *et al.*, 2004; Muldoon *et al.*, 2009a, 2009b). It is an extraordinarily rich repository for five species of extinct giant lemurs: *Palaeopropithecus ingens*, *Megaladapis madagascariensis*, *Archaeolemur majori*, *Daubentonia robusta*, and *Pachylemur* (Wunderlich *et al.*, 1996; Jungers *et al.*, 1997, 2005; Godfrey *et al.*, 1999; Hamrick *et al.*, 2000; Simons *et al.*, 2004; Shapiro *et al.*, 2005).

All of the subfossil sites are strictly localized, and all are of comparatively recent age. Most radiocarbon dates that have been obtained so far cluster in the period between about 2,500 and 1,000 years ago, and only one or two stretch back to the final millennia of the last Ice Age, which ended around 10,000 years ago. These are not very ancient ages by any standard, and they show that subfossil and living lemurs all form part of the same contemporary fauna; the extinct lemurs are in no way the precursors of those that still survive.

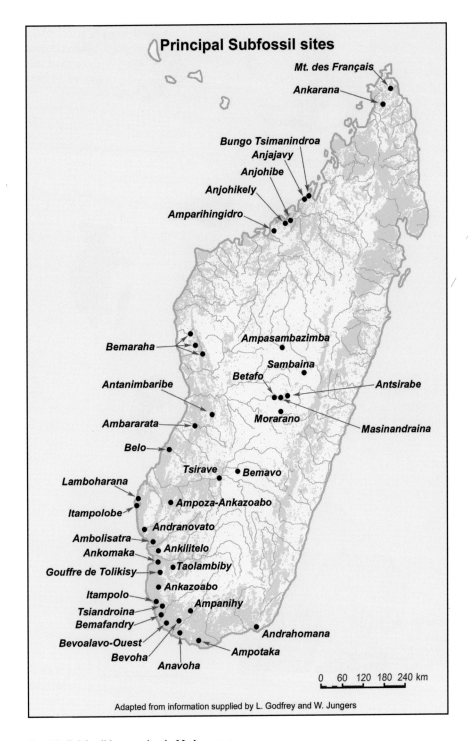

Fig. 3.2: Subfossil lemurs sites in Madagascar.

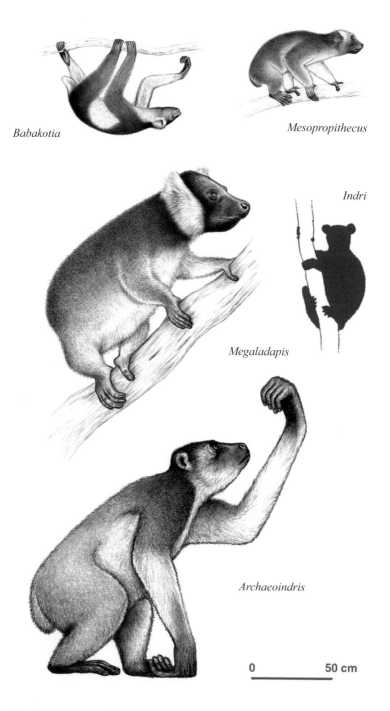

Babakotia

Mesopropithecus

Indri

Megaladapis

Archaeoindris

0   50 cm

Fig. 3.3 and 3.4: Above and next page: Reconstructions of the eight subfossil lemur genera already extinct in Madagascar. The indri, the largest of the living genera, is included in silhouette to show scale (artwork by S. D. Nash, based on information provided by L. R. Godfrey and W. L. Jungers).

0   50 cm

Pachylemur

Indri

Palaeopropithecus

Hadropithecus

Archaeolemur

Fig. 3.4.

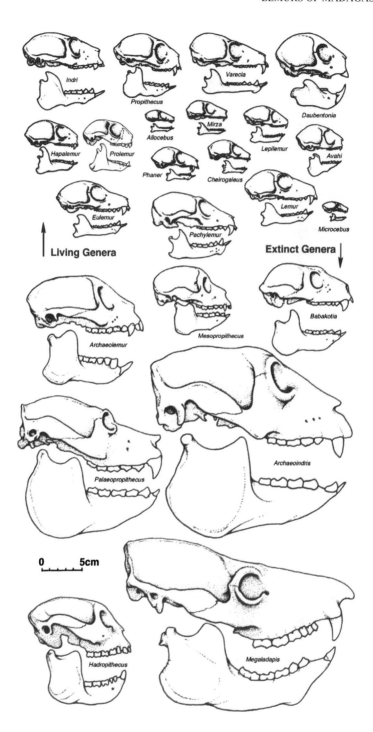

Fig. 3.5: Skulls of living and extinct lemur genera, drawn to scale. Note the great diversity in this radiation of primates and the enormous size achieved by some of the extinct genera. The living genera are indicated in blue (drawings by S. D. Nash).

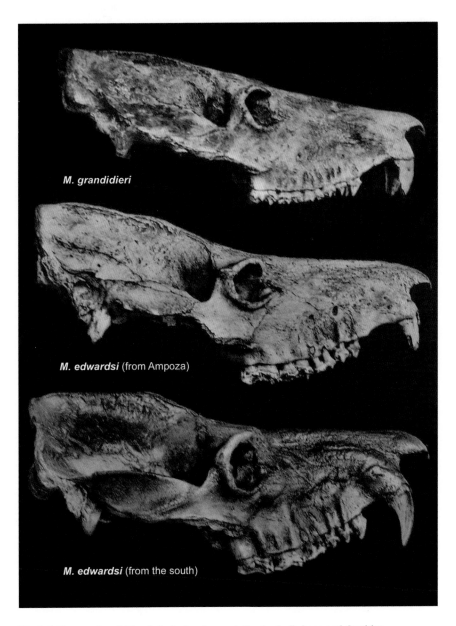

Fig. 3.6: Two species of *Megaladapis* showing variation in skull shape and dentition.

Affinities of the Subfossil Lemurs

Of the subfossil lemurs, at least three families, eight genera, and 17 species are extinct. Virtually all of the extinct species were larger than any of the living lemurs. When the living and subfossil lemurs are considered together, they form an adaptive spectrum that rivals, or even surpasses, the variety achieved in the major continental areas where primates occur (the Neotropics, Africa and Asia), all of them many times larger than the island of Madagascar. In other words, Madagascar's concentration of primate diversity in recent times (and even today) was truly unsurpassed. The 17 extinct subfossil species are listed below by family and genus:

Family Lemuridae
     Genus *Pachylemur* Lamberton, 1948
         Pachylemur insignis Filhol, 1895
         Pachylemur jullyi G. Grandidier, 1899 (b)
Family Archaeolemuridae
     Genus *Archaeolemur* Filhol, 1895
         Archaeolemur edwardsi Filhol, 1895
         Archaeolemur majori Filhol, 1895
     Genus *Hadropithecus* Lorenz von Liburnau, 1899
         Hadropithecus stenognathus Lorenz von Liburnau, 1899
Family Palaeopropithecidae
     Genus *Palaeopropithecus* G. Grandidier, 1899
         Palaeopropithecus ingens G. Grandidier, 1899 (b)
         Palaeopropithecus maximus Standing, 1903
         Palaeopropithecus kelyus Gommery *et al.*, 2009
     Genus *Archaeoindris* Standing, 1909
         Archaeoindris fontoynontii Standing, 1909
     Genus *Babakotia* Godfrey *et al.*, 1990
         Babakotia radofilai Godfrey *et al.*, 1990
     Genus *Mesopropithecus* Standing, 1905
         Mesopropithecus dolichobrachion Simons *et al.*, 1995
         Mesopropithecus globiceps Lamberton, 1936
         Mesopropithecus pithecoides Standing, 1905
Family Megaladapidae
     Genus *Megaladapis* Forsyth-Major, 1894
         Megaladapis edwardsi (G. Grandidier, 1899) (a)
         Megaladapis grandidieri Standing, 1903
         Megaladapis madagascariensis Forsyth-Major, 1894
Family Daubentoniidae
     Genus *Daubentonia* É. Geoffroy St. Hilaire, 1795
         Daubentonia robusta (Lamberton, 1934)

Adaptations and Habitats of Extinct Lemurs

Family Lemuridae

The only extinct genus of the family Lemuridae thus far discovered is *Pachylemur* (Fig. 3.4), which is represented by at least two species, *Pachylemur insignis* (Fig. 3.7) and *P. jullyi*. Individuals are estimated to have weighed 10–13 kg and are known from sites in central and southwestern Madagascar (Godfrey and Jungers, 2002). Skull structure is very close to that of *Varecia*, with dental microwear and tooth morphology suggesting a mixed diet dominated by fruits (Godfrey *et al.*, 2004a). The heavy-boned postcranial skeleton of *Pachylemur* was initially interpreted to indicate a more terrestrial lifestyle, but more recent interpretations are that this genus was largely arboreal and engaged in some suspensory behavior (Jungers *et al.*, 2002). It apparently survived in the extreme south of Madagascar until at least A.D. 1280–1420 (Burney *et al.*, 2004).

Family Archaeolemuridae

This family had relatively large brains, the tooth combs that characterize the strepsirrhines were replaced in favor of thick nipping incisors, and they had bilophodont teeth (two transverse ridges on the crowns of the molar teeth). For these reasons, they are commonly referred to as the "monkey lemurs." They were stocky and had hands and feet with broad terminal phalanges on all the digits (Godfrey and Jungers, 2002). They were clearly terrestrial but would also have climbed in trees. In trying to envisage their general lifestyle, they have been compared to macaques and baboons (Lamberton, 1938; Tattersall, 1973a, 1982) (Figs. 3.4 and 3.8).

The genus *Archaeolemur*, represented by at least two species (*Archaeolemur edwardsi* and *A. majori*), is perhaps the most widely distributed of all the subfossil lemur genera, having been found in abundance at sites in the south, southwest, center, northwest and north of Madagascar. Body weight is estimated at 15–25 kg (Jungers *et al.*, 2002). The molar teeth resemble those of Old World monkeys in being bilophodont, with two

Fig. 3.7: Mounted skeleton of *Pachylemur insignis* in the Musée de l' Académie Malgache in Antananarivo (photo by S. D. Nash).

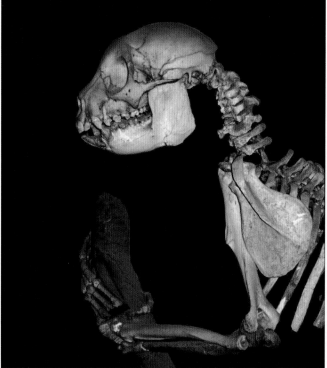

Fig. 3.8: A mounted skeleton of *Archaeolemur* in the Musée de l' Académie Malgache in Antananarivo (photos by S. D. Nash).

transverse crests, which suggests a diversified diet that might have included frugivory, seed predation, and omnivory (Godfrey *et al.*, 2004a). *Archaeolemur* was a deliberate quadruped and among the most terrestrial of the extinct lemurs, although it seems likely that it also frequented trees to feed and sleep. It is believed to have survived in northern and northwestern Madagascar until A.D. 1047–1280, and possibly later (Burney *et al.*, 2004).

The genus *Hadropithecus* is considered a sister taxon to *Archaeolemur*. and only one species is thus far known—*Hadropithecus stenognathus,* which weighed approximately 27–35 kg (Jungers *et al.*, 2002) (see Fig. 3.4). Like *Archaeolemur*, it is also thought to have had a varied diet and to have been a semi-terrestrial quadruped that spent at least some time in the trees (Jungers *et al.*, 2002; Godfrey *et al.*, 2004a). It was less agile than *Archaeolemur*, having no suspensory or leaping abilities (Walker *et al.,* 2008), and it apparently died out much sooner, populations persisting in southwestern Madagascar only until about A.D. 444–772 (Burney *et al.*, 2004).

In 1995, Burney and Ramilisinona (1998) interviewed elderly Malagasy in three villages on the southwest coast of Madagascar. Several of the elders related having seen and heard animals that do not match any of today's species. One of these was the *Kidoky*, the description of which the authors concluded was "decidedly lemur-like." Their descriptions of the animal and its behaviors were like those of creatures detailed in historical accounts and folklore recorded in Madagascar between the mid-1600s and the end of the 19th century. Conferring with W. L. Jungers, the authors concluded the likelihood that, considering its reported size (perhaps 25 kg), terrestriality, and baboon-like gait, the most plausible candidates for the *Kidoky* were *Archaeolemur* and *Hadropithecus.*

Family Palaeopropithecidae

The apparent commitment of this family to arboreal suspensory locomotion has earned it the nickname of "sloth lemurs," with the genus *Palaeopropithecus* probably being the most specialized of the group (Fig. 3.4). It had a wide distribution in Madagascar, having been found at sites in the south, southwest, center, northwest, and north of the island. For many years, its locomotor adaptations were the subject of heated debate, but this was resolved in the mid-1980s with the discovery of an associated and relatively complete skeleton in the cave of Anjohibe in northwest Madagascar. As in other dedicated suspensory forms, joints throughout the skeleton of this lemur are built for flexibility rather than for stability and strength. The exception is in the digits of the hand and feet, where stability is most needed when hanging below branches. The first digit is missing and the long, curved phalanges of the rest have tongue-in-groove joints that limit movement to one plane and maximize power grasping. Three species of *Palaeopropithecus* have been described, *Palaeopropithecus ingens, P. maximus*, and *P. kelyus*, but some experts do not distinguish between the first two. *P. kelyus*, on the other hand, which was only recently discovered in northwestern Madagascar, is smaller and quite distinct (W. L. Jungers, unpubl.) (Figs. 3.9 and 3.10). Body weight estimates for the genus range from 35–50 kg (Jungers *et al.*, 2002), and the diet probably consisted largely of fruits and seeds (Godfrey *et al.*, 2004a). Subfossil specimens from Ankilitelo provide a date for *Palaeopropithecus* of 510–680 years ago (Simons *et al.*, 1995), and relict populations may have survived until as late as A.D. 1300–1620 (Burney *et al.*, 2004).

Archaeoindris fontoynontii was a much larger lemur, closer to the size of a male gorilla, and very possibly tipped the scales at approximately 200 kg (Godfrey and Jungers 2002). It is known only from the site of Ampasambazimba on the central plateau, and even there only from rare fossils. Its very large size argues for more of a terrestrial existence than

Fig. 3.9: A skull of the extinct sloth lemur *Palaeopropithecus kelyus* Gommery *et al.*, 2009 still *in situ* in a cave at Anjajavy in northwest Madagascar (photo by R. A. Mittermeier).

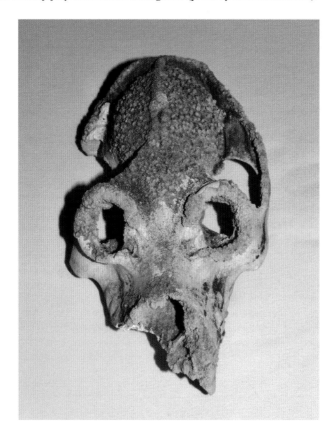

Fig. 3.10: A second specimen of *Palaeopropithecus kelyus* from Anjajavy (photo by R. A. Mittermeier).

that of *Palaeopropithecus*, perhaps more akin to the giant ground sloths of the Americas that became extinct at the end of the last Ice Age (Lamberton, 1934b; Jungers, 1980). Its postcranial anatomy, especially its hip joint mobility, however, does suggest some sort of adaptation to an arboreal lifestyle (Vuillaume-Randriamanantena, 1988), and Godfrey and Jungers (2002) speculated that it is a "capable, but deliberate, scansorial browser, and that it also frequented the ground to feed and travel." Experts believe that this species was still living on the high plateau of Madagascar when people arrived on the west coast at about B.C. 350 (Burney *et al.*, 2004).

Babakotia radofilai was another suspensory arboreal lemur from northern Madagascar that, at only 16–20 kg, was significantly smaller than either *Archaeoindris* or *Palaeopropithecus* (Godfrey and Jungers, 2002; Jungers *et al.*, 2002) (Figs. 3.3 and 3.11). It is believed to have been a fruit and seed eater, an adaptation that fits with its smaller size (Godfrey *et al.*, 2004a). Its skull very much resembles that of *Indri*, but the forelimbs are much more elongated, and the hands and feet appear to have been more adapted for strong grasping. The hind foot was also comparatively reduced, which is not characteristic of animals that leap. The single radiocarbon date available for this species places it on the Ankarana Massif at roughly BP 5000, well before humans arrived on Madagascar.

The genus *Mesopropithecus* contained the smallest of the sloth lemurs (Fig. 3.3). Remains of three species, *Mesopropithecus dolichobrachion*, *M. globiceps*, and *M. pithecoides*, have been found in central and southern Madagascar, and their crania most closely resemble those of modern day sifakas (*Propithecus*). Post-cranial material, however, is very different from that of modern day indriids. Forelimbs, rather than hind limbs, are elongated, favoring suspensory postures and de-emphasizing leaping as a form

Fig. 3.11: Reconstruction of *Babakotia*, a subfossil lemur that probably had a sloth-like lifestyle (artwork by S. D. Nash).

of locomotion. Estimated body weights range from 10–14 kg (Jungers *et al.*, 2002). The consensus is that *M. pithecoides*, which inhabited the high plateau, was largely a folivore, while the other two species were mixed feeders, eating mostly fruits and seeds (Godfrey *et al.*, 2004a). As a group, these species were more quadrupedal than other members of the family, but did engage in suspensory behavior to some degree. Subfossil remains indicate that *Mesopropithecus* survived at least until A.D. 245–429 (Burney *et al.*, 2004).

Family Megaladapidae

Megaladapis, the sole genus of this family, contains three species, *Megaladapis edwardsi*, *M. grandidieri*, and *M. madagascariensis,* known collectively as the "koala lemurs." Details of their molar teeth and various aspects of skull structure originally led experts to believe they were most closely related to the genus *Lepilemur*, but studies of

Fig. 3.12: Some scientists believe that muscle attachments on the snout of *Megaladapis* indicate that it had a prehensile upper lip, which may have been useful in foraging for leaves (artwork by S. D. Nash).

ancient DNA now seem to indicate closer phylogenetic ties to the Lemuridae (A. Yoder, pers. comm.). Body weight estimates range from 45 to 85 kg (the heaviest being similar in weight to a female gorilla, see Figs. 3.4 and 3.14), and leaves were almost certainly the dietary staple for this group (Jungers *et al.*, 2002; Godfrey *et al.*, 2004a). The skull of *Megaladapis* is highly elongated, to a degree found in no other primate, and the face is tilted upwards and connected to a relatively small neurocranium via enormous frontal sinuses (Figs. 3.12 and 3.13). The hole through which the spinal cord exited from the braincase faces fully rearwards, as do the joint surfaces by which the skull articulated with the spine. In combination, these adaptations would have turned the long head into a functional extension of the neck, maximizing the radius within which this heavy animal could have cropped leaves from a single sitting position. *Megaladapis* would have eaten using the horny pad that presumably replaced the adult incisors that are missing in the front of the mouth; an overhanging shelf of bone above the nasal aperture also hints at the presence of a mobile snout (Fig. 3.12).

The body skeleton of *Megaladapis* was no less unusual (Figs. 3.12 and 3.13), apparently finding its closest analogue in the marsupial koala of Australia. Its extraordinarily long hands and feet, highly adapted for strong grasping, make very clear that it was an arboreal animal. However, its arms and legs were rather short, and, in combination with its high body weight, suggest that *Megaladapis* had very limited leaping abilities. Like the koala, these primates would have climbed slowly and cautiously in the trees (Figs. 3.1 and 3.12). Furthermore, they may well have adopted a variety of suspensory postures, perhaps emphasizing the hind limbs, since the feet were even more elongated and specialized for powerful grasping than were the hands. Specimens from the Ankilitelo pit cave in southwest Madagascar show that *Megaladapis* was alive 630–650 years ago (Simons *et al.*, 1995), and based on Carbon-14 dates, this genus persisted in southwestern Madagascar until at least A.D. 1280–1420 (Burney *et al.*, 2004).

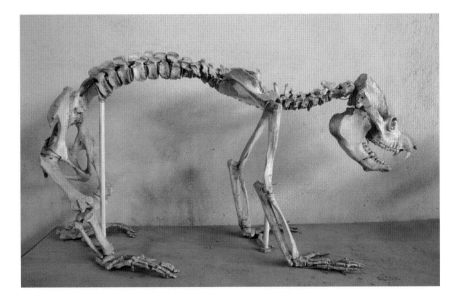

Fig. 3.13: One of the reconstructed subfossil skeletons (*Megaladapis edwardsi*) on exhibit in the Musée de l' Académie Malgache in Antananarivo. Note that this is an early reconstruction. It may be that not all of the bones are properly associated, and that the animal's posture may be unnatural (photo by P. Oxford).

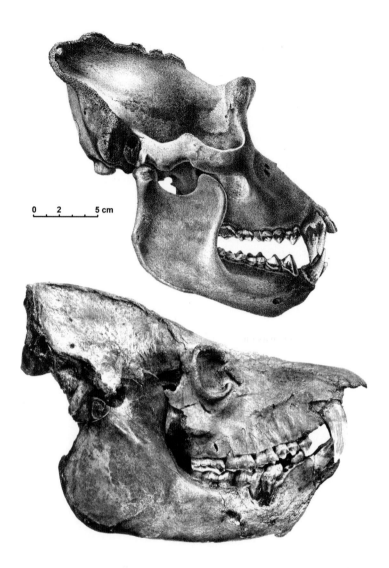

Fig. 3.14: A comparison of the skulls of *Gorilla gorilla* and *Megaladapis edwardsi*. The lemur is from Lorenz von Libernau (1905) and the gorilla from 'Des Caracteres Anatomiques des Grands Singes Pseudo-Anthropomorphes', 'Archives du Museum d'Histoire Naturelle' (1853).

Family Daubentoniidae

In addition to the eight lemur genera that have gone extinct in Madagascar, another extant genus, *Daubentonia*, is represented by a larger extinct species, the giant aye-aye (*Daubentonia robusta*), together with the living aye-aye (*D. madagascariensis*). The difference in size between the extinct form (approximately 14 kg) and the living species (less than 3 kg) is significant (Jungers *et al.,* 2002), although it is believed that giant aye-ayes probably had a similar diet of nuts and invertebrate larvae (Godfrey *et al.*, 2004a). Postcranial skeletal remains also suggest that subfossil aye-ayes were arboreal quadrupeds and had limited leaping abilities, much the same as their modern relatives. *Daubentonia robusta* is known to have survived at least until A.D. 891–1027 in southern Madagascar.

Extinction of the Subfossil Lemurs

One of the most notable results of the early discovery of subfossil sites in central Madagascar was to draw attention to the fact that this region, almost treeless today, must formerly have been forested. It was obvious that most, if not all, of the extinct lemurs were forest-living animals, and their bones were also found in association with those of extant forms that we know to be confined to forest areas. However, the degree to which the plateau was forested when the subfossil bones were accumulating remains a subject of discussion. Early workers, especially the French botanist Henri Humbert, developed the notion that Madagascar had once been entirely covered by forests, but that these were largely destroyed by fire following the arrival of humans who cleared the land for grazing and cultivation (Humbert, 1927; Humbert and Cours Darne, 1965). Others, noting that many of the southern and southwestern subfossil sites are marshes that have to one extent or another dried out, proposed that natural drying of the climate, at least locally, had deprived the large extinct lemurs of needed habitat.

Recent paleoenvironmental work by David Burney and colleagues has shown that the forests of Madagascar have fluctuated in extent over the past several millennia (Burney *et al.*, 2004). The grasslands of the central plateau are thus not entirely anthropogenic in origin, although Humbert was clearly right in identifying cutting, burning and grazing as the greatest current threats to the island's natural vegetation and thus to the habitat of the surviving lemurs. Nonetheless, substantial areas of forest still support large populations of lemurs, and this fact points to the selective nature of the recent extinctions. All of the lemur species that disappeared were larger than any existing species, and they were likely slower-moving as well.

As Burney's work suggests, Madagascar was not immune to the environmental vicissitudes that are well known to have afflicted northern latitudes during the Ice Ages. It may well be that climatic changes in the past reduced and/or modified the habitat available to the precursors of the living and subfossil lemurs. Nonetheless, the now-vanished lemur lineages and the still extant forms had obviously survived these climatic stresses. In the absence of any evidence that the most recent climatic oscillations were particularly severe (they probably were not), the only evident candidate for such a factor is the appearance of humans in Madagascar.

Those lemur (and other vertebrate) species that went extinct were both the most attractive as a food source (because of their large size) and the most vulnerable to human predation (because of their slow-moving habits) (Godfrey and Jungers, 2003a). For the lemurs, inferences concerning their reproductive rates indicate that they were low; they all likely had interbirth intervals of at least two years. But those with the lowest rates were not necessarily the largest. Catlett *et al.* (2010) concluded that those with the largest brains were the slowest breeders, and that low reproductive rates (less resilience to hunting) and large body size contributed, both independently and together, as factors in the extinction of the different species.

In sum, the extinct lemurs were those that would be expected to succumb most readily to human hunting pressures and to severe habitat fragmentation. The same threats face living lemurs, except that the range of human activities placing them at risk has increased both in magnitude and complexity.

Fig. 4.1: A ring-tailed lemur (*Lemur catta*) from the Chinese Emperor Ganlong's private zoological collection, as painted in 1761 by the Italian missionary Giuseppe Castiglione (1688-1766). From the collection of the Taipei Gugong National Museum.

CHAPTER 4

DISCOVERY AND STUDY OF THE
LIVING LEMURS

The remarkable lemur fauna of Madagascar must surely have been known to Arab and Portuguese sailors long before the 17th century. But the earliest reference to any lemur of which we are aware dates back to the year 1608, and was published in 1625. The vehicle was an enormous compilation of voyages, titled *Hakluytus Posthumus* or "Purchas his Pilgrimes," which Samuel Purchas edited in the latter year in celebration of the early successes of the East India Company of London. In this work, Purchas included parts of an account of a visit to Sainte Augustin's Bay (just south of modern Toliara) by several of the company's ships. William Finch, one of the expedition's merchants, recorded that "*In the woods neere about the [Onilahy] River, is a great store of beasts, as big as Munkies, ash-coloured, with a small head, long taile like a Fox, garled with white and blacke, the fur very fine.*" Clearly this was *Lemur catta*, appropriately described by Finch's companion Captain Keeling as "the beautifull beast."

In the following years anecdotal accounts of lemurs proliferated, among the most engaging being those of the Cornish merchant Peter Mundy, who was the first to record a lemur from the Comores. In a journal entry for 1655, Mundy described a mongoose lemur (*Eulemur mongoz*) that had been taken aboard his ship when it called at the island of Anjouan. It was "*exceeding nimble, thatt itt would skip from rope to rope [...] with such agilitie thatt itt seemed rather to flie than leape. And soe famigliar to every one thatt hee would leape on their shoulders, take them fast about the necks and licke their mouths and faces.*" This is a most evocative description for anyone familiar at first-hand with these charming primates.

However, the most famous of the early accounts of lemurs is that of the French merchant Etienne de Flacourt, who spent from 1648 to 1665 at Fort-Dauphin (= Tolagnaro) as "Directeur de la Compagnie Françoise de l'Orient and Commandant pour sa Majesté dans [Madagascar] and és Isles adjacentes." During his stay at the island's southern tip, this remarkable man compiled an account of Madagascar's people and natural wonders that remained definitive for two centuries. In a famous passage, Flacourt described at least seven living species of lemurs, including the black-and-white ruffed lemur (*Varecia variegata*), the bamboo lemur (*Hapalemur griseus*), the sifaka (*Propithecus verreauxi*), the ring-tailed lemur (*Lemur catta*), the mouse lemur (*Microcebus murinus*), the brown lemur (*Eulemur fulvus*), and maybe the woolly lemur (*Avahi laniger*).

In addition, Flacourt described the "tretretretre" or "tratratratra," which is often interpreted as *Megaladapis*, one of the largest of Madagascar's extinct lemurs. Given the interest of this animal, we translate Flacourt's description of it here in full: "*An animal as big as a two-year-old calf, with a round head and a human face: the front feet are monkeylike, and the rear ones as well. It has frizzy hair, a short tail and humanlike ears. [...] One has been seen near Lake Lipomami, around which it lives. It is a very solitary animal; the local people fear it greatly and flee from it as it does from them.*" (de Flacourt, 1658). Given what we know of *Megaladapis*, Flacourt's description is not entirely convincing, and it is anyway far from clear that Flacourt ever saw a "tretretretre" himself. However, this may be about as close as we will ever come to an eyewitness description of one of the extraordinary giant extinct lemurs of Madagascar.

Throughout the 17th century, travelers continued to supply accounts of Malagasy lemurs, but it was not until 1703 that one of these primates is recorded as having reached a European capital where it could be examined by the savants of the day. In that year, a mongoose lemur from Anjouan was described and illustrated by James Petiver, a London apothecary. Petiver had some difficulty in classifying this primate, and eventually equated it with one of the African monkeys that had been described by the eminent anatomist John Ray.

Fig. 4.2: An early depiction (1790) of a ring-tailed lemur (*Lemur catta*) by Sowerby, from Shaw's *Museum Leverianum*, 1792–1796.

As early as 1638, Peter Mundy had recorded seeing a lemur that had been taken by sailors to the Indian town of Surat, so almost from the beginning these animals had evidently found their way at least occasionally onto merchant ships passing through Madagascar or the Comores. In view of this, it is perhaps rather surprising that almost 40 years seem to have passed after Petiver's description before any further published notice of lemurs appeared. This came from the pen and brush of the London illustrator George Edwards, who in 1751 described and illustrated a mongoose lemur, which he clearly recognized as distinct from any monkey. It was, indeed, on another of Edwards' illustrations that Carolus Linnaeus, the Swedish inventor of the modern system of classifying living things, based the species description of *Lemur catta* in the definitive 1758 (10th) edition of his great work *Systema Naturae*. *Lemur* was one of only three genera into which Linnaeus classified all primates then known, and *L. catta* was the only Malagasy primate among the several species allocated to this genus.

Two years earlier, however, the French naturalist Brisson had been able to describe at least three species of what he called "*Prosimia*," and which in today's terminology were undoubtedly *Lemur catta*, *Eulemur mongoz* and *Eulemur fulvus*, from specimens belonging to the Count de Réaumur in Paris. By 1756, Edwards himself had added the "Black Maucauco" and some others to his gallery of lemurs illustrated from life. The Black Maucauco was later designated the type (definitive) specimen of *Eulemur macaco* by Linnaeus, in his 12th edition of *Systema Naturae* in 1766. This animal, kept by Mr. Critington of the Royal College of Surgeons, appears to have had rather eclectic dietary tastes; while Edwards had it to illustrate "*it eats cakes, bread and butter, and summer fruits, it being in July.*"

It may seem a little odd that after 40 years of obscurity, lemurs appear suddenly to have abounded in London and Paris in the 1750s. However, at around this time the collection of exotic animals had become something of a craze among the wealthy, and naturalists began to benefit from the trend. In Paris during the 1760s and 1770s, for example, such eminent scientists as Buffon and Daubenton were able to provide descriptions of the anatomy of several lemur species.

In addition to their appearance in Europe, lemurs were also being imported into East Asia during the 18th century, perhaps by Arab trading ships, by way of Vietnam. This is demonstrated by the fact that Emperor Ganlong of the Qing Dynasty of China kept a ring-tailed lemur (*L. catta*) in his private zoological collection, along with a number of gibbons (*Hylobates*), lorises (*Loris*), and other exotic animals. The Italian missionary Giuseppe Castliglione (1688–1766), who had served under the emperor, left us a drawing of this animal (Fig. 4.1).

This was also the time when more substantial accounts of lemurs and their native habitat began to be furnished by traveling naturalists. In 1771, Joseph-Philibert Commerson made his classic statement about Madagascar: "*I can announce to naturalists that this is the true Promised Land. Here Nature seems to have created a special sanctuary whither she seems to have withdrawn to experiment with designs different from any she has used elsewhere. At every step, one finds more remarkable and marvellous forms of life.*" None too soon, Madagascar was finally beginning to be seen as the extraordinary home of an endemic and astonishing fauna.

Commerson, alas, failed to survive the return journey to France, although his illustrations provided the basis on which Étienne Geoffroy Saint-Hilaire first described the dwarf lemurs (*Cheirogaleus*) in 1812. Commerson's colleague, Sonnerat, was more fortunate, visiting Madagascar on several occasions between 1774 and 1781, and recording a variety of lemur species in the 4th Book of his *Voyage aux Indes orientales et à la Chine*. Sonnerat's "firsts" included illustrations of the aye-aye (later *Daubentonia*) and the woolly lemur (later *Avahi*).

The 19th century ushered in a period during which published references to new lemurs came thick and fast as specimens flooded into Europe. The resulting proliferation of new zoological names led to a nomenclatural thicket which later systematists were obliged to work hard and long to disentangle. From mid-century on, most lemur specimens came to the attention of museum curators in England and continental Europe through the efforts of a new category of explorers—professional collectors whose expeditions had as their primary objective the collection of specimens for museums, menageries and cabinets. The first major foray of this kind to Madagascar was undertaken in 1864 and subsequent years by François Pollen and J. C. van Dam of the Rijksmuseum van Natuurlijke Historie in Leiden, Holland. Pollen and van Dam's collection from the north and northwest of Madagascar and on the island of Mayotte in the Comores still forms perhaps the central resource for systematic studies of lemurs from these regions. These collections were splendidly complemented during 1876–1879 by the German collector Josef-Peter Audebert, who obtained numerous specimens from Madagascar's northeast for the same museum.

Hard on the heels of Pollen and van Dam came the Englishman Alfred Crossley, who crisscrossed Madagascar in search of bird and mammal specimens between 1865 and his premature death in 1870. Unfortunately, Crossley's marvelous collections were dispersed through commercial dealers (in whose care much documentation was lost), but many of his specimens found a permanent home in the British Museum, where they form the core of another of the world's outstanding collections of Malagasy birds and mammals.

Another cause for dispersal of unified collections during this period was a general "postage stamp" mentality among naturalists. It was considered vastly preferable to have one specimen of each of ten species than to have 10 of one species, and this led to the widespread trading of specimens between individuals and institutions, as those responsible strove to maximize the breadth of their collections, inevitably at the expense of their depth. This activity, and the mindset behind it, did much to impede the appreciation by systematists of the variation in external appearance that naturally occurs between individuals of the same species.

One naturalist who clearly understood the importance of such variation was the French explorer Alfred Grandidier, who devoted his life to the documentation of the peoples and natural history of Madagascar. His efforts culminated in the publication of a magnificent series of volumes between 1875 and 1930. Unfortunately, while several folios of lemur illustrations appeared (Vols. 9 and 10), only one volume of explanatory text was completed (Vol. 6 on the Indriidae). This is particularly regrettable since Grandidier was rather innovative in his use of names to identify the lemurs that he so magnificently illustrated. Confusion inevitably resulted when later workers used his plates to identify specimens that came before them. Compounding this is the fact that virtually all of the collections on which Grandidier's illustrations were based appear subsequently to have disappeared.

Several other major collections were made during the last two decades of the 19th century, in the years leading up to the French takeover of Madagascar in 1895. Notable among them were those made by the German J. M. Hildebrandt for the Berlin Museum, W. W. Abbott for the Smithsonian Institution, and C. I. Forsyth Major for the British Museum (Natural History). Other important contributions were also made during this period by missionaries, in particular by William Deans Cowan and other emissaries of the London Missionary Society. Back in Europe, the efforts of numerous museum systematists such as John Edward Gray and Albert Günther in London and A. Schlegel in Leiden ensured that the supply of new names kept up with that of new specimens. As a result, by the early years of the twentieth century a large number of competing nomenclatures existed for the lemurs of Madagascar.

The nomenclatural chaos of the late nineteenth century gradually gave way to a more ordered approach during the 1920s. The identification of the many specimens collected during the Mission Zoologique Franco-Anglo-Américaine of 1929–1931 (a resource divided today between the great natural history museums of New York, London and Paris) show that by this time the familiar modern nomenclature had more or less taken on its present form. This was enshrined in a landmark publication by Ernst Schwarz in 1931, which provided the starting point for all subsequent systematic work on lemurs.

While a firm framework of nomenclature for the lemurs of Madagascar had thus been laid well before the middle of the 20th century, those interested in aspects of the behavior and ecology of these primates were limited until the 1950s to the anecdotal accounts of 19th century explorers and collectors. It was not until late in the 1950s that French scientist

The Mongooz.

Fig. 4.3: One of the earliest depictions of the mongoose lemur (*Eulemur mongoz*) by George Edwards in the mid-18th century.

Fig. 4.4: An illustration of a female *Eulemur mongoz* from *L'histoire Naturelle des Mammifères* by É. Geoffroy Saint-Hilaire (1819).

Jean-Jacques Petter (1962a, 1962b) undertook a survey of Madagascar's primate fauna in which he included observations on the ecology and social groupings of a variety of lemurs at different sites on the island. American researcher Alison Jolly (1966) followed in 1963 with a more detailed study of the diet and social behavior of the ring-tailed lemur (*Lemur catta*) and Verreaux's sifaka (*Propithecus verreauxi*) at the now famous site of Berenty in Madagascar's far south (Jolly, 2004; Jolly *et al.*, 2006a, 2006b). Between them, these two individuals ushered in a new era of research on lemur ecology and behavior, including, in recent years, intense concern for the conservation of these remarkable animals.

Although Petter was one of the great pioneers of lemur research and made many contributions to our knowledge of them, much of it summarized in his book in the *Faune de Madagascar* series (Petter *et al.*, 1977), he did not have a long-term field site. In contrast, Jolly began her work in the Berenty Private Reserve in 1963, and has continued it to the present; a total of 47 years at the time of writing. Her work on ring-tailed lemurs (*L. catta*) and on Verreaux's sifakas (*P. verreauxi*) have resulted in many publications over the years, both by Jolly herself and by the hundreds of researchers and students from various countries who have spent time in this site and are ongoing (e.g., Jolly, 1966, 2003; Jolly *et al.*, 1982a, 1982b, 2006a, 2006b; Jolly and Pride, 1999; Mertl-Milhollen, 1976 and subsequent publications: Blumenfeld-Jones *et al.*, 2006). Other long-term studies at Berenty include those first initiated in the 1970s by Marcel Hladik and others on feeding ecology, and by another French team under Pierre Charles-Dominique, focusing on social behavior. Both studies have since been inherited by a team from the National Museum of Natural History in Paris, which focuses primarily on the feeding ecology of several species (Simmen *et al.*, 2003, 2006a, 2006b, 2007; Simmen, 2006). Equally important is the work being carried out on ring-tailed lemurs by a team from Kyoto University, Japan, which was first headed by Naoki Koyama and now by Takayo Soma (Koyama *et al.*, 2001, 2002, 2006, 2008; Soma, 2006). This long-term study analyzes population dynamics, social interactions, and feeding ecology. The team also carries out laboratory studies on molecular genetics and morphology (Koyama *et al.*, 2002; Nakamichi *et al.*, 1997; Takahata *et al.*, 2008). More recently, an Italian team from Pisa University has begun focusing on sifaka and ring-tailed lemur ecology (Palagi and Norscia, 2009; Palagi *et al.*, 2008), and a Malagasy team from Antananarivo University under Hanta Rasamimanana began sending Malagasy students to work there in the late 1990s (Rasamimanana, 1999, 2006; Rasamimanana *et al.*, 2006). While most of these studies have focused on ring-tailed lemurs and Verreaux's sifakas, there are a few being conducted on other species as well, such as on the reserve's hybrid *Eulemur* population (Pinkus *et al.,* 2006) and on the ecology of the grey-brown mouse lemur (*Microcebus griseorufus*) (Génin, 2008).

Several other important studies of lemur behavior and ecology were undertaken in the late 1960s and early 1970s elsewhere in the country, prior to a hiatus imposed by political events of the mid-1970s. These included the first detailed study of mouse lemurs (*Microcebus murinus*) by Robert D. Martin (1972a, 1973), and of the sportive lemur (*Lepilemur leucopus*) by Marcel Hladik and Pierre Charles-Dominique in 1970 (published in 1974), comparative studies of *Propithecus verreauxi* at sites in the northwest and south by Alison Richard (1973 and subsequent publications), studies of sympatric ring-tailed lemurs (*Lemur catta*) and the red-fronted brown lemur (at that time *Lemur fulvus rufus*, now *Eulemur rufifrons*) in southwestern Madagascar by Bob Sussman (1974 and subsequent publications), and the pioneer rain forest study of *Indri indri* by Jon Pollock (1975a, 1975b) at Périnet (= Andasibe). This period also saw the first studies of lemurs living in the Comoros Islands, the mongoose lemur (*Eulemur mongoz*) on Mohéli and Anjouan (Tattersall, 1976a, 1976b) and the brown lemur (*Eulemur fulvus = mayottensis*) on Mayotte (Tattersall, 1977b).

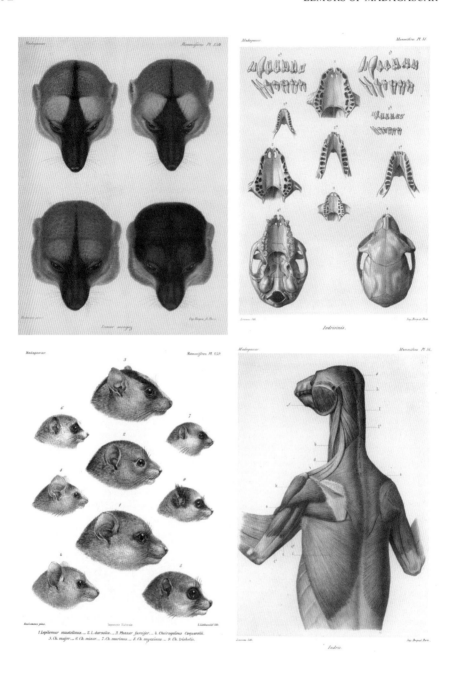

Fig. 4.5: Four plates of lemurs from volume 10 of Alfred Grandidier's classic 32-volume series of books on Madagascar, volumes 6, 9, and 10 of which dealt with some of the lemur genera. The accompanying text to the volume on the Indridae, the only one completed, was published in 1875.

Fig. 4.6: Four more plates of lemurs from Alfred Grandidier's classic series. The plates here are from volume 9.

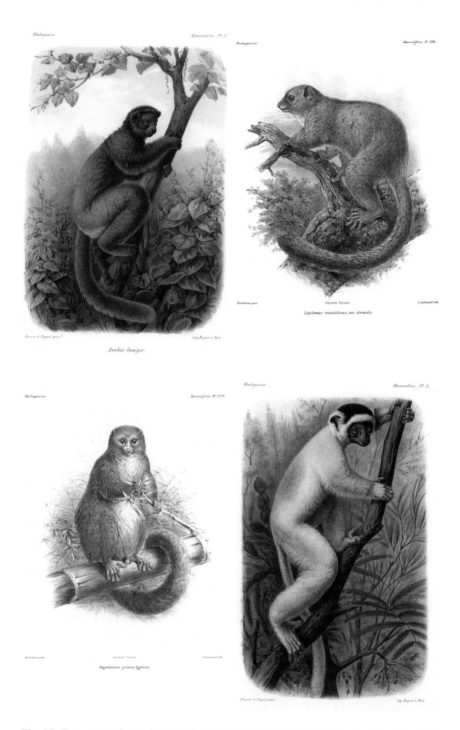

Fig. 4.7: Four more plates of lemurs from Alfred Grandidier's classic series. Top left: *Avahi laniger*; **top right:** *Lepilemur dorsalis*; **bottom left:** *Hapalemur griseus*; **bottom right:** *Propithecus verreauxi*.

Field activity waned in the aftermath of Madagascar's revolution from 1972 to 1974, but in the early 1980s field studies of the lemurs resumed with great vigor, due in part to the renewed involvement of the Duke University Primate Center (now the Duke Lemur Center) under the direction of Elwyn Simons and, subsequently, Ken Glander. A notable result of this was the establishment, through the efforts of Patricia Wright, of a research base and national park at Ranomafana in the eastern rain forest. Since the mid-1980s, there has been a proliferation of studies of rain forest lemurs at that site, including research on Milne-Edwards' sifaka (*Propithecus edwardsi*) (Wright, 1988), red-bellied lemur (*Eulemur rubriventer*) (Overdorff, 1988, 1991), red-fronted brown lemur (*Eulemur rufifrons*) (Overdorff, 1991), and the first report of the previously undescribed golden bamboo lemur (*Hapalemur aureus*) (Meier *et al.*, 1987).

More recently, the Institute for the Conservation of Tropical Environments (ICTE) was established at Stony Brook University in 1994 to encourage and promote scientific research, training, and conservation in the tropics, with a particular focus on Madagascar. ICTE coordinates and catalogs the work of hundreds of natural and social scientists at Ranomafana National Park and other parts of Madagascar, organizes and conducts biodiversity surveys and ecological assessments of tropical ecosystems, and trains scientists at all levels through field-based courses, collaborations, and academic exchanges. ICTE was the impetus behind the development and construction of the Centre ValBio Research Station, directly adjacent to the park. This research station is one-of-a-kind in Madagascar, providing logistical support, modern facilities, and access to technology for this globally important rain forest park. Its health, hygiene and education projects extend to villages all around the southeast of Madagascar. Recent research projects there include the conservation of *Prolemur simus* at Ranomafana and Ivato, and studies of aging in lemurs (L. Donovan, pers. comm.).

Also noteworthy is the study site for lemurs of the southwestern deciduous and spiny forests established by Alison Richard and Malagasy collaborators at Beza-Mahafaly in 1985. Detailed demographic records of Verreaux's sifaka (Richard *et al.*, 1991, 1993) and of the ring-tailed lemur (Sauther, 1991; Sussman, 1991) emerged from long-term studies carried out there.

In the northwest, Jörg Ganzhorn and others (Ganzhorn and Abraham, 1991) renewed research interest in what was then the Ankarafantsika Nature Reserve (now a national park). To the north of this, near Maromandia, Koenders *et al.* (1985a) were able to confirm the separate identity of the blue-eyed black lemur (*Eulemur flavifrons*), and David Meyers and colleagues (Meyers *et al.*, 1989) later documented the geographical relationship between this taxon and the black lemur (*Eulemur macaco*), which itself became the subject of several studies.

Still further north, the Ankarana Massif at last began to attract the attention it deserved, both from zoologists and ecologists (Hawkins *et al.*, 1990) and from paleontologists (Simons *et al.*, 1992; Wilson *et al.*, 1995; Godfrey *et al.*, 1996). It was on the Ankarana that Jane Wilson and colleagues (Wilson *et al.*, 1989; Wilson, 1995) undertook the first field study of the crowned lemur, *Eulemur coronatus*. Close to the northern tip of Madagascar, David Meyers (Meyers and Ratsirarson, 1989) also conducted the first detailed field study of Tattersall's sifaka (*Propithecus tattersalli*). Finally, the island of Nosy Mangabe in the Bay of Antongil in the northeast was the site of two pioneering studies, one by Morland (1991a) on the northern black-and-white ruffed lemur (*Varecia variegata subcincta*) and another by Sterling (1993b) on the elusive aye-aye (*Daubentonia madagascariensis*).

Fig. 4.8: A series of plates of various lemurs from *Récherches sur la Faune de Madagascar et de ses Dépendances*, by F. P. L. Pollen and D. C. van Dam, published in Leiden in 1868.

Since the publication of the first edition of this field guide in 1994, a great many new field studies have been carried out. What is particularly heartening is that more and more Malagasy scientists are engaging in such fieldwork, since they are truly the future of research and conservation in this globally important country; indeed several of them are coauthors of and contributors to this third edition. Also of great importance is the fact that there has been an explosion of new species' discoveries in Madagascar since 1994. Much of that has taken place since 2000, and it has resulted in a doubling of the known living

Lemur pufillus Geoffr.

Fig. 4.9: *"Lemur pusillus"* **from** *Die Säugthiere in Abbildungen nach Natur* **by Johann Christian Daniel Schreber, published by Wolfgang Walther in Erlangen, Germany in 1795. Although this illustration does not look very much like a mouse lemur, the name** *"Lemur pusillus"* **is a synonym of** *Microcebus murinus.*

Fig. 4.10: An *Avahi* **depicted by De Seve in Livre XIII (***Les Quadrupèdes***) of the** *Histoire Naturelle Générale et Particulière* **by George-Louis Leclerc, Comte de Buffon (1783).**

lemur fauna, from 50 taxa (32 species) in the first edition of this field guide to 71 taxa in the second edition just three years ago, to 101 and counting in this latest version. Rather than trying to summarize all of these, we refer the reader to the individual species accounts that include new information from studies that have taken place since the appearance of the first (1994) and second (2006) editions of this book. However, a summary review of the major organizations involved in research and conservation, and of the various research groups conducting fieldwork, is in order and follows here.

Building on early studies on the ecology of lemurs in the dry deciduous forest of the Menabe (Charles-Dominique *et al.*, 1980), the University of Tübingen under Jörg Ganzhorn initiated another long-term Malagasy/Swiss/German research program in the Kirindy Forest (Kirindy/CFPF) in 1987. This effort has now been continued by the German

Primate Center (DPZ), beginning in 1993. New approaches in these studies include measurements of lemur metabolism in the field and documented torpor and hibernation of lemurs under field conditions (Ortmann *et al.*, 1997; Drack *et al.*, 1999; Schmid, 2000; Dausmann *et al.*, 2000, 2004). The German Primate Center's recently completed studies there include the first comprehensive field observations of the behavioral ecology of the red-tailed sportive lemur (*Lepilemur ruficaudatus*) (Hilgartner *et al.*, 2008), the pale fork-marked lemur (*Phaner pallescens*) (Schülke, 2003a, 2003b, 2005; Schülke and Kappeler, 2003), and Madame Berthe's mouse lemur (*Microcebus berthae*) (Dammhahn and Kappeler, 2008a, 2008b, 2009). Ongoing studies focus on aspects of sexual selection, such as reproductive strategies (Kappeler and Port, 2008; Kappeler and Schäffler, 2008; Mass *et al.*, 2009; Port *et al.*, 2009), as well as inter- and intragroup communication in *Propithecus verreauxi* and *Eulemur fulvus* (Barthold *et al.*, 2009; Benadi *et al.*, 2008; Fichtel, 2008). In addition, the distribution and coexistence of sympatric cheirogaleids is being studied in the central Menabe region as a whole, with particular attention being given to the status of *M. berthae* throughout its entire range. Recently completed and ongoing projects also focus on phylogeographic questions relating to *Cheirogaleus* (see Groeneveld *et al.*, 2009, in press), *Microcebus*, *Eulemur*, and western *Propithecus*. A large-scale study of the social system of the fossa (*Cryptoprocta ferox*) should also yield some interesting information about predation on lemurs.

Long-term research has been carried out by the University of Hanover, Germany, under Elke Zimmermann and Ute Radespiel, at the field station of Ampijoroa in Ankarafantsika National Park. There the focus has been on evolution of lemurs, with emphasis on nocturnal genera, the mouse lemurs (*Microcebus*), the sportive lemurs (*Lepilemur*) and the woolly lemurs (*Avahi*). Since 1994, this group has been studying socioecology, population ecology, communication, cognition, and conservation genetics, along with their phylogeny and phylogeography. The primary goals are to explore and to further develop hypotheses on the evolution of primates, and to collect the necessary information to improve the management and conservation of these taxa. Research methods include radio-tracking, mark-recapture procedures, morphometric measurements, focal observations, ecological census techniques, plant phenology, bioacoustics, psychoacoustics, playback experiments, GIS-based spatial analyses, genotyping, and genetic analyses. With this research, they aim to develop competence in tropical biodiversity research in Madagascar by integrating local scientists and students. They also conduct courses on tropical ecology at the Ampijoroa Field Station for students of biology and veterinary medicine, and cooperate closely with the University of Antananarivo, the University of Mahajanga, and Madagascar National Parks.

In the far south, in the region of Fort-Dauphin (= Tolagnaro), a team led by Jörg Ganzhorn is collaborating with the environmental program of an international mining operation to support the protection of remaining littoral forests in that region (Ganzhorn *et al.*, 2007). Since 1997, natural and artificial forest fragments have been used in a semi-experimental research design to assess possibilities for the controlled translocation of lemurs (Donati *et al.* 2007), studying the links and interactions between parasite infection, forest fragmentation, immune genetics (Major Histocompatibility Complex), and native and introduced mammals as vectors for disease transmission (Schad *et al.*, 2005; Raharivololona *et al.*, 2007; Raharivololona and Ganzhorn, 2009). These forests represent the humid end of a short but steep environmental gradient that allows for investigation of the behavioral and physiological flexibility of a number of lemur species (Lahann *et al.*, 2006; Lahann, 2007; Donati *et al.*, 2009; Schmid and Ganzhorn, 2009; Kobbe and Dausmann, 2009), and under conditions that lead to speciation and hybridization (Gligor *et al.*, 2009).

Fig. 4.11: Watercolor paintings of various lemurs by Charles-Alexandre Lesueur (1787-1846), produced during the Baudin Expedition, 1801-1804. The species depicted are likely *Eulemur collaris*, perhaps *Eulemur cinereiceps*, and *Varecia rubra*.

It is also noteworthy that researchers are increasingly linking lemur research to conservation and development activities. Mitchell Irwin, Jean-Luc Raharison and Karen Samonds have partnered since 2000 to study the 10 lemurs found in high-altitude rainforest at Tsinjoarivo in the central part of the eastern rain forest. Their research has focused mainly on the diademed sifaka (*Propithecus diadema*), documenting its response to habitat disturbance and fragmentation in terms of diet (Irwin, 2008a), ranging (Irwin, 2008b), predation risk (Irwin *et al.*, 2009), and social behavior (Irwin, 2007), as well as body mass and growth, parasite ecology, nutrition, and physiology. This ongoing project's main goals are to document the conditions of lemur-human co-existence (including understanding the causes of local extinctions), and to undertake research that will assist efforts to ensure that coexistence continues in the future. In 2008, these researchers created a new NGO called Sadabe (<http://www.sadabe.org>) centered on Tsinjoarivo with the goal of promoting lemur research, ensuring habitat conservation, and improving human lives through development and humanitarian assistance.

Long-term research on the silky sifaka (*Propithecus candidus*), one of Madagascar's most critically endangered lemurs, has been ongoing since 2001 in the majestic montane rain forests of Marojejy National Park (reviewed in Patel, 2009a). Current projects include population surveys and an intensive study of diet and ranging behavior. Past research has examined scent-marking (Patel, 2006b), vocal communication (Patel, 2002; Patel *et al.*, 2006), and aspects of conservation (Patel *et al.*, 2005a; Patel, 2007b).

A team based at the University of Calgary and led by Steig Johnson has conducted research on brown lemurs (*Eulemur*) across the southeast since the 1990s. White-collared brown (*Eulemur cinereiceps*) and red-fronted brown lemurs (*Eulemur rufifrons*) form a hybrid zone at Andringitra National Park, and Johnson and colleagues have investigated this zone from the social group to the population level, including the ecology of hybrid and parental groups, population surveys, and morphological and genetic analyses to assess adaptation and gene flow (e.g., Wyner *et al.*, 2002; Johnson *et al.*, 2005; Johnson, 2006). The aim is to draw inferences from the present interaction of these taxa as to the factors that may lead to speciation. Additional recent work has focused on allopatric populations of the endangered *E. cinereiceps*, including studies on population genetics, socioecology, forest fragmentation and edge effects, and taxonomy (e.g., Johnson *et al.*, 2008). Research and conservation initiatives have been conducted in close collaboration with NGOs active in the region (Durrell, Missouri Botanical Garden, ICTE, and the Madagascar Biodiversity and Biogeography Project).

Among the most important lemur research teams currently in operation is the Madagascar Biodiversity and Biogeography Project (MBP) fielded by the Henry Doorly Zoo of Omaha, Nebraska, in the United States. It was initiated in 1998 by Edward E. Louis Jr., one of the authors of this book. Louis and his teams have carried out extensive fieldwork on the island for the past 12 years in order to develop baseline molecular, distribution, and census data on lemurs and other Malagasy flora and fauna. The MBP team, which now includes 50 Malagasy employees, has successfully immobilized, collected material from, and released over 4,000 lemurs from 112 sites across Madagascar. What is particularly exciting is that the MBP has been responsible for a large part of the explosion of new species discoveries over the past decade, a total of 21 thus far, with more still to come, and resulting in a major rewrite of lemur taxonomy. At the same time, the new data they have collected has resulted in a much better understanding of lemur distributions, including a redefinition of the ranges of many known species, and a much clearer picture of conservation priorities. In addition, the project is responsible for successfully re-establishing two lemur species, the diademed sifaka (*Propithecus diadema*) and the southern black-and-white ruffed lemur (*Varecia variegata editorum*), into their historical habitat in Analamazaotra Special Reserve, where they had been extirpated by humans decades before. In 2003, Dolch *et al.* (2004), working with the Association Mitsinjo, were able to confirm a population of the Critically Endangered greater bamboo lemur (*Prolemur simus*) at the Torotorofotsy Ramsar site, near Andasibe (Dolch *et al.*, 2008). Conservation efforts for this species have since continued, with the MBP also launching a multifaceted program involving research, community outreach and education at Kianjavato, near Ranomafana in the southeast, intimately connecting the local people with the environment (Wright *et al.*, 2008). What is more, the group has created and distributed 15,000 conservation-based coloring and activity books to Malagasy primary school children, and supports 40 Malagasy graduate students. Lastly, the MBP works with the Malagasy national zoo, the Parc Botanique et Zoologique de Tsimbazaza, and has built several new facilities there, including a large and impressive nocturnal house.

In terms of conservation efforts, few organizations have done as much for Madagascar and its lemurs as has Durrell. This NGO started out as a small private zoo founded by British author Gerald Durrell on the island of Jersey. Long acknowledged as an innovator in captive breeding as an aid to conservation, by the late 1980s it had also started to establish *in situ* projects around the world, and specially in Madagascar. In 1990, it sent a special expedition to the island, primarily to collect specimens of the Alaotran bamboo lemur (*Hapalemur alaotrensis*) and aye-aye (*Daubentonia madagascariensis*) (Carroll and Beattie, 1993; Feistner and Rakotoarinosy, 1993). In this they were successful, quickly establishing captive colonies both in Jersey as well as in a number of other zoos that, combined, now serve as a safeguard against extinction for both species. In addition, Durrell has been conducting field research and developing community-based conservation strategies for the Alaotran bamboo lemur since the early 1990s (Feistner and Rakotoarinosy, 1993; Mutschler and Feistner, 1995; Nievergelt *et al.*, 2002a, 2002b). *Hapalemur alaotrensis* is found only in the marshes of Lake Alaotra, the largest lake in Madagascar, and Durrell has supported the creation of a protected area which will ensure the survival of the bamboo lemur, and also help maintain fish stocks in the lake, a vital resource for thousands of people there. Durrell is also carrying out research and developing conservation strategies for two other highly endangered lemurs—the white-collared brown lemur (*Eulemur cinereiceps*) and southern black-and-white ruffed lemur (*Varecia variegata editorum*)—in the lowland rain forest of Manombo, in southeastern Madagascar. These activities focus on the censusing of populations and mapping habitats, and on working directly with local communities and stakeholders to help them manage their natural resources.

A number of European zoos have been involved in efforts to protect the last remaining habitat of the blue-eyed black lemur (*Eulemur flavifrons*) on the Sahamalaza Peninsula since the late 1980s, when the zoos of Mulhouse, Cologne and Saarbrücken, and the University of Strasbourg founded a consortium for lemur research and conservation. This initiative has developed into the *Association Européenne pour l'Etude et la Conservation des Lémuriens* (AEECL), which today counts 31 member zoos from all over Europe. The association is based in Mulhouse, France, and is steered by a board of directors that includes one of the authors of this book (C. Schwitzer). Together with its partners, the Wildlife Conservation Society (WCS) and Madagascar National Parks, AEECL has, since its creation, been working on the implementation of a UNESCO Biosphere Reserve (established in 2001) and a national protected area on the Sahamalaza Peninsula (inaugurated in 2007).

During 2004, a field research and conservation station and a scientific working group were established by scientists of AEECL and the universities of Antananarivo and Mahajanga in the Ankarafa Forest, situated in the Sahamalaza – Iles Radama National Park. Recently

¹⁄₅

Maki mit weisser Stirne. (Mån. u. Weib).
Lemur albifrons.
Maki a front blanc, mâle et femelle.

Der Mokoko.
Lemur Catta.
Le Mokoko.

Fig. 4.12: Lemur illustrations from *Naturhistorische Abbildungen der Saugetier*, published in Zurich, 1827, by Karl Joseph Brodtmann. The species at the top is a female white-fronted lemur (*Eulemur albifrons*) with young, below it is the male. On the bottom branch is *Lemur catta*.

MURINE LEMUR.

HEART-MARKED LEMUR.

800.Jan.1.London.Publish'd by G.Kearsley Fleet Street.

Fig. 4.13: Two plates of lemurs from *General Zoology* by Shaw (1826). The animal above is a mouse lemur (*Microcebus murinus*) and the one below is most likely a crowned lemur (*Eulemur coronatus*).

completed and ongoing studies address the conservation ecology of the blue-eyed black lemur (Randriatahina and Rabarivola, 2004; Schwitzer *et al.*, 2006, 2007a, 2007b, 2009; Polowinsky and Schwitzer, 2009; Randriatahina and Roeder, in press), the newly described Sahamalaza Peninsula sportive lemur (*Lepilemur sahamalazensis*) (Andriaholinirina *et al.*, 2006a) and Mittermeier's sportive lemur, *Lepilemur mittermeieri* Rabarivola *et al.*, 2006, as well as other lemurs living in the region. The knowledge gained in these studies is being used to help implement effective conservation measures for the endangered lemurs of north-western Madagascar. Together with the local communities living around Sahamalaza – Iles Radama National Park, AEECL has established a community-based natural resource management programme (CBNRM) in the area. The two objectives are to maintain and strengthen natural processes and the condition of terrestrial and marine ecosystems, and to improve natural resource-use techniques to improve the standard of living of the local human populations.

AEECL has also funded and implemented a number of research projects in other areas of Madagascar. A team based at the University of Strasbourg, working with the Universities of Antanananarivo and Mahajanga, and the German Primate Center (Göttingen), and AEECL, has been researching the taxonomy of several genera, including *Hapalemur* (Fausser *et al.*, 2002a, 2002b; Rabarivola *et al.*, 2007) *Avahi* (Razafindrainibe *et al.*, 2000; Zaramody *et al.*, 2006), *Propithecus* (Andriaholinirina *et al.*, 2004; Razafindrainibe *et al.*, 2000) and *Lepilemur* (Ravoarimanana, 2001; Rumpler *et al.*, 2001; Ravoarimanana *et al.*, 2001, 2004; Zaramody *et al.*, 2005; Andriaholinirina *et al.*, 2005, 2006a, 2006b; Rabarivola *et al.*, 2006). Andriaholinirina *et al.* (2006a) even named one of their newly described species of *Lepilemur* after the association, calling it *Lepilemur aeeclis*. Ongoing programs are also focusing on the distributional limits of *Hapalemur* (*H. gilberti* and *H. ranomafanensis*), *Lepilemur* (*L. mittermeieri* and *L. sahamalazensis*) and the eastern *Propithecus*. Last, but not least, the AEECL member zoos have initiated captive propagation programs for the blue-eyed black lemur as well as for a number of other lemur species.

Last but not least, an increasing amount of lemur research is now also being undertaken by Malagasy specialists. For example, GERP (*Groupe d'Etude et de Recherche sur les Primates de Madagascar*) is a Malagasy non-profit association, the membership of which consists of primate researchers and students from different national and international institutions, and with a range of expertise from behavioral ecology and conservation to medicine and genetics. Its main objectives are to conduct research on both subfossil and extant lemurs, as well as to ensure the proper application of legislation and regulations governing lemur conservation. In the process, it also works to improve the livelihood of human populations in the peripheral zones of protected areas where lemurs are living. GERP has carried out research and education/conservation activities at various sites, including Ambato, Maromizaha, Sahafina and Makira. In 2008, GERP staff discovered a new species of mouse lemur, *Microcebus macarthurii*, in the forest of Makira. Also that year, the Ministry of the Environment and Forests assigned GERP the responsibility of managing the Maromizaha Forest, a new protected area in the Ankeniheny-Zahamena corridor. Maromizaha is 4 km from Andasibe, one of the country's most popular tourist lemur-watching destinations. It has more lemur species than Andasibe; 12 in all, including *Indri indri*, *Propithecus diadema*, *Varecia variegata*, and the rare *Allocebus trichotis*.

Fig. 5.1: "Dancing" Verreaux's sifaka (*Propithecus verreauxi*) in the tourist area of the Berenty Reserve (photo by R. A. Mittermeier).

CHAPTER 5

CONSERVATION OF LEMURS

Biodiversity in Madagascar

The island of Madagascar is a major priority not just for primates; it is considered by many to be the single highest biodiversity conservation priority on Earth. Its exceptional diversity and endemism, combined with the fact that much of its original forest cover and some of its most spectacular species have already been lost, make it both one of the world's most endangered "hotspots" and one of the top five of the world's 18 "megadiversity" countries. What is more, recent information on endemic families and genera (Mittermeier *et al.*, 2004) indicate that it is one of the world leaders in these categories as well, with many more unique evolutionary lineages than any other hotspot (Tables 5.1 and 5.2).

Table 5.1. Top Five Hotspots for Endemic Families of Plants and Vertebrates

Hotspot	Endemic plant families	Endemic vertebrate families	Total
Madagascar and Indian Ocean Islands	8	17	25
Southwest Australia	4	3	7
New Zealand	1	6	7
Chilean Winter-Rainfall Valdivian Forests	3	4	7
Forests of New Caledonia	5	1	6

Madagascar's privileged position in terms of biodiversity is based on its geological history and geographic placement. The world's largest oceanic island and the fourth largest island overall, it has been separated from all other land masses for at least 90 million years, meaning that most of its plant and animal life has evolved in isolation. This has resulted in very high levels of endemism, both at the species level and, more importantly, at higher taxonomic levels, with Madagascar having numbers of endemic plant and animal families and genera rivaled only by Australia, which is 13 times larger.

Table 5.2. Top Five Hotspots for Endemic Genera of Plants and Vertebrates

Hotspot	Endemic plant genera	Endemic vertebrate genera	Total
Madagascar and Indian Ocean Islands	310	168	478
Caribbean Islands	205	64	269
Sundaland	117	82	199
Western Afromontane	44	134	178
Cape Floristic Region	160	2	162

Madagascar is situated largely in the tropics (between 11°57'S and 25°37'S) and also has very high species diversity, especially given its relatively small size (587,041 km²). For example, although Madagascar occupies only about 1.9% of the land area of the African region, it has more orchids than all of mainland Africa, and indeed is home to as much as one-third of all African plants. Its total plant diversity is estimated at 14,000–15,000 species, of which about 83% are endemic (Goodman and Benstead, 2005). For animals, the proportion is usually even higher, the best example being the primates; 100% of the island nation's 97 species and 101 taxa occur naturally only on Madagascar (Tables 5.3 and 5.4). Two species, the brown lemur (*Eulemur fulvus*) and the mongoose lemur (*Eulemur mongoz*), also live on the nearby Comoros Islands, but they were almost certainly introduced there from Madagascar by our own species in relatively recent times.

Table 5.3. Top Five Countries on Earth for Nonhuman Primate Species Diversity

Country	Families	Genera	Species	Taxa
Brazil	5	18	114	135
Madagascar	5	15	97	101
Indonesia	5	10	44	68
DRC	4	16	34	56
Colombia	5	12	39	50

At the generic and family levels, Madagascar's primate diversity is even more striking, with fully five primate families and 15 genera found nowhere else. Compare this to Brazil, the richest country in primate species with 114, but none of its five primate families are endemic, and it has only four endemic genera out of 18. In terms of species numbers, Madagascar is second highest on the world list, exceeded only by Brazil; in genera it is only three behind Brazil, in spite of the fact that it is only 7% its size.

Table 5.4. Primate Endemism in the Most Diverse Countries on Earth

Country	Families	Genera	Species	Endemism
Madagascar	5/5	15/15	97/97	100%
Brazil	0/5	4/18	71/114	62%
Indonesia	0/5	1/10	26/44	58%
Colombia	0/5	0/12	7/39	18%
DRC	0/4	1/16	5/34	15%

Other vertebrate groups exhibiting comparable levels of diversity and endemism include the amphibians and the reptiles. All of its 235 native amphibians (about 3.8% of the world total) are endemic, and new species are being described every year (Glaw and Vences, 2007). Glaw and Vences (2007) reported that a further 150 amphibians have been identified but have yet to be named, bringing the count to about 400 species on the island. Reptiles are even more diverse. There are 21 reptile lineages in Madagascar (compared to six for amphibians) and 92% of the country's 363 non-marine reptiles are endemic (Raxworthy, 2003; Glaw and Vences, 2007).

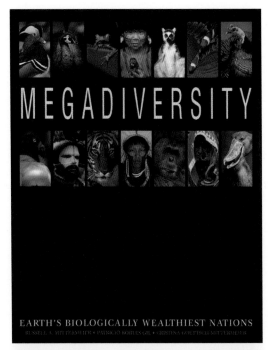

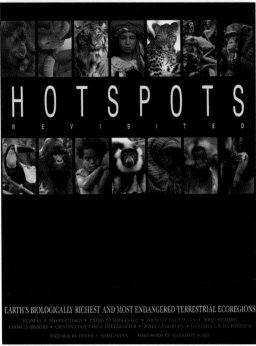

Fig. 5.2: Two books produced by the Mexican cement company CEMEX and Conservation International, which highlight the global importance of Madagascar (Mittermeier *et al.*, 1997, 2004).

In terms of birds, the total number of breeding bird species (209: Hawkins and Goodman, 2003) is relatively low, but endemism is high (109 species or 52%). What is more, five bird families and 37 genera are endemic, a remarkably high number given Madagascar's size (Hawkins and Goodman, 2003).

Madagascar's very high levels of diversity for certain groups, its endemism at both the species and higher taxonomic levels, and its high endemism per unit area all help to push this country to the top of the global conservation priority list. A hectare of forest lost in Madagascar has a greater negative impact on global biodiversity than a hectare lost almost anywhere else, the only regions of comparable importance being some of the other endangered "hotspots" such as the Philippines, parts of Indonesia, the Tropical Andes and Atlantic Forest of South America, and a handful of islands such as New Caledonia in the South Pacific. Unfortunately, many hectares are still being cut every year in Madagascar, and a great deal has already been lost in recent times. The lemur extinctions referred to in the previous chapter and the disappearance of many other spectacular creatures such as eight species each of elephant bird (*Aepyornis* and *Mullerornis*), three of pygmy hippopotamus (*Hippopotamus*), two species of giant tortoise, and two species of an aardvark-like creature (*Plesiorycteropus*) now placed in its own order, are the most striking examples, but others exist as well (see chapter 2). Only the extinctions in the Hawaiian Islands and New Zealand, caused first by Polynesians and then by Europeans, the recent losses in some of the other Indian Ocean islands such as Mauritius and La Reunion, and the impact of the Europeans in Australia can match the great losses in Madagascar that have taken place over the past 2,000 years. Furthermore, as discussed in the individual species profiles in the remainder of this book, it is clear that many of the living lemurs are at great risk of disappearing as well.

What are the threats to lemurs and other forms of life in Madagascar? In this chapter, we discuss these threats, and also what is being done to prevent further lemur extinctions, both through *in situ* conservation in parks and reserves and international *ex situ* captive breeding efforts. We provide an outlook for the future of lemurs in the wild, and comment on how their chances for survival can be improved by demonstrating their long-term economic value to Madagascar and its people. In spite of the many serious problems faced by lemurs and their natural habitats, we believe that the prospects for their long-term survival are still good, and we are optimistic that all of the species alive today can be saved from extinction.

Major Threats to Lemurs

The specific threats to wild lemurs (and indeed to all primates) are many, and can be divided into three main categories: habitat destruction, hunting for food or other purposes, and live capture (Mittermeier and Coimbra-Filho, 1977; Mittermeier, 1987). The impacts of these factors vary considerably from species to species and from region to region, but habitat destruction is usually the major threat.

Habitat Destruction

The most severe threat to primate populations worldwide is the destruction and degradation of tropical forest habitats, where more than 90% of the world's primates reside (Mittermeier, 1987). Lemurs are no exception. As mentioned earlier, it is estimated that more than 90% of Madagascar's original forest cover has already been converted for agriculture and pasture, for mining, for the extraction of precious hardwoods, for firewood and other products, and for a variety of other uses (Fig. 5.3).

Fig. 5.3: Clockwise from top left: Baobab forest burning in the Analabe region of the Menabe Forest of southwestern Madagascar, 1984; severe erosion and burning to the west of the Makira Forest in northern Madagascar, 2004; and erosion, burning, and siltation in the high plateau region of central Madagascar, not far from Antananarivo, 2004 (photos by R. A. Mittermeier).

The causes of forest destruction in Madagascar are many. The human population as of 2009 is about 20 million people in an area of 587,041 km², not very high compared to many other developing countries (and roughly comparable to the populations of Mexico City or São Paulo in an area nearly the size of Texas). Nonetheless, it is growing at 3%, with a doubling time of 25 years; definitely a cause for concern. Perhaps more telling is the fact that there are only 30,000 km² of arable land in a country that is 80% dependent on small-scale agriculture (rice, coffee, vanilla, spices), meaning that there is already great land-use pressure (Fig. 5.4). Another factor is that the Malagasy are relative newcomers to their island, arriving there from southeast Asia, Africa, and intermediate points as recently as 1,500–2,000 years ago and bringing with them a mix of land-use practices not well adapted to Madagascar's delicate ecosystems, including rice-growing from southeast Asia and cattle-raising from East Africa.

The rates of forest loss since the arrival of humans on Madagascar are cause for much concern. It is difficult to ascertain the full extent of forest that existed when people first arrived in Madagascar, but it seems likely that the combination of fire and grazing resulted in the loss of at least 50–60% of all forest between then and the start of the 20th century, much of this in the first 500 years of occupation. Essentially, this involved almost all forest that would burn without first being cut. Since then, the latest estimates show that about 44% of all remaining forest was lost between 1950 and 2000, most of it in the tropical humid zone of eastern Madagascar. Initial rates of loss in the western and southern forest during this period were relatively low, but have increased dramatically since the early 1970s, mainly due to a reversion to rural lifestyles (e.g., slash-and-burn agriculture) and a continually increasing human population. The rate of forest loss has been slowing since 1990, following investments made by the Malagasy government and the international

Fig. 5.4: Paddy rice production in the eastern rain forest region (photo by R. A. Mittermeier), and the drying of vanilla beans in northern Madagascar (photo by W. R. Konstant).

community to address the root causes of poverty and lack of governance (Harper *et al.*, 2007), and is now around 0.53% per year.

Madagascar is mostly covered in a thick layer of extremely weathered bedrock called laterite that contains little organic material. This laterite is extremely infertile, and is not suited to intensive agricultural use. When exposed to the weather it erodes rapidly into sand, leaving much of the country's central plateau a moonscape of baked red earth (Fig. 5.3), giving rise to Madagascar's popular, albeit tragic, nickname, "Le Grande Ile Rouge" ("Great Red Island"). The red sand and dust washes into rivers (Fig. 5.5) and the surrounding ocean during the rainy season, leaving a red ring around the island so striking that it has been observed by astronauts from space. The results of this situation have been disastrous. In the 1980's the World Bank estimated that some $100–300 million of future potential were being lost each year due to this widespread erosion, and it is likely that the figures are now even higher.

The case of rice helps to illustrate some of Madagascar's critical land-use problems. Rice is the mainstay of life in Madagascar, and its cultivation is the primary livelihood of 70% of the country's population; indeed, the Malagasy have the highest level of per capita rice consumption of any country. Traditionally, about 70% of Madagascar's rice is grown in paddies (Fig. 5.4), which can be maintained year after year and have relatively high productivity (though not yet comparable to those of southeast Asia). Paddy rice is grown in the valleys and low plains, especially in the area surrounding Lac Alaotra in the east and the Marovoay plains of the lower Betsiboka River in the west. The remainder is grown as rain-fed rice through slash-and-burn cultivation or *tavy*. Where this involves primary forest, it is not only disastrous for lemurs and other forest wildlife, it also exacerbates erosion and destroys the watershed for paddy rice in the valleys below.

Fig. 5.5: A river in northwestern Madagascar showing the heavy silt load resulting from severe erosion (photo by R. A. Mittermeier).

In the normal *tavy* process used in dry rice cultivation, a plot of forest is cleared of its natural vegetation, which is then burned. The resultant ash provides sufficient nutrients to the otherwise poor soil to allow for a couple of seasons of crop production. When the nutrients are exhausted, the farmer moves on to another plot, leaving the original land to lie fallow and the forest to regenerate before returning, ideally 10–15 years later. In situations where population pressure is low, such shifting techniques can be sustainable, but in Madagascar demands for agricultural land are so great that cultivators are frequently forced to either return to their fields before the forest can fully regenerate or to open new plots. Average fallow time in the agricultural lands surrounding the Zahamena National Park, for example, is seven years or less (F. Boltz, pers. comm.).

The effects of upstream erosion after deforestation can be dramatic. In the first few years, a sudden flush of sand from the deforested laterite slopes is washed downstream and into irrigation channels and rice fields, rendering them unproductive or even barren. This process is of particular importance around the key rice-growing areas of Lac Alaotra and the Marovoay basin.

The widespread use of inappropriate land practices has led to some of the most dramatic examples of erosion on our planet (Figs. 1.6, 1.7, 5.3 and 5.5). Sadly, restoring such land to forest is difficult and costly, and would likely take more than a generation to achieve even if resources were available. Clearly, the top priority to prevent further disastrous erosion must be to conserve whatever natural ecosystems remain intact.

In the past, Madagascar was spared the major depredations of loggers suffered by countries such as Malaysia and Indonesia, partly because its trees are generally smaller and in more difficult terrain than in those countries but also because national policy has favored local small-scale operations. Most native forest in Madagascar has already been subjected to the removal of high-value trees by artisanal loggers, transported out on portable billets. Compared to intensive commercial exploitation, this has not had an immediate or profound impact, but secondary consequences, such as increased hunting, the introduction of alien species, and localized drying of forests leading to increased fire risk, have been significant. Regrowth rates in western Madagascar are so low that trees of exploitable diameter (>35 cm) may be more than 300 years old. Data for the eastern forests are incomplete, but the ebonies and rosewoods favored for the export market may be of similar or greater age. Consequently, it is clear that any form of timber exploitation, other than for limited local use, is unsustainable. In 2004, the President of Madagascar recognized this and called for a suspension of all logging permits and a ban on the export of hardwoods. Sadly, since the political crisis in early 2009, illegal logging is again on the upswing, even in important protected areas such as the national parks of Marojejy and Masoala in the northeastern part of the country (Fig. 5.6). Some effort has been made to curtail this trade, but it is unclear how effective this will be.

Once native forest has been heavily disturbed, either through logging or slash-and-burn practices, there are a range of aggressive invasive species waiting to take over. This results, even after 50 years, in a wooded landscape of little value for endemic biodiversity and which, based on current evidence, will not regenerate to native forest (Brown and Gurevitch, 2004). Malagasy trees are slow to regenerate, and once native forest has been cleared, secondary invasive species such as strawberry guava (*Psidium cattleianum*) tend to take over in areas that are not intensively cultivated. Lemurs can use this habitat, and tend to do so if they are not persecuted. Indeed, certain mouse lemurs (*Microcebus*), giant mouse lemurs (*Mirza zaza*: Markolf et al., 2008a), and eastern forest bamboo lemurs (*Hapalemur*) may be more common in these secondary forests than in primary forests, and

Fig. 5.6: Above: Rosewood logs from the national parks of Marojejy and Masoala in storage in the port city of Vohemar, awaiting export, January, 2010. Below: The port of Vohemar. Note the storage depot (circled in yellow) towards the center of the picture (photos by R. A. Mittermeier).

aye-ayes can occur in coconut plantations in the eastern rain forest area. Even sifakas and brown lemurs can be found in plantations of mango and tamarind in the west, sometimes even in the middle of villages if they are not hunted locally.

The issue of invasive species, especially plants, has received relatively little attention to date, but is another prominent threat to remaining habitat. For example, extensive areas of the well-known Montagne d'Ambre National Park in northern Madagascar have been invaded by lantana or red sage (*Lantana camara*) and Jimson weed (*Datura*), and parts of Andohahela National Park in the south have been invaded by sisal (*Agave sisalana*) and prickly pear cactus (*Opuntia*) originally brought in from Mexico. The gallery forest of the Berenty Reserve in the south is also invaded by a succulent vine, *Cissus quadrangularis*, which smothers tamarind trees and results in a dramatic drying of the forest (Fig. 5.7). Although not as immediately threatening as clear-cutting, this issue is serious in many parts of the country.

Another subsistence-level land use issue is fuelwood. Every year, large areas of natural forest are cut down to provide firewood and charcoal for cooking. The problem is especially severe in the southern spiny desert region, where very poor tribesmen convert

Fig. 5.7: A tamarind tree which was smothered and ultimately destroyed by an invasive succulent vine (*Cissus quadrangularis*), Berenty Private Reserve (photo by R. A. Mittermeier).

Fig. 5.8: Above: Charcoal production in the southern spiny desert of Madagascar is a major conservation problem, destroying large expanses of habitat rich in endemic species. This photo was taken in 1985 on the road to Beza-Mahafaly. Below: Charcoal for sale along road at Ranomainty (photos by R. A. Mittermeier).

large areas of slow-growing spiny forest into bags of charcoal and stacks of firewood for sale to townspeople (Fig. 5.8). Dozens of roadside stands selling these low value products can be seen along major roads in the southern part of Madagascar. Needless to say, such use of these unique forests, with 95% plant endemism at the species level and close to 50% at the generic level, is very sad indeed. The charcoal producers depend on this activity for revenue, so finding alternative sources of economic activity for them (through, for example, handicrafts or the creation of plantations for charcoal) is a key conservation need. What is more, since this region is sunny throughout the year, their own fuel needs could be met by solar box coolers. Fuel-efficient stoves are another option.

Yet another problem is the tradition of cattle-raising (Fig. 5.9). There are as many cattle in Madagascar as there are people, and overgrazing, clearance of forest for cattle pasture, and periodic burning to provide a "green bite" of new grass have gradually eroded the edges of forest fragments, prevented regeneration, and introduced alien species into primary forest. In Madagascar, the problem is concentrated in the west and the south. Cattle are wealth for people such as the Antandroy, the Sahalava, and Mahafaly, and they are rarely eaten except at huge funeral ceremonies, at which time many are slaughtered for a single event. As in East Africa, the cattle-raising people of Madagascar are very closely tied to their herds, and changing this tradition will be very difficult. In some areas, the cattle culture can have a certain positive impact, as in parts of the south and west where the forest is used, and therefore protected, as a refuge against cattle thieves. However, this is minor compared to the overall negative impacts of cattle. In particular, burning for the "green bite" can occur over very extensive areas, even in regions with very low human and cattle populations, and effectively promotes erosion and prevents natural regeneration.

Mining has also had significant impact on Madagascar's natural environments. The country has been shown in recent years to be rich in many valuable minerals, and mining has taken two distinct trajectories, large-scale commercial mining by major companies

Fig. 5.9: Cattle on a muddy dirt road approaching the Highway of the Baobabs (photo by R. A. Mittermeier).

and small-scale mining by itinerant local prospectors. The more alarming is the free-for-all approach epitomized at Ilakaka, right on the boundary of Isalo National Park, where tens of thousands of poor migrants have dug deep holes in search of sapphires. In the late 1990s, the same thing took place right at the edge of Ankarana National Park in the north. The other end of the spectrum is represented by the large, long-term titanium ore mining complex in the southeastern corner of Madagascar near Tolagnaro (= Fort-Dauphin), where the Rio Tinto mining company has put in place a variety of environmental safeguards and has supported a lot of biodiversity survey work in the area to be affected. Madagascar has some of the world's largest deposits of titanium ore, and this mineral is potentially worth hundreds of millions of dollars to the country. Other mineral deposits of great value include bauxite and nickel. The Ambatovy/Analamay mining operation for nickel, in the heart of the eastern rain forest near Andasibe, provides a clear opportunity for engaging multinational mining interests to promote conservation and sustainable development. Conservation International and other organizations have been working with the promoters of such projects to ensure that the environmental impacts of such major upheavals are minimized. The principal that is emerging for such projects is that of "net positive impact on biodiversity," meaning that the companies in question will support regional conservation programs as well as those in the immediate vicinity of the mine site.

In the past, multilateral and bilateral donors funded projects with negative impacts on Madagascar's enivironment. However, over the last couple of decades, the development banks and bilateral aid agencies have contributed significantly to biodiversity conservation. The World Bank was instrumental in preparing the Environmental Action Plan for Madagascar in the mid 1980s (World Bank *et al.*, 1988) and later joined with Conservation International to establish a Critical Ecosystem Partnership Fund (CEPF) to support programs in hotspot regions. The US Agency for International Development (US-AID) has been exemplary in its biodiversity conservation efforts. Indeed, US-AID has supported key biodiversity projects since the early 1980s, and biodiversity has been a major component of its overall assistance program for Madagascar. Unfortunately, the political crisis of early 2009 resulted in the suspension of most aid to Madagascar, meaning that many government-funded programs of major importance have been suspended. A case in point is US-AID, which, at the time of writing, has closed its office in Antananarivo.

Increasingly, the private sector has been involved in supporting conservation and community development efforts, particularly through the purchase of carbon credits (for avoiding deforestation) and through increasing investments in ecotourism infrastructure (see below). Some of these have continued through the period of political instability, providing an effective buffer against these unfortunate upheavals.

Hunting

Worldwide, hunting is the second most important threat to primate populations after habitat loss. Primates are hunted around the world as food items, as bait, for medicinal purposes, as crop pests, for their skins and other body parts as ornamentation, as evil omens or for other quasi-religious reasons, and often simply for sport (Mittermeier, 1987). Hunting pressure generally increases with the size of the species; larger animals simply provide more meat, skin, bait or other products, while small ones barely recompense the hunter for the cost of a shotgun shell or the effort involved. This is probably why all the lemurs that have already gone extinct were larger than any of the extant taxa (Godfrey and Irwin, 2007). Even today, hunting is likely to be a greater threat to the larger lemurs than to the smaller nocturnal animals because of hunting behavior and species' life history characteristics. However, taste preferences are also a factor. According to Christopher

Fig. 5.10: Recent research has shown that lemur hunting is more of a problem than previously believed. On the left, a typical noose-trap used by hunters. On the right, a white-fronted brown lemur (*Eulemur albifrons*) killed using this kind of trap, Andapa region, northeastern Madagascar (photos by C. Golden).

Golden (pers. comm.), hunters in the northeast are often more likely to kill a smaller, better-tasting dwarf lemur (*Cheirogaleus*) than a larger, less appealing woolly lemur (*Avahi*). Ruffed lemurs (*Varecia*) and white-fronted brown lemurs (*Eulemur albifrons*) are considered especially delicious, and in some areas in the Makira region of northeastern Madagascar it is considered prestigious to eat meat of the indri (*Indri indri*) (Golden, 2005). Some species provide the hunter with products other than meat. In the Makira region, for example, hunters use hair from the neck of the black-and-white ruffed lemur (*Varecia variegata*) to make a tea that—tradition has it—relieves discomfort from persistent cough (Golden, 2005).

Fortunately, in many parts of the country there are also strong taboos against hunting certain species of lemur, known in Malagasy as *fady*. These *fady* vary not only from ethnic group to ethnic group but also from family to family. The killing of the indri, for example, is prohibited in some communities (but not others) of the Betsimasaraka people of the eastern rain forest, and the killing of Verreaux's sifaka (*Propithecus verreauxi*) is *fady* among the Antandroy and Mahafaly of the southern spiny desert.

Despite such local traditions, however, the subsistence hunting of lemurs for food is widespread. It is illegal both inside and outside of protected areas, but in regions far from authority and outside protected areas it can still have a major effect on wild lemur populations. In the north and east of the country, species such as the northern bamboo lemur (*Hapalemur occidentalis*) and diademed sifaka (*Propithecus diadema*) have been eliminated from many areas, and the black-and-white ruffed lemur (*Varecia variegata*) and several species of *Eulemur* have become very scarce. In the Makira region in the northeast, Golden (2009) has shown that the hunting of northern black-and-white ruffed lemur (*Varecia variegata subcincta*), white-fronted brown lemur (*Eulemur albifrons*), northern bamboo lemur, and indri (*Indri indri*) is unsustainable. In most cases, such hunting is for local consumption, but in some areas commerce may link hunter and consumer over dozens of kilometers. Several days of hiking by the hunter to go from forest to market is uncommon, but does occur for very valuable forest products. Since the beginning of Madagascar's political unrest, hunting has seemingly increased in many areas where opportunistic loggers have camped out in the forest and depend at least in part on the forest for their food.

Where local taboos remain strong or where conservation policy is strictly enforced, it is not unusual for even the larger species to be prominent and conspicuous. Indri are still present in many small forest fragments, and the sight of Decken's sifaka (*Propithecus deckenii*) in the middle of towns in western Madagascar is powerful evidence of the conditions that this species can tolerate in the absence of hunting. In the Ankarana region in the north, crowned lemurs (*Eulemur coronatus*) even come into camps and steal chocolate and other food, such is their familiarity with people. Unfortunately, in many other parts of the country these taboos only protect certain species and not others, and in many cases they are breaking down. The result is that lemurs are becoming increasingly difficult to see outside protected areas.

Fig. 5.11: An aye-aye (*Daubentonia madagascariensis*) killed for meat in the Makira region, northeastern Madagascar (photo by C. Golden).

Methods that have been reported for hunting lemurs are similar to those used for primate hunting in other parts of the tropics, and range from snaring, trapping with nooses and wooden traps, hunting with dogs, tree-felling, and stone throwing (Tattersall, 1982), to the use of slingshots, blowguns and rifles (Fig. 5.10). The main reason for hunting lemurs is for food, and the majority of published and anecdotal accounts of hunting cite the target animals as being the larger species, especially *Propithecus* or *Varecia*, which would provide the greatest amount of food. Nonetheless, small genera such as *Cheirogaleus* and *Lepilemur* are regularly captured for food as well, the usual methods being trapping or simple removal of the animals from their daytime nesting sites, some of which can be almost at ground level. Lemurs as small as mouse lemurs are even eaten on a regular basis (Golden, 2009).

Although most killing of lemurs is for food, one well-known exception is the tradition of killing the aye-aye (*Daubentonia madagascariensis*) because it is considered an evil omen that signals impending death or disaster. If an aye-aye passes through a village, one *fady* requires that it be killed immediately. In some cases, the appearance of an aye-aye even requires that the entire village be abandoned. Aye-ayes may be killed for more practical reasons as well, since they apparently raid coconut and lychee plantations and are regarded as crop "pests" in some areas. However, recent evidence indicates that even the aye-aye may be killed for food in some communities, and that animals killed as a bad omen may also later be eaten (C. Golden, pers. comm.) (Fig. 5.11).

Since the hunting of lemurs is illegal in Madagascar, knowledge of its impact is difficult to obtain. However, it is certainly worthy of further study and monitoring, along the lines of recent, detailed research carried out by Christopher Golden (Golden, 2009). Movement of human populations is on the rise throughout Madagascar, as families search for new arable land and sources of employment. Migration is often accompanied by a decline in traditional values. As food becomes scarce, and in the absence of social pressure from the community to prevent hunting, local people may be driven to kill lemurs that were once considered *fady* in a last-ditch effort to put food on the table. Alternatively, families without taboos for a particular lemur may move into an area with a large population of that species, where the animals, previously protected because of the *fady*, are unafraid. The result can be rapid local extermination by immigrant hunters. The situation can be even more complex. Golden (2005), for example, noted that people for whom eating lemurs is taboo may nonetheless be willing to hunt them for sale to others who have no such restrictions.

Although there has been a tendency in the past to consider lemur hunting less of a threat than habitat destruction, and less severe than in places like Central and West Africa and southeast Asia, recent information, especially from studies by Golden (2009) in the Makira region, indicate that it may be much more significant than previously recognized. In the absence of alternative sources of meat, the hunting of lemurs is unlikely to decline. Increased monitoring and better enforcement practices are necessary, but better livestock-raising practices and the introduction of alternative protein sources are likely to be more effective.

Conservation incentive mechanisms are a promising strategy to address the issue of hunting. Durrell has pioneered this approach in Madagascar and it is now being used by a number of other organizations. Communities agree to conserve populations of lemurs or other threatened species for a performance-related investment that offers significant benefits. This approach merits wider testing and application.

Live Capture

Fortunately, the live capture of lemurs for local use as pets or for export does not appear to be a serious threat, even though it has been a major factor in the decline of other primates such as the Colombian cotton-top tamarin (*Saguinus oedipus*) (Mast *et al.*, 1993), the African chimpanzee (*Pan troglodytes*) (Mack and Mittermeier, 1984), and the orangutans (*Pongo*) of Indonesia and Malaysia. A few of the hardier lemurs, such as *Lemur catta*, *Varecia* and *Eulemur*, are sometimes kept as pets by local people, but this is much less of a problem than in most other regions where primates occur. Indeed, most lemurs are difficult to keep in captivity, especially the folivores such as *Lepilemur* and the indriids. Since they usually perish quickly, there is little incentive to keep them. One exception to this is the frequent capture of live *Hapalemur alaotrensis* by villagers in the Lac Alaotra area. This practice is apparently quite common there, and is probably a major factor in the decline of this now Critically Endangered species (Fig. 5.12).

Although a visitor may see an occasional lemur kept as a pet by local people, this is usually not cause for major concern. Nonetheless, since there is relatively little information on this topic, we would welcome hearing from you if you do see lemurs in captivity. Data on the species in question—including where it is being kept, where it originated, and how it was captured—are all of interest, and a photograph would be helpful as well. Information on how to contact us is given at the end of this book.

Lemur export also does not appear to be a serious issue. Although there is a substantial legal and illegal trade in plants, amphibians and reptiles, lemur export has been prohibited for decades and has been relatively well enforced. All lemurs are protected by law in Madagascar, and all species are listed in the appendices of CITES, the Convention on International Trade in Endangered Species. Indeed, the only documented lemur exports over the past two decades have been for scientific purposes, particularly for conservation-oriented captive breeding programs such as those at the Duke Lemur Center in the US, and Durrell on the island of Jersey in the UK (formerly, the Durrell Wildlife Conservation Trust). These programs have taken only a very small number of individuals from the wild and do not constitute a threat in any way.

Nonetheless, we must remain vigilant in relation to the export issue. There are rumours that several lemur species are being kept in private collections in parts of Asia, where their importation was almost certainly illegal.

Fig. 5.12: Local girl with a pet Lac Alaotra bamboo lemur (*Hapalemur alaotrensis*), Andreba Village, Lac Alaotra (photo by R. A. Mittermeier).

Endangered reptiles such as the Angonoka tortoise (*Geochelone yniphora*) and the radiated tortoise (*Geochelone radiata*) are now showing up in pet markets and even on dealer websites in China, Malaysia, Thailand, and other Asian countries, and it may well be that lemurs have made their way to these countries as well. Since enforcement in general has declined since the start of the current political crisis in early 2009, potential for illegal lemur export certainly exists.

Lemur Conservation Efforts

A diversified approach is needed to ensure the survival of viable populations of all lemur species, and it requires elements of each of the following:

1) effective management of existing protected areas with significant lemur populations;
2) creation of new protected areas for species and ecosystems that are not yet covered in the existing park and reserve network;
3) special efforts, aimed at Endangered and Critically Endangered taxa, to reduce the impact of hunting, particularly through conservation incentive mechanisms;
4) captive breeding programs for target species, both for possible reintroduction in the future, and also to learn more of their basic biology and for their genetic management;
5) continued survey work in poorly-known areas to learn more of the geographic distribution and conservation status of lemurs in the wild;
6) continued and expanded long-term research efforts to learn more of lemur ecology and behavior in the wild;
7) continued field and laboratory research to better understand the taxonomy of lemurs and to identify new species;
8) conservation education and public awareness efforts both within Madagascar and internationally, using lemurs as "flagship species" and "ambassadors" for their habitats and for the country as a whole;
9) training of Malagasy conservation professionals to carry the cause of lemur conservation and research into the future; and
10) development of economic incentives for the conservation of lemurs and their habitats, especially through research and ecotourism.

In the final section of this chapter, we discuss these different aspects of lemur conservation, including some of the activities already underway and others that need to be developed or expanded in the near future. This section is divided into four main headings: conservation status of lemurs, conservation in the wild, conservation in captivity, and incentives for lemur conservation.

Conservation Status of Lemurs

The lemurs of Madagascar have been recognized as a conservation priority since the earliest days of the modern conservation movement. In his classic work, *Extinct and Vanishing Mammals of the Old World*, Harper (1945) discussed 40 lemur taxa, and gave what was for the time a good account of their status. Twenty-one years later, the first volume of the *IUCN Red Data Book, Mammalia* (Simon, 1966) listed most of the then recognized lemurs as Endangered or Vulnerable; a total of 24 taxa in all. The 1972 version of the mammal *Red Data Book* (Goodwin and Holloway, 1972) continued to recognize the same taxa as those of the 1966 edition, with some updating of information.

In 1990, IUCN published an entire volume focusing exclusively on the lemurs, entitled *Lemurs of Madagascar and the Comoros: The IUCN Red Data Book* (Harcourt and Thornback, 1990). This greatly updated the information in the earlier volumes. Of the 52 species and subspecies that they recognized, they assessed 16 as Endangered, 16 as Vulnerable, nine as Rare, one as Insufficiently Known, and four as Abundant. Two years later, we introduced a somewhat different rating system in the IUCN/SSC Primate Specialist Group's *Lemurs of Madagascar: An Action Plan for their Conservation, 1993– 1999* (Mittermeier *et al.*, 1992). We focused on priorities for conservation action using a system to assess each species that weighted them by taking into account taxonomic uniqueness, degree of threat and level of protection. This resulted in an analysis that recognized 12 taxa as of Highest Priority, 11 as of High Priority, seven as Priority, and 20 as Not of Conservation Concern.

In the first edition of this field guide (Mittermeier *et al.*, 1994), we carried out yet another analysis of lemur conservation status; this time based on the then new and greatly expanded IUCN Red List categories of threat (IUCN, 1994). These new categories resulted from a profound revision of the criteria for assessing the threatened status of all species, which began with a workshop held at the IUCN General Assembly in Madrid in 1984. The revision continued in a series of workshops and studies spearheaded by the IUCN Species Survival Commission (SSC) and Georgina Mace and Russell Lande, two leading conservation biologists. Their first attempt at more rigorous analysis was published as *Assessing Extinction Threats: Toward a Re-evaluation of IUCN Threatened Species Categories* (Mace and Lande, 1991). This was then widely circulated and substantially revised, resulting in a still more extensive analysis that was presented at the IUCN General Assembly in Buenos Aires in January 1994.

Further revisions in subsequent years resulted in a second version of the categories and criteria, published in 2001 as Version 3.1 (IUCN, 2001). These are the categories and criteria that are used today. A Conservation Assessment and Management Plan (CAMP) Workshop, organized by the IUCN/SSC Conservation Breeding Specialist Group, was then held in Mantasoa, Madagascar, in May, 2001, initiating the process of re-assessing the status of all the lemurs using these new criteria. This provided an interim list.

A more detailed reassessment then took place in April 2005 in an Antananarivo-based workshop carried out as part of the IUCN/SSC's initiative to assess all of the mammals, known as the Global Mammal Assessment. In this 2005 review, 11 species and subspecies were assessed as Critically Endangered, 16 as Endangered, 18 as Vulnerable, six as Least Concern, and 14 as Data Deficient. Next, we have the 2008 IUCN Red List (IUCN, 2008), which draws largely from the Global Mammal Assessment, including all the taxa evaluated in the 2005 workshop, as well as 24 species and subspecies that were described after the workshop had taken place (Table 5.5). Most of these new species were placed in the Data Deficient category. In addition, a further seven species have been described very recently, and have not been evaluated. Lastly, in preparing this field guide, we re-assessed the blue-eyed black lemur (*Eulemur flavifrons*), listed as Endangered by IUCN (2008), and concluded that it should be Critically Endangered.

In all, eight species and subspecies are now recognized as Critically Endangered, 18 Endangered, and 15 Vulnerable. Four are Near Threatened, eight are of Least Concern, 41 are Data Deficient, and seven have yet to assessed (Table 5.5). IUCN (2008) lists *Cheirogaleus adipicaudatus* and *Cheirogaleus ravus* as Data Deficient, but we no longer recognize them as valid taxa.

Table 5.5. IUCN Conservation Status of Lemur Species and Subspecies (as of 2008)

Critically Endangered
Hapalemur alaotrensis
Prolemur simus
Eulemur flavifrons
Varecia variegata variegata
Varecia variegata editorum
Varecia variegata subcincta
Propithecus candidus
Propithecus perrieri

Endangered
Microcebus berthae
Microcebus ravelobensis
Microcebus sambiranensis
Microcebus tavaratra
Lepilemur ankaranensis
Lepilemur septentrionalis
Hapalemur aureus
Eulemur sanfordi
Eulemur cinereiceps
Varecia rubra
Avahi occidentalis
Avahi cleesei
Propithecus coronatus
Propithecus coquereli
Propithecus tattersalli
Propithecus diadema
Propithecus edwardsi
Indri indri

Vulnerable
Phaner parienti
Phaner electromontis
Lepilemur edwardsi
Hapalemur griseus griseus
Hapalemur meridionalis
Hapalemur occidentalis
Eulemur fulvus
Eulemur albifrons
Eulemur collaris
Eulemur macaco
Eulemur coronatus
Eulemur rubriventer
Eulemur mongoz
Propithecus verreauxi
Propithecus deckenii

Lower Risk–Near Threatened
Mirza coquereli
Lemur catta
Eulemur rufifrons
Daubentonia madagascariensis

Lower Risk–Least Concern
Microcebus murinus
Microcebus griseorufus

Microcebus rufus
Cheirogaleus medius
Cheirogaleus major
Phaner furcifer
Phaner pallescens
Avahi laniger

Data Deficient
Microcebus myoxinus
Microcebus bongolavensis
Microcebus danfossi
Microcebus mamiratra
Microcebus jollyae
Microcebus lehilahytsara
Microcebus simmonsi
Microcebus mittermeieri
Mirza zaza
Allocebus trichotis
Cheirogaleus sibreei
Cheirogaleus crossleyi
Cheirogaleus minusculus
Lepilemur mustelinus
Lepilemur betsileo
Lepilemur microdon
Lepilemur jamesorum
Lepilemur wrightae
Lepilemur fleuretae
Lepilemur seali
Lepilemur milanoii
Lepilemur ruficaudatus
Lepilemur dorsalis
Lepilemur tymerlachsonorum
Lepilemur mittermeieri
Lepilemur sahamalazensis
Lepilemur grewcockorum
Lepilemur otto
Lepilemur aeeclis
Lepilemur ahmansonorum
Lepilemur randrianasoloi
Lepilemur hubbardorum
Lepilemur petteri
Lepilemur leucopus
Hapalemur griseus gilberti
Eulemur rufus
Avahi peyrierasi
Avahi betsileo
Avahi ramanantsoavanai
Avahi meridionalis
Avahi unicolor

Not Evaluated
Microcebus margotmarshae
Microcebus arnholdi
Microcebus macarthurii
Lepilemur hollandorum
Lepilemur scottorum
Hapalemur griseus ranomafanensis
Avahi mooreorum

Those species described since the 2005 workshop and included as Data Deficient in the 2008 edition of the IUCN Red List have not yet been subjected to any kind of serious assessment. However, since many of these new animals have tiny ranges or are known only from their type localities in areas of fragmented forest, it is likely that many of them will wind up in the Critically Endangered or Endangered categories. The same is true for those seven described since the 2008 Red List. A reassessment of the lemurs is urgently needed in order to fit these new taxa into lemur conservation plans and to determine if there have been significant changes in the status of the assessed taxa since 2005.

Conservation in the Wild

The principal focus of lemur conservation efforts has to be on natural habitat, and protected areas of various kinds are the most important element in ensuring the survival of these very special animals. It is obvious that certain species will need more attention than others, either because of their Critically Endangered status or because they require large areas of intact forest to survive. Other species may be more adaptable and capable of surviving in altered habitats and secondary forests adjacent to human habitation. These will need less attention than their more demanding relatives, but will also benefit from habitat conservation efforts for the more endangered lemurs. Among the adaptable species are most (but not all) *Microcebus*, some of the more widespread *Cheirogaleus* and *Lepilemur*, some of the *Eulemur* species, and some sifakas, especially *Propithecus verreauxi* and *P. deckenii*, all of them capable of surviving in human-modified habitats. The most demanding species include many of the larger forms, such as the indri, the ruffed lemurs, the larger eastern and northern *Propithecus*, *Hapalemur aureus*, and *Prolemur simus*. These require tracts of undisturbed habitat and special management efforts to ensure their survival. Indeed, all of the Critically Endangered and Endangered species and subspecies in Table 5.5 will need special, species-focused management programs in addition to maintenance of their natural habitats. In other words, setting aside protected areas for them is not by itself sufficient; these species will need further attention to protect them from hunting and to learn more about their behavioral and ecological needs.

The national parks and reserves network in Madagascar was initiated in 1927 and now consists of 47 protected areas (corresponding to IUCN categories I, II and IV). This network is managed by Madagascar National Parks (formerly ANGAP) and covers 2.3 million ha, including an extension of 500,000 ha that has been added as part of the Durban Vision (see Box). These are shown in Figs. A.5 and A.6 in Appendix A, and also in the accompanying map in this chapter (Fig. 5.13).

In addition, there are 27 new protected areas covering 2.6 million ha that are managed directly by the Ministry of the Environment and Forests in partnership with community groups and NGOs (these correspond to IUCN Protected Area categories III, V and VI). A further 40 areas covering 1.1 million ha have been identified as priorities, and the work to protect these sites is in the early stages. International non-governmental organizations such as Conservation International, the Wildlife Conservation Society, Durrell, and the World Wide Fund for Nature, as well as national non-governmental organizations such as Fanamby are working closely with Madagascar National Parks to manage effectively the original 47 protected areas and a number of new partnerships have been developed to manage the new ones that have resulted from the Durban Vision.

The collective name for all of Madagascar's protected areas is now SAPM, the System of Protected Areas of Madagascar, and it incorporates both the original network of 47 parks and reserves managed by Madagascar National Parks and the areas created under the

Durban Vision. The location of both the original 47 parks and reserves and the new ones in various stages of creation are shown in Fig. 5.13.

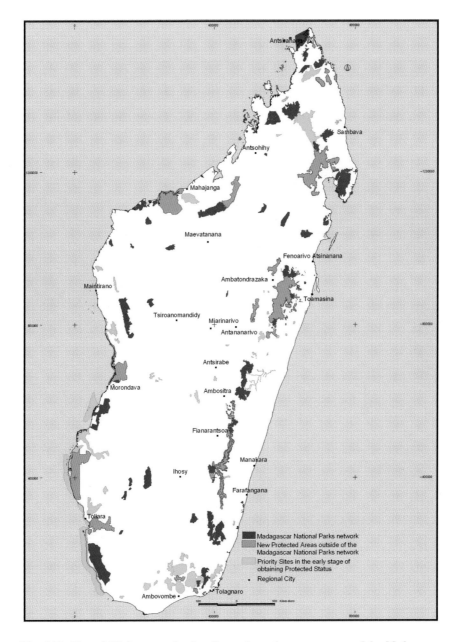

Fig. 5.13: Map of Madagascar showing the parks and reserves managed by Madagascar National Parks (dark green), new protected areas outside of the Madagascar National Parks network (green), and priority sites in the early stages of obtaining protected status (pale green) (Map courtesy of Conservation International/Madagascar).

The Durban Vision: An Historic Opportunity

In the 1990s and the early years of the 21st century, conservationists continued to make the point that the existing protected area network of Madagascar did not fully cover the country's unique biodiversity, with several people, including some of the authors of this book, pushing for a substantial increase in coverage, perhaps a 50% increase or even a doubling. This concept did not gain traction under previous administrations, but took a quantum leap forward with the election of President Marc Ravalomanana in December, 2002. After consulting with several of the leading conservation organizations, Ravalomanana made a truly historic announcement at the World Parks Congress in Durban, South Africa in September, 2003. To everyone's surprise and delight, he committed not just to a doubling, but rather a tripling, of the country's protected area network over the next five years.

To make this a reality, he asked the international community to help his government finance such activities. In January, 2005, this became a reality with the creation of a trust fund, the Madagascar Foundation for Protected Areas and Biodiversity, the objective of which was to cover part of the recurrent costs of protected areas. The Foundation's original fundraising target for 2012 was $50 million, and it stimulated a great deal of interest on the part of the international community. The Malagasy government, Conservation International and WWF joined forces to make the first contributions to the new Foundation's capital. The government's contribution came from the cancellation of German government debt valued at €1.7 million and Conservation International and WWF each provided $1 million. Shortly thereafter the World Bank and the French Government (through AfD and the FFEM) came on board with larger commitments, and the Malagasy government donated a further €13.3 million from the cancellation of French government debt. The German government (through KfW) also contributes funding to national parks through the Foundation with a "sinking fund" that does not add to the capital but will instead be used up over several years. By July, 2010, five years after its creation, the Foundation had raised US$33.7 million and was in negotiations with the GEF, KfW and Conservation International for further contributions that, if successful, would secure the $50 million goal.

The Government of Madagascar also kept its promise and protected the first additional 1 million ha in December, 2005, and has continued adding further areas to the protected area system since then. By July, 2010, there were 4.9 million ha of protected areas in Madagascar, and the government, NGOs and community groups were actively working to create yet another 1.1 million ha.

The increase in size of the national protected area system envisaged under the Durban Vision includes several new types of management categories, many of them under the direct control of local communities. While each new protected area will have a core where economic activity will be limited, much of the peripheral area of these new zones will be managed according to agreements brokered with local communities that allow for harvesting of forest products such as medicinal plants, fibers, or essential oils, and for ecotourism enterprises. The emphasis will be on significant and sustainable economic benefits that complement and augment the benefits of ecosystem services, such as sustainable water supplies and erosion prevention.

Its goals are:
- To conserve the Malagasy cultural heritage associated with biodiversity;
- to conserve the full array of the unique biodiversity of Madagascar (ecosystems, species and genetic variability); and
- to maintain ecosystem services and foster wise use of natural resources in order to contribute to poverty alleviation and sustainable development.

In the case of many of the new protected areas, there is strong interest on the part of communities in having management rights over forest resources, including water sources, access to medicinal plants and other non-timber forest products, and to provide shelter for cattle. More recently, the value of forests for providing global goods such as carbon storage has also emerged, and has created new and greatly increased economic opportunities for local people, demonstrating more strongly than ever the value of standing forest.

Conservation in Captivity

Although wild populations of lemurs should always be the principal focus of conservation efforts, zoo-based initiatives can be important as well. Captive colonies provide a safety net against possible extinctions in the wild, they are a source of animals for possible future reintroduction programs, they serve a very important public awareness and conservation education function, and they should be a focal point for research into diet, reproductive behavior, handling. transport, and genetic management that complement and augment field-based research activities (Porton, 1993). Indeed, it is essential that captive and field-based conservation activities no longer be treated as separate endeavors; rather, they should be viewed as points on a collaborative continuum, the ultimate goal of which should be to ensure the continued survival of all living lemurs.

A number of lemur species are represented in captivity, but most are not. The world's largest collection of lemurs is maintained at the Duke Lemur Center in Durham, North Carolina, USA, which houses 20 species, including one (*Propithecus diadema*) that is not in captivity anywhere else outside of Madagascar. Other noteworthy lemur collections include those of Durrell (the former Durrell Wildlife Conservation Trust on the Island of Jersey), the Mulhouse and Vincennes (Paris) Zoos in France, and the St. Louis, Denver, San Francisco and Philadelphia zoos in the United States. There are also several collections in Madagascar that are well worth seeing, notably Parc Tsimbazaza, Parc Ivoloina, and Lemurs Park, which are discussed in Appendix C of this guide.

By and large, *ex situ* lemur conservation programs are managed under the auspices of several international associations including the American Zoo and Aquarium Association (AZA), the European Association of Zoos and Aquaria (EAZA), and the Australasian Regional Association of Zoological Parks and Aquaria (ARAZPA) (Zeeve and Porton, 1997). Each of these associations has targeted a number of lemur taxa as conservation priorities and has developed a series of coordinated programs aimed at securing their survival. Examples include the AZA's Species Survival Programs (SSPs) for black and blue-eyed black lemurs (*Eulemur macaco, Eulemur flavifrons*), the mongoose lemur (*Eulemur mongoz*), and ruffed lemurs (*Varecia*), EAZA's corresponding Endangered Species Programmes (EEPs) for both the *Eulemur* and *Varecia* taxa listed above, as well as the red-bellied lemur (*Eulemur rubriventer*), Lac Alaotra bamboo lemur (*Hapalemur alaotrensis*), greater bamboo lemur (*Prolemur simus*), crowned sifaka (*Propithecus coronatus*), and aye-aye (*Daubentonia madagascariensis*), and ARAZPA's Australasian Species Management Plan (ASMP) for the ring-tailed lemur (*Lemur catta*) and ruffed lemurs. In addition, regional and international studbooks are managed by a number of participating institutions and cover the following lemur genera: *Cheirogaleus*, *Daubentonia*, *Eulemur*, *Hapalemur*, *Lemur*, *Microcebus*, *Mirza*, *Propithecus*, and *Varecia*.

Each of the programs listed above has existing or potential links to *in situ* lemur conservation initiatives. Within the AZA, for example, the Prosimian Taxonomic Advisory Group (TAG) provides recommendations and opportunities for member institutions to become actively involved in field conservation projects. The Prosimian TAG produces regional collection plans for lemurs intended to ensure optimum use of captive space by collaborating institutions, to share relevant information on lemur genetics and husbandry, and to make recommendations regarding research and field conservation efforts. The IUCN/ SSC Conservation Breeding Specialist Group (CBSG) also assists zoos by evaluating the role of captive breeding programs in maintaining overall genetic diversity for the target species.

A number of zoos have chosen to support *in situ* lemur conservation by joining associations such as the Madagasacar Faunal Group (MFG) and the Association Européenne pour l'Etude et la Conservation des Lémuriens (AEECL). The MFG, for example, was formed following a 1986 meeting at St. Catherine's Island, Georgia (USA), at which Malagasy government officials asked the international zoo community for assistance with habitat protection, species propagation, research, and training. One of the authors of this book, Russ Mittermeier, was present at this inaugural meeting and instrumental in the creation of this group, as was the late Warren Thomas, then Director of the Los Angeles Zoo. Its conservation objectives and authorization to work in Madagascar have been established through a Protocol of Collaboration with the Government of Madagascar. Participating institutions help the MFG achieve its wildlife conservation mission through a nine-point strategy:

1) Connecting zoos, aquariums, botanical gardens and their constituencies to the flora and fauna of Madagascar;
2) stimulating the flow of funds from zoos, aquariums, botanical gardens, and their constitutencies to conservation in Madagascar;
3) building the capacity for conservation in Madagascar;
4) building partnerships with the Government of Madagascar and other organizations;
5) setting priorities for research and conservation action;
6) protecting sites to maintain the diversity of wildlife;
7) acting to conserve the most endangered species;
8) fostering a conservation ethic among the people of Madagascar; and
9) encouraging and facilitating the development of exciting and informative exhibits and programs at member institutions.

Both the AZA Prosimian TAG and the Madagascar Fauna Group are headquartered at the St. Louis Zoo. Approximately 30 North American and European institutions are current MFG members or supporters. Flagship conservation projects for MFG include captive breeding, public awareness, and education initiatives at Parc Ivoloina in Toamasina (= Tamatave) (Katz and Welch, 2003) and field research, habitat protection, and lemur reintroduction efforts at the nearby Betampona Strict Nature Reserve (Britt *et al.*, 2003).

Another zoo-based conservation program is that of the Henry Doorly Zoo of Omaha, Nebraska, headed by another of the authors of this book, Edward E. Louis Jr. This is a very comprehensive program that includes a wide range of field surveys in Madagascar, as well as the construction of captive facilities in Parc Tsimbazaza. The training of Malagasy

Fig. 5.14: Mitchell Irwin of the State University of New York at Stony Brook with field team members and local villagers in the region of Tsinjoarivo, central eastern Madagascar. Behind the group are educational panels depicting local lemur species (photo courtesy of M. Irwin).

conservationists, both in Omaha as well as in Madagascar itself, is also an important aspect. It is described in more detail in the previous chapter.

Incentives for Lemur Conservation

In order to achieve long-term conservation objectives, the people of Madagascar must derive direct benefit from conservation. Three key ingredients for this to happen are:

1) developing recognition of and appreciation for their country's globally unique wildlife heritage on the part of the Malagasy people themselves;
2) training a cadre of Malagasy conservation professionals to carry the cause of biodiversity conservation into the future; and, most important of all,
3) demonstrating the concrete economic value of lemurs and other wildlife to local people and to the nation as a whole, especially through ecotourism.

Lemurs will be instrumental in achieving all of these goals. Madagascar's greatest shadow asset is the often-unappreciated value of its wildlife and natural ecosystems, as well as the country's global reputation as a biodiversity "hotspot." Biodiversity in Madagascar exceeds all other resources in terms of potential for future sustainable economic gain and is without a doubt the country's strongest international "brand". What is more, lemurs are the best known symbols of this wonderful natural diversity—the "flagship" species that serve as the global ambassadors for the rest of the country's wildlife.

President Marc Ravalomanana took significant steps to capitalize on the marketing value of Madagascar's biodiversity, especially to stimulate the growth of ecotourism. This effort was greatly assisted by the animated film "Madagascar," which was produced by the

Fig. 5.15: Fanomezana Ratsoavina, a Malagasy graduate student from the University of Antananarivo, with a silky sifaka (*Propithecus candidus*), Anjanaharibe-Sud Special Reserve (photo by E. E. Louis Jr.).

Hollywood company DreamWorks Pictures and premiered in May, 2005. The original film, which has now been seen by an estimated 100 million people in theaters around the world and by some 200–300 million in its DVD version, was recently followed by an equally successful sequel, "Madagascar II," with yet another sequel currently in production. There can be no question that these have greatly increased awareness of Madagascar, and surely provided a major stimulus to ecotourism. Indeed, many of you reading this book may have first been stimulated to go to Madagascar because of these films.

Fig. 5.16: "Madagascar", produced by Dreamworks, appeared in 2005 and it was set in Madagascar. It featured a number of lemur characters, including King Julien XIII (a ring-tailed lemur with a Jamaican accent), an aye-aye named Maurice, and a mouse lemur named Mort (a constant irritation to King Julien), among many other lemurs and other Malagasy animals.

Furthermore, local people must benefit from ecotourism and other sustainable forms of resource use, as it is only with support from the grass roots that long-term conservation efforts can succeed. Fortunately, ecotourism in Madagascar has enormous potential and is likely to experience dramatic growth in the years to come. An ecotourism industry focusing on lemurs as the principal "flagship" species, but incorporating many other components of Madagascar's rich wildlife, has the potential to contribute substantially to the reduction of poverty in Madagascar and eventually to become the country's most important industry. The example of Costa Rica, where ecotourism is now a major source of revenue for the country, and that of Rwanda, where tourism based on a single primate species, the mountain gorilla (*Gorilla beringei beringei*), is one of the country's top foreign exchange earners, are models that Madagascar should follow. To be sure, some ecotourism already exists in Madagascar, but it should be increased by at least five-fold over the next decade. Only a handful of lemur-watching sites are now heavily visited (e.g., Berenty, Andasibe [= Périnet], Ranomafana, Nosy Be, Nosy Mangabe, Montagne d'Ambre, Kirindy), but others continue to be developed.

Indeed, locally-based ecotourism of this kind should provide strong incentives to rural communities to conserve forests in their regions. Andasibe provides an excellent example of this type of tourism operation. In the Analamazaotra Special Reserve, right next to Andasibe and home to a small number of habituated indris, there are now nearly 100 guides divided into three guide associations—well-organized groups that provide high quality standardized guide services. The oldest of these is the Association des Guides d'Andasibe (Fig. 5.17), a true grassroots effort and a model that is already being emulated elsewhere in Madagascar (e.g., Ranomafana, Masoala, Montagne d'Ambre). The second is the Association Mitsinjo, which actually has its own reserve, right across the road from the government reserve. And the third is the recently-created Association Tambatra. Tourists should recognize the importance of these local initiatives and encourage them through generous and regular support. In many ways, the future of lemurs and other wildlife depends heavily on local people, who must be viewed as major partners in the conservation of Madagascar's biological heritage.

The five year (2007–2012) governmental plan, referred to as the Madagascar Action Plan (MAP), had tourism as one of the pillars of the future development of Madagascar, including especially ecotourism. The objective announced for 2012 was 500,000 visitors, generating an estimated $500 million in revenue and 40,000 direct jobs. Between 1990 and 2007, Madagascar had enjoyed a steady growth of 11% per year in the number of tourists, rising to 345,000 visitors (non-residents) in 2007 and 375,000 in 2008. It was estimated that 62% (217,000) of these visitors were real tourists and not French and Malagasy people living abroad coming to the country to visit their relatives. In 2007, tourism generated $300 million and created 25,000 direct jobs, and about 55% of the visitors were ecotourists. In 2008, the income in foreign currency increased by 44%, and created 25,662 direct jobs, 68% of the visitors went to national parks and other protected areas. Madagascar was on

Fig. 5.17: Senior author Russ Mittermeier with members of the Association des Guides d'Andasibe, a local organization of nature tour guides for visitors to the Analamazaotra Special Reserve and the nearby Mantadia National Park (photo by W. R. Konstant).

track to achieve its objective defined in the MAP. With textile, vanilla, and shrimp, tourism was one of the main sources of foreign exchange.

In 2009, however, the combination of the world economic crisis and the political turmoil affecting Madagascar had a very negative impact on tourism, with the political crisis playing an even larger role than the economic crisis. Indeed only 163,000 visitors came to Madagascar, compared to 375,000 in 2008.

It is hoped that tourism activities will resume once the political crisis ends. However, it will take time to regain the confidence of investors in this highly competitive market and to convince world tour operators to put Madagascar back on top of their list of favorite destinations. The 2012 objective of 500,000 announced in the MAP now seems difficult to reach. Fortunately, the uniqueness of Madagascar's biodiversity continues to fascinate, and at least some ecotourists have continued to travel there in spite of the problems. Once the crisis ends, it should be possible to increase tourism to the country once again, and enable everyone there to benefit. However, this will only be possible if the lemurs and the rest of the country's wildlife are protected, and not lost to rampant short-term exploitation.

In order to further stimulate interest in lemurs worldwide, Russ Mittermeier, one of the authors of this book, has come up with the concept of Primate Life-Listing and the establishment of Primate-Watching as a hobby, based in large part on the great global success of Birdwatching. Given the number of lemur species and the ease of seeing most of them in their natural habitat, Lemur-Watching would be a major component of this new endeavor. This concept of Primate Life-Listing and Primate-Watching is explained in more detail in Appendix D.

Education and public awareness in Madagascar is a priority at all levels, from government decision-makers to city-dwellers to local people living in the remotest villages (Fig. 5.14). Education efforts, using lemurs and other species, have been carried out sporadically in the past, employing materials such as t-shirts (Figs. 5.17 and 5.18), posters, stickers, pins, brochures and a variety of other products. However, these efforts must be greatly increased and undertaken in earnest, with the goal of changing attitudes toward the environment on a national scale and making it clear to all decision-makers that Madagascar's biodiversity—best symbolized by its lemurs—represents the country's greatest competitive advantage in the international arena.

Last but not least, training is also critical for the future. Although much lemur field research has been carried out in Madagascar, the number of Malagasy researchers, though growing, remains relatively small. A major focus on such training is a key element in any overall conservation program.

In closing, we hope that this book will help all researchers, including those from Madagascar itself, to become more involved in lemur study and conservation, that it will stimulate the general public to become much more interested in Madagascar's magnificent natural heritage, and that ultimately it will make at least a small contribution to ensuring the survival of this unique global asset. You, the reader, are already making a contribution by coming to Madagascar, and we hope that you will encourage others to do the same.

Fig. 5.18: The Maki brand, which originated in Madagascar, now sells t-shirts and other clothing throughout the Indian Ocean islands (photo by R. A. Mittermeier). Maki is the Malagasy name for the ring-tailed lemur, but the face portrayed is that of a sifaka. A brand like this is indicative of the growing popularity of lemurs in Madagascar and regionally.

Fig. 5.19: A black-and-white ruffed lemur welcomes visitors to Lemur Island, Hotel Vakona, Andasibe (photo by R. A. Mittermeier).

Fig. 5.20: Brigitte, a young lemur enthusiast from Seattle, and a brown lemur on Lemur Island, Hotel Vakona, Andasibe (photo by R. A. Mittermeier).

Fig. 6.1: Indri (*Indri indri*) mother and infant, Andasibe (photo by R. A. Mittermeier).

CHAPTER 6

THE LIVING LEMURS

Classification of the Living Lemurs

Family Cheirogaleidae Gray, 1873

Microcebus É. Geoffroy, 1828 Mouse lemurs
  Microcebus murinus (J. F. Miller, 1777) Gray mouse lemur
  Microcebus griseorufus Kollman, 1910 Gray-brown mouse lemur
  Microcebus berthae Rasoloarison *et al.*, 2000 Madame Berthe's mouse lemur
  Microcebus myoxinus Peters, 1852 Peters' mouse lemur
  Microcebus ravelobensis Zimmermann *et al.*, 1997 Golden-brown mouse lemur
  Microcebus bongolavensis Olivieri *et al.*, 2007 Bongolava mouse lemur
  Microcebus danfossi Olivieri *et al.*, 2007 Ambarijeby mouse lemur
  Microcebus margotmarshae Louis *et al.*, 2008 Margot Marsh's mouse lemur
  Microcebus sambiranensis Rasoloarison *et al.*, 2000 Sambirano mouse lemur
  Microcebus mamiratra Andriantompohavana *et al.*, 2006 Nosy Be mouse lemur
  Microcebus tavaratra Rasoloarison *et al.*, 2000 Tavaratra mouse lemur
  Microcebus arnholdi Louis *et al.*, 2008 Montagne d'Ambre mouse lemur
  Microcebus rufus (Lesson, 1840) Rufous mouse lemur
  Microcebus jollyae Louis *et al.*, 2006 Jolly's mouse lemur
  Microcebus lehilahytsara Roos and Kappeler, 2005 in Kappeler *et al.*, 2005
    Goodman's mouse lemur
  Microcebus simmonsi Louis *et al.*, 2006 Simmons' mouse lemur
  Microcebus macarthurii Radespiel *et al.*, 2008 Anjiahely mouse lemur
  Microcebus mittermeieri Louis *et al.*, 2006 Mittermeier's mouse lemur

Mirza Gray, 1870 Giant mouse lemurs
  Mirza coquereli (A. Grandidier, 1867) Coquerel's giant mouse lemur
  Mirza zaza Kappeler and Roos, 2005 in Kappeler *et al.*, 2005 Northern giant mouse
    lemur

Allocebus Petter-Rousseaux and Petter, 1967 Hairy-eared dwarf lemur
  Allocebus trichotis (Günther, 1875) Hairy-eared dwarf lemur

Cheirogaleus É. Geoffroy, 1812 Dwarf lemurs
  Cheirogaleus medius É. Geoffroy, 1812 Fat-tailed dwarf lemur
  Cheirogaleus sibreei (Forsyth Major, 1896) Sibree's dwarf lemur
  Cheirogaleus major É. Geoffroy, 1812 Greater dwarf lemur
  Cheirogaleus crossleyi A. Grandidier, 1870 Crossley's dwarf lemur
  Cheirogaleus minusculus Groves, 2000 Lesser iron-gray dwarf lemur

Phaner Gray, 1871 Fork-marked lemurs
  Phaner furcifer (de Blainville, 1839) Masoala fork-marked lemur
  Phaner pallescens Groves and Tattersall, 1991 Pale fork-marked lemur
  Phaner parienti Groves and Tattersall, 1991 Sambirano fork-marked lemur
  Phaner electromontis Groves and Tattersall, 1991 Montagne d'Ambre fork-marked
    lemur

Family Lepilemuridae Gray, 1871

Lepilemur I. Geoffroy, 1851 Sportive lemurs
  Lepilemur mustelinus I. Geoffroy, 1851 Weasel sportive lemur
  Lepilemur betsileo Louis *et al.*, 2006 Betsileo sportive lemur
  Lepilemur microdon (Forsyth Major, 1894) Small-toothed sportive lemur
  Lepilemur jamesorum Louis *et al.*, 2006 Manombo sportive lemur
  Lepilemur wrightae Louis *et al.*, 2006 Wright's sportive lemur
  Lepilemur fleuretae Louis *et al.*, 2006 Andohahela sportive lemur
  Lepilemur hollandorum Ramaromilanto *et al.*, 2009 Mananara-Nord sportive lemur
  Lepilemur seali Louis *et al.*, 2006 Seal's sportive lemur
  Lepilemur scottorum Lei *et al.*, 2008 Masoala sportive lemur
  Lepilemur milanoii Louis *et al.*, 2006 Daraina sportive lemur
  Lepilemur ankaranesis Rumpler and Albignac, 1975 Ankarana sportive lemur
  Lepilemur septentrionalis Rumpler and Albignac, 1975 Sahafary sportive lemur
  Lepilemur dorsalis Gray, 1871 Gray's sportive lemur
  Lepilemur tymerlachsonorum Louis *et al.*, 2006 Nosy Be sportive lemur
  Lepilemur mittermeieri Rabarivola *et al.*, 2006 Mittermeier's sportive lemur
  Lepilemur sahamalazensis Andriaholinirina *et al.*, 2006 Sahamalaza sportive lemur
  Lepilemur grewcockorum Louis *et al.*, 2006 Anjiamangirana sportive lemur
  Lepilemur otto Craul *et al.*, 2007 Ambodimahabibo sportive lemur
  Lepilemur edwardsi (Forsyth Major, 1894) Milne-Edwards' sportive lemur
  Lepilemur aeeclis Andriaholinirina *et al.*, 2006 Antafia sportive lemur
  Lepilemur ahmansonorum Louis *et al.*, 2006 Tsiombikibo sportive lemur
  Lepilemur randrianasoloi Andriaholinirina *et al.*, 2006 Bemaraha sportive lemur
  Lepilemur ruficaudatus A. Grandidier, 1867 Red-tailed sportive lemur
  Lepilemur hubbardorum Louis *et al.*, 2006 Zombitse sportive lemur
  Lepilemur petteri Louis *et al.*, 2006 Petter's sportive lemur
  Lepilemur leucopus (Forsyth Major, 1894) White-footed sportive lemur

Family Lemuridae Gray, 1821

Hapalemur I. Geoffroy, 1851 Bamboo or Gentle lemurs
  Hapalemur griseus griseus Link, 1795 Gray bamboo lemur
  Hapalemur griseus gilberti Rabarivola *et al.*, 2007 Beanamalao bamboo lemur
  Hapalemur griseus ranomafanensis Rabarivola *et al.*, 2007 Ranomafana bamboo
    lemur
  Hapalemur meridionalis Warter *et al.*, 1987 Southern bamboo lemur
  Hapalemur occidentalis Rumpler, 1975 Northern bamboo lemur
  Hapalemur alaotrensis Rumpler, 1975 Lac Alaotra bamboo lemur
  Hapalemur aureus Meier *et al.*, 1987 Golden bamboo lemur

Prolemur (Gray, 1871) Greater bamboo lemur
  Prolemur simus (Gray, 1871) Greater bamboo lemur

Lemur Linnaeus, 1758 Ring-tailed Lemur
  Lemur catta Linnaeus, 1758 Ring-tailed lemur

Eulemur Simons and Rumpler, 1988 True lemurs
  Eulemur fulvus (É. Geoffroy, 1796) Brown lemur
  Eulemur rufus (Audebert, 1799) Rufous brown lemur

Eulemur rufifrons (Bennett, 1833) Red-fronted brown lemur
Eulemur albifrons (É. Geoffroy, 1796) White-fronted brown lemur
Eulemur sanfordi (Archbold, 1932) Sanford's brown lemur
Eulemur cinereiceps (A. Grandidier and Milne-Edwards, 1890) White-collared brown
    lemur
Eulemur collaris (É. Geoffroy, 1812) Red-collared brown lemur
Eulemur macaco (Linnaeus, 1766) Black lemur
Eulemur flavifrons (Gray, 1867) Blue-eyed Black lemur
Eulemur coronatus (Gray, 1842) Crowned lemur
Eulemur rubriventer (I. Geoffroy, 1850) Red-bellied lemur

Varecia Gray, 1863 Ruffed lemurs
    Varecia variegata variegata (Kerr, 1792) Variegated black-and-white ruffed lemur
    Varecia variegata editorum (Hill, 1953) Southern black-and-white ruffed lemur
    Varecia variegata subcincta (A. Smith, 1833) Northern black-and-white ruffed lemur
    Varecia rubra (É. Geoffroy, 1812) Red ruffed lemur

Family Indriidae Burnett, 1828

Avahi Jourdan, 1834 Woolly lemurs or Avahis
    Avahi laniger (Gmelin, 1788) Eastern woolly lemur
    Avahi mooreorum Lei *et al.*, 2008 Masoala woolly lemur
    Avahi peyrierasi Zaramody *et al.*, 2006 Peyriéras' woolly lemur
    Avahi betsileo Andriantompohavana *et al.*, 2007 Betsileo woolly lemur
    Avahi ramanantsoavanai Zaramody *et al.*, 2006 Manombo woolly lemur
    Avahi meridionalis Zaramody *et al.*, 2006 Southern woolly lemur
    Avahi occidentalis (Lorenz von Liburnau, 1898) Western woolly lemur
    Avahi cleesei Thalmann and Geissmann, 2005 Bemaraha woolly lemur
    Avahi unicolor Thalmann and Geissmann, 2000 Sambirano woolly lemur

Propithecus Bennett, 1832 Sifakas
    Propithecus verreauxi A. Grandidier, 1867 Verreaux's sifaka
    Propithecus deckenii Peters, 1870 Decken's sifaka
    Propithecus coronatus Milne-Edwards, 1871 Crowned sifaka
    Propithecus coquereli A. Grandidier, 1867 Coquerel's sifaka
    Propithecus tattersalli Simons, 1988 Tattersall's sifaka
    Propithecus diadema Bennett, 1832 Diademed sifaka
    Propithecus edwardsi A. Grandidier, 1871 Milne-Edwards' sifaka
    Propithecus candidus A. Grandidier, 1871 Silky sifaka
    Propithecus perrieri Lavauden, 1931 Perrier's sifaka

Indri É. Geoffroy and G. Cuvier, 1796 Indri or Babakoto
    Indri indri (Gmelin, 1788) Indri

Family Daubentoniidae Gray, 1863

Daubentonia É. Geoffroy, 1795 Aye-aye
    Daubentonia madagascariensis (Gmelin, 1788) Aye-aye

Cheirogaleidae

Fig. 7.1: A Nosy Be mouse lemur (*Microcebus mamiratra*) in forest right next to the Ampasipohy Beach, Lokobe Strict Nature Reserve (photo by R. A. Mittermeier).

CHAPTER 7

FAMILY CHEIROGALEIDAE Gray, 1873

The family Cheirogaleidae has five genera and 30 species: *Microcebus*, the mouse lemurs (18 species); *Allocebus*, the hairy-eared dwarf lemur (one species); *Mirza*, giant mouse lemurs (two species); *Cheirogaleus*, the dwarf lemurs (five species); and *Phaner*, the fork-marked lemurs (four species). No subspecies are recognized at the present time. Cheirogaleid lemurs range in size from the world's smallest primate at about 30 g to almost 600 g. All move quadrupedally and most have elongated bodies with short legs. At least one species of cheirogaleid can be found in any natural forest of reasonable size in Madagascar.

All members of this family are nocturnal, sleeping during the day in small nests of dead leaves, in tree holes, or in holes in the ground. Some cheirogaleids undergo prolonged periods of seasonal torpor.

Microcebus É. Geoffroy, 1828
Mouse Lemurs

The genus *Microcebus* includes the smallest of the lemurs and indeed the smallest of all living primates. These tiny animals range in weight from 30 to 87 g and in length from about 23 to 29 cm (including tail), and all are nocturnal in habit. Until recently, very few species were recognized in this genus. Schwarz (1931), for example, recognized only one with two subspecies. Field work by Martin (1972a) indicated that the two subspecies were in fact distinct species, *Microcebus rufus* and *M. murinus*. Petter *et al.* (1977) continued to recognize two subspecies, but noted that there was geographical variation in both the eastern and western areas of their distribution. Subsequent field studies in western and northern Madagascar in the 1990s led to the resurrection of the name *myoxinus* (see Schmid and Kappeler, 1994) and the discovery of a new species, *M. ravelobensis* Zimmermann *et al.*, 1997. Later still, more field work in western Madagascar, coupled with genetic analyses, resulted in the addition of three new species, *M. berthae*, *M. sambiranensis* and *M. tavaratra*, a clarification of the status of *M. myoxinus*, and the elevation of a previously described subspecies to a full species, *M. griseorufus* (see Rasoloarison *et al.*, 2000; Yoder *et al.*, 2000b; Hapke *et al.*, 2003a). These researchers also indicated that eastern *M. rufus* might also include more than a single species, and Groves (2001) drew attention to differences between northeastern and southern specimens within the form recognized as *M. rufus*. This has now been confirmed by recent field and laboratory studies that have resulted in the description of an additional ten species as we go to press in 2010, all in what was formerly considered the range of *M. rufus*. These include *M. lehilahytsara* described in Kappeler *et al.* (2005), *M. danfossi* and *M. bongolavensis* described by Olivieri *et al.* (2007a), *M. mamiratra* described by Andriantompohavana *et al.* (2006), *M. jollyae*, *M. mittermeieri* and *M. simmonsi* described by Louis *et al.* (2006a), *M. macarthurii* described by Radespiel *et al.* (2008), and *M. arnholdi* and *M. margotmarshae* described by Louis *et al.* (2008). In this field guide we provide full accounts for all 18 presently-recognized species while at the same time recognizing that the taxonomy of this genus will continue to undergo further revision. Anticipated are formal descriptions of two more species mentioned in Louis *et al.* (2006a) (from Manombo and Vevembe, respectively) and one species mentioned in Radespiel *et al.* (2008).

Mouse lemurs are present throughout Madagascar wherever suitable natural habitat remains, including primary and secondary forest and even disturbed habitats. They are often among the most abundant mammals in areas where they occur. Typically, mouse lemurs are sympatric with at least one other nocturnal lemur, and very often three, four, or even five. Two *Microcebus* species may be sympatric in some areas as well.

In the field, *Microcebus* can be distinguished from *Cheirogaleus* by its much smaller size and more active movements, and from *Mirza* by its smaller size. *Phaner* is larger, much more vocal, and easily distinguished by its fork-mark and its bobbing movements. *Lepilemur*, *Avahi*, and *Daubentonia* are all much larger and cannot be confused with *Microcebus*. The one genus which presents problems is *Allocebus*, since both *Microcebus* and *Allocebus* are small, and the latter's hairy ears are only distinguishable if a very clear, close view is obtained. Mouse lemurs tend to use the lower forest layers and to prefer habitat edges, moving quadrupedally and jumping in rapid bursts. During daylight hours, they seek shelter in tree holes, dense tangles of vegetation, or nests, where they congregate in small groups. During the austral winter, certain species may enter periods of daily and seasonal torpor during which they lose a significant percentage of their body mass, previously stored as fat. Their diet consists mainly of fruit, but also includes small invertebrates, gums and insect excretions. Mouse lemurs are preyed upon by several mammals, and by owls, vangas (Vangidae), and snakes.

Home ranges vary from one to two hectares, those of multiple males and females overlapping. Mouse lemurs can begin to reproduce during their first year of life, typically giving birth once or twice (rarely three times) each year, and often producing twins. Much of what is currently known about mouse lemurs is well summarized in Kappeler and Rasoloarison (2003).

There are many opportunities for visitors to Madagascar to see mouse lemurs in the wild, but only if they are willing to don a headlamp or flashlight and embark on a night walk. Be prepared to listen for high-pitched, squeaking vocalizations and to look for the tiny eyes shining back in the beam of your flashlight from the shrub layer up to the middle levels of the forest. However, do not expect the mouse lemur to sit in your beam for too long, as would be the case with the less active *Cheirogaleus* or *Lepilemur*. Mouse lemurs are active and will move away from the light, although you can usually follow them for short distances. Occasionally, with a little luck, one will freeze in the beam of your light, allowing you to approach to within a meter or so and perhaps even take a photo.

Fig. 7.2: *Microcebus* **postural and behavioral drawings (next page):**
> **a.** *Microcebus* **sitting in a tree**
> **b.** *Microcebus* **climbing upside down on twigs**
> **c.** *Microcebus* **standing on a horizontal branch**
> **d.** *Microcebus* **standing on a twig**
> **e.** *Microcebus* **mating**

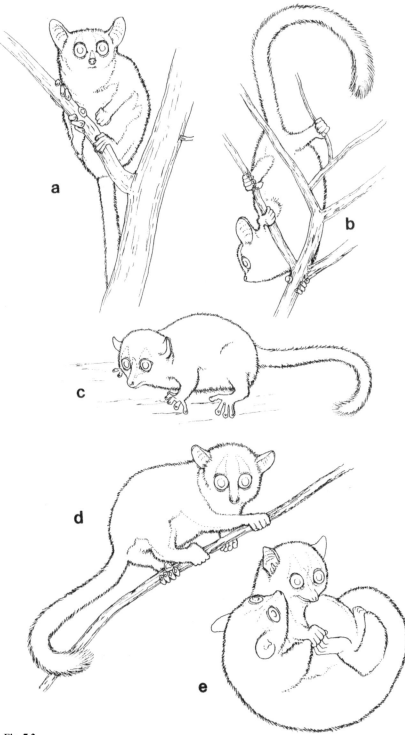

Fig. 7.2.

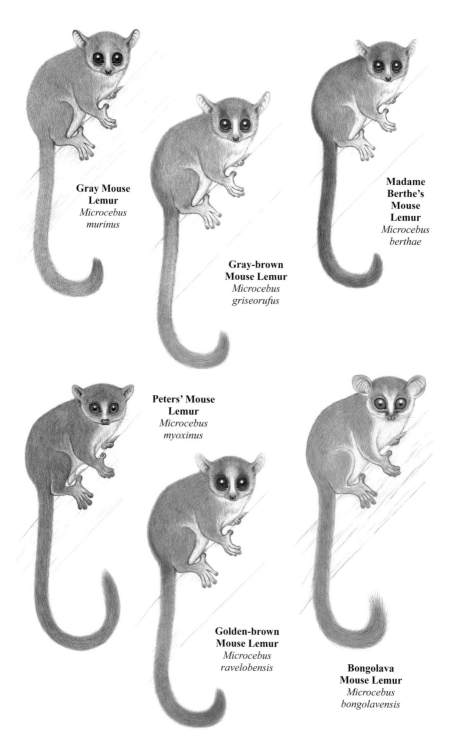

**Gray Mouse
Lemur**
*Microcebus
murinus*

**Gray-brown
Mouse Lemur**
*Microcebus
griseorufus*

**Madame
Berthe's
Mouse
Lemur**
*Microcebus
berthae*

**Peters' Mouse
Lemur**
*Microcebus
myoxinus*

**Golden-brown
Mouse Lemur**
*Microcebus
ravelobensis*

**Bongolava
Mouse Lemur**
*Microcebus
bongolavensis*

Fig. 7.3.

Ambarijeby Mouse Lemur
Microcebus danfossi

Sambirano Mouse Lemur
Microcebus sambiranensis

Margot Marsh's Mouse Lemur
Microcebus margotmarshae

Nosy Be Mouse Lemur
Microcebus mamiratra

Montagne d'Ambre Mouse Lemur
Microcebus arnholdi

Tavaratra Mouse Lemur
Microcebus tavaratra

Fig. 7.4.

Cheirogaleidae

Cheirogaleidae

**Rufous Mouse
Lemur**
Microcebus rufus

**Jolly's
Mouse
Lemur**
*Microcebus
jollyae*

**Goodman's
Mouse
Lemur**
*Microcebus
lehilahytsara*

**Simmons'
Mouse Lemur**
*Microcebus
simmonsi*

**Anjiahely
Mouse Lemur**
*Microcebus
macarthurii*

**Mittermeier's
Mouse Lemur**
*Microcebus
mittermeieri*

Fig. 7.5.

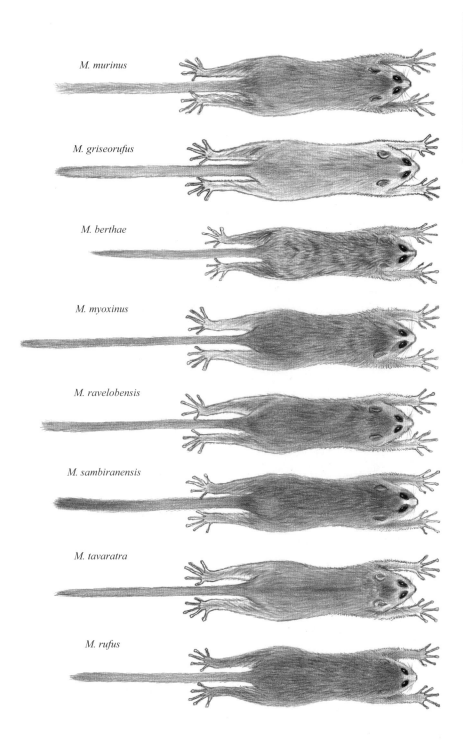

M. murinus

M. griseorufus

M. berthae

M. myoxinus

M. ravelobensis

M. sambiranensis

M. tavaratra

M. rufus

Fig. 7.6.

Cheirogaleidae

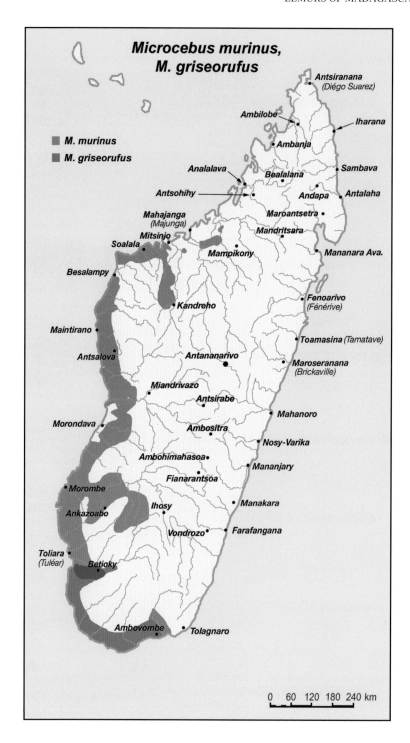

Fig. 7.7: Distibution of western *Microcebus* species. Note that *M. griseorufus* is sympatric with *M. murinus* over most (or possibly all) of its range.

Fig. 7.8: Distribution of Western *Microcebus* species. Question marks indicate the presence of mouse lemur species that are either not yet described or are of uncertain identity.

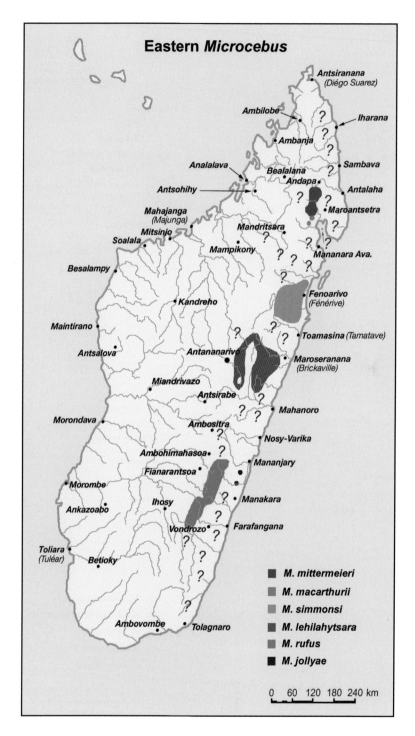

Fig. 7.9: Distribution of Eastern *Microcebus* species. Question marks indicate the presence of mouse lemur species that are either not yet described or are of uncertain identity.

Cheirogaleidae

Fig. 7.10: Goodman's mouse lemur (*Microcebus lehilahytsara*), Andasibe (photo by R. A. Mittermeier).

Cheirogaleidae

Microcebus murinus (J. F. Miller, 1777)
Gray Mouse Lemur

Other English: Lesser Mouse Lemur
French: Cheirogale mignon, Cheirogale nain, Microcèbe murin, Petit Microcèbe
German: Grauer Mausmaki
Malagasy: Tsidy (north), Koitsiky, Titlivaha, Pondiky (Tolagnaro = Fort-Dauphin)

Identification

The gray mouse lemur has a head-body length of 12–14 cm, a tail length of 13–14.5 cm, a total length of 25–28 cm, and a weight of 58–67 g (Rasoloarison *et al.*, 2000). The dorsal coat is brownish-gray with various reddish tones, the flanks are light gray to beige, and the ventral fur has discrete dull beige or whitish-beige patches along portions of the belly. A pale white patch occurs above the nose and between the eyes; some individuals have dark orbital markings. The furred portions of the hands and feet are off-white. The ears are long and fleshy in comparison to the shorter, more concealed ears of *Microcebus rufus*.

This species can be distinguished from the often sympatric *Cheirogaleus medius* by its smaller size and more active movement, and from *Mirza coquereli* by its smaller ears and smaller size. *Phaner*, *Lepilemur*, and *Avahi* are all considerably larger and unlikely to be confused with this species. It is sympatric with at least four other mouse lemur species over its large range; for ways to distinguish them, see the accounts for *M. griseorufus*, *M. berthae*, *M. ravelobensis*, and *M. tavaratra*.

Geographic Range

The distribution of *M. murinus* is currently believed to extend throughout western Madagascar from the Onilahy River in the south to Ankarana in the north. A disjunct population is also found in the southeast up to the littoral forests of the Mandena Conservation Zone. This species is sympatric with *M. griseorufus* at Beza-Mahafaly, Mikea, and Berenty, with *M. berthae* in Kirindy Forest, with *M. ravelobensis* at Ankarafantsika (Rasoloarison *et al.*, 2000; Goodman *et al.*, 2002; Yoder *et al.*, 2002; Kappeler and Rasoloarison, 2003; Ganzhorn and Randrianamalina, 2004; Rasoazanabary, 2004), and with *M. tavaratra* at Ankarana.

Natural History

Microcebus murinus inhabits lowland tropical dry forest, sub-arid thorn scrub, gallery forest, spiny forest and secondary forest formations from sea level to 800 m, and is one of Madagascar's most abundant small native mammals (Radespiel, 2000). Studies at Ankarafantsika indicate that individuals may take shelter in three to nine different tree holes within their range and remain in a given shelter for several days in succession. Females tend to share nests with several conspecifics, while males tend to sleep alone (Radespiel *et al.*, 1998). Two or more females will form breeding groups and raise their young cooperatively (Eberle and Kappeler, 2006).

The diet is varied, consisting largely of invertebrates (particularly beetles), but also fruits, flowers, gums, nectar, and small amphibians and reptiles. The Long-eared Owl (*Asio madagascariensis*) is an important predator of this species (Goodman *et al.*, 1993a).

Activity patterns appear to differ between populations and sexes. Males and females at Ankarafantsika exhibit daily, rather than seasonal, torpor (Zimmermann, 1998). At the Kirindy Forest both sexes show the same daily torpor, but most adult females also hibernate for significant periods, while males remain active during these same periods. In fact, the males become extremely active several weeks before the females emerge from their torpor (Schmid and Kappeler, 1998; Rasoazanabary, 2001; Génin, 2003).

Recent studies of gray mouse lemur social behavior confirm that male home ranges tend to be twice as large as those of females, and also increase in size during the mating season (Buesching *et al.*, 1998; Radespiel, 2000; Eberle and Kappeler, 2002). Ranges of both sexes overlap, those of females less so than those of males, while the ranges of all members of a "neighborhood" overlap in a central area. Recent genetic studies of *M. murinus* populations at Kirindy suggest that females tend to arrange themselves spatially in clusters of related individuals, while males tend to emigrate from their natal groups (Wimmer *et al.*, 2002).

Fig. 7.11: Gray mouse lemur (*Microcebus murinus*), Kirindy Forest (photo by R. A. Mittermeier).

Cheirogaleidae

The mating system is characterized as multi-male/multi-female (Radespiel, 2000; Eberle and Kappeler, 2002, 2004). Females become receptive every 45–55 days from September to March, during which time the male's testes increase greatly in size. Typically, two young are born after a gestation of approximately 60 days.

Although *M. murinus* is reported to inhabit secondary forests and degraded habitats, at least one recent study suggests that decreased habitat quality may have adverse effects on population dynamics. According to Ganzhorn and Schmid (1998), fewer large tree holes in secondary forests result in fewer opportunities to save energy through periods of torpor, and may increase levels of stress and mortality.

Conservation Status

Microcebus murinus was classified as Least Concern (LC) in the most recent IUCN Red List assessment (2008). Loss of habitat for slash-and-burn agriculture and live capture to supply local pet trades are the two most significant threats to this species, the latter being more prominent in the southern and northern parts of its range. It is present in six national parks (Andohahela, Ankarafantsika, Baie de Baly, Isalo, Tsingy de Namoroka, and Zombitse-Vohibasia), six special reserves (Andranomena, Ankarana, Bemarivo, Beza-Mahafaly, Kasijy, and Maningoza), the Berenty Private Reserve, and other privately-protected forests within the Mandena Conservation Zone, as well as in Kirindy Forest (part of the Menabe-Antimena Protected Area).

As of 2009, there were about 150 individuals in captivity around the world (ISIS, 2009). This species is still used in a small number of medical laboratories as well (I. J. Porton, pers. comm.).

Where to See It

With a little patience, this species can be seen easily almost anywhere within its large range. Particularly good opportunities exist at the Beza-Mahafaly Special Reserve, the Kirindy Forest, Ankarafantsika National Park, and the Berenty Private Reserve. In Berenty, this species occurs only in the gallery forest, while the adjacent spiny forest is occupied by *M. griseorufus*. Excursions to Kirindy, which has comfortable bungalows, can be arranged through hotels in Morondava, such as Chez Maggie and the Baobab Hotel. Excursions to Ankarafantsika can easily be arranged through hotels in Mahajanga (= Majunga), or through an Antananarivo-based tour operator. The Ampijoroa campsite has been upgraded recently and now contains the locally managed "Gîte de Ampijoroa" with comfortable rooms and a restaurant. In addition, more upscale chalets have recently opened at Lac Ravelobe across the road.

Cheirogaleidae

Fig. 7.12: Gray mouse lemur (*Microcebus murinus*), Mandena (photo by A. Hapke).

Cheirogaleidae

Microcebus griseorufus Kollman, 1910
Gray-brown Mouse Lemur

Other English: Reddish-gray Mouse Lemur, Rufous-gray Mouse
Lemur
French: Microcèbe gris-roux
German: Graubrauner Mausmaki
Malagasy: Pondiky, Tsidy

Identification

Microcebus griseorufus is a large mouse lemur, with a head-body length of 12–13 cm,
a tail length of 14–15 cm, a total length of 26–28 cm, and a body weight of 46–79 g
(Rasoloarison *et al.*, 2000). The dorsal coat is light gray, split by a cinnamon midline stripe
that runs from either the crown or the shoulders to the end of the tail, which is largely
cinnamon above and beige beneath. The anterior portion of the ventral coat is light grayish-
white, the posterior portion tending more toward gray.

An inhabitant of the spiny forest of southern Madagascar, this species is sympatric
in some areas with *M. murinus*, from which it can readily be distinguished by its more
prominent, darker mid-dorsal stripe (Rasoloarison *et al.*, 2000; Goodman *et al.*, 2002;
Yoder *et al.*, 2002; Ganzhorn and Randriamanalina, 2004). It is often in the same forests
with two other nocturnal genera, *Cheirogaleus* and *Lepilemur*, as well, and can easily be
distinguished from both of these by its much smaller size and more rapid movements.

Geographic Range

Kollman (1910) described the new subspecies
Microcebus minor griseorufus from southern Madagascar.
Tattersall (1982) considered it to be a synonym of *M.
murinus*. In a recent review of the genus, Rasoloarison *et
al.* (2000) elevated it to a full species as *M. griseorufus*. It is
found in the spiny forest region of southern and southwestern
Madagascar, where it ranges from Lamboharana south to
the Toliara (= Tuléar) region, to the Beza-Mahafaly Special
Reserve (south of the Onilahy River) in the southeast, and
to Tsimanampetsotsa, Berenty, and Petriky in the extreme
south. At Beza-Mahafaly and Mikea it is sympatric with
M. murinus, whereas in Berenty it is found in spiny forest
patches but not in the immediately adjacent gallery forest
that is occupied by *M. murinus*.

Natural History

Microcebus griseorufus is a common inhabitant of spiny
forest and dry thorn scrub from sea level to 250 m. In the
Beza-Mahafaly Special Reserve it is also found in gallery forest, while in the Berenty
Private Reserve it is replaced in that habitat by *M. murinus* (see Rasoazanabary, 2004).
In Beza-Mahafaly and in the nearby Ihazoara Valley, both species are among the prey of
the Barn Owl (*Tyto alba*) and the Madagascar Long-eared Owl (*Asio madagascariensis*)
(Goodman *et al.*, 1993a, 1993b). This species feeds mainly on gums, especially during

Fig. 7.13: Gray-brown mouse lemur (*Microcebus griseorufus*), Manakaralahy (photo by R. Randrianampionona).

periods of drought. Daily torpor and opportunistic seasonal fattening have been observed when food availability is high (Génin, 2008).

The reproductive season is relatively long, lasting as it does from September to May. Estrus is not synchronized. Mating occurs between September and January. Males have been observed to mate-guard. Gestation in one female lasted 52 days, and litters of up to three have been reported. Alloparenting has been observed. Young males disperse. Females and, less frequently, males associate in same-sex pairs that sometimes combine to form larger sleeping groups (Génin, 2008).

Conservation Status

Microcebus griseorufus was classified as Least Concern (LC) in the most recent IUCN Red List assessment (2008). The most significant threats to its survival are deforestation for charcoal production and land clearance for commercial maize production. This species is known to occur in the Tsimanampetsotsa National Park, the Beza-Mahafaly Special Reserve, and the Berenty Private Reserve, and may also be present in two other national parks (Isalo and Zombitse-Vohibasia).

As of 2010, this species was not being kept in captivity (I. J. Porton, pers. comm.).

Where to See It

The easiest place to see this mouse lemur is in the spiny forest patches of the Berenty Private Reserve, where it is quite common. Another good place is the Beza-Mahafaly Special Reserve, located 35 km northeast of Betioky Sud, about a five-hour drive from Toliara (= Tuléar) in a four-wheel-drive vehicle (Bradt, 2007; Ratsirarson, 2003). *Microcebus griseorufus* may also be readily observed in the forest called "PK 32" near Ifaty, north of Toliara, and in Tsimanampetsotsa National Park. Night walks at PK 32 are possible from many of the hotels in the Ifaty Mangily coastal tourism area, one hour north of Toliara. Tsimanampetsotsa National Park is a two-hour drive from Anakao (another coastal tourist spot with several hotels), and a 45-minute boat ride south of Toliara.

Fig. 7.14: Gray-brown mouse lemur (*Microcebus griseorufus*), spiny desert of Berenty (photo by R. A. Mittermeier).

Cheirogaleidae

Microcebus berthae Rasoloarison *et al.*, 2000
Madame Berthe's Mouse Lemur

Other English: Berthe's Mouse Lemur
French: Microcèbe de Madame Berthe
German: Madame Berthe's Mausmaki
Malagasy: Tsidy bitika an' i-Berthe

Identification

Microcebus berthae is the smallest of the mouse lemurs and very likely the smallest primate in the world. It has a head-body length of 9–9.5 cm, a tail length of 13–14 cm, a total length of 22–23 cm, and it weighs only about 30 g (Rasoloarison *et al.*, 2000). The dorsal coat is rufous with a distinct, darker midline stripe that extends from just behind the shoulders to the tip of the tail. The fur of the head is brighter than that of the back. The ventral coat is pale yellow-brown to pale gray in color. A dull white patch occurs above the nose, the region around the eyes is cinnamon, and the crown and ears are tawny. The ears are very short and the orbits are surrounded by a narrow black band. The furred portions of the hands and feet are dull beige.

This species can be confused with the sympatric gray mouse lemur (*Microcebus murinus*), which is only a little larger, and especially with young *M. murinus*, which are sometimes "parked" by their mothers. The most reliable characteristic is the warmer rufous back and flanks of Madame Berthe's mouse lemur, but the difference can be difficult to confirm at night. If a small mouse lemur sits for any length of time, it may be a young "parked" *M. murinus*, rather than the very active *M. berthae*.

Geographic Range

West-central Madagascar. *M. berthae* is the name given to the diminutive, rufous-colored mouse lemur that was discovered in the Kirindy Forest in 1992, and was originally thought to be *Microcebus myoxinus* (see Schmid and Kappeler, 1994). This species inhabits dry deciduous lowland forests (from sea level to 150 m) in the Menabe region south of the Tsiribihina River, where it is sympatric with the larger *Microcebus murinus* (see Schmid and Kappeler, 1994; Schwab and Ganzhorn, 2004). In addition to the Kirindy Forest, *M. berthae* has been reported from the Andranomena Special Reserve (Schwab and Ganzhorn, 2004), and used to occur in the forests of Analabe, just a few kilometers to the northwest (based on a photograph taken in 1985, Fig. 7.15), and in Ambadira. However, the forests of Analabe have been heavily degraded over the past two decades, so it is uncertain if the species still occurs there. Densities in Ambadira tend to be higher than in Kirindy (L. M. Schäffler and P. M. Kappeler, unpubl. data).

Natural History

Dammhahn and Kappeler (2005) describe *M. berthae* as a solitary forager characterized by extensively overlapping home ranges, those of the males (4.9 ha) being much larger than those of the females (2.5 ha). Daily ranges appear to be significantly greater than (more than double) those of the larger *M. murinus*. Population densities have been estimated at 30–100 individuals/km² (Schwab and Ganzhorn, 2004). In addition, while both sexes of *M. berthae* engage in daily periods of torpor, they do not enter prolonged torpor during the dry season and do not seem to take shelter in tree holes during the day as does *M. murinus*. The two sympatric mouse lemurs seem to avoid interspecific competition by spatial segregation, making the distributions of both species very patchy (Schwab and Ganzhorn, 2004; Dammhahn and Kappeler, 2008a). In general, *M. berthae* appears to be more localized than the gray mouse lemur.

This tiny primate feeds on fruit and gum, and relies on sugary insect excretions and animal matter during the harsh dry season (Dammhahn and Kappeler, 2008b). Madam Berthe's lemurs are subject to predation by many different species in the forests where they occur, even more so than the larger *M. murinus* (M. Dammhahn, pers. comm.).

Conservation Status

The most recent IUCN Red List assessment (2008) classified *M. berthae* as Endangered (EN). Habitat destruction for slash-and-burn agriculture and logging is the principal threat. Its population was estimated at no more than 8,000 mature individuals and it is known from only a handful of forests, most of which are still at risk of destruction and fragmentation

Fig. 7.15: Madame Berthe's mouse lemur (*Microcebus berthae*) photographed in 1985 (15 years before the species was described) in the Analabe forest near Kirindy, in the Manabe region of southwestern Madagascar (photo by R. A. Mittermeier).

(Schwab and Ganzhorn, 2004). The recently-established 125,000-ha Menabe-Antimena Protected Area encompasses the 30,000-ha strict conservation zone that includes the Kirindy Forest, and the currently unprotected Ambadira forests, all of which provide protection for this species. It probably still occurs in the Andranomena Special Reserve as well, an old reserve immediately adjacent to the new protected area. It used to occur in the Analabe Private Reserve, but this has now been severely degraded, so it is unclear whether the species still survives there.

As of 2009, this species was not being kept in captivity (ISIS, 2009).

Where to See It

The best chances for seeing *M. berthae* in the wild are in the Kirindy Forest, operated by the Centre National pour la Formation, Education, Recherche en Environnement et Foresterie (CNFEREF), Morondava. Tourists can reach Kirindy from Morondava (some 60 km to the southwest) via the regular taxi-brousse service which drops you off 5 km from the camp, or by renting a car through one of the Morondava hotels such as Chez Maggie or the Baobab Hotel. An overnight stay at the CNFEREF camp is required to see this and other nocturnal species. The tourist camp, which was constructed here in 1996 and renovated and expanded in 2007, features simple but comfortable bungalows. Reservations should be made at the CNFEREF bureau in Morondava. Both Madame Berthe's and the gray mouse lemur (*M. murinus*) can be seen during night walks in close proximity to the camp area, but some trails are much better than others, so a local guide is essential.

Fig. 7.16: Russ Mittermeier holding Madame Berthe's mouse lemur (*Microcebus berthae*), the smallest primate in the world (photo by R. A. Mittermeier).

Cheirogaleidae

Fig. 7.17: Madame Berthe's mouse lemur (*Microcebus berthae*) from the Kirindy Forest (photo by J. Zoanarivelo).

Microcebus myoxinus Peters, 1852
Peters' Mouse Lemur

Other English: Pygmy Mouse Lemur, Dormouse Lemur
French: Microcèbe de Peters, Microcèbe pygmée
German: Zwergmausmaki
Malagasy: Tsidy, Malajira

Identification

Microcebus myoxinus is one of the smaller mouse lemurs, with a head-body length
of 12–13 cm, a tail length of 14–15 cm, a total length of 26–28 cm, and a body weight
of 43–55 g (Rasoloarison *et al.*, 2000). The dorsal coat is rufous-brown with a distinct
reddish-brown midline stripe. The ventral coat is pale yellow-brown to pale gray in color.
The tail is darker toward the tip. The ears are relatively short. A light cinnamon patch
between the eyes darkens to reddish behind the orbits and to a tawny crown and ears. The
dark eyebrows are prominent. Furred portions of the hands and feet are whitish-gray to
whitish-beige.

Although this species may be sympatric with other mouse lemurs, it is difficult to give
precise information on how to distinguish between them. Since some of the sympatric
species may still be undescribed, further research on western mouse lemurs is clearly
needed. In addition, *Microcebus myoxinus* is sympatric with several other nocturnal
genera, including *Cheirogaleus*, *Mirza*, *Phaner*, and *Lepilemur*, but can be distinguished
from them by its smaller size.

Geographic Range

West-central Madagascar. Peters (1852) returned from
a collecting expedition to Madagascar with three western
mouse lemur specimens that he named *M. myoxinus*, but
Schwarz (1931) later declared them synonymous with
Microcebus murinus. Schmid and Kappeler (1994) later
concluded that two mouse lemur species were present in
the Kirindy Forest north of Morondava, one of them a
smaller rufous animal for which they resurrected the name
M. myoxinus. Re-examination of the specimens collected by
Peters (1852) indicated that the Kirindy animals were not
M. myoxinus, but rather an entirely new species that was
named *Microcebus berthae* Rasoloarison *et al.*, 2000, and
that the name *M. myoxinus* actually applies to populations
found farther north.

Microcebus myoxinus is reported to range from the
north bank of the Tsiribihina River north to Baie de Baly
in western Madagascar, and to occur in the forests of Belo-
sur-Tsiribihina and Aboalimena, the Tsingy de Bemaraha
National Park and Strict Nature Reserve, and the Tsingy de Namoroka National Park.
In Tsingy de Namoroka and Baie de Baly, it occurs in sympatry with *M. murinus* (see
Hawkins *et al.*, 1998; Rasoloarison *et al.*, 2000; CBSG, 2002).

In Tsingy de Bemaraha National Park, this species is sympatric with at least one other form of *Microcebus* that remains to be identified (Rakotoarison *et al.*, 1993; Thalmann and Rakotoarison, 1994; Ausilio and Raveloarinoro, 1998).

Natural History

Microcebus myoxinus has been found in tropical dry deciduous lowland forests (sea level to 900 m) in the Tsingy de Bemaraha Strict Nature Reserve and the Andramasy forests north of Belo-sur-Tsiribihina, along the border of heavily degraded deciduous forest and savanna at Aboalimena, and in mangrove forests in the Baie de Baly region (Hawkins *et al.*, 1998; Rasoloarison *et al.*, 2000). Its ecology and behavior remain to be studied.

Conservation Status

There is insufficient information to determine the conservation status of *M. myoxinus*, and the latest IUCN Red List assessment (2008) classified it as Data Deficient (DD). It occurs in two national parks (Tsingy de Bemaraha and Tsingy de Namoroka), the Tsingy de Bemaraha Strict Nature Reserve, and likely in Baie de Baly National Park as well, but little is known of its populations in these areas.

As of 2009, this species was not being kept in captivity (ISIS, 2009).

Where to See It

The best chances for seeing *M. myoxinus* in the wild are in the Tsingy de Bemaraha, where there are now two lodges to accommodate visitors. Excursions to the area can be arranged through the Hotel Chez Maggie in Morondava or through most Antananarivo-based tour operators. However, distinguishing it from the sympatric, possibly undescribed, species may be difficult.

Fig. 7.18: Peters' mouse lemur (*Microcebus myoxinus*), Tsingy de Bemaraha National Park (photo by E. E. Louis Jr.).

Cheirogaleidae

Cheirogaleidae

Microcebus ravelobensis Zimmermann *et al.*, 1997
Golden-brown Mouse Lemur

Other English: Lac Ravelobe Mouse Lemur
French: Microcèbe doré
German: Goldbrauner Mausmaki
Malagasy: Tsidy

Identification

Microcebus ravelobensis is the largest of the western Madagascar mouse lemurs. It has a head-body length of 12–13 cm, a tail length of 15–17 cm, a total length of 27–30 cm, and a body weight of 56–87 g (Rasoloarison *et al.*, 2000; Andriantompohavana *et al.*, 2006). The dorsal coat, including the crown and ears, is rufous and mottled; the mid-dorsal stripe is poorly defined. The lighter ventral fur is also mottled or bicolored. The region between the eyes is pale grayish, changing to cinnamon toward the crown. Tail color darkens toward the tip (Zimmermann *et al.*, 1997, 1998).

Microcebus ravelobensis is sympatric with *M. murinus*, and can be confused with it in the wild. However, *Microcebus ravelobensis* has a longer tail and is rufous in coloration.

Geographic Range

The type specimen for this species was collected adjacent to Lac Ravelobe in Ankarafantsika National Park, in northwestern Madagascar. It also occurs in the Mariarano Classified Forest, just north of Mahajunga (Zimmermann *et al.*, 1997, 1998; E. E. Louis Jr., pers. obs.).

Natural History

Microcebus ravelobensis inhabits dry deciduous lowland forests up to 500 m, and can be observed even in degraded patches. It appears to prefer forests with a lower canopy height and more lianas than those inhabited by *M. murinus*, and also uses tree holes less often. The social behavior of the two species seems to be similar (Radespiel *et al.*, 2003; Rendigs *et al.*, 2003; Weidt *et al.*, 2004).

Conservation Status

According to the 2008 IUCN Red List assessment, *M. ravelobensis* is Endangered (EN). Principal threats include habitat loss due to slash-and-burn cultivation and seasonal brush fires, and predation by feral cats and dogs. Ankarafantsika National Park is the only protected area where the golden-brown mouse lemur is known to occur, but it has been reported from two classified forests. Surveys are needed to determine the full extent of its range. In addition, consideration should be given to establishing a protected area that includes the Mariarano Classified Forest.

As of 2009, this species was not being kept in captivity (ISIS, 2009).

Where to See It

This species can be seen with relative ease during night walks in forests surrounding Lac Ravelobe near the tourist camp at Ampijoroa in Ankarafantsika National Park. However, it can be difficult to distinguish from *M. murinus* unless one gets a very clear sighting. Be sure to take an experienced guide to help distinguish the two species.

Cheirogaleidae

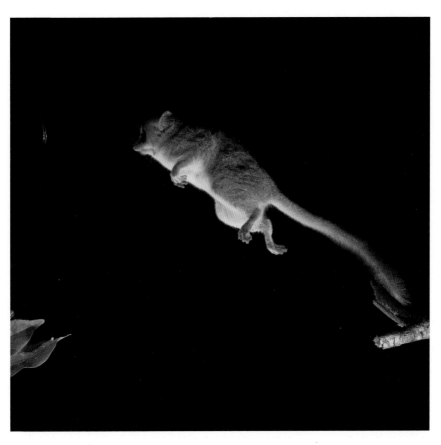

Fig. 7.19: Golden-brown mouse lemur (*Microcebus ravelobensis*) leaping, Ankarafantsika National Park (photo by I. Relanzón).

Microcebus bongolavensis Olivieri *et al.*, 2007
Bongolava Mouse Lemur

Other English: None
French: Microcèbe du Bongolava
German: Bongolava-Mausmaki
Malagasy: Tsidy

Identification

A large, reddish form, difficult to distinguish in the field from *Microcebus danfossi* and *Microcebus ravelobensis* found north and south of its range, respectively. The head-body length is 9–12.2 cm, the tail length 14.7–17.4 cm, the total length 24.7–29.4 cm, and the body weight about 55 g (E. E. Louis Jr., unpubl. data). The fur is short and dense, being maroon on the dorsum with an orange tinge (sometimes showing a faint dorsal line). The ventrum is creamy white, and the tail is the same color as the body, although the fur changes from short and dense on the proximal part to longer and more sparse at the tip. The color of the head varies between individuals even within a population. In some (possibly young) individuals, the head is uniformly rufous to brown, while others show this color only at a triangularly-shaped part over the eyes, with the crown being pale grayish. The ears are rufous. As with other mouse lemurs, there is a distinct white stripe on the bridge of the nose. The hands and feet are white and poorly-haired (Olivieri *et al.*, 2007a).

Geographic Range

Northwestern Madagascar. This species is known only from three small forest fragments in the area around Port-Bergé, between the Mahajamba Est and Sofia rivers, including the type locality Ambodimahabibo (Olivieri *et al.*, 2007a). Prior to its description, the mouse lemur in this region was presumed to be *M. ravelobensis*.

Natural History

This species has not been studied in the wild. It is known to inhabit the primary forests of the Bongolava Mountains (Olivieri *et al.*, 2007a).

Conservation Status

The most recent IUCN Red List assessment (2008) classified *M. bongolavensis* as Data Deficient (DD). It is not known to occur in any protected area, although it may occur in the Bongolava Classified Forest. Surveys are needed to determine the full extent of its range. Consideration should be given to establishing a protected area that includes the Bongolava Classified Forest, the only relatively large forest fragment left that is in its known range.

As of 2010, this species was not being kept in captivity (I. J. Porton, pers. comm.).

Where to See It

At this time, the best place where one can see this species is the type locality at Ambodimahabibo.

Fig. 7.20: Bongalava mouse lemur (*Microcebus bongolavensis*), Ambodimahabibo Classified Forest (photo by J. F. Ranaivoarisoa).

Cheirogaleidae

Microcebus danfossi Olivieri *et al.*, 2007
Ambarijeby Mouse Lemur

Other English: Danfoss' Mouse Lemur
French: Microcèbe d'Ambarijeby, Microcèbe de Danfoss
German: Danfoss-Mausmaki
Malagasy: Tsidy

Identification

Microcebus danfossi is a large mouse lemur, difficult to distinguish in the field from *M. bongolavensis* and *M. ravelobensis*. The head-body length is 12.7–13.6 cm, the tail length is 16.5–17.3 cm, the total length is 29.5–30.7 cm, and the body weight is about 63 g (Olivieri *et al.*, 2007a; E. E. Louis Jr., unpubl. data). The fur is short, dense and bicolored, being maroon on the dorsum with an orange tinge (sometimes showing a faint dorsal line), while the underside is creamy-white. The tail is the same color as the dorsum, although the fur changes from short and dense on the proximal part to longer and scarcer at the tip. There is a distinct white stripe between the eyes, and the ears are rufous. The hands and feet, though poorly haired, are of the same white as between the eyes (Olivieri *et al.*, 2007a).

Geographic Range

Northwestern Madagascar. This species is currently known only from six forest fragments between the Sofia and Maevarano rivers (Olivieri *et al.*, 2007a). Prior to its description, the mouse lemur in this region was assumed to be *M. ravelobensis*.

Natural History

As of 2010, there had been no field studies of this species.

Conservation Status

The most recent IUCN Red List assessment (2008) classified *M. danfossi* as Data Deficient (DD). This species is presently known to occur in two protected areas, the Bora Special Reserve and the forest of Anjiamangirana I (Randrianambinina *et al.*, 2003; Olivieri *et al.*, 2007a). However, surveys are needed to determine the full extent of its range. Both Bora and Anjiamangirana are small and have very little infrastructure to implement efficient protection. The forest of Bora is already very degraded (Randrianambinina *et al.*, 2003b; Olivieri *et al.*, 2005). Furthermore, due to the small size, the genetic diversity of *M. danfossi* in these two protected areas could be too low to ensure its long-term survival. An effort is needed to reinforce the infrastructure and protection within Anjiamangirana I, and to establish another protected zone in Marosakoa, another fragment in which it occurs (E. E. Louis Jr., pers. obs.).

As of 2010, this species was not being kept in captivity (I. J. Porton, pers. comm.).

Where to See It

With a bit of effort, this species may be seen in the Bora Special Reserve and the forest of Anjiamangirana I.

Fig. 7.21: Ambarijeby mouse lemur (*Microcebus danfossi*), Andalirano Classified Forest (photo by J. F. Ranaivoarisoa).

Microcebus margotmarshae Louis *et al.*, 2008
Margot Marsh's Mouse Lemur

Other English: Antafondro Mouse Lemur
French: Microcèbe de Margot Marsh
German: Margot Marsh's Mausmaki
Malagasy: Tsidy

Identification

Microcebus margotmarshae is a small mouse lemur with a head-body length of about 11–12 cm, a tail length of about 14 cm, a total length of 25–26 cm, and a body weight of 41–50 g (Louis *et al.*, 2008). The dorsal and tail pelage is predominantly reddish-orange with gray undertones, the ventral fur is white to cream, and the head is largely bright reddish-orange. The muzzle and the area surrounding the eyes are light brown, and there is a small, bright white spot on the nose ridge between the eyes. The ears are small (Louis *et al.*, 2008).

Geographic Range

Northwestern Madagascar. This newly-described species is currently known only from its type locality, the Antafondro Classified Forest south of the Andranomalaza River and north of the Maevarano River (Andriantompohavana *et al.*, 2006; Louis *et al.*, 2008). Further research is needed to determine the precise limits of its distribution (Louis *et al.*, 2008). Formerly, the mouse lemurs from this region were thought to be *M. sambiranensis*.

Natural History

As of 2010, this species had not been studied in the wild.

Conservation Status

The conservation status of this species has not yet been assessed. It is present in the Antafondro Classified Forest, and possibly at high-elevations in the Tsaratanana Special Reserve as well (Louis *et al.*, 2008).

As of 2010, *M. margotmarshae* was not being kept in captivity (I. J. Porton, pers. comm.).

Where to See It

The only confirmed locality for this species is in the Antafondro Classified Forest (Louis *et al.*, 2008).

Fig. 7.22: Margot Marsh's mouse lemur (*Microcebus margotmarshae*), Antafondro Classified Forest (photo by R. Andriantompohavana).

Microcebus sambiranensis Rasoloarison *et al.*, 2000
Sambirano Mouse Lemur

Other English: None
French: Microcèbe du Sambirano
German: Sambirano-Mausmaki
Malagasy: Tsidy, Tsitsihy, Vokimbahy

Identification

Microcebus sambiranensis is one of the smallest of the mouse lemurs, with a head-body length of 11–12 cm, a tail length of 13.5–14.5 cm, a total length of 25–27 cm, and a body weight of just 38–50 g (Rasoloarison *et al.*, 2000; Andriantompohavana *et al.*, 2006). The dorsal coat is a bright reddish-cinnamon with a poorly defined, amber midline stripe that extends from just beyond the shoulders to the end of the tail. The ventral coat is a duller whitish-beige. There is a pale patch between the eyes, which are surrounded by dark orbital rings. The crown and ears are amber.

Geographic Range

Northwestern Madagascar. This species is presently known only from the Manongarivo Special Reserve (Rasoloarison *et al.*, 2000; Goodman and Soarimalala, 2002), north of the Andranomalaza River and south of the Sambirano River (Louis *et al.*, 2006a). It is possibly also found in isolated populations on the Ampasindava Peninsula and in the Tsaratanana Massif (Randrianambinina *et al.*, 2003c; Louis *et al.*, 2008). Prior to the description of this species, the mouse lemur of Manongarivo was thought to be *M. rufus* (see Tattersall, 1982).

Natural History

The Sambirano mouse lemur is named for the Sambirano region of northern Madagascar, where elements of the country's humid eastern and dry western forests meet. It can also be found in disturbed habitats and in forests bordering agricultural sites. No systematic studies of the ecology or behavior of this species have been conducted to date, and there are no estimates of population size or density.

Conservation Status

Microcebus sambiranensis is Endangered (EN) according to the IUCN Red List assessment of 2008. The principal threat is habitat loss due to slash-and-burn agriculture, firewood collection, and charcoal production. It is protected in the Manongarivo Special Reserve.

As of 2009, this species was not being kept in captivity (ISIS, 2009).

Where to See It

So far, the only place to see *M. sambiranensis* in the wild is in the Manongarivo Special Reserve. The reserve can be reached by four-wheel-drive vehicle from Ambanja, which is about 60 km to the north. It is probably best to contact an Antsiranana- or Nosy Be-based tour operator to arrange such a trip, and it is important to get permission from Madagascar National Parks in advance to enter this reserve. It is not easy to reach. There are several hotels in Ambanja and at least two very good ones in nearby Ankify.

Fig. 7.23: Sambirano mouse lemur (*Microcebus sambiranensis*), Manongarivo Special Reserve (photo by J. F. Ranaivoarisoa).

Fig. 7.24: Sambirano mouse lemur (*Microcebus sambiranensis*), Mariarano (photo by E. E. Louis Jr.).

Cheirogaleidae

Microcebus mamiratra Andriantompohavana *et al.*, 2006
Nosy Be Mouse Lemur

Other English: Claire's Mouse Lemur
French: Microcèbe de Nosy Be, Microcèbe de Claire
German: Nosy Be-Mausmaki
Malagasy: Valovi (Lokobe)

Identification

Microcebus mamiratra is similar to *M. sambiranensis* except that it is slightly larger, with a a head-body length of about 12.7 cm, a tail length of about 14.3 cm, a total length of 27 cm, and a body weight of 50–60 g (Andriantompohavana *et al.*, 2006). The fur is dense and short, with the upper body and head (including the ears) being a light reddish-brown (becoming a brighter reddish-brown on the dorsum and crown cap), and white to creamy below. There is sometimes a faint, light grayish-brown dorsal line. The tail changes gradually from rufous-brown on the proximal part to dark brown at the tip. The hands and feet, though poorly-haired, are gray or white. A whitish midline stripe is found on the anterior part of the muzzle, which is wider and more diffuse between the eyes (Andriantompohavana *et al.*, 2006).

Shortly after the description of this species, Olivieri *et al.* (2007a) described the same animal, giving it the name *lokobensis*. However, since this name was published after the name *M. mamiratra*, it becomes a junior synonym.

Geographic Range

This species is confined to the island of Nosy Be in northwestern Madagascar, principally within the Lokobe Strict Nature Reserve (Andriantompohavana *et al.*, 2006).

Natural History

As of 2010, there had been no field studies of this species.

Conservation Status

The most recent IUCN Red List assessment (2008) classified *M. mamiratra* as Data Deficient (DD). It occurs in Lokobe Strict Nature Reserve. Unfortunately, although the infrastructure of this reserve is good, its total area is small. Consequently, this species should be considered Endangered or perhaps even Critically Endangered.

As of 2010, there were four individuals of this species in captivity, all in the Tsimbazaza Zoo in Antananarivo, Madagascar (E. E. Louis Jr., pers. obs.).

Where to See It

This species can be seen in the Lokobe Strict Nature Reserve on Nosy Be, in close proximity to tourist accommodations on the beach at Ampasipoly where there are two comfortable hotels. However, it is much harder to find than sympatric Nosy Be sportive lemurs (*Lepilemur tymerlachsonorum*), which are quite abundant there. Indeed, during a two-night visit to Ampasipoly in September 2006, Mittermeier found 24 *Lepilemur* and only a single *Microcebus mamiratra*.

Fig. 7.25: A Nosy Be mouse lemur (*Microcebus mamiratra*) in forest right next to the Ampasipohy Beach, Lokobe Strict Nature Reserve (photo by R. A. Mittermeier).

Cheirogaleidae

Microcebus tavaratra Rasoloarison *et al.*, 2000
Tavaratra Mouse Lemur

Other English: Northern Brown Mouse Lemur, Northern Rufous
Mouse Lemur
French: Microcèbe roux du nord
German: Nördlicher Brauner Mausmaki
Malagasy: Tsidy

Identification

Microcebus tavaratra is a relatively large mouse lemur with a head-body length of
12–14 cm, a tail length of 15–16 cm, a total length of 28–29 cm, and a body weight of
45–77 g (Rasoloarison *et al.*, 2000; Andriantompohavana *et al.*, 2006). The dorsal coat
is brownish-black with a distinct midline stripe that extends either from the crown or
from between the shoulders to the base of the tail. The ventral fur is typically bicolored, a
mixture of whitish-beige and gray. The crown and ears are rufous, the region between the
eyes is grayish-white, and there are distinct black markings around the anterior portions
of the orbits. Although somewhat similar in appearance to *M. ravelobensis* (known only
from the region of Ankarafantsika about 450 km to the southwest), this species is slightly
smaller and less robust.

Geographic Range

Northern Madagascar. *M. tavaratra* is one of the most
northerly of the mouse lemurs, occurring in the Ankarana,
Analamerana, Andavakoera and Andrafiamena regions
(Rasoloarison *et al.*, 2000; Louis *et al.*, 2008). Earlier
records from Ankarana suggested the occurrence of two
mouse lemurs, *M. rufus* and *M. murinus*, but the records
of the former are now attributed to *M. tavaratra* (see
Nicoll and Langrand, 1989). Whether *M. murinus* is indeed
sympatric with *M. tavaratra* in this region remains to be
determined.

Natural History

This species inhabits tropical dry deciduous lowland
and gallery forests (20–250 m above sea level), which
include deep canyons and steep rugged limestone pinnacles
referred to as "tsingy." Basic aspects of its ecology and
behavior remain to be studied.

Conservation Status

The most recent IUCN Red List assessment (2008) classified *M. tavaratra* as Endangered
(EN). The principal threat is habitat loss due to illegal logging, mining for sapphires,
uncontrolled brush fires, and charcoal production. It is reported from two protected areas
(Analamerana Special Reserve and Ankarana National Park), in the newly-protected forest
of Andrafiamena adjacent to Analamerana, and in Andavakoera as well. Field surveys and
genetic studies of mouse lemur populations are needed within this broader region.

As of 2009, this species was not being kept in captivity (ISIS, 2009).

Where to See It

This species is relatively easy to see in Ankarana National Park, the Analamerana Special Reserve, and in the Andriafamena and Andavakoera Forests. Organized excursions are available from some hotels and through local tour operators in Antsiranana (= Diégo-Suarez). There are basic campsites in Ankarana and very simple accommodations at the Mahamasina entrance along RN6, 108 km from Antsiranana. The best campsite is the Encampment des Anglaises (English Camp), located in a forested canyon accessible from the west by four-wheel drive vehicle in the dry season and by hiking from Mahamasina all year round. For those who prefer not to camp, there is a comfortable hotel in nearby Ambilobe, a drive of about 45 minutes from the reserve entrance at Mahamasina.

Cheirogaleidae

Fig. 7.26: Above: Tavaratra mouse lemur (*Microcebus tavaratra*) taken in the Analamerana Special Reserve (photo by R. A. Mittermeier). Below: Another Tavaratra mouse lemur from the Ankarana National Park (photo by E. E. Louis Jr.).

Microcebus arnholdi Louis *et al.*, 2008
Montagne d'Ambre Mouse Lemur

Other English: Arnhold's Mouse Lemur
French: Microcèbe de la Montagne d'Ambre, Microcèbe
d'Arnhold
German: Arnhold's Mausmaki
Malagasy: Tsidy

Identification

Microcebus arnholdi is a medium-sized mouse lemur with a head-body length of 10–
12.6 cm, a tail length of 10.6–13.6 cm, a total length of 20.6–26.2 cm, and a body weight
of 50 g (Louis *et al.*, 2008). The overall dorsal pelage is a mixture of dark brown, red and
gray. There is a dark brown midline dorsal stripe that runs down to the base of the tail. The
tail is dark brown near the tip. The ventral fur is white to cream with gray undertones. The
head is predominantly red with dark brown on the muzzle and surrounding the eyes, with a
white nose ridge that stops at the distal end of the muzzle (Louis *et al.*, 2008).

Geographic Range

Northern tip of Madagascar. The most northerly-
occurring mouse lemur, this species is known only from
Montagne d'Ambre National Park and Special Reserve,
northwest of the Irodo River (Louis *et al.*, 2008).

Natural History

As of 2010, there had been no field studies of this
species, but it is known to live in montane rain forest (Louis
et al., 2008).

Conservation Status

The conservation status of *M. arnholdi* has not yet been
assessed. It is known to occur in two protected areas, the
adjacent Montagne d'Ambre National Park and Montagne
d'Ambre Special Reserve (Louis *et al.*, 2008).

As of 2010, this species was not being kept in captivity
(I. J. Porton, pers. comm.).

Where to See It

This species is relatively easy to see in the Montagne d'Ambre National Park and
Montagne d'Ambre Special Reserve (Louis *et al.*, 2008).

Fig. 7.27: Montagne d'Ambre mouse lemur (*Microcebus arnholdi*) from Montagne d'Ambre (photo by E. E. Louis Jr.).

Cheirogaleidae

Microcebus rufus (Lesson, 1840)
Rufous Mouse Lemur

Other English: Brown Mouse Lemur, Eastern Rufous Mouse
Lemur
French: Microcèbe roux
German: Brauner Mausmaki, Östlicher Mausmaki
Malagasy: Pondiky, Antsidy Mena, Tsidy, Tsitsidy, Tsitsihy

Identification

Microcebus rufus is a relatively small mouse lemur with a head-body length of 12 cm,
a tail length of 10.9–12.5 cm, a total length of 22.5–24.9 cm, and a weight of 39.5–47.9 g
(Kappeler, 1991; Atsalis, 1999b; Louis *et al.*, 2006a). The head and forelimbs are reddish-
brown, blending into a grayish-brown dorsum and tail, and the underside is grayish-white.
A black midline stripe runs the length of the back. The face sports a conspicuous white
rostral patch that does not extend past the level of the eyes (Tattersall, 1982). The nose is
slightly less prominent than in *Microcebus murinus*.

Petter *et al.* (1977) noted geographic variation in morphology (especially ear size)
throughout the range of this species, and Groves (2001) suggested that northern specimens
were darker and shorter-tailed than those from the south. Part of the variation that they
observed can be accounted for by the identification of new species from within the large
range once thought to be occupied by just this one species (see, for example, Louis *et al.*
[2006a], and the descriptions of other new eastern mouse lemur species in this book).

This species can be distinguished from *Cheirogaleus major*, with which it is often
sympatric, by its much smaller size and more rapid movements.

Geographic Range

Until recently, the geographic range of *M. rufus* was
believed to extend throughout Madagascar's eastern forests
from Tolagnaro (= Fort-Dauphin) in the south perhaps as
far as the Tsaratanana Massif and just south of the Makira
region in the north. However, recent field work and analyses
of molecular data have resulted in the identification of
several new species within this distribution, including
Microcebus lehilahytsara, *M. mittermeieri*, *M. simmonsi*,
M. jollyae, and *M. macarthurii*. On top of this, it is likely
that still more eastern mouse lemur species will emerge
from ongoing studies. These new discoveries have resulted
in a significantly reduced range size for *M. rufus,* and
clarification of the ranges of recently-described species are
sure to reduce its range still further (Louis *et al.*, 2008).
The map for this species gives some indication of what we
believe the range of this mouse lemur to be at this time,
roughly from Ranomafana National Park to Andringitra
National Park (including the corridor between the two sites)
in southeastern Madagascar (E. E. Louis Jr., pers. obs.).

Fig. 7.28: Rufous mouse lemur (*Microcebus rufus*) from the Sainte-Luce region of southeastern Madagascar (photo by A. Hapke).

Natural History

As originally described, *M. rufus* is reported to occur at high densities in tropical moist lowland and montane forests, and sometimes in adjacent secondary forest formations, bamboo forests, old plantations, and even *Eucalyptus* groves, from sea level to 2,000 m (Ganzhorn, 1987a, 1988; Duckworth *et al.*, 1995; Atsalis, 1999a, 2000). It is omnivorous, subsisting mainly on fruits, but also flowers, insects, gums, and occasionally young leaves (Atsalis, 1998a, 1998b). Fruit of the mistletoe *Bakerella*, which has a high fat and high fiber content, seems to be a particularly important dietary component, and beetles were the insects most frequently eaten (Atsalis, 1999b). This species is usually seen feeding in shrubs and low trees. Fat storage in the tail seems to be less important than in *M. murinus*.

Rufous mouse lemur ecology and social behavior have been studied in Ranomafana (Atsalis 1999a, 1999b, 2000). Individuals scent mark with urine and feces, a behavior that helps delimit ranges and communicate presence to conspecifics (Tattersall, 1982). This species sleeps in tree holes and leaf nests during the day, and has even been observed to use old bird's nests (Martin, 1973; Pollock, 1979b). Predators include the ring-tailed mongoose (*Galidia elegans*), Madagascar Harrier-hawk (*Polyboroides radiatus*), owls, dogs and cats (Goodman *et al.*, 1993c; Langrand and Goodman, 1996).

Male territories often overlap those of two or more females (Atsalis, 1999a). Mating takes place in September and October, during which time the male's testes increase significantly in size. One to three young are born following a two-month gestation. During the austral winter, from May through September, most females and some males enter a state of torpor, losing from 5 to 35 g in body weight (Atsalis, 1998a, 1998b, 1999a). Males begin becoming active again in August, while females remain torpid for one or two more months.

It should be noted that many of the studies of "*Microcebus rufus*," were actually of some of the newly-described taxa, expecially those by Ganzhorn at Analamazaotra Special Reserve (at Andasibe), which are now known to refer to *M. lehilahytsara*.

Conservation Status

The most recent IUCN Red List assessment (2008) classifies *M. rufus* as Least Concern (LC). As with most members of the genus *Microcebus*, the principal threat is habitat loss due to slash-and-burn agriculture. It is present in two national parks (Andringitra and Ranomafana) and in Pic d'Ivohibe Special Reserve (Nicoll and Langrand, 1989; Feistner and Schmid, 1999; Wright and Porter, 2004; Louis *et al.*, 2008).

As of 2009, there were four individuals of this species in captivity, all in the Tsimbazaza Zoo in Antananarivo, Madagascar (E. E. Louis Jr., pers. obs.).

Where to See It

The rufous mouse lemur can readily be observed in Ranomafana National Park. This important park now has several good hotels, among them the Centrest Sejour and the Domaine Nature Lodge.

Fig. 7.29: Above: Rufous mouse lemur (*Microcebus rufus*) eating a cockroach at Tsimbazaza Zoo, Antananarivo (photo by R. A. Mittermeier). Below: Another rufous mouse lemur eating a piece of fruit at Belle Vue, Talatakely, Ranomafana National Park (photo by E. E. Louis Jr.).

Cheirogaleidae

Microcebus jollyae Louis *et al.*, 2006
Jolly's Mouse Lemur

Other English: None
French: Microcèbe de Jolly
German: Jolly's Mausmaki
Malagasy: Tsidy an'i-Jolly

Identification

Microcebus jollyae has a head-body length of 13 cm, a tail length of just over 12 cm, a total length of 25 cm, and an average adult weight of just over 60 g (based on measurements of three adults from one site) (Louis *et al.*, 2008). The dorsal coat is a uniform reddish-brown on both the body and the head. There are small white patches on the rostrum and under the mandible, the latter blending with the gray ventral coat (Louis *et al.*, 2006a).

Geographic Range

Microcebus jollyae occurs in the lowland coastal forest of eastern central Madagascar at Kianjavoto (its type locality), just south of the Mananjary River in the province of Fianarantsoa, and also Mananjary nearby, just to the northeast (Louis *et al.*, 2006a).

Natural History

This species is known to occur in lower altitudinal coastal rain forest, but as of 2009 it had not been studied in the wild (Louis *et al.*, 2006).

Conservation Status

There is insufficient information to determine the conservation status of *M. jollyae*, and the latest IUCN Red List assessment (2008) classified it as Data Deficient (DD). Its presence in a number of forests has been verified, but no estimates of population size are available. It occurs in the Kianjavato Forest near Ranomafana, which, although not an official government reserve, does receive some degree of local protection (Louis *et al.*, 2006a).

As of 2009 there were four individuals of this species in captivity, all in the Tsimbazaza Zoo in Antananarivo, Madagascar (E. E. Louis Jr., pers. obs.).

Where to See It

This mouse lemur can be seen in the wild in Kianjavato, a short distance by car from Ranomafana National Park. It is present as well in the forest along the road in the commune of Kianjavato. Lemur research projects have been undertaken in the forests of Kianjavato, and limited hotel accommodation is available.

Fig. 7.30: Jolly's mouse lemur (*Microcebus jollyae*), Tsimbazaza Zoo, Antananarivo (photo by R. A. Mittermeier).

Fig. 7.31: Jolly's mouse lemur (*Microcebus jollyae*), Kianjavato Classified Forest (photo by E. E. Louis Jr.).

Cheirogaleidae

Microcebus lehilahytsara Roos and Kappeler, 2005 in Kappeler *et al.*, 2005
Goodman's Mouse Lemur

Other English: None
French: Microcèbe de Goodman
German: Goodman's Mausmaki
Malagasy: Tsidy an' i-Goodman

Identification

Microcebus lehilahytsara is one of the smaller mouse lemurs. It has a head-body length of approximately 9 cm and a weight of 45–48 g (Kappeler *et al.*, 2005). The fur is short and dense. The dorsal coat is bright maroon with an orange tinge on the back, head, and tail, turning creamy-white on the ventrum. A distinct white stripe runs from the nose to the forehead. The ears are short and round. The scrotum is furred and the testes are noticeably large.

This species is very similar in size and appearance to *Microcebus rufus*, with which it might easily be confused. It is also found in the same forests with two other small nocturnal genera, *Allocebus* and *Cheirogaleus*. *Allocebus* is very similar in size and has very distinctive tufted ears, but it would be difficult to distinguish between the two unless one obtained a very good look at the animal. *Cheirogaleus* is larger still and tends not to move as rapidly.

Geographic Range

At present this species is known only from the type locality of Andasibe and neighboring areas, for example, Maromizaha Forest (Randrianambinina and Rasoloharijaona, 2006), the Analamazaotra Special Reserve, the Anjozorobe Angavo Protected Area and Mantadia National Park in eastern Madagascar (Kappeler *et al.*, 2005; Roos and Kappeler, 2006; Louis *et al.*, 2008). These mouse lemurs were previously considered to be *M. rufus*.

Natural History

The ecology and behavior has been studied at Andasibe (Périnet) (Ganzhorn, 1987a, 1988, 1989). Ganzhorn (1987) observed *M. lehilahytsara* not only in the natural forest of the region but also regularly, if in lower numbers, in adjacent patches of old eucalyptus plantations where the understory was sufficiently developed to allow travel without descending to the ground. Generally solitary, it feeds on fruits and insects in shrubs and low trees as well as in the upper canopy of the forest (Ganzhorn, 1988, 1989). Population density at Andasibe was estimated at 110 ±34 individuals/km² (Ganzhorn, 1988). These studies were published using the name *M. rufus* for this species.

Conservation Status

There is insufficient information to determine the conservation status of *M. lehilahytsara*, and the latest IUCN Red List assessment (2008) classified it as Data Deficient (DD). Its geographic range is poorly known. It occurs in the Mantadia National Park, the Analamazaotra Special Reserve, Maromizaha forest, and in the Anjozorobe Angavo Protected Area, managed by the NGO Fanamby (Kappeler *et al.*, 2005; Louis *et al.*, 2008). Its presence in Mangerivola Special Reserve has yet to be ascertained (Roos and Kappeler, 2006).

As of 2009 there were approximately two dozen individuals of this species in captivity, most of them in Switzerland and in the Tsimbazaza Zoo in Antananarivo, Madagascar (E. E. Louis Jr., pers. obs.; I. J. Porton, pers. comm.).

Where to See It

Goodman's mouse lemur can be readily observed in the Analamazaotra Special Reserve near Andasibe (= Périnet), about three hours drive east of Antananarivo. There are four lodges to choose from: the upscale Vakona Forest Lodge, the conveniently located Hotel Feon'ny Ala, the quaint Mikalo Hotel, which also has a row of new higher quality chalets, and the Eulophiella Lodge close to the Andasibe and Mantadia Reserves. The Saha Forest Camp, managed by the NGO Fanamby, provides for tours of the Anjozorobe Angavo Protected Area.

Fig. 7.32: Goodman's mouse lemur (*Microcebus lehilahytsara*) at Sahanody in the Vohidrazana massif, a little north of Andasibe in east central Madagascar (photo by S. M. McGuire).

Cheirogaleidae

Microcebus simmonsi Louis *et al.*, 2006
Simmons' Mouse Lemur

Other English: None
French: Microcèbe de Simmons
German: Simmons' Mausmaki
Malagasy: Tsidy an'i-Simmons

Identification

Microcebus simmonsi is the most robust of the eastern Madagascar mouse lemurs, with a head-body length of 12.8 cm, a tail length of just under 15 cm, a total length of around 27.5 cm, and an adult weight of 75–78 g (Louis *et al.*, 2006a). The dorsal coat, head and forelimbs are dark reddish-brown to orange-brown, sometimes with a mid-dorsal stripe, while the ventral coat is grayish-white to white. There is a distinctive white patch on the rostrum, and hairs on the middle of the crown have black tips (Louis *et al.*, 2006a).

Geographic Range

Northeastern Madagascar. This species is known only from the regions of Betampona, Zahamena and Tampolo (Louis *et al.*, 2008).

Natural History

As of 2009, this species had not been studied in the wild.

Conservation Status

The most recent IUCN Red List assessment (2008) classified *M. simmonsi* as Data Deficient (DD). It is currently known only from two strict nature reserves (Betampona and Zahamena) and Zahamena National Park.

In 2009, there were four individuals of this species in captivity, all in the Tsimbazaza Zoo in Antananarivo, Madagascar (E. E. Louis Jr., pers. obs.).

Where to See It

Betampona is the best place to see *M. simmonsi*. It is a small reserve located about 40 km northwest of the major port city of Toamasina (= Tamatave), and is the site of a long-term lemur field research program. It can be reached by car, followed by hiking, and excursions can be arranged through tour operators in Antananarivo. This species can also readily be seen in Tampolo Classified Forest. Finding it at Zahamena is possible as well, but this area is much more difficult to reach.

Fig. 7.33: Above: Simmons' mouse lemur (*Microcebus simmonsi*) in the Tsimbazaza Zoo, Antananarivo (photo by R. A. Mittermeier). Below: Another Simmons' mouse lemur in the Betampona Special Reserve (photo by E. E. Louis Jr.).

Cheirogaleidae

Microcebus macarthurii Radespiel *et al.*, 2008
Anjiahely Mouse Lemur

Other English: MacArthur's Mouse Lemur
French: Microcèbe d'Anjiahely, Microcèbe de MacArthur
German: MacArthurs' Mausmaki
Malagasy: Kandrandra

Identification

Microcebus macarthurii is a large mouse lemur with a head-body length of 11–12 cm, a tail length of 14.7 cm, a total length of 26 cm, and a body weight of around 53 g (Radespiel *et al.*, 2008). The dorsum is covered in short, dense, reddish-brown fur from head to tail, with a broad, dark rufous midline stripe. The head is rufous, turning orange on the cheeks; it is dark brownish around the eyes, but with the characteristic white interocular stripe of the genus. The ears are a darker rufous. A lighter reddish color extends towards the outer upper legs and arms. The tail is reddish-brown and densely furred, being darker on the dorsal than the ventral side, and middle-brown towards the tip. The ventrum is yellowish-orange with a creamy-white coloration on the ventral throat and the genital region. The hands and feet are sparsely haired with grayish-white (Radespiel *et al.*, 2008).

This species can be distinguished from *Microcebus mittermeieri* by its larger size (Radespiel *et al.*, 2008).

Geographic Range

Northeastern Madagascar. This newly-described species is known only from its type locality near the village of Anjiahely, about 26 km west of Maroantsetra (Radespiel *et al.*, 2008). The precise limits of its distribution and its relationship to neighboring taxa remain to be determined. It appears to be sympatric with *M. mittermeieri* at Anjiahely (Radespiel *et al.*, 2008).

Natural History

This species was described in 2008, and has not been studied in the wild.

Conservation Status

The conservation status of *M. macarthurii* has not been assessed. However, considering its presumably minute distribution and the present rate of deforestation in the region in which it lives, it is very likely threatened. It may occur in the Makira Forest, which is currently under temporary government protection awaiting final conservation status, and may prove to be the mouse lemur in the Nosy Mangabe Special Reserve as well.

As of 2009, this species was not being kept in captivity.

Where to See It

At the time of writing, the only confirmed locality for this species is Anjiahely (Radespiel *et al.*, 2008). However, it may also turn out to be the mouse lemur regularly seen in the Nosy Mangabe Special Reserve.

Cheirogaleidae

Fig. 7.34: A mouse lemur from Nosy Mangabe, which may be *Microcebus macarthurii* (photo by E. E. Louis Jr.).

Cheirogaleidae

Microcebus mittermeieri Louis *et al.*, 2006
Mittermeier's Mouse Lemur

Other English: None
French: Microcèbe de Mittermeier
German: Mittermeier's Mausmaki
Malagasy: Tsidy an'i-Mittermeier

Identification

Microcebus mittermeieri is the smallest mouse lemur in Madagascar's eastern rain forests, and indeed ranks with *M. myoxinus* and *M. berthae* in body size. The head-body length is just 8 cm, with a 12 cm tail, a total length of about 20 cm, and an average adult weight of just over 40 g (Louis *et al.*, 2006a). The head and dorsal coat are light reddish-brown to rust, with an orange tint at the base of the forelimbs and hindlimbs, while the ventral coat is whitish-brown. The tail is brown above with a darker brown mid-dorsal stripe and a black tip. A distinctive white patch extends along the rostrum past the level of its eyes, which are underlined with yellow. The latter coloration is also present under the chin and extends along the ventral aspect of the neck. According to Louis *et al.* (2006a), the overall color is lighter than that of *M. rufus*.

Geographic Range

Northeastern Madagascar. This species occurs in and around the Anjanaharibe-Sud Special Reserve (Louis *et al.*, 2006a), and is known to be sympatric with *M. macarthurii* over some of its range (Radespiel *et al.*, 2008).

Natural History

This species has not been studied in the wild.

Conservation Status

The most recent IUCN Red List assessment (2008) classified *M. mittermeieri* as Data Deficient (DD). The only protected area in which it is known to occur is the Anjanaharibe-Sud Special Reserve.

As of 2009, there were four individuals of this species in captivity, all in the Tsimbazaza Zoo in Antananarivo (E. E. Louis Jr., pers. obs.).

Where to See It

Excursions to Anjanaharibe-Sud can be arranged in advance through Sambava Voyages, a local tour operator in Sambava that also organizes trips to Marojejy National Park. Anjanaharibe-Sud can be reached by car from Andapa, but finding this species requires hiking well into the reserve and camping overnight in the forest.

Fig. 7.35: Mittermeier's mouse lemur (*Microcebus mittermeieri*), Anjanaharibe-Sud (photo by E. E. Louis Jr.).

Cheirogaleidae

Mirza Gray, 1870
Giant Mouse Lemurs

The genus *Mirza* contains at least two species of small, omnivorous, nocturnal, nest-dwelling lemurs reported from several disjunct areas in Madagascar's western lowland dry deciduous forests and the Sambirano region. *Mirza coquereli* was originally described by Alfred Grandidier (1867) as a species of *Cheirogaleus*, apparently based on its resemblance to the fork-marked lemur, *Phaner*, which Grandidier knew in his time as *Chirogale furcifer*. It was subsequently placed in the genus *Microcebus* by Petter *et al.* (1977), in spite of the fact that—at approximately 300 g—Coquerel's giant mouse lemur is more than three times the size of the largest mouse lemur (Petter *et al.*, 1977). In 1982, Tattersall placed this species in its own genus, *Mirza*, and Groves (2001) agrees with this, citing both dental characters and behavior as justification for recognizing *Mirza* as distinct from other cheirogaleids.

Recent analyses of morphometric, genetic, and behavioral data has resulted in the recognition of a second species of *Mirza*. *Mirza coquereli* is the larger of the two, with the center of its distribution in southwestern Madagascar, while the newly-described, smaller *Mirza zaza* is found in the Sambirano region of the far northwest (Kappeler *et al.*, 2005). Additional research will be required to determine the taxonomic status of intermediate populations which occur in the Tsingy de Bemaraha, and Tsingy de Namoroka (S. M. Goodman, pers. comm.), the Befotaka region (Randriatahina and Rabarivola, 2004), and the Sahamalaza region (Markolf *et al.*, 2008a), and it is quite possible that additional species will be discovered.

Fig. 7.36: *Mirza zaza* in an old banana plantation behind Benavony (photo by R. A. Mittermeier).

Fig. 7.37: *Mirza* postural and behavioral drawings (next page):
    a. *Mirza* resting on a large branch
    b. *Mirza* preparing to leap
    c. *Mirza* in an upside-down clinging posture
    d. Close-up of the face of *Mirza* (note the large ears)
    e. *Mirza* clinging sideways on a vertical branch while looking around
    f. *Mirza* crouched on a branch looking around
    g. *Mirza* in a sitting posture

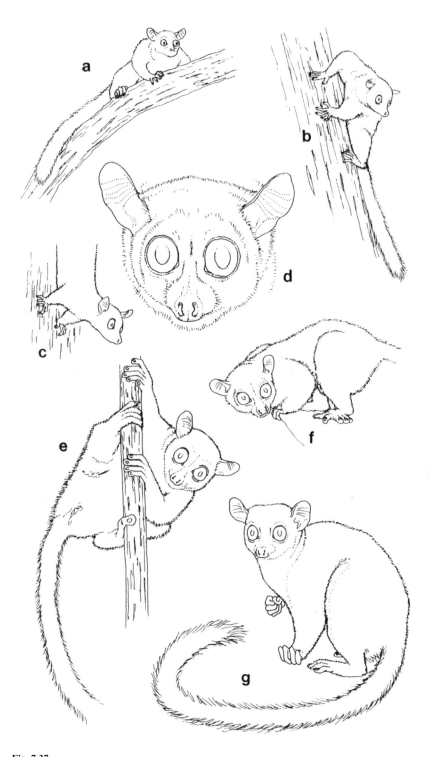

Fig. 7.37.

**Coquerel's Giant
Mouse Lemur**
Mirza coquereli

**Northern Giant
Mouse Lemur**
Mirza zaza

Coquerel's Giant Mouse Lemur
Mirza coquereli

Northern Giant Mouse Lemur
Mirza zaza

Fig. 7.38.

Fig. 7.39: Distribution of *Mirza*.

Cheirogaleidae

Mirza coquereli (A. Grandidier, 1867)
Coquerel's Giant Mouse Lemur

Other English: Coquerel's Dwarf Lemur, Southern Giant Mouse
Lemur
French: Microcèbe géant de Coquerel
German: Coquerel's Riesenmausmaki, Südlicher Riesenmausmaki
Malagasy: Tsiba, Tilitilivaha, Siba (Morondava), Setohy

Identification

   Mirza coquereli is a small nocturnal lemur with a long body and a long tail. It has a
head-body length averaging 25 cm, a tail length of 31–32 cm, a total length of 56–57 cm,
and a body weight of 300–320 g (Pagès, 1978; Stanger *et al.*, 1995; Kappeler *et al.*, 2005).
The dorsal coat is rich brown or gray-brown, but rose or yellow shades are often found as
well. Ventrally, the gray hair base is visible beneath rusty or yellow tips. The tail, which is
longer than the body, is thin but has long hair, giving it a slightly "bushy" appearance, and
it is darker towards the tip.

   The large, evident ears, and its quadrupedal running, serve to distinguish *Mirza*
from *Cheirogaleus*, which has more concealed ears and is slower moving. *Mirza* can
be distinguished from sympatric *Microcebus* species by its much larger size and very
distinctive ears, and from sympatric *Lepilemur* by its much smaller size, prominent ears,
and more rapid quadrupedal movements. *Lepilemur* is usually far more sedentary and a
vertical clinger and leaper, as opposed to a quadrupedal runner. In the Menabe region north
of Morondava, and especially in the Kirindy Forest, *Mirza* is also sympatric with *Phaner*,
another active, medium-sized, nocturnal lemur. There, it can be distinguished from *Phaner*
again by its larger ears and shorter muzzle. *Phaner* also has a prominent forked pattern on
its head, has very loud, distinctive vocalizations, and has a very distinctive habit of head-
bobbing. It should be noted, however, that *Mirza* is highly active, often making it difficult
to get a good look and confirm its identity.

Geographic Range

   Coquerel's giant mouse lemur is found in lowland dry
forests of western Madagascar, from sea level to 700 m
(Petter *et al.*, 1971; Kappeler *et al.*, 2005). Its distribution
is best described as patchy, reflecting the fragmentation of
the forests throughout this region. One nucleus is in the
southwest between the Onilahy River in the south and the
Tsiribinha River in the north, including Zombitse-Vohibasia
National Park (Ganzhorn, 1994) and Isalo National Park
(Hawkins, 1999). To the north of the Tsiribihina River,
Mirza has also been reported from the the Andranomena
Special Reserve and Tsingy de Bemaraha National Park
(Kappeler, 2003), and recent sightings confirm its presence
in Tsingy de Namoroka National Park as well (S. M.
Goodman, pers. comm.). For the present, these disjunct
populations are attributed to *M. coquereli*. Still farther
north, *M. zaza* inhabits the Sambirano region.

Natural History

Ecological and behavioral studies of *M. coquereli* have been conducted in the Beroboka, Kirindy, and Marosalaza forests just north of Morondava (Petter *et al.*, 1971; Pagès, 1978, 1980; Kappeler, 1997). Population densities reported from Marosalaza range from 30 individuals/km² (Hladik *et al.*, 1980) to 50 individuals/km² (Petter *et al.*, 1971) but, in the latter study, reached as high as 210 individuals/km² in forests running along rivers. Ausilio and Raveloarinoro (1993) recorded densities of 100 individuals/km² in the forests of Tsimembo, while Kappeler (1997) recorded 120 individuals/km² in Kirindy. However, the latter population underwent an inexplicable decline after remaining steady for several years (Markolf *et al.*, 2008b).

Fig. 7.40: Coquerel's giant mouse lemur (*Mirza coquereli*), Tsingy de Bemaraha National Park (photo by E. E. Louis Jr.).

Home ranges of 1 to 4 ha overlap extensively and all individuals studied seem to make heavy use of smaller core areas, which they defend aggressively (Pagès, 1978, 1980; Kappeler, 1997). Male ranges tend to overlap those of several females as well as those of other males. In the Kirindy Forest, their ranges more than quadruple in the mating season (Kappeler, 1997, 2003). Males interact positively (grooming, contact calling) with females when they make contact, and pairs travel together for short periods even during the dry season.

Coquerel's giant mouse lemur is typically solitary when foraging, and does not nest communally. It spends its daytime hours in a spherical nest of up to 50 cm in diameter (Kappeler, 2003), usually placed 2–10 m high in the fork of a large branch or among dense lianas (to discourage predators), and constructed of interlaced lianas, branches, leaves, and twigs chewed off from nearby trees (Petter *et al.*, 1971; Pagès, 1980; Sarikaya and Kappeler, 1997). Pagès (1980) and Kappeler (1997) found only females and their offspring sharing nests. Each individual uses as many as 10 or 12 nests, changing its sleeping site every few days (Kappeler, 2003).

Fig. 7.41: Coquerel's giant mouse lemur (*Mirza coquereli*), Kirindy Classified Forest (photo by J. R. Zoanarivelo).

Individuals leave the nest around dusk, at which time they begin feeding or self-grooming, or continue resting. Travel and foraging usually occur at heights of 5 to 10 m, though *M. coquereli* does come to the ground on occasion (Kappeler, 2003). During the latter half of the night they are more likely to be involved in social activities (Pagès, 1978, 1980). While they are likely to return to the nest for the second half of the night during the cold winter, they remain active year round and do not enter into a state of torpor. Some may make "loud calls," usually at the beginning of their nightly activity, and they make soft *hon* calls while moving about (Kappeler, 2003). Individuals scent-mark objects using saliva, urine or anogenital secretions (Petter and van der Sloot, 2000).

Coquerel's giant mouse lemur is omnivorous, feeding on fruits, flowers, buds, gums, insects, insect excretions, and spiders, frogs, chameleons, and small birds (Pagès, 1980). It may even prey on smaller *Microcebus* species (Goodman, 2003). Another seemingly important food source during the dry season (June–July) are the excretions of cochineal and homopteran larvae (Pagès, 1980).

Based on the results of comparative studies, reproductive activity of *M. coquereli* in the Kirindy Forest begins in November (Pagès, 1978, 1980; Kappeler, 2003). Gestation lasts about three months (Petter-Rousseaux, 1980) and two infants (occasionally one) leave the nest after about three weeks. The young are carried in their mother's mouth for several weeks and are left in vegetation while she forages (Stanger *et al.*, 1995; Kappeler, 1998). After three months infants forage alone, but maintain vocal contact with the mother (Pagès, 1980, 1983).

Conservation Status

The most recent IUCN Red List assessment (2008) classified *M. coquereli* as Near Threatened (NT). It appears to be adaptable, can survive in secondary forest, and occurs in fairly high densities in some parts of its range (Petter *et al.*, 1977). This species is believed to be present in two national parks (Tsingy de Bemaraha and Zombitse-Vohibasia), the Tsingy de Bemaraha Strict Nature Reserve, the Andranomena Special Reserve, the Kirindy Forest (part of the Menabe-Antimena Protected Area), and the Ampataka Classified Forest (Mittermeier *et al.*, 1994; Ganzhorn, 1994).

According to ISIS (2009), there were about half a dozen individuals of this species in captivity in the United States and Europe. However, it would appear that they are all, in fact, examples of *Mirza zaza* (A. Katz, pers. comm.), and in any event are a non-breeding population (I. J. Porton, pers. comm.).

Where to See It

Coquerel's giant mouse lemur is easily seen in the Kirindy Forest north of Morondava, where it is sympatric with five other nocturnal species (*Microcebus berthae*, *M. murinus*, *Cheirogaleus medius*, *Lepilemur ruficaudatus*, and *Phaner pallescens*). Zombitse-Vohibasia National Park is also a good place to observe this species.

Cheirogaleidae

Mirza zaza Kappeler and Roos, 2005 in Kappeler *et al.*, 2005
Northern Giant Mouse Lemur

Other English: Northern Dwarf Lemur
French: Microcèbe géant du nord
German: Nördlicher Riesenmausmaki
Malagasy: Tanta, Fitily (north of Ambanja)

Identification

Mirza zaza is the smaller of the two species currently recognized in this genus. Based on specimens from Ambato, it has a head-body length of about 27 cm, a tail length of 27–28 cm, a total length of 54–55 cm, and a body weight of 287–299 g (Kappeler *et al.*, 2005). The dorsal coat is grayish-brown and the hairs are short. The ventral coat is gray. The hindlimbs are slightly longer than the forelimbs, and the tail is bushy and darker towards the tip. The ears are shorter than those of *Mirza coquereli* and are rounded.

Larger ears and quadrupedal locomotion help to distinguish *M. zaza* from *Cheirogaleus medius*, which has more concealed ears and is slower moving. It can also be distinguished from sympatric *Microcebus* species by its much larger size and very distinctive ears, and from sympatric *Lepilemur* by its much smaller size, prominent ears, and more rapid quadrupedal movements, *Lepilemur* usually being far more sedentary and a vertical clinger and leaper. *Mirza zaza* is also sympatric with *Phaner parienti*, another active, medium-sized, nocturnal lemur. *Phaner* has a prominent forked pattern on its head and has very loud, distinctive vocalizations. It should be noted, however, that *Mirza* is highly active, often making it difficult to get a good look to confirm an identification.

Geographic Range

Type specimens for *M. zaza* come from the region of the Ampasindava Peninsula in northwestern Madagascar, specifically from Ambato and Pasandava. It is known to occur between the rivers Mahavavy Nord and Maeverano in the northwest of the island (between Manehoko in the north and Ankaibe in the south) (Markolf *et al.*, 2008a). Christoph Schwitzer (pers. obs.) has recorded it in the Sahamalaza region in the Anakarafa Forest. Sightings attributed to *M. coquereli* in the Mahalaka Forest (Randrianambinina *et al.*, 2003c) and in Ankarafa, Andranobe and Ambendrana (Randriatahina and Rabarivola, 2004) are probably *M. zaza* (see Markolf *et al.*, 2008a). Populations from the Befotaka region a bit farther to the south may also be this species (Randriatahina and Rabarivola, 2004), but this remains uncertain.

Natural History

Andrianarivo (1981) and Kappeler (1997) have recorded high population densities for *M. zaza*. Indeed, their estimates of 385 individuals/km² and 1,086 individuals/km² are several times higher than those obtained for *M. coquereli* in the

Fig. 7.42: Northern giant mouse lemur (*Mirza zaza*) in an old banana plantation behind Benavony (photo by R. A. Mittermeier).

Cheirogaleidae

Kirindy Forest. The concentration of animals in more isolated forest fragments and the presence of mango, cashew, and other introduced food tree species in the Ambato region may help explain the higher densities (Markolf *et al.*, 2008a).

This species is typically solitary, choosing to forage alone. It spends daytime hours in a spherical nest of up to 50 cm in diameter, usually placed 2–10 m high in the fork of a

Fig. 7.43: Northern giant mouse lemur (*Mirza zaza*) photographed in captivity at the Duke Lemur Center in Durham, North Carolina. "Zaza" is the Malagasy word for "child" (photos by D. Haring/DLC).

large branch or among dense lianas (to discourage predators), and constructed of interlaced lianas, branches, leaves, and twigs chewed off nearby trees. It would seem that they are more social nesters than *M. coquereli*. Kappeler (2003) found nests in Ambanja with adult males, females and young, and an average occupancy of four individuals (Kappeler *et al.*, 2005). Markolf *et al.* (2008a) also found that they showed more social tendencies than is typical of *M. coquereli* (perhaps associated with higher recorded densities) and were also more vocal.

Mirza zaza is omnivorous, feeding on fruits, flowers, buds, gums, insects, insect secretions, spiders, frogs, chameleons, and small birds. Cashew fruits are an important food source during the dry season (June–July).

Reproductive activity in *M. zaza*, based on studies of animals from the Ambanja region (Kappeler *et al.*, 2005), begins in August, several months earlier than when *M. coquereli* begins to mate in the Kirindy Forest of southwestern Madagascar (Pagès, 1978, 1980; Kappeler, 2003).

Conservation Status

There is insufficient information to determine the conservation status of *M. zaza*, so the latest IUCN Red List assessment (2008) classified it as Data Deficient (DD). However, given that *M. coquereli* is currently listed as Near Threatened (NT), *M. zaza* must be considered at least as threatened (Markolf *et al.*, 2008a) and could very well be Endangered. Kappeler *et al.* (2005) described its type locality as a highly degraded forest of only about 4 ha. A subsequent visit in 2007 by Markolf *et al.* (2008a) found that the forest had been almost entirely eliminated. They did see *M. zaza* there (four individuals in 20 minutes of walking), but they concluded that the extirpation of the population was only a matter of time. Markolf *et al.* (2008a) visited a further four sites in search of this species—Ankiabe, Andranobe, Ambendrana and Ankarafa. At Ankiabe, they saw a few individuals in a degraded 4-5 km forest along a hillside near the River Maevarano. The forests at Andranobe and Ambendrana were very small and similarly degraded but with many mango trees. There they were able to see *M. zaza* with some ease. The forest at Ankarafa was better preserved and they were able to confirm their presence there, although in fewer numbers than at Andranobe and Ambendrana, concluding that the mango trees were an important food source in the degraded forests. This species is known to occur in two national parks, Tsingy de Namoroka and Sahamalaza-Iles Radama (U. Radespiel, pers. comm.), and in the protected area at Ankarafa (Markolf *et al.*, 2008a). Markolf *et al.* (2008a) concluded that the range of *M. zaza* is limited to just a few highly degraded forest fragments, and that, even though individuals are regularly seen together, population densities are low in all of them.

According to ISIS, as of 2009 this species was not represented in captivity. However, it would appear that the half-dozen speciemens of *Mirza* in the United States and Europe, currently being exhibited as *M. coquereli*, are in fact *M. zaza* (A. Katz, pers. comm.).

Where to See It

Mirza zaza is easily seen in secondary forests near Ambanja, especially in abandoned cashew orchards. It can also be readily viewed in forest right next to the town of Benavony, about 6 km from Ambanja, and in the Andoke-Be Forest right at the edge of the Manongarivo Special Reserve (R. A. Mittermeier, pers. obs.). The Benavony Forest is also very good for *Hapalemur occidentalis*.

Fig. 7.44: Hairy-eared dwarf lemur (*Allocebus trichotis*), Mitsinjo Section, Andasibe (photo by G. Davies).

Allocebus Petter-Rousseaux and Petter, 1967
Hairy-eared Dwarf Lemur

The genus *Allocebus* contains a single species, *Allocebus trichotis*, a tiny nocturnal lemur from the rain forests of eastern Madagascar. The first specimens were assigned to the genus *Cheirogaleus* when originally described by Günther in 1875, but distinct cranial and dental features ultimately elevated the species to its own genus (Petter-Rousseaux and Petter, 1967; Yoder, 1996). Initial attempts to determine the relationships of *Allocebus* to the other cheirogaleids were inconclusive (Rumpler *et al.*, 1995), but later work suggested that it is a sister group to the clade formed by *Mirza* and *Microcebus* (Pastorini *et al.*, 2001a; Roos *et al.*, 2004). The hairy-eared dwarf lemur's most distinguishing characteristic, as its name indicates, are the tufts of hairs that adorn its ears.

Until 1989, this species was known from only five museum specimens, three of which were collected in the late 19th century. The fourth specimen was discovered in Stockholm, having been misidentified as "*Cheirogaleus murinus*." The fifth was captured by Peyriéras in 1965, and had the only well-defined locality data of the specimens collected up to that time (Meier and Albignac, 1991). It is only in recent years that we have begun to understand the distribution of *Allocebus*. In 1989, it was found again in the forest of Andranomahitsy, west of Mananara, where Peyriéras' 1965 specimen was taken (Meier and Albignac, 1989). Over the next two decades, populations were discovered in the Mananara-Nord, Mantadia, Marojejy, and Masoala National Parks and in the Analamazaotra and Anjanaharibe-Sud Special Reserves (Rakotoarison, 1995a, 1995b; Rakotoarison *et al.*, 1997; Schütz and Goodman, 1998; Goodman and Raselimanana, 2002). Although it remains a rare and elusive animal, it now appears to be more widely distributed in the eastern rain forests than previously imagined, and we believe it likely that other populations will be found.

Fig. 7.45: A hand-colored lithograph of the hairy-eared dwarf lemur (*Allocebus trichotis*) published in the *Proceedings of the Zoological Society of London*, 1875.

Fig. 7.46: Hairy-eared dwarf lemur (*Allocebus trichotis*) feeding on gum, Mitsinjo Section, Andasibe (photo by G. Davies).

Fig. 7.47: *Allocebus* postural and behavioral drawings:
  a. *Allocebus* climbing down twigs
  b. *Allocebus* standing quadrupedally on a branch
  c. *Allocebus* standing bipedally
  d. *Allocebus* clinging upside-down on a vertical branch
  e. *Allocebus* bridging between two supports
  f. *Allocebus* standing quadrupedally and looking around

Fig. 7.47.

Cheirogaleidae

Fig. 7.48: Distribution of *Allocebus*.

**Hairy-eared Dwarf
Lemur**
Allocebus trichotis

Fig. 7.49.

Cheirogaleidae

Allocebus trichotis (Günther, 1875)
Hairy-eared Dwarf Lemur

Other English: Hairy-eared Mouse Lemur
French: Allocèbe; Cheirogale à oreilles poilues, Cheirogale à oreilles velues
German: Büschelohrmaki, Büschelohriger Mausmaki
Malagasy: Tsidiala, Antsidy Mavo

Identification

Allocebus trichotis is superficially very similar to the mouse lemurs (*Microcebus*). It has a head-body length of 13–16 cm, a tail length of 14–20 cm, a total length of 27–36 cm, and a body weight of 65–90 g (Meier and Albignac, 1991; Biebouw, 2009). The most obvious external character is the long tufted hair around the ears. The dorsal coat is a rosy brownish-gray and the ventral coat is light gray. The long tail is the same color as the body, becoming darker and bushier at its end. Dark rings surround the eyes, and there is sometimes a pale white stripe that extends between the eyes and the tip of the nose.

This lemur is comparable in size to *Microcebus* and smaller than *Cheirogaleus*. Distinguishing this small animal from eastern *Microcebus* in the field can be quite difficult, unless one is close enough to get a good look at the ear tufts or actually has the animal in hand.

Geographic Range

The range of *A. trichotis* is still not well known, although it has become clearer over the past 20 years. Up until 1989, animals had been sighted only along the Mananara River and the species was thought to be restricted to lowland rain forests of that area (Meier and Albignac, 1991). Since 1994, however, its presence has been documented in Marojejy National Park (Goodman and Raselimanana, 2002), Anjanaharibe-Sud Special Reserve (Schütz and Goodman, 1998; Schmid and Smolker, 1998), Masoala National Park (Sterling and Rakotoarison, 1998), Mananara-Nord National Park, the Marotandrano Special Reserve (J. Ralison, pers. comm.), Zahamena Strict Nature Reserve (Rakotoarison, 1995a, 1995b), Analamazaotra Special Reserve (Garbutt, 2001; R. A. Mittermeier, pers. obs.), Maromizaha Forest (J. Zaonarivelo, pers. comm.), Vohidrazana Forest (Rakotoarison *et al.*, 1997), Ambavoty Classified Forest (E. E. Louis Jr., pers. obs.), and the forests of Vohimana (N. Garbutt, pers. comm.). Overall, sightings have been few (probably no more than a few dozen in total).

The species appears to be very rare wherever it occurs, with an estimated 11–19 individuals per km² in the one study that has been conducted (Biebouw, 2009). *Allocebus* has mostly been found in intact tropical moist lowland and mid-altitude forest up to 1,000 m, but some populations appear to occur in montane forests (e.g., the Marotandrano Special Reserve) up to 1,600 m. It also seems to tolerate moderate levels of human activity (Schütz and Goodman, 1998).

Natural History

Relatively little was known about the behavior and ecology of the hairy-eared dwarf lemur until recently (Biebouw, 2009; Biebouw *et al.*, 2009). It is nocturnal and has been observed in pairs (presumably male and female) with offspring, as well as singly. It appears to have much larger home ranges (5.4–15.4 ha) than other Cheirogaleidae (Biebouw, 2009). Groups of two to six nest in holes of larger trees and prefer to line the nest with dry plant material, even covering themselves with it in captivity (Meier and Albignac, 1991). Individuals use from four to five tree holes, showing high nest fidelity (Biebouw *et al.*, 2009). Additionally, the species has been seen to share a tree hole with white-tailed tree rats (*Brachytarsomys albicauda*) (Biebouw *et al.*, 2009). Individuals are often seen in tangles of brush or lianas, and evidently forage at lower levels in the forest.

Fig. 7.50: Hairy-eared dwarf lemur (*Allocebus trichotis*) in the Ambatovy Classified Forest (photo by E. E. Louis Jr.).

The teeth and nails suggest a gum-eating diet, and the long tongue is suited for gathering nectar. Indeed, this lemur prefers fruit, insects and honey in captivity. Insectivory has been observed in the wild, along with feeding on gums, primarily of *Terminalia* (Biebouw, 2009). According to earlier reports, prior to undergoing aestivation in the cooler, less rainy austral winter (May/June–September/October), *A. trichotis* accumulates large amounts of fat and its body weight peaks at about 140% of the minimum (Rakotoarison *et al.*, 1997). During this supposed torpor, it is said to consume most of its fat reserves, but emerges ready to breed. However, more recent research indicates that *Allocebus* does not, in fact, undergo periods of torpor at all. Moreover, these same researchers did not observe significant weight being gained prior to the winter months (Biebouw, 2009; E. E. Louis Jr., pers. obs.). We still have much to learn about this unusual animal.

Conservation Status

Allocebus trichotis was classified as Data Deficient (DD) in the most recent IUCN Red List assessment (2008). Threats include destruction of eastern rain forest habitat, as well as hunting and trapping in certain regions (Yoder, 1996). Fortunately, this species is known to occur in at least five national parks (Mananara-Nord, Mantadia, Marojejy, Masoala, and Zahamena), the Zahamena Strict Nature Reserve, and three special reserves (Analamazaotra, Anjanaharibe-Sud, and Marotandrano). Range-wide surveys are needed to assess population densities and conservation status, and more detailed field studies should also be carried out to complement the single in-depth study by Biebouw (2009). In addition, a detailed long-term study of this species would be highly desirable to gain a better understanding of its behavior and ecology.

As of 2009, this species was not being kept in captivity (ISIS, 2009).

Where to See It

Under normal circumstances, this is one of the most difficult lemurs to find in the wild. Indeed many experts who have worked for decades in Madagascar have yet to see one. If you are lucky enough to catch what you think is one in your flashlight beam, you will have to get close enough to see the hair on its ears to be sure it is actually *A. trichotis*. Currently, the best opportunity for viewing it is at Andasibe (Perinét), in the Mitsinjo-managed section of the forest. There, in recent years, a particular individual *Allocebus* religiously visits a *Terminalia* tree virtually every night to eat gum. You can get to within a couple of meters or so of the animal as it feeds low down on the tree. This *Allocebus* is very regular in its habits, and appears to only visit the *Terminalia* between 19:00 and 19:45 hrs. One can, therefore, be reasonably sure of seeing it by staking out this tree over two or three nights (G. Davies, pers. comm.). Other places for viewing this species are at the Analamazaotra Special Reserve itself and the Forêt de Vohidrazana near the village of Fanovana, about 12 km east of Andasibe (Rakotoarison *et al.*, 1997), although its observation in these areas remains very unpredictable. The recent unfortunate policy of closing government reserves to night walks makes seeing nocturnal species in protected areas such as Analamazaotra very difficult, and we hope that the government will soon drop this unnecessary and counter-productive policy in the near future. However, this policy does not affect private areas such as Mitsinjo and Vohidrazana.

Fig. 7.51: Hairy-eared dwarf lemurs (*Allocebus trichotis*) photographed in lowland rain forest near Mananara-Nord, northeastern Madagascar in 1989 (photo by B. Meier).

Cheirogaleus É. Geoffroy, 1812
Dwarf Lemurs

The dwarf lemurs (*Cheirogaleus*) are small and nocturnal, and the only primates known to undergo extended seasonal periods of torpor akin to hibernation. A common English name for one species, "fat-tailed dwarf lemur," stems from their ability to store fat in the tail as a nutritional reserve during such periods. Dwarf lemurs are larger than mouse lemurs (*Microcebus*), reaching total lengths of 40–50 cm, 40–50% of which is tail. Body weights tend to vary seasonally, as do activity levels. The highest weights are recorded just prior to torpor and can reach 600 g. The lowest weights are recorded upon emergence from the seasonal lethargic state and can be less than 50% of the pre-torpor body mass. Since these species enter a torpid state during the austral winter, they are typically not seen from May to mid-September.

This genus is found throughout much of Madagascar. Until just a few years ago, only two species were recognized, the fat-tailed dwarf lemur (*Cheirogaleus medius*), an inhabitant of dry, deciduous forests and spiny forest in western and southern Madagascar, and the greater dwarf lemur (*C. major*), thought to occur only in the moist forests of eastern and northern Madagascar. However, Groves (2000, 2001) divided *Cheirogaleus* into two species groups: the *C. major* group (composed of *C. major*, *C. crossleyi*, *C. minusculus*,

Fig. 7.52: A possible new species of *Cheirogaleus* from Manongarivo (photo by J. F. Ranaivoarisoa).

C. ravus and *C. sibreei*) and the *C. medius* group (*C. medius* and *C. adipicaudatus*). Of these, three (*C. adipicaudatus*, *C. crossleyi*, and *C. sibreei*) had been described in the past but had subsequently been considered junior synonyms, and two were new and named by Groves himself (*C. minusculus*, *C. ravus*). These dwarf lemurs he distinguished according to differences in body size, pelage, ear size and covering, tail length, skull shape, and dentition.

These seven species were included in the second edition of this field guide, published in 2006. However, since that time, Groeneveld *et al.* (2009) have provided detailed new evidence regarding this genus. They confirmed the exclusivity of three of the *Cheirogaleus* species, *C. major*, *C. medius*, and *C. crossleyi*, and found that, genetically, *C. sibreei* fell within the *C. major* clade but that its morphology made it difficult to place. At the same time, Groeneveld *et al.* (2009) indicated that *C. adipicaudatus* is a synonym of *C. medius*, and that *C. ravus* is synonymous with *C. major*, so we no longer recognize these two as valid taxa. Until very recently, *C. minusculus* and *C. sibreei* had never been found in the field (Hapke *et al.* 2005; Groeneveld *et al.* 2009, 2010). However, Blanco *et al.* (2009) found two dwarf lemur species at Tsinjoarivo, 80 km south-southeast of Antananarivo, just west of the eastern escarpment of the central plateau and on the north bank of the Onive River; although *C. major* was presumed to be the species occurring there, they concluded that one was probably *C. crossleyi* and the second was possibly *C. sibreei* or a new species. Genetic analyses by Groeneveld *et al.* (2010) subsequently confirmed the two as *C. crossleyi* and *C. sibreei*, and, based on this new data, they concluded that *C. sibreei*, resurrected by Groves (2000), is indeed a valid species. Groeneveld *et al.* (2009) were unable to resolve the taxonomic status of *C. minusculus* due to insufficient data—it is known only from the type specimen, and genetic material was not available. We maintain *C. minusculus* as a valid taxon pending further field and laboratory studies. The distributions of these dwarf lemurs is far more complex than previously believed, and are described in more detail below under each individual species.

What is of particular interest is that Groeneveld *et al.* (2009) found eight, fully resolved terminal clades in their *C. crossleyi* clade, five in their *C. medius* clade, and three in their *C. major* clade. Each of these, in the opinion of some, could represent distinct species. Although Groeneveld *et al.* (2009) made no determination as to species status for these terminal clades, it appears likely that more species will emerge from this genus. Field data currently being gathered by one of the authors of this book, E. E. Louis Jr., also indicate that a number of new *Cheirogaleus* species likely await description.

Dwarf lemurs typically walk quadrupedally along branches at all levels of the forest and tend to jump less and move more slowly than the closely-related mouse lemurs, although they are capable of leaping when necessary. They are easily distinguishable from *Microcebus* and *Mirza* in the field, being larger and generally more sedentary, and having dark rings around the eyes and a muzzle-like pink nose. The anus is located a short distance along the tail, but this feature can be observed only at close range or if the animal is in the hand (Mittermeier *et al.*, 1994). They also move more slowly than *Lepilemur* and do not adopt the vertical clinging posture typical of that genus.

When only two species were recognized in this genus, both were considered widespread and abundant, and neither was considered threatened. At present, no *Cheirogaleus* species appear as threatened on the IUCN Red List, but there is a need to reassess the conservation status of those that were resurrected from the literature. Some of them have very restricted distributions, may not occur in any protected areas, and could possibly be threatened.

Cheirogaleidae

J.Smit lith.   Hanhart imp.

CHIROGALEUS MILII.

Fig. 7.53: Hand-colored lithograph by J. Smit of *Cheirogaleus milii* (= *Cheirogaleus major*), published in the *Proceedings of the Zoological Society of London* in 1879.

Fig. 7.54: *Cheirogaleus* postural and behavioral drawings (next page):
     a. *Cheirogaleus* standing quadrupedally
     b. *Cheirogaleus* standing on twigs
     c. *Cheirogaleus* clinging sideways to a branch
     d. *Cheirogaleus* feeding
     e. *Cheirogaleus* clinging to branches

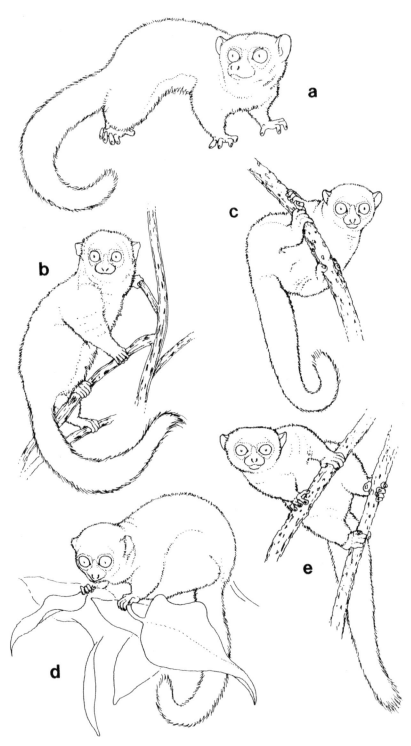

Fig. 7.54.

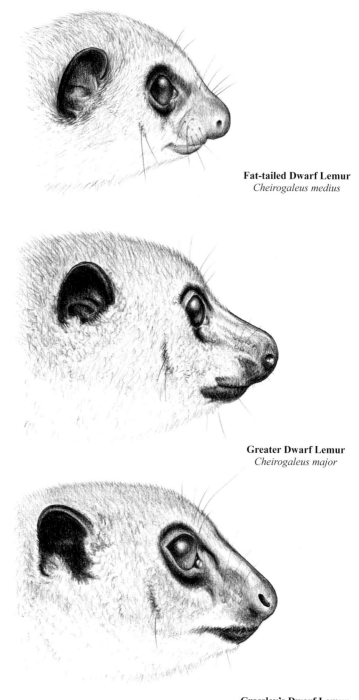

Fat-tailed Dwarf Lemur
Cheirogaleus medius

Greater Dwarf Lemur
Cheirogaleus major

Crossley's Dwarf Lemur
Cheirogaleus crossleyi

Fig. 7.55: Profiles of three *Cheirogaleus* species.

Cheirogaleidae

Fat-tailed Dwarf Lemur
Cheirogaleus medius

Sibree's Dwarf Lemur
Cheirogaleus sibreei

Greater Dwarf Lemur
Cheirogaleus major

Crossley's Dwarf Lemur
Cheirogaleus crossleyi

**Lesser Iron-gray
Dwarf Lemur**
Cheirogaleus minusculus

Fig. 7.56.

Fig. 7.57: Distributions of *Cheirogaleus medius*, *C. crossleyi*, *C. minusculus*, **and** *C. sibreei*.

Fig. 7.58: Distribution of *Cheirogaleus major*.

Cheirogaleidae

Fig. 7.59: A hand-colored lithograph of *Opolemur milii* by C. Burjeau from the *Proceedings of the Zoological Society of London*, 1872. Groves (2000) considered *Opolemur milii* to be a junior synonym of *Cheirogaleus major*.

Fig. 7.60: A plate from the *Naturgeschichte und Abbildungen der Säugethiere* by Carl Joseph Brodtmann, Zürich, 1827, depicting three species of *Cheirogaleus*.

Cheirogaleus medius É. Geoffroy, 1812
Fat-tailed Dwarf Lemur

Other English: Lesser Dwarf Lemur, Western Fat-tailed Dwarf
Lemur, Spiny Forest Dwarf Lemur
French: Petit Cheirogale, Cheirogale moyen, Cheirogale à gross
queue, Cheirogale à queue grasse
German: Fettschwanzmaki
Malagasy: Tsidihy, Kelybehohy, Matavyrambo, Bodonohy (in the
south near Tolagnaro [= Fort-Dauphin])

Identification

The fat-tailed dwarf lemur is one of the smaller members of the genus *Cheirogaleus*.
Head-body length is 17–23 cm, tail length is 19–27 cm, total length is 40–50 cm, and
body weight varies seasonally from 120 to 270 g (Petter, 1978; Fietz and Ganzhorn, 1999;
Müller, 1999b; Groves, 2000). According to Groves (2000), the dorsal coat is a light frosted
fawn-gray with a brown midline stripe. The ventral coat is creamy or yellowish, somewhat
more yellow toward the median. There is a partial but sharply marked white collar that
extends well up the sides of the neck. A white median facial stripe is offset by dark brown
eye rings. The hands and feet are white.

In his revision of the genus, Groves (2000) considered populations from the tropical
dry lowland forests and spiny forest regions of the southwest to be a distinct species,
and resurrected the name *Cheirogaleus adipicaudatus* (A. Grandidier, 1868). In terms of
morphology, this taxon was said to be similar to *C. medius*, but with less contrasting colors
and a tail that was longer than the head-body length. Groves (2000) examined specimens
from three southern Madagascar sites: Tabiky, Tolagnaro (= Fort-Dauphin), and a third
unnamed location 170 km east of Toliara (= Tuléar). Most likely representing a collection
in dry spiny forest to the west of Tolagnaro. The presence of *C. adipicaudatus* in the region
of Tolagnaro was not supported by Hapke *et al.* (2005), whose findings indicated instead the
presence of three other *Cheirogaleus* species from that region (*C. crossleyi, C. major* and *C.
medius)*. It may be that the features on which this species was differentiated from *C. medius*
(see Groves, 2001) characterize only a particular population of restricted distribution (C. P.
Groves, pers. comm.). In any case, as indicated above, we follow Groneveld *et al.* (2009)
in considering *C. adipicaudatus* a synonym of *C. medius*. Groneveld *et al.* (2009) found
five terminal clades within *C. medius*, however, which may turn out to be distinct species.

In the field, *Cheirogaleus* is most likely to be confused with *Lepilemur* or *Mirza*, and
possibly *Microcebus*, although it tends to move more slowly than any of these three. It can
be distinguished from *Lepilemur* by its distinctive lighter underparts, by the form of its tail,
and by body posture and movement; *Lepilemur* is more likely to adopt a vertical posture
and to leap, whereas *Cheirogaleus* walks slowly and quadrupedally (although it is capable
of leaping as well). Sportive lemurs are three to eight times the size of *C. medius*. *Mirza*
has large distinctive ears and moves both rapidly and constantly. *Microcebus* also has
highly visible ears, moves more than does *Cheirogaleus*, and is much smaller. Confusion
with *Phaner* is unlikely, since *Phaner* moves constantly, vocalizes loudly, bobs its head
back and forth, and has a more elongate face and telltale fork-mark pattern on its head.
Distinguishing among species of *Cheirogaleus* is possible through the geographic location
and using the detailed descriptions found in this section.

Geographic Range

When *C. medius* was one of only two recognized dwarf lemur species, it was believed to occur throughout the west and south of Madagascar, from Tolagnaro (= Fort-Dauphin) in the southeast, west through the southern spiny desert to the southwestern side of the island, and then north along the western dry deciduous forest as far as the Sambirano region. It was also reported from several scattered northern sites such as Ambilobe, Ankarana, and Daraina (Nicoll and Langrand, 1989; Mittermeier *et al.*, 1994). Groves (2000), in his revision of the genus, limited the range of this species to the dry forests of western Madagascar, with *C. adipicaudatus* in the southern spiny desert. Subsequent field studies and genetic analyses have now eliminated *C. adipicaudatus* as a valid species, and have again extended the range of *C. medius* into the southern spiny desert and all the way east to the evergreen humid forest of Sainte-Luce, 40 km northeast of Tolagnaro in extreme southeastern Madagascar (Hapke *et al.*, 2005). In the southeast, *C. medius* also occurs in the littoral forests of Petriky and Mandena, and in humid forest remnants in the Lavasoa-Ambatotsirongorongo mountains (west of Fort-Dauphin) (A. Hapke, pers.comm.). *Cheirogaleus major* is also known from Mandena and possibly occurs in Sainte Luce as well (A. Hapke, pers.comm.). Groeneveld *et al.* (2009, 2010) further confirm that this species occurs in the Tolagnaro region in the southeast, and also in the region of the Bay of Pasandava (north of the Ampasindava Peninsula) in the northwest. In addition, it extends as far northwest as Ankarana and in at least two sites in the northeast, Bekaraoka and Sambava, and it may be the species present in the Daraina area in the northeast, but this remains to be confirmed (Mittermeier *et al.*, 1994).

Fig. 7.61: Juvenile fat-tailed dwarf lemur (*Cheirogaleus medius*), Tsingy de Bemaraha National Park (photo by E. E. Louis Jr.).

Natural History

Cheirogaleus medius inhabits dry deciduous forests at densities estimated to range from 40 to 400 individuals/km^2 (Hladik *et al.*, 1980; Fietz, 1999a). Individual home ranges are 1–2 ha. Territories are defended, and marked using feces (Schilling, 1980; Ganzhorn and Kappeler, 1996; Fietz, 1999a). Small family groups consist of the reproductively-active pair and their offspring from one or two breeding seasons (Fietz, 1999b; Müller, 1999a). Despite the family structure, about 40% of the offspring are fathered by other males (Fietz *et al.*, 2000). Individuals of both sexes disperse from their natal range, and local populations a few kilometers apart can vary greatly in population density and sex ratio (Fredstedt *et al.*, 2007). Fruits, flowers and seeds are dietary staples, with invertebrates being eaten in small amounts and small vertebrates taken on occasion. Gums and insect excretions round out the diet. Daylight hours are spent in tree holes, with up to five individuals occupying a single shelter (Petter, 1978).

The most notable characteristic of this species and other members of the genus *Cheirogaleus* is the ability to become torpid for six months or more during the austral winter, a time of food and water scarcity (Pagès and Petter-Rousseaux, 1980; Fietz, 2003; Dausmann *et al.*, 2004). In preparation for the dry season, animals begin to eat greater quantities of fruits with high sugar content and to accumulate significant quantities of fat, much of it stored in the tail. Individuals enter the same tree holes used as daily shelters and

Fig. 7.62: Fat-tailed dwarf lemur (*Cheirogaleus medius*), Kirindy Forest (photo by R. A. Mittermeier).

remain totally inactive during prolonged hibernation. Unlike other hibernating mammals, the body temperatures of torpid dwarf lemurs do not remain lower and stable, but closely track ambient temperatures (Dausmann *et al.* 2000, 2004). Emergence from torpor typically occurs just before the seasonal rains in November. Body mass may decline by more than half during this period. The return to an active state also stimulates the onset of mating behavior, resulting in births a couple of months later. Litter sizes range from one to four, but twins are the most common and the young are born covered with fur and with eyes open (Foerg, 1982b). As the next dry season draws near, juvenile dwarf lemurs tend to remain active about a month longer than do adults. Sexual maturity is reached during the second year of life.

Predators of *C. medius* include the fossa (*Cryptoprocta ferox*), the boas *Sanzinia madagascariensis* and *Acrantophis madagascariensis*, the Madagascar Harrier-hawk (*Polyboroides radiatus*), the Madagascar Buzzard (*Buteo madagascariensis*), and the owls *Tyto alba* and *Asio madagascariensis* (Goodman and Langrand, 1996a; Gilbert and Tingay, 2001; Goodman, 2003).

Conservation Status

The 2008 IUCN Red List assessment classified *C. medius* as Least Concern (LC). Although it is an apparently widespread and abundant species at present, the discovery of new species within its formerly broad range will affect its overall status and some of the new taxa may be Endangered. It is reported from seven national parks (Andohahela, Ankarafantsika, Ankarana, Baie de Baly, Tsimanampetsotsa, Tsingy de Namoroka, and Zombitse-Vohibasia) and four special reserves (Andranomena, Bemarivo, Beza-Mahafaly and Maningoza), as well as in the Kirindy Forest (part of the Menabe-Antimena Protected Area), in Daraina (Loky-Manambato Protected Area), and in the Sainte-Luce Private Reserve (O'Connor *et al.*, 1986; Harcourt and Thornback, 1990; Feistner and Schmid, 1999).

According to ISIS, there are approximately 50 individuals of what are considered to be *Cheirogaleus medius* in captivity in the USA and in Europe (ISIS, 2009).

Where to See It

The fat-tailed dwarf lemur can be seen in many places throughout its range, but usually only in the rainy season (October through April). Particularly good sites for viewing it are the Kirindy Forest (Menabe-Antimena Protected Area) in the southwest, Ankarafantsika National Park in the northwest, and the dry forest near Daraina (Loky-Manambato Protected Area) in northeastern Madagascar, where it seems to be particularly abundant. Visits to Daraina are now being arranged by a number of international tour operators, mainly for seeing Tattersall's sifaka (*Propithecus tattersalli*).

In southern Madagascar, the best locations for viewing what we believe to be this species of *Cheirogaleus* are the Beza-Mahafaly Special Reserve to the east of Toliara (= Tuléar), Tsimanampetsotsa National Park, and Zombitse-Vohibasia National Park, which can be reached by car from Toliara in about two hours. The latter is also a good location for seeing the ring-tailed lemur (*Lemur catta*) and Verreaux's sifaka (*Propithecus verreauxi*). Andohahela National Park's dry forest parcels also offer opportunities to see dwarf lemurs during nocturnal walks. The park has excellent trails and camping facilities. Curiously, the species appears to be absent from the Berenty Private Reserve.

Cheirogaleidae

Cheirogaleus sibreei (Forsyth Major, 1896)
Sibree's Dwarf Lemur

Other English: None
French: Cheirogale de Sibree
German: Sibree's Fettschwanzmaki
Malagasy: Tsitsihy

Identification

Cheirogaleus sibreei is one of five dwarf lemurs identified by Groves (2000, 2001) as belonging to the *C. major* group. This species was first described by Forsyth Major in 1896, but subsequently considered a junior synonym of *C. major*. Groves (2000) resurrected this species based on four skins in museum collections (the type specimen in the British Museum, a skin from Imerina in the Humboldt Museum, Berlin, and two specimens from Pasandava Bay, north of the Ampisandava Peninsula, in Naturalis (the Rijksmuseum in Leiden). No more recent information was available concerning its range in the wild until the species was identified in a small patch of forest in Tsinjoarivo by Blanco *et al.* (2009). Blanco *et al.* (2009) measured 15 individuals: head-body length with a mean of 21.8 ±0.9 cm (range 20.5–23.5 cm), tail length 23.5 cm ±1.3 cm (range 22.0– 26.5 cm), and body mass with a mean of 272.1 ±35.6 g (range 219.0–359.5 g).

This species has gray-fawn fur on the dorsum and cap, with or without a darker dorsal median line (see Fig. 7.64). There is light gray or creamy fur (with whitish tips and darker roots) on the ventrum, this lighter coloration continuing cranially as bands extending onto the sides of the neck, but not the back, though it does extend up the flanks and along the outsides of the thighs. The orbits are surrounded by distinct, broad and very black eye rings. There may be thin extensions of this black coloration (or none at all) delineating the sides of the muzzle, but the dominant color of the muzzle is only slightly grayer than the dorsal fur and very uniform, and the rhinarium tends to be pink. The ears are naked, and the pinnae are dark with sparse hair on their inner and outer surfaces. The hands and feet are pink ventrally and gray-brown dorsally (Blanco *et al.*, 2009; M. Blanco, pers. comm.; see also Groves, 2000).

Geographic Range

This species was long known only from museum specimens collected from three localities in Madagascar's Central Domain (Groves, 2000). The type locality, Ankeramadinika, a "day's journey east of Antananarivo" (Groves, 2000), is just east of the Mangoro River, 1,408 m above sea level (Blanco *et al.*, 2009; Groeneveld *et al.*, 2010). Blanco *et al.* (2009) recorded sympatric dwarf lemurs about 100 km south of Ankeramadinika, in the mid- and high-altitude forests of the Tsinjoarivo region, a forest block isolated by two rivers (the Onive in the south and the Mangoro in the east) and bounded by the high-altitude central plateau in the west. They identified *C. crossleyi* in extensive forest at a site called Vatateza at about 1,390 m above sea level, and (tentatively at the time) *C. sibreei*, in a forest patch of 228 km² at Andasivodihazo at about 1,660 m above sea level. Blanco *et al.* (2009) based

Fig. 7.63: A juvenile *Cheirogaleus sibreei* trapped for study at Andasivodihazo, a forest fragment in the Tsinjoarivo area. These and the photos on the next page may be the first ever taken of this species (photos by M. B. Blanco).

their identifications on morphometric traits. Subsequent molecular genetic studies by Groeneveld *et al*. (2010) confirmed their conclusion: "the individuals from Andasivodihazo are distinct from *C. medius*, *C. major* and *C. crossleyi* and thus represent a fourth species" (p.10). Groeneveld *et al*. (in press) carried out further morphometric analyses of the Andasivodihazo dwarf lemurs, comparing them with the *C. sibreei* holotype in the British Museum, and concluded that they were indeed the same species.

As reported by Groeneveld *et al*. (2010), three localities were sampled at Tsinjoarivo on two occasions between 2006 and 2009. *Cheirogaleus crossleyi* was subsequently also found at Andasivodihazo, and *C. sibreei* alone was recorded at a nearby site called Ankadivory at about 1,470 m above sea level. They indicated that *C. sibreei* may be restricted by the Onive and Mangoro rivers, Anjozorobe, and the corridor to the western half of the Tsinjoarivo forest above 1,400 m altitude, in an area of less than 2,000 km².

Rasolofoson *et al.* (2007a, 2007b) reported it far to the north, in the Makira Forest. It seems that this locality is a rather large range extension, and it may be that a closely related species, thus far undescribed, is involved (C. P. Groves, pers. comm.). Groeneveld *et al.* (2010) determined that the Naturalis material from Pasandava Bay examined by Groves (2000), was aligned, morphometrically and genetically, with *C. medius*, not *C. sibreei*.

Figs. 7.64 and 7.65 (next page): A juvenile of *Cheirogaleus sibreei* trapped for study at Andasivodihazo, a forest fragment in the Tsinjoarivo area (photos by M. B. Blanco).

Natural History

As of 2010, this species had not been studied in the wild.

Conservation Status

The latest IUCN Red List assessment (2008) classified *C. sibreei* as Data Deficient (DD). Its range may well be the smallest of the dwarf lemurs. Furthermore, if, as Groeneveld *et al.* (2010) surmised, it occurs only at higher altitudes (above about 1,400 m), it may be restricted to just a very few subpopulations along the western margin of the eastern rain forest corridor between the Onive and Mangoro rivers. Groeneveld *et al.* (2010) reported on the status of these forests. While the lower parts near the plateau escarpment are remote and reasonably undisturbed, the higher areas are flatter, continuous with the plateau, and broadly accessible to "substantial human settlement." The forest cover in this western part of Tsinjoarivo has been reduced to about half its original extent, and is highly fragmented (Irwin, 2006). As reported by Groeneveld *et al.* (2010), the forest there is slated for future protection, but there are as yet no safeguards to ensure its permanence. Habitat loss and fragmentation could well be a threat to its survival.

As of 2010, this species was not being kept in captivity (I. J. Porton, pers. comm.).

Where to See It

The only site where we know with certainty that this species can be found is Andasivodihazo, in the Tsinjoarivo region. However, this location is difficult to reach, and we do not recommend it for first time visitors to Madagascar.

Fig. 7.65.

Cheirogaleus major É. Geoffroy, 1812
Greater Dwarf Lemur

Other English: Geoffroy's Dwarf Lemur
French: Grand Cheirogale
German: Grosser Fettschwanzmaki
Malagasy: Tsitsihy, Tsidy, Hataka, Kelybehohy (southeast)

Identification

The greater dwarf lemur is one of the larger members of the genus *Cheirogaleus*. Its head-body length is 23–25 cm, tail length 25–28 cm, total length 50–55 cm, and its body weight averages 350–400 g, with a seasonal variation from 250 to 500 g (Fietz, 2003). The dorsal coat is gray-brown, and the ventral coat is gray. The dark reddish dorsal midline stripe, when present, is not very distinct. The mid-facial zone is pale and lacks a distinct stripe. This lighter region does not extend above the level of the eyes, the eye rings themselves are not distinct, and the snout is dark. The ears are naked. As indicated above in the generic description for *Cheirogaleus*, Groeneveld *et al.* (2009) found three terminal clades within *C. major*, which may well turn out to be distinct species. *Cheirogaleus major* may easily be confused with other sympatric species of *Cheirogaleus* in the few places where such sympatry occurs (see below).

Geographic Range

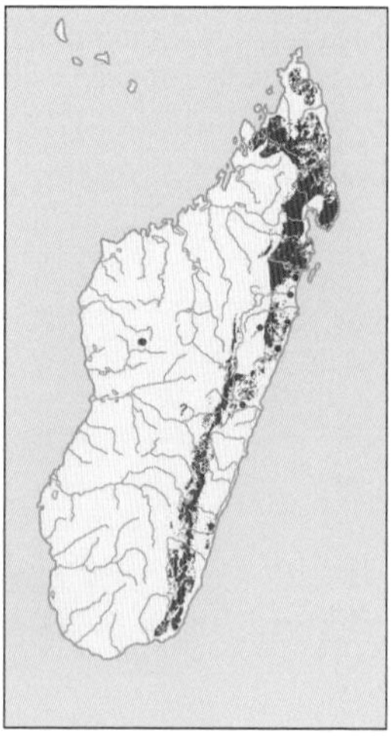

According to the most recent information from Groeneveld *et al.* (2009), *C. major* is found in eastern lowland rain forest from the southeastern tip of Madagascar near Tolagnaro (= Fort-Dauphin) as far north as Maroantsetra. The southern limit of its distribution is particularly interesting, since *C. medius* and *C. crossleyi* can also be found the same general region, although not to date in the same forests (Hapke *et al.*, 2005). Andreas Hapke has found *C. major* in the humid forests of the Vohimena and Anosy mountains and the littoral forest at Mandena, and believes it might also occur in Sainte Luce, but this has yet to be confirmed (pers. comm.). *Cheirogaleus crossleyi* and *C. medius*, on the other hand, occur in humid forest remnants in the Lavasoa-Ambatotsirongorongo mountains (west of Fort- Dauphin), and *C. medius* also in the littoral forests of Petriky, Mandena and Sainte Luce. *Cheirogaleus major* is sympatric with *C. crossleyi* in Ranomafana National Park (P. C. Wright, pers. comm.).

Natural History

Cheirogaleus major is an inhabitant of Madagascar's eastern lowland and montane forests (sea level to 1800 m), where conditions of water and food availability are not as seasonally severe as in the drier western deciduous forests. Nonetheless, the greater dwarf lemur does prepare for hibernation by storing excess fat in its tail, perhaps taking up, as much as 30% of its total body mass. Also, as is the case with *C. medius*, *C. major* hibernates in tree holes and hollows (Wright and Martin, 1995).

Fig. 7.66: Greater dwarf lemur (*Cheirogaleus major*), Midongy du Sud (photo by J. F. Ranaivoarisoa).

Fig. 7.67: Greater dwarf lemur (*Cheirogaleus major*), Midongy du Sud (photo by J. F. Ranaivoarisoa).

Relatively little is known of the social behavior of *C. major*. Home ranges of adult females extend up to 4 ha, and appear to include those of adult males and juveniles as well. Sleeping groups of up to three adult animals have been observed both in tree holes and clumps of vegetation. Population densities have been estimated at 75–110 individuals/km^2 (Pollock, 1979b). However, it should be noted that a number of these observations, cited here and below, were made in Andasibe (= Périnet), which would mean that they refer to *C. crossleyi* under the new taxonomic arrangement of Groves (2000).

Mating behavior ensues shortly after emergence from torpor in October and November, females giving birth to two to three infants in January after a gestation of about 70 days (Petter-Rousseaux, 1964). Young are born in leaf nests constructed by the females 6–12 m above the ground. Newborn greater dwarf lemurs are born furred but with eyes closed. They are first carried in their mother's mouth, but soon cling to the fur on her back (Fietz, 2003).

Cheirogaleus major feeds mainly on nectar, fruits, young leaves, and buds, with insect prey constituting only a minor part of the diet (Ganzhorn, 1988; Wright and Martin, 1995). Nectar seems to be a particularly important food item just after it emerges from hibernation, and studies suggest that *C. major* may be an important pollinator for at least one species of liana (Nilson *et al.*, 1993). Predators of *C. major* include the fossa (*Cryptoprocta ferox*), the ring-tailed mongoose (*Galidia elegans*), and the Madagascar tree boa (*Sanzinia madagascariensis*) (Goodman, 2003).

Conservation Status

In the most recent IUCN Red List assessment (2008), *C. major* was classified as Least Concern (LC). It is reported to occur in eight national parks (Andohahela, Andringitra, Mananara-Nord, Marojejy, Masoala, Midongy du Sud, Montagne d'Ambre, and Ranomafana), two strict nature reserves (Betampona and Tsaratanana), and three special reserves (Anjanaharibe-Sud, Mangerivola and Pic d'Ivohibe) (O'Connor *et al.*, 1986; Nicoll and Langrand, 1989; Sterling and Rakotoaraison, 1998; Feistner and Schmid, 1999; Sterling and McFadden, 2000; Wright and Porter, 2004).

Based on the new *Cheirogaleus* taxonomy, the dwarf lemur species occurring in Zahamena National Park, Mantadia National Park, and the Analamazaotra Special Reserve at Andasibe (= Périnet), previously believed to be *C. major*, would now be *C. crossleyi*.

As of 2009, there were five individuals of this species in captivity, four in the Tsimbazaza Zoo in Antananarivo, Madagascar, and one in the Zürich Zoo, Switzerland (ISIS, 2009; I. J. Porton, pers. comm.).

Where to See It

This species is readily seen in Ranomafana National Park and the littoral forest of the Mandena Conservation Zone (northeast of Tolagnaro = Fort-Dauphin). *Cheirogaleus medius* also occurs in Mandena. The two species can be seen only during the wet season (October through April). As with most other nocturnal species, it is most easily found by using a flashlight or headlamp to locate eye shine. Most sightings are in the understory and lower to middle levels of the forest canopy, but this species also can be seen high up in the canopy as well.

Cheirogaleus crossleyi A. Grandidier, 1870
Crossley's Dwarf Lemur

Other English: Furry-eared Dwarf Lemur
French: Cheirogale de Crossley
German: Crossley's Fettschwanzmaki
Malagasy: Matavirambo, Tsitsihy (northeast)

Identification

Cheirogaleus crossleyi is one of several dwarf lemur species that re-emerged from the former *Cheirogaleus major* as a result of the taxonomic revision by Groves (2000). Its head-body length is 22–26 cm, its tail length 21–27 cm, and its average total length is 50 cm. The dorsal coat is reddish-brown, and the ventral coat is gray, turning creamy toward the midline. The mid-facial zone is yellowish, this coloring extending above the eyes, which are surrounded by blackish rings. The ears are heavily pigmented, and covered with black fur both inside and out, and help to distinguish this species from *C. major*, along with its reddish color and blacker, more pronounced eye rings. As indicated above in the generic description for *Cheirogaleus*, Groeneveld *et al.* (2009) found five terminal clades within *C. crossleyi*, which may well turn out to be distinct species. This species can easily be confused with *C. major* in areas where the two are sympatric.

Geographic Range

The range of *C. crossleyi* remains to be fully determined. Groves (2000) describes it as running inland to that of *C. major* in eastern Madagascar and extending further to the north. Localities in eastern central Madagascar include Lac Alaotra, Andasibe (= Périnet), Imerina, and the mid- to low-altitude forests at Tsinjoarivo where Blanco *et al.* (2009) and Groeneveld *et al.* (2010) recorded it at Talatakely and Vatateza and, sympatric with *C. sibreei*, at Andasivodihazo. *Cheirogaleus crossleyi* is also sympatric with *C. major* in Ranomafana National Park (P. C. Wright, pers. comm.). Localities in the northeast include Sambava, Manatenina, and Vohémar (Groeneveld *et al.*, 2009, 2010). According to Hapke *et al.* (2005), this is one of three dwarf lemurs found west of Tolagnaro (= Fort-Dauphin). *Cheirogaleus major* and *C. medius* are also found in the region, although not to date in the same forests. Both *C. crossleyi* and *C. medius* occur in humid forest remnants in the Lavasoa-Ambatotsirongorongo mountains (west of Fort-Dauphin) (A. Hapke, pers. comm.). Despite its apparently wide distribution, there are thus far no indications of geographic differences within this species (C. P. Groves, pers. comm.).

Natural History

Although there are no studies of the behavior and ecology of this species published under the name *C. crossleyi*, those studies conducted on *C. major* in Andasibe (= Périnet) would refer to this animal (e.g., Petter-Rousseaux, 1964; Pollock, 1979b).

Cheirogaleidae

Fig. 7.68: Crossley's dwarf lemur (*Cheirogaleus crossleyi*), Andasibe (photo by R. A. Mittermeier).

Cheirogaleidae

Conservation Status

There is insufficient information to determine the conservation status of *C. crossleyi*, so the latest IUCN Red List assessment (2008) classified it as Data Deficient (DD). It is believed to be present in a number of protected areas, including the Zahamena Strict Nature Reserve, the Analamazaotra Special Reserve, and at least two national parks, Mantadia and Zahamena.

As of 2010, this species was not being kept in captivity (I. J. Porton, pers. comm.).

Where to See It

A good place to see this species in the wild is the Analamazaotra Special Reserve near Andasibe (= Périnet). Dwarf lemurs are quite common there in the wet season (November through April), and can sometimes be seen feeding on traveler's palm (*Ravenala madagascariensis*) sap right next to the Feon'ny Ala Hotel at the edge of the forest. Indeed, one sometimes sees groups of 30–40 tourists clustered around a few traveler's palms right next to the restaurant of this hotel, observing two or three individuals of this species happily feeding without any fear of their human admirers. They are also fond of moving back and forth on power lines at this location. Both *C. major* and *C. crossleyi* can also be seen in Ranomafana National Park.

Fig. 7.69: Above: Crossley's dwarf lemur (*Cheirogaleus crossleyi*), Andringitra (photo by J. F. Ranaivoarisoa).

Fig. 7.70: Above: A Crossley's dwarf lemur (*Cheirogaleus crossleyi*), Analamazaotra Special Reserve (photo by O. Langrand). Below: Another Crossley's dwarf lemur feeding on on the sap of *Ravenala*, Andasibe (photo by R. A. Mittermeier).

Cheirogaleus minusculus Groves, 2000
Lesser Iron-gray Dwarf Lemur

Other English: Large Iron-gray Dwarf Lemur
French: Grand Cheirogale gris-acier
German: Graufettschwanzmaki
Malagasy: Tsitsiha

Identification

Cheirogaleus minusculus is one of the dwarf lemur species formerly considered to be *C. major* that was resurrected by Groves (2000). Groeneveld *et al.* (2009) did not have sufficient material of this form for their genetic analysis of the genus. The dorsal coat is iron-gray with brownish tones and a vague midline stripe. The ears are furred along the rims. The digits are white. It is intermediate in size between the larger *C. major* group and smaller *C. medius* group species.

In his revision of the genus in 2000, Groves considered populations from Ambositra to be a distinct species, the lesser iron-gray dwarf lemur (*Cheirogaleus minusculus*), differentiating it from the greater iron-gray dwarf lemur (*Cheirogaleus ravus*). As indicated above, we continue to recognize *C. minusculus*, but no longer consider *C. ravus* a valid taxon. This species is presently known only from a single museum specimen from the type locality, Ambositra, north of Fianarantsoa in east-central Madagascar. Groves (2000) believed that this is also the species recorded from the Bongolava Massif northwest of the type locality (Thalmann and Rakotoarison, 1994), but photographs from that region, shown recently to Groves by Urs Thalmann, indicate that this is not the case. It is possible that a further undescribed species exists on Bongolava (C. P. Groves, pers. comm.).

Geographic Range

At present this species is known only from a single museum specimen, collected from the type locality, Ambositra, north of Fianarantsoa in east-central Madagascar. It is not known whether it still survives in forest fragments in that region.

Natural History

As of 2010, this species had not been studied in the wild.

Conservation Status

There is insufficient information to determine the conservation status of *C. minusculus*, so the latest IUCN Red List assessment (2008) classified it as Data Deficient (DD). It is not known to occur in any protected areas within what appears to be a very restricted range.

As of 2010, this species was not being kept in captivity (I. J. Porton, pers. comm.).

Where to See It

There are currently no sites that we can recommend for seeing *C. minusculus* in the wild.

Fig. 7.71: Lesser iron-gray dwarf lemur (*Cheirogaleus minusculus*).

Fig. 7.72: Pale fork-marked lemur (*Phaner pallescens*), Kirindy (photo by J. Zaonarivelo).

Phaner Gray, 1870
Fork-marked Lemurs

The nocturnal fork-marked lemurs, or fork-marked dwarf lemurs, are one of the two large genera of cheirogaleids, along with *Cheirogaleus*. The pelage is light grayish-brown dorsally and creamy-white to yellow ventrally. A distinctive black, Y-shaped line starts above each eye and joins together as a single line on the top of the head, creating the fork that gives these animals their common name. From there, a stripe of varying width and intensity extends rearward along the dorsal midline to the tail. The tip of the tail is typically black. The eyes are circled by dark rings that may also extend down the muzzle.

Fork-marked lemurs have a discontinuous distribution in the forests of the west, the north, and the east, but are absent from the southern spiny forest of the far south. They appear to be absent from the southeastern part of the eastern rain forest as well, with the possible exception of Andohahela National Park (see below). The first description of a *Phaner* was by de Blainville in 1839, who used the name *Lemur furcifer*. The animal was later placed in the genus *Phaner* by Gray (1870).

Until relatively recently, *Phaner* contained a single species, *Phaner furcifer*. Groves and Tattersall (1991) were the first to point out differences in color and anatomy between isolated populations and proposed four subspecies—*furcifer, electromontis, pallescens*, and *parienti*—based on examination of museum specimens. Groves (2001) raised the four taxa to full species. However, there are indications that other forms may yet be described. In 1995, R. A. Mittermeier first observed a population of *Phaner* in Daraina, pointing out that it might be a new species, an opinion shared by Groves (2001). In 1999, Feistner and Schmid reported *Phaner* from the rain forest parcel of Andohahela National Park. More recently, E. E. Louis Jr. and his team have indicated that there are potentially undescribed forms from other parts of the island. However, for now, until more information becomes available, we continue to follow Groves (2001) in recognizing four species of *Phaner*.

Phaner are very vocal lemurs, particularly just after dusk and at dawn, and their loud calls help to find and identify them in the field (Charles-Dominique and Petter, 1980). Bursts of high-pitched whistling cries routinely alert the visitor to their presence. When spotted, their mode of locomotion is also a distinguishing feature. They tend to run rapidly along horizontal tree branches and to jump from one branch to the next without pausing. When an animal stops, it often bobs its head up and down or wags it sideways, creating a very distinctive pattern of eye-shine that is unique to this genus.

Based on the studies of *Phaner pallescens* from the region of Kirindy, this genus has a very unusual diet among lemurs, feeding heavily on gums and other exudates. Fork-marked lemurs feed especially on the gum exuded by trees of the genus *Terminalia* (Family Combretaceae) (called *Talinala* in Malagasy), which have suffered from attacks by beetle larvae boring between the wood and bark. Gums are usually eaten when they seep directly on the bark or exude from crevices, but they often bite at the bark to open up the insect galleries with their heavy, horizontal lower incisors and canines, which form a toothcomb specialized as a scraping tool. They have a long tongue to lick up the gums, and an enlarged (elongated) cecum where the relatively indigestible gums can be fermented. Gums may provide the bulk of the diet at certain times of the year (March–May) (Charles-Dominique and Petter, 1980). They also eat nectar, for example from the flowers of *Crateva greveana* (Capparidaceae) (Petter *et al.*, 1971, 1975), and the syrupy excretions of sap-feeding homopterans (Machaerotidae) on *Rhopalocarpus lucidus* (Rhopalocarpaceae) trees

Cheirogaleidae

(Charles-Dominique and Petter, 1980). They have long, sharpened nails which give them particular agility on large tree trunks and branches where they search for gums.

Compared to other cheirogaleids and indeed to most lemurs, members of the genus *Phaner* remain little studied and poorly known. Most of what is known about them comes from studies of the pale fork-marked lemur, *P. pallescens*, in the dry deciduous forests of the Kirindy region in southwestern Madagascar (Petter *et al.*, 1971, 1975; Pariente, 1974; Charles-Dominique and Petter, 1980; Hladik *et al.*, 1980; Schülke, 2003a, 2003b, 2005; Schülke and Kappeler, 2003; Schülke *et al.*, 2002, 2004).

CHIROGALI — *Chirogaleus*

Fig. 7.73: A plate from the 1863 book *Atlante Zoologico* by Boschi. The animal at lower left is a *Cheirogaleus* and the one at upper right is a fork-marked lemur (*Phaner*).

Fig. 7.74: *Phaner* **postural and behavioral drawings (next page):**
    a. *Phaner* **clinging sideways to a vertical branch**
    b. *Phaner* **in characteristic upside-down vertical clinging posture on a tree trunk**
    c. *Phaner* **walking quadrupedally on a branch**
    d. *Phaner* **eating gum on the trunk of a taly tree**
    e. *Phaner* **clinging vertically to a branch**
    f. *Phaner* **clinging sideways to a branch**
    g. *Phaner* **clinging sideways to the trunk of a tree**
    h. Close-up of *Phaner***'s specialized lower dentition, the "tooth-comb" used to gouge holes to feed on tree exudates**
    i. *Phaner* **in an upside-down vertical clinging posture feeding on tree exudates**

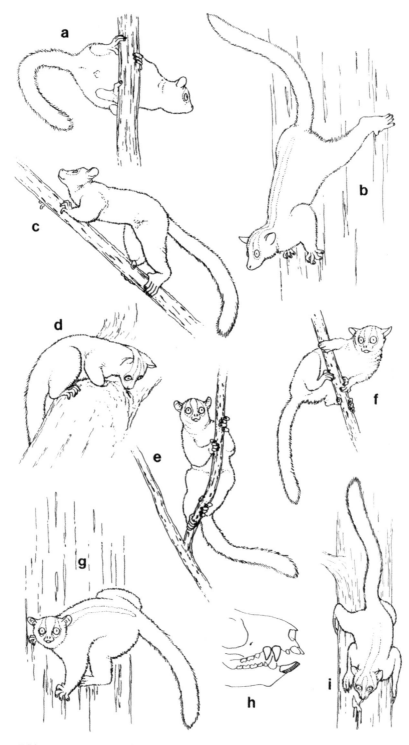

Fig. 7.74.

Cheirogaleidae

**Pale
Fork-marked Lemur**
Phaner pallescens

**Masoala
Fork-marked Lemur**
Phaner furcifer

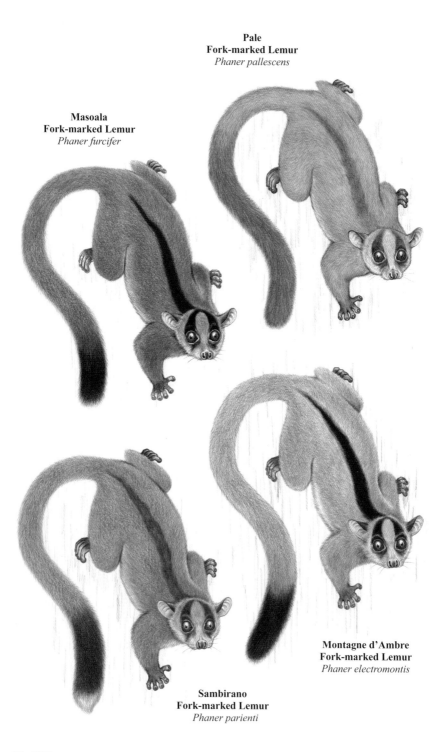

**Montagne d'Ambre
Fork-marked Lemur**
Phaner electromontis

**Sambirano
Fork-marked Lemur**
Phaner parienti

Fig. 7.75.

Fig. 7.76: Distribution of *Phaner*.

Cheirogaleidae

Phaner furcifer (de Blainville, 1839)
Masoala Fork-marked Lemur

Other English: Eastern Fork-marked Lemur
French: Phaner oriental, Lémurien à fourche oriental, Phaner à fourche oriental
German: Masoala Gabelstreifenmaki
Malagasy: Tantana, Tanta, Vakiandrina

Identification

Phaner furcifer is the darkest of the fork-marked lemur species, and has long, dense fur. The dorsal coat is dark brown and the underside creamy to buffy-gray. The markings on the crown are thick, black and distinct, and the dorsal midline stripe that emanates from the head does not reach the base of the tail. There are no published measurements or weights for this species. The hands and feet are also dark. As with all *Phaner*, location is the best indicator as to which species is being seen in the wild.

This species is sympatric with several other nocturnal lemur genera, including *Microcebus*, *Cheirogaleus*, and *Lepilemur*. However, it can readily be distinguished from *Microcebus* by its size, and from all others by its rapid movements, the forked pattern on the crown, the very loud and distinctive vocalizations, and the unusual head-bobbing movements, which are readily visible in the beam of a flashlight.

Geographic Range

Phaner furcifer is found in northeastern Madagascar from Toamasina (= Tamatave) north to and including the Masoala Peninsula. It inhabits tropical moist lowland forests from sea level to 1,000 m.

Natural History

As of 2010, the ecology and behavior of this species had not been studied.

Conservation Status

The most recent IUCN Red List assessment (2008) classified *P. furcifer* as Least Concern (LC). The principal threat to its survival is habitat loss due to slash-and-burn agriculture and illegal logging. However, it appears to be widely distributed and is reported from two national parks (Masoala and Zahamena), two strict nature reserves (Betampona and Zahamena), the Ambatovaky Special Reserve, and the forests of Makira, and it may occur in the Mananara-Nord National Park.

As of 2009, this species was not being kept in captivity (ISIS, 2009).

Cheirogaleidae

Where to See It

The Masoala fork-marked lemur is most easily seen in Masoala National Park, especially near the Lohatrozona campsite. Lodging is available on the mainland at Maraontsetra, notably in the excellent Relais du Masoala Ecolodge, and excursions to the Masoala Peninsula can be arranged through hotels in Maraontsetra or through an Antananarivo-based tour operator.

THE FORKED MOUSE-LEMUR ($\frac{1}{4}$ nat. size).

Fig. 7.77: A plate from Brehms' *Tierleben* (1860) depicting a fork-marked lemur.

Cheirogaleidae

Phaner pallescens Groves and Tattersall, 1991
Pale Fork-marked Lemur

Other English: Western Fork-marked Lemur
French: Phaner occidental, Lémurien à fourche occidental, Phaner pâle
German: Westlicher Gabelstreifenmaki
Malagasy: Tanta, Tantaraolana, Vakivoho

Identification

Phaner pallescens is the palest and possibly the smallest of the fork-marked lemurs. Tattersall (1982) reported head-body lengths ranging from 23–29 cm and tail lengths from 29–37 cm. Schülke (2003a) measured 18 adults: head-body length 26.3 ±0.9 cm; tail length 31.9 ±1.2 cm; and a weight of 327 ±1.2 g. Twelve animals from Zombitse (8) and Kirindy (4) measured by E. E. Louis Jr. (unpubl.) averaged 23.7 ±0.9 cm in head-body length; 32.1 ±1.3 cm in tail length, and 340 ±30 g in weight. The dorsal coat is light gray with a silvery sheen. The crown fork and the dorsal midline stripe are poorly defined, but the stripe does reach the rump. The terminal half to three-fourths of the tail is dark, as are the hands and feet. As with all *Phaner*, location is the best indicator as to which species is being seen in the wild.

This species is sympatric with several other nocturnal lemur genera, including *Microcebus*, *Cheirogaleus*, *Mirza*, and *Lepilemur*. However, it can readily be distinguished from *Microcebus* by its size, and from all others by its rapid movements, the forked pattern on the crown, the very loud and distinctive vocalizations, and the unusual head-bobbing movements, which are readily visible in the beam of a flashlight.

Geographic Range

The pale fork-marked lemur is patchily distributed along a narrow strip of western Madagascar forests from just south of the Fiherenana River, including the Forêts de Mikea (Ganzhorn and Randriamanalina, 2004), north as far as Soalala (Groves and Tattersall, 1991), and it also occurs in the very important forest of Kirindy. It inhabits lowland forests from sea level to 800 m. Fork-marked lemurs have also been recorded calling in and around Parcel 2 of Andohahela National Park in the southeast of the country, but it is not known whether the form in question is *P. pallescens*, *Phaner furcifer*, or an undescribed species (Feistner and Schmid, 1999).

Natural History

This is the best-studied of the four *Phaner* species. It is found in tropical dry deciduous forests and can even survive in exotic tree plantations. Population density estimates derived from studies in the Kirindy Forest and from Marosalaza are consistent at about 50–70 individuals/km² (Charles-Dominique and Petter, 1980), but Ausilio and Raveloarinoro (1993) estimated densities of 300–400

Fig. 7.78: Pale fork-marked lemur (*Phaner pallescens*), Kirindy (photo by J. Zaonarivelo).

individuals/km² in the forests of Tsimembo. Family groups, consisting of an adult pair and their offspring, occupy and defend territories ranging from 3–10 ha (Schülke, 2003a), but the adults spend very little time together (Schülke and Kappeler, 2003). The male has a large cutaneous throat gland (see Fig. 7.79), which he rubs on the head, shoulders, and the back of the female in a stereotypical manner during social grooming (Charles-Dominique and Petter, 1980; Ganzhorn and Kappeler, 1996). To avoid competition with other nocturnal lemurs, this species tends to use the highest sleeping sites, taking shelter in tree holes and leaf nests constructed by the sympatric *Mirza coquereli* (Kappeler, 2003; Schülke, 2003a).

Figs. 7.79 and 7.80 (next page): Two views of a fork-marked dwarf lemur (*Phaner pallescens*), Kirindy Forest (photo by R. A. Mittermeier). Note the large cutaneous gland in the throat of the male above.

Phaner pallescens has an unusual diet with a high percentage of tree exudates. It is well adapted to its specialized diet, having a long tongue, an elongated cecum and nearly horizontal lower front incisors and canines that serve as scrapers. At Kirindy, two species of *Terminalia* trees provide the bulk of the exudates eaten by *Phaner*. Apparently, this food provides a good source of protein, to the point that invertebrate prey is not sought to the same degree that it is by other cheirogaleids (Hladik *et al.*, 1980). Females appear to be dominant to males in terms of access to feeding sites. Predators of *P. pallescens* include the fossa (*Cryptoprocta ferox*), the Madagascar Buzzard (*Buteo brachypterus*) and

Fig. 7.80.

Fig. 7.81: Pale fork-marked lemur (*Phaner pallescens*) from Analabe, in the Menabe region of southwestern Madagascar, photographed in 1985 (photo by R. A. Mittermeier).

the Madagascar Cuckoo-hawk (*Aviceda madagascariensis*) (Rasoloarison *et al*., 1995; Goodman, 2003). Schülke (2003a) believes that Madagascar Harrier-hawks (*Polyboroides radiatus*) take *Phaner* from their sleeping holes, using their long legs to investigate hollow trees and crevices (Langrand, 1990; Gilbert and Tingay, 2001).

Communication within and between groups is largely vocal and frequent. At least four different types of calls have been identified (Charles-Dominique and Petter, 1980). Females tend to be dominant in contacts with strange males from neighboring groups (Schülke, 2003a). Fork-marked lemurs generally leave their sleeping sites just before dusk and they are most active (including vocalizing) in the first hour after sunset. Early studies of *Phaner* reproductive behavior (Petter *et al*., 1971, 1975) suggest a much earlier onset of mating activities than those more recently observed by Schülke (2003a), but a single infant appears to be born during the austral summer.

Conservation Status

The most recent IUCN Red List assessment (2008) classified *P. pallescens* as Least Concern (LC). The principal threats to its survival are habitat loss due to illegal logging, annual burning to create pasture, and slash-and-burn agriculture. *Phaner pallescens* is reported to occur in three national parks (Tsingy de Bemaraha, Tsingy de Namoroka, and Zombitse-Vohibasia), the Tsingy de Bemaraha Strict Nature Reserve, and the Andranomena Special Reserve. Reports of this species from the region of Andohahela National Park remain unconfirmed. Of particular importance to its survival is the Menabe-Antimena Protected Area, which has within it the Kirindy Forest Station.

As of 2009, this species was not being kept in captivity (ISIS, 2009).

Where to See It

Phaner pallescens is most easily seen in the Kirindy Forest north of Morondava, where it is common, and in the Zombitse-Vohibasia National Park. The CNFEREF Ecotourism Station in Kirindy is an especially good site and now has bungalow accommodations available. Excursions to Kirindy can be arranged through the Hotel Chez Maggie or the Baobab Hotel in Morondava.

Fig. 7.82: Fork-marked dwarf lemur from Zombitse-Vohibasia National Park; presumably
Phaner pallescens, but its identity is uncertain (photo by R. A. Mittermeier).

Fig. 7.83: Pale fork-marked dwarf lemur (*Phaner pallescens*) in the Kirindy Forest (photo by R. A. Mittermeier).

Phaner parienti Groves and Tattersall, 1991
Sambirano Fork-marked Lemur

Other English: Pariente's Fork-marked Lemur
French: Phaner de Pariente, Lémurien à fourche de Pariente
German: Sambirano-Gabelstreifenmaki
Malagasy: Tanta, Valvihy

Identification

Phaner parienti is darker than *Phaner pallescens* to the south and *Phaner electromontis* to the north. The dorsal coat is dark brown, while the ventral coat is buffy and often tinted with red. The crown fork is broad, black, well defined, and continuous with the dorsal midline stripe that extends to the base of the tail. The distal third of the tail is also dark, but sometimes tipped with white (Groves, 2001). There are no published weights or measurements available for this species, but three animals (one male and two females) from Antafondro measured by E. E. Louis Jr. (unpubl.) averaged 23.8 ±0.9 cm in head-body length; 40.1 ±1.8 cm in tail length, and 360 ±50 g in weight. As with all *Phaner*, location is the best indicator as to which species is being seen in the wild.

The Sambirano fork-marked lemur is sympatric with several other nocturnal lemurs, including *Microcebus*, *Cheirogaleus*, and *Lepilemur*. However, it can readily be distinguished from *Microcebus* by its size, and from all others by its rapid movements, the forked pattern on the crown, the very loud and distinctive vocalizations, and the unusual head-bobbing movements, which are readily visible in the beam of a flashlight.

Geographic Range

Phaner parienti inhabits tropical moist lowland forests from sea level to 800 m in the Sambirano region of northwest Madagascar south of Ambanja, with a range that includes the Ampasindava Peninsula and extends south to the Andranomalaza River. It can also survive in remnant forest canopies that shade coffee plantations (U. Thalmann, pers. comm.).

Natural History

As of 2010, this species had not been studied in the wild.

Conservation Status

The most recent IUCN Red List assessment (2008) classified *P. parienti* as Vulnerable (VU). The principal threat is habitat destruction due to slash-and-burn agriculture, in some cases for the illegal growing of *Cannabis*. The species is reported to occur in the Tsaratanana Strict Nature Reserve and the Manongarivo Special Reserve, but neither is well protected at this time. Significant tracts of suitable forest habitat remain within its range, and these should be the focus of efforts to expand and link existing protected areas.

As of 2009, this species was not being kept in captivity (ISIS, 2009).

Where to See It

This species is most readily seen in the forests of Beraty, west of RN6 about 45 km south of Ambanja, and in forests along the road between Ambanja and Benavony. Excursions to Beraty and the Ambanja area can be arranged by tour operators based in Antsiranana (= Diégo-Suarez) or Nosy Be. There is basic accommodation in Ambanja and two good hotels at Ankify nearby. Intact forests on the the Ampasindava Peninsula are also a possibility, although finding the animals there is by no means certain.

Fig. 7.84: A Sambirano fork-marked lemur (*Phaner parienti*), along the road between Benavony and Ambanja (photo by R. A. Mittermeier). This is the only available photo of this species.

Cheirogaleidae

Phaner electromontis Groves and Tattersall, 1991
Montagne d' Ambre Fork-marked Lemur

Other English: Amber Mountain Fork-marked Lemur
French: Phaner de la Montagne d'Ambre, Lémurien à fourche de
la Montagne d'Ambre
German: Montagne d' Ambre-Gabelstreifenmaki
Malagasy: Tanta

Identification

Phaner electromontis is a light gray species of fork-marked lemur. There are no
published body measurements available for this species, but three animals from Montagne
d'Ambre (one male and two females) measured by E. E. Louis Jr. (unpubl.) averaged 27.2
±0.4 cm in head-body length; 34.4 ±0.2 cm in tail length, and 387 ±35 g in weight. The
dorsal and ventral coats are light gray. The crown fork is thick and black, and a well-
defined dorsal midline stripe extends all the way to the rump. The distal third of the tail
is dark, as are the hands and feet. As with all *Phaner*, location is the best indication as to
which species is being seen in the wild.

This species is sympatric with several other nocturnal lemurs, including *Microcebus*,
Cheirogaleus, and *Lepilemur*. However, it can readily be distinguished from *Microcebus*
by its size, and from all others by its rapid movements, the forked pattern on the crown, the
very loud and distinctive vocalizations, and the unusual head-bobbing movements, which
are readily visible in the beam of a flashlight.

Geographic Range

The Montagne d'Ambre fork-marked lemur is restricted
to northern Madagascar in the region of Montagne d'Ambre
and Ankarana, where it inhabits both tropical moist forest
and dry forest. Fork-marked lemurs also occur in the
Daraina area, but it remains to be determined whether they
are *P. electromontis* or a new species.

Natural History

In the region of Montagne d'Ambre, population densities
are reported to be high (Ganzhorn *et al.*, 1997). However, as
of 2010, this species had not been studied in detail.

Conservation Status

The most recent IUCN Red List assessment (2008)
classified *P. electromontis* as Vulnerable (VU). The principal
threat is localized habitat loss due to annual burning. It is
common in Montagne d'Ambre National Park, and present

as well in Ankarana National Park, two special reserves (Analamerana and Forêt d'Ambre),
and in the Sahafary Classified Forest (Nicoll and Langrand, 1989; Hawkins *et al.*, 1990; A.
Razafimanantsoa, pers. comm.). It is possible that the unidentified *Phaner* first seen in the
region of Daraina (now the Loky-Manambato Protected Area) by Mittermeier in 1995 is
this form, but it is more likely that it is an entirely new species.

As of 2009, this species was not being kept in captivity (ISIS, 2009).

Where to See It

Phaner electromontis is most easily seen in Montagne d'Ambre National Park and in the Forêt d'Ambre Special Reserve, where it is quite common. Particularly good sites include the forestry station (Les Roussettes) and botanical garden of the Montagne d'Ambre National Park. There are now two excellent lodges at Montagne d'Ambre, Domaine de Fontenay and the Nature Lodge, and the park is easily reached by car from Antsiranana (= Diégo-Suarez), a trip of about 45 minutes.

Cheirogaleidae

Fig. 7.85: Above: *Phaner electromontis* from Montagne d'Ambre. Below: *Phaner electromontis* or an as-yet-unnamed species from Daraina (photos by E. E. Louis Jr.).

Lepilemuridae

Fig. 8.1: White-footed sportive lemur (*Lepilemur leucopus*) in a daytime sleeping site, Berenty Private Reserve (photo by R. A. Mittermeier).

CHAPTER 8

FAMILY LEPILEMURIDAE Gray, 1870

Most previous authors placed the sportive lemurs of the genus *Lepilemur* in the separate family Lepilemuridae. Groves (2001) placed *Lepilemur* together with the extinct giant lemur, genus *Megaladapis*, in the Megaladapidae but, based on recent genetic analyses (Yoder *et al.*, 1999b; Karanth *et al.*, 2005), other experts have decided that the relationship between these two lineages is not as close as Groves indicated, and have gone back to separating out the Lepilemuridae. We prefer this arrangement, and return to recognizing Lepilemuridae as separate from the Megaladapidae, and containing a single genus, *Lepilemur*.

Lepilemur I. Geoffroy, 1851
Sportive Lemurs

The genus *Lepilemur* contains at least 26 named species, most of which have been described in the past ten years. All are medium-sized, largely folivorous, and nocturnal. Sportive lemurs generally weigh less than one kilogram and are approximately half a meter in length, including the tail. They are vertical clingers and leapers, with legs that are elongated compared to their trunks and arms. The face of *Lepilemur* is covered with short hairs. Its identification in the field would most likely be confused with the genus *Avahi*, another medium-sized, nocturnal lemur, but sportive lemurs tend to be a bit smaller, have more prominent ears, and lack the highly visible white patches on the back of the thighs that are so typical of *Avahi*. *Avahi* also has a strong tendency to huddle tightly with family members in clusters of two to four animals, sometimes even during the night when they are active. *Lepilemur* will do this in its daytime sleeping sites, but rarely at night, making this behavior a reasonably good field characteristic. At first glance, or in poor viewing conditions, *Lepilemur* may also be confused with the larger dwarf lemurs, especially *Cheirogaleus major* and *Cheirogaleus crossleyi* in Madagascar's eastern rain forests. However, *Lepilemur* is a vertical clinger and leaper, whereas *Cheirogaleus* moves quadrupedally, and *Cheirogaleus* species usually have a contrasting white belly. Sportive lemurs can also be readily differentiated from most other nocturnal lemur species by their loud screams, except for *Phaner* which vocalizes even more loudly. However, this field character is useful only at certain times of the year, when these animals are vocally active.

Sportive lemurs are the smallest of the folivorous primates (Ganzhorn, 1993). Leaves constitute the bulk of the diet, with flowers, buds, and sometimes fruit taking on greater importance toward the end of the dry season. Most populations appear to inhabit low- and mid-altitude evergreen and deciduous forests. Most of what is known about *Lepilemur* ecology and behavior comes from studies of western and southern species. During the day, sportive lemurs routinely take shelter and sleep in tree holes or tangles of branches, vines, or lianas, and sometimes can be seen resting in the fork of a tree if such shelters are not available. *Lepilemur ruficaudatus* and *Lepilemur edwardsi* live in pairs (Ganzhorn and Kappeler, 1996; Thalmann, 2001; Zinner *et al.*, 2003). The social behavior of the other *Lepilemur* remains unclear and may vary between species. Significant differences in vocal behavior are very apparent, with rain forest species being relatively silent (Petter *et al.*, 1977) while those from more open, drier forests are more vociferous.

The taxonomy of *Lepilemur* has been fairly complicated over the past 50 years, and continues to be interesting. Petter and Petter-Rousseaux (1960) recognized a single species, *Lepilemur mustelinus*, with five subspecies, but Petter *et al.* (1977) increased this to seven species, with one (*Lepilemur septentrionalis*) having four subspecies. Tattersall (1982) provisionally recognized a single species (*L. mustelinus*) with six subspecies, but later concurred with Jenkins (1987) that the genus was represented by seven distinct species. This arrangement was supported by at least one genetic analysis (Ishak *et al.*, 1992) and was accepted by most authors in the 1990s (e.g., Mittermeier *et al.*, 1994).

Rumpler *et al.* (2001), investigating the cytogenetics of *L. septentrionalis*, identified karyotypes attributable to two species—*L. septentrionalis* and *L. andrafiamensis*—each with two subspecies and with no evidence of hybridization between populations. Groves (2001), in contrast, regarded this assemblage as two subspecies of *L. septentrionalis*—*L. s. septentrionalis* to the north and *L. s. ankaranensis* from the forests of Ankarana and Andrafiamena to the south and west—and suggested that the name *ankaranensis* has priority over Rumpler's *andrafiamensis*. Subsequently, Ravoarimanana *et al.* (2004) and Rumpler (2004) presented data regarding the geographic range of these taxa, elevating these two forms to species and suggesting that the range of *L. septentrionalis* was restricted to the forests of Sahafary, a very tiny area in the far eastern part of the range of northern *Lepilemur*.

In the previous edition of this field guide (2006) we recognized eight full species. Since that time a number of scientific papers have been published, and the taxonomy of the genus has been extensively revised, resulting in an explosion of new species. In 2006, Louis *et al.* described an incredible 11 new species in a single paper—*Lepilemur fleuretae*, *Lepilemur seali*, *Lepilemur betsileo*, *Lepilemur wrightae*, *Lepilemur jamesorum*, *Lepilemur ahmansonorum*, *Lepilemur hubbardorum*, *Lepilemur petteri*, *Lepilemur grewcockorum*, *Lepilemur tymerlachsonorum*, and *Lepilemur milanoii*. That same year, Andriaholinirina *et al.*, described a further three species (*Lepilemur. aeeclis*, *Lepilemur randrianasoloi* and *Lepilemur sahamalazensis*), and Rabarivola *et al.* described *Lepilemur mittermeieri*. In 2007, Craul *et al.* described two more new species (*Lepilemur otto* and *Lepilemur manasamody*), in 2008, Lei *et al.* described *Lepilemur scottorum*, and most recently, in 2009, Ramaromilanto *et al.* described *Lepilemur. hollandorum*. *Lepilemur manasamody* has since been synonymized with *L. grewcockorum* (Zinner *et al.*, 2007). There is also some dispute over the precise taxonomy of the forms from the region of Nosy Be and the nearby mainland, which has not yet been resolved. However, the net result has been a tripling of species in this genus since the publication of the last edition of this field guide in 2006. We now recognize 26 species, and anticipate that more may be described in the years to come.

Lepilemuridae

Lepilemuridae

Fig. 8.2: Ankarana sportive lemur (*Lepilemur ankaranensis*), Ankarana National Park (photo by R. Andriantompohavana).

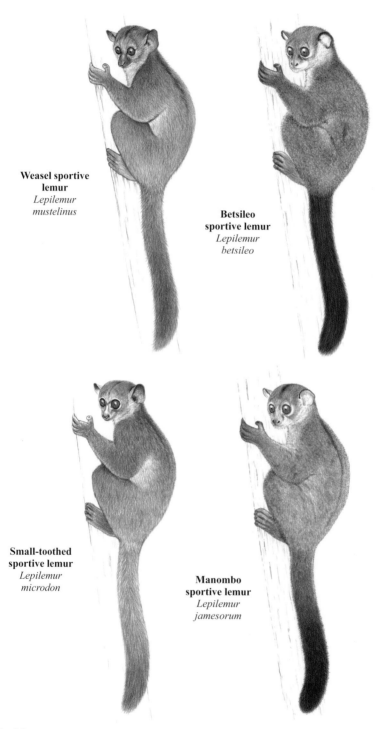

**Weasel sportive
lemur**
*Lepilemur
mustelinus*

**Betsileo
sportive lemur**
*Lepilemur
betsileo*

**Small-toothed
sportive lemur**
*Lepilemur
microdon*

**Manombo
sportive lemur**
*Lepilemur
jamesorum*

Fig. 8.3.

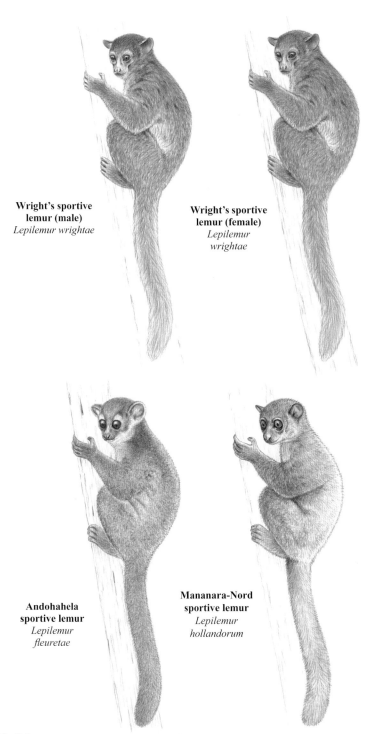

Wright's sportive lemur (male)
Lepilemur wrightae

Wright's sportive lemur (female)
Lepilemur wrightae

Andohahela sportive lemur
Lepilemur fleuretae

Mananara-Nord sportive lemur
Lepilemur hollandorum

Lepilemuridae

Fig. 8.4.

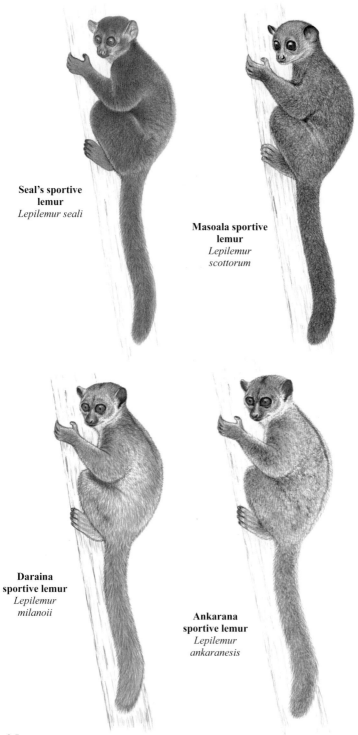

Seal's sportive lemur
Lepilemur seali

Masoala sportive lemur
Lepilemur scottorum

Daraina sportive lemur
Lepilemur milanoii

Ankarana sportive lemur
Lepilemur ankaranesis

Fig. 8.5.

**Sahafary
sportive lemur**
*Lepilemur
septentrionalis*

**Gray's
sportive lemur**
*Lepilemur
dorsalis*

**Nosy Be sportive
lemur**
*Lepilemur
tymerlachsonorum*

**Mittermeier's
sportive lemur**
*Lepilemur
mittermeieri*

Fig. 8.6.

Lepilemuridae

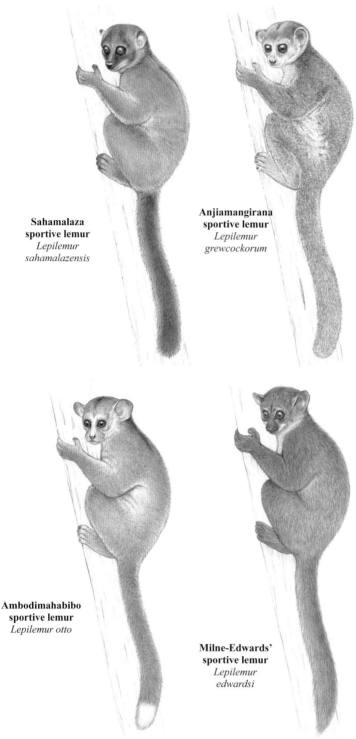

**Sahamalaza
sportive lemur**
*Lepilemur
sahamalazensis*

**Anjiamangirana
sportive lemur**
*Lepilemur
grewcockorum*

**Ambodimahabibo
sportive lemur**
Lepilemur otto

**Milne-Edwards'
sportive lemur**
*Lepilemur
edwardsi*

Fig. 8.7.

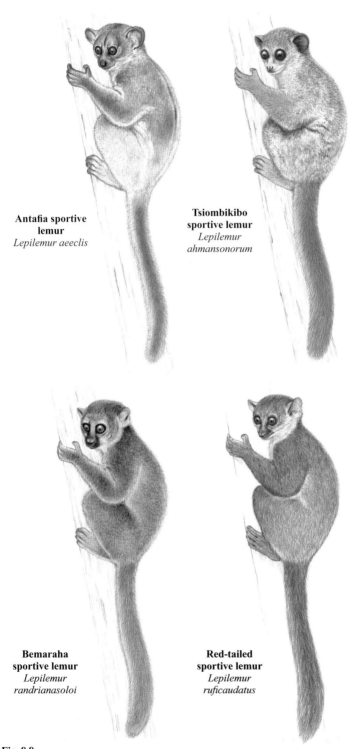

Antafia sportive lemur
Lepilemur aeeclis

Tsiombikibo sportive lemur
Lepilemur ahmansonorum

Bemaraha sportive lemur
Lepilemur randrianasoloi

Red-tailed sportive lemur
Lepilemur ruficaudatus

Fig. 8.8.

Lepilemuridae

Lepilemuridae

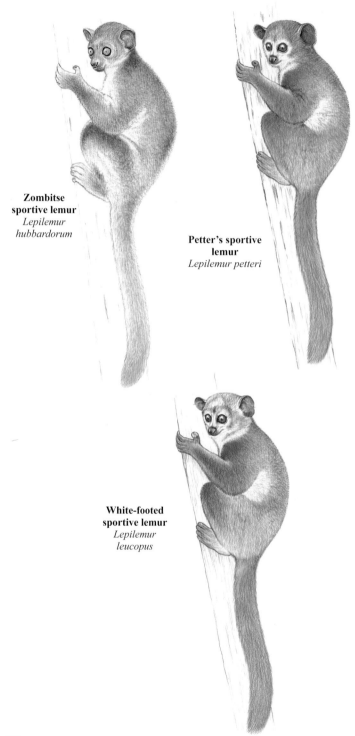

**Zombitse
sportive lemur**
*Lepilemur
hubbardorum*

**Petter's sportive
lemur**
Lepilemur petteri

**White-footed
sportive lemur**
*Lepilemur
leucopus*

Fig. 8.9.

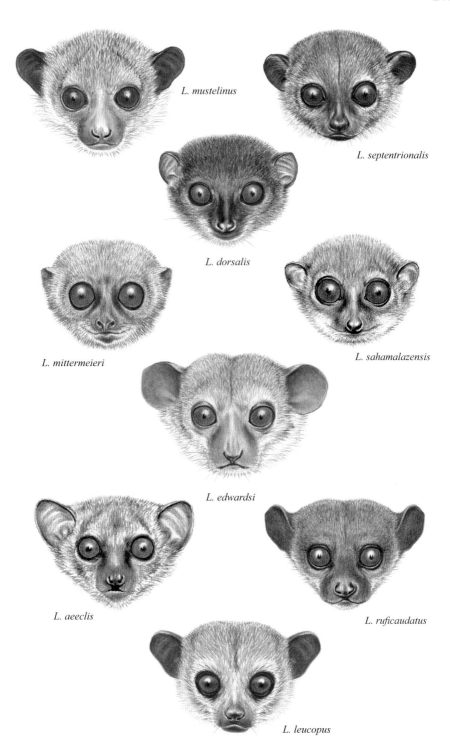

L. mustelinus

L. septentrionalis

L. dorsalis

L. mittermeieri

L. sahamalazensis

L. edwardsi

L. aeeclis

L. ruficaudatus

L. leucopus

Fig. 8.10: Portraits of several *Lepilemur* species.

Soul pinx.   *Imprimerie Nationale.*   *L.Léchaudel lith.*

Lepilemur mustelinus, var. leucopus.

Fig. 8.11: *Lepilemur leucopus* from Volume 10 of Alfred Grandidier's *Histoire Physique, Naturelle et Politique de Madagascar*, published in Paris in 1875.

Fig. 8.12: *Lepilemur* postural and behavioral drawings (next page):
    a. *Lepilemur* in an aggressive posture
    b. *Lepilemur* resting in a daytime sleeping site in the fork of a tree
    c. *Lepilemur* peering out from a daytime sleeping hole
    d. Mother and infant *Lepilemur* resting in a vertical clinging posture
    e-f. *Lepilemur* leaping and twisting in mid-air from a vertical clinging posture
    g. *Lepilemur* in a resting posture
    h-k. Sequence of images showing *Lepilemur* landing on a vertical trunk
    l. Side view of head

Fig. 8.12.

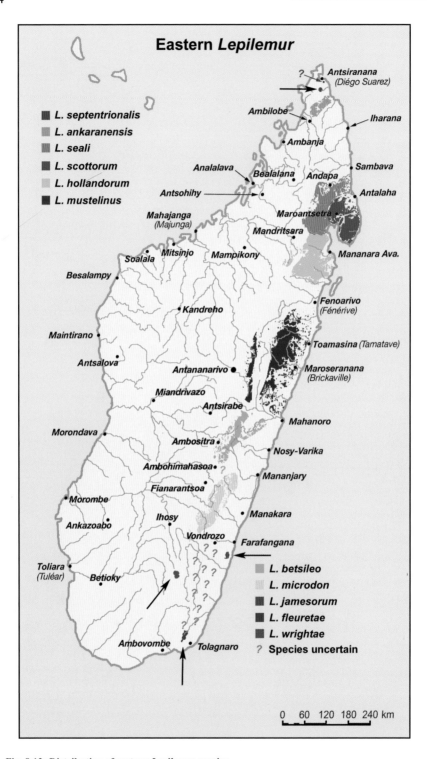

Fig. 8.13: Distribution of eastern *Lepilemur* species.

Fig. 8.14: Distribution of western and southern *Lepilemur* species.

Lepilemur mustelinus I. Geoffroy, 1851
Weasel Sportive Lemur

Other English: Greater Sportive Lemur, Weasel Lemur, Greater
Weasel Lemur
French: Lépilémur
German: Westlicher Wieselmaki
Malagasy: Hataka, Trangalava, Kotrika, Fitiliky, Kotriana

Lepilemuridae

Identification

Lepilemur mustelinus is a large sportive lemur with a head-body length of 26–30 cm, a
tail length of 25–29 cm, a total length of 51–59 cm, and a weight of about 1 kg (Harcourt
and Thornback, 1990; Louis *et al.*, 2006b; Garbutt, 2007; Lei *et al.*, 2008). The fur is rather
long and dense, being a variable chestnut-brown dorsally, and often with a dark midline
stripe. The face is gray or brown, the cheeks, throat and abdomen a bit lighter. The tail
darkens toward the tip.

There are also cases of bright orange *L. mustelinus* with populations of naturally colored
members of these species. See, for example, Figure 8.16, which depicts an individual from
the Anamalazaotra Special Reserve at Andasibe (G. Davies, pers. comm.).

This species is most likely to be confused with the similar-sized *Avahi*, which also
adopts a vertical clinging posture, and to a lesser extent with *Cheirogaleus*, which moves
about quadrupedally. Closer observation will reveal that the weasel sportive lemur has
prominent ears and lacks the white thigh patches of *Avahi*, and that it is significantly larger
than *Cheirogaleus* and moves about by leaping.

Geographic Range

The weasel sportive lemur is found in the rain forests
of eastern Madagascar from the Nesivolo and Mangoro
rivers north at least to the Maningory River. Additional
survey work is required to determine the northern and
southern extent of the distribution, particularly in light of
discoveries of new species within the larger area in which it
was previously thought to occur.

Natural History

Although this species is widespread and apparently
common throughout its eastern rain forest range, it is not
well studied in the wild. Ratsirarson and Rumpler (1988)
reported that it occupies territories of 1.5 ha, and that it
sleeps in tree holes 6–12 m above the ground during the dry
season. It takes shelter during the day in tangles of vines
and leaves during the wet season. *L. mustelinus* is solitary
and eats leaves, flowers, and fruits (Ganzhorn, 1988). It
also seems to be out-competed by *Avahi* for leaves of high
nutritional value, subsisting on leaves of lower nutritional value and eating foods with high
levels of alkaloids.

Fig. 8.15: Weasel sportive lemur (*Lepilemur mustelinus*), Analamazaotra Special Reserve, Andasibe (photo by R. A. Mittermeier).

Conservation Status

There is insufficient information to determine the conservation status of *L. mustelinus*, and the latest IUCN Red List assessment (2008) classified it as Data Deficient (DD). Many questions still remain regarding its overall distribution and relationship to *L. microdon* and other species. The main threats are habitat destruction (for slash-and-burn agriculture) and hunting. This species is reported to occur in two national parks (Mantadia and Zahamena), two strict nature reserves (Betampona and Zahamena) and in the Analamazaotra Special Reserve at Andasibe (Nicoll and Langrand, 1989; Safford *et al.*, 1989; Schmid and Smolker, 1998; Britt *et al.*, 1999).

As of 2009, this species was not being kept in captivity (ISIS, 2009).

Where to See It

It is possible to find the weasel sportive lemur in the protected areas listed above, but there is no single site that ensures encountering it in the wild. As with other *Lepilemur* species, this form is located by its eyeshine in your flashlight beam at night, but can also be located during the day in sleeping sites that are sometimes only a few meters above the ground. The use of experienced local guides is highly recommended, since they usually know of regularly used sleeping holes or vine tangles that offer good viewing conditions.

Fig. 8.16: An unusual orange variant of the weasel sportive lemur (*Lepilemur mustelinus*), Anamalazaotra Special Reserve, Andasibe (photo by G. Davies).

Lepilemuridae

Fig. 8.17: Weasel sportive lemur (*Lepilemur mustelinus*), Mantadia National Park (photo by H. N. T. Randriahaingo)

Lepilemur betsileo Louis *et al.*, 2006
Betsileo Sportive Lemur

Other English: None
French: Lépilémur du Betsileo
German: Betsileo-Wieselmaki
Malagasy: Hataka, Trangalava, Kotrika, Fitiliky, Kotriana

Identification

Lepilemur betsileo is a large sportive lemur, with a head-body length of 25 cm, a tail length of 28 cm, a total length of 53 cm, and an approximate weight of 1.1–1.2 kg. The color pattern is predominantly grayish to reddish-brown, the fur being a mixture of dark to light gray and reddish-brown, and darker dorsally than ventrally. The tail is black and contrasts sharply with the rest of the body. The anterior portion of the mandible is white, with the remainder of the face being gray. The fur in the ear pinna is noticeably lighter and bordered by dark brown to black along the outer edge (Louis *et al.*, 2006b).

Geographic Range

This species is currently known only from the Fandriana region of central-eastern Madagascar. The southern and northern extents of the range need to be determined, but are believed to be the Mangoro and Namorona rivers (Louis *et al.*, 2006b).

Natural History

As of 2010, this species had not been studied in the wild.

Conservation Status

There is insufficient information to determine the conservation status of this species and the latest IUCN Red List assessment (2008) classified it as Data Deficient (DD).

As of 2010, this species was not being kept in captivity (I. J. Porton, pers. comm.).

Where to See It

At this time, the only place to look for this species is in the Fandriana Classified Forest.

Lepilemuridae

Fig. 8.18: Betsileo sportive lemur (*Lepilemur betsileo*), Fandriana Classified Forest (photo by E. E. Louis Jr.).

Lepilemur microdon (Forsyth Major, 1894)
Small-toothed Sportive Lemur

Other English: Small-toothed Weasel Lemur
French: Lépilemur aux petits dents
German: Kleinzahn-Wieselmaki
Malagasy: Fitiliky, Hataka, Trangalavaka, Kotrika

Identification

Lepilemur microdon is a large sportive lemur with a head-body length of 27–32 cm, a tail length of 25–29 cm, a total length of 55–64 cm, and a body weight of 900 g–1.2 kg (Louis *et al.*, 2006b; Garbutt, 2007). The dorsal coat is thick and reddish-brown, and sports a dark midline stripe, while the underside, including the face and neck, are a pale gray-brown, sometimes with a yellowish tinge on the abdomen. The forelimbs and shoulders are a rich chestnut-brown, and the tail darkens toward the tip. This species is very similar in appearance to *L. mustelinus*, and indeed the two are almost impossible to distinguish under field conditions, making geographic location the best means of identifying individuals seen in the wild.

This species is most likely to be confused with the similar-sized *Avahi*, which also adopts a vertical clinging posture, and to a lesser extent with *Cheirogaleus*, which moves about quadrupedally. Closer observation will reveal that the small-toothed sportive lemur has prominent ears and lacks the white thigh patches of *Avahi*, and that it is significantly larger than *Cheirogaleus* and moves about by leaping.

Geographic Range

Southeastern Madagascar. The range of this species currently appears to extend in a northeast to southwest trajectory from Ranomafana National Park to Andringitra National Park (Louis *et al.*, 2006b). However, the relationships between the various *Lepilemur* taxa of southeastern Madagascar are in need of much further study, and what is presented here in terms of range must be considered tentative and likely to be modified in the near future.

Natural History

The small-toothed sportive lemur is nocturnal and solitary, and spends its days asleep hidden in a tree cavity or in a tangle of vines and leaves. It feeds on leaves, fruits, and flowers (Ganzhorn, 1988). Petter *et al.* (1977) pointed out that this species and *L. mustelinus,* both of which inhabit densely vegetated eastern rain forests, appear to vocalize far less than do sportive lemurs of more open and drier forested regions.

Lepilemuridae

Conservation Status

There is insufficient information to determine the conservation status of *L. microdon* and the latest IUCN Red List assessment (2008) classified it as Data Deficient (DD). It is reported to occur in two national parks (Andringitra and Ranomafana). It is also provisionally listed as occurring in Midongy du Sud National Park in the extreme south of its range, though the population there may perhaps be *L. fleuretae*.

As of 2009, this species was not being kept in captivity (ISIS, 2009).

Where to See It

Small-toothed sportive lemurs are most easily seen in Ranomafana National Park in the Vohiparara region. Although tourists typically do not visit this region of the park, arrangements for nocturnal hikes can be arranged with local guides at the park headquarters.

Fig. 8.19: Small-toothed sportive lemur (*Lepilemur microdon*), Vohiparara, Ranomafana National Park (photo by E. E. Louis Jr.).

Lepilemuridae

Lepilemur jamesorum Louis *et al.*, **2006**
Manombo Sportive Lemur

Other English: James' Sportive Lemur
French: Lépilémur de Manombo, Lépilémur de James
German: James' Wieselmaki
Malagasy: Hataka, Trangalava, Kotrika, Fitiliky, Kotriana

Identification

Lepilemur jamesorum is a medium-sized sportive lemur with a head-body length of 26 cm, a tail length of 30 cm, a total length of 56 cm, and a body weight of 780 g (Louis *et al.*, 2006b). The pelage is short and smooth, being generally brown above and a lighter grayish-brown on the belly and ventral surface of the extremities. The tail is brown proximally, gradually becoming a darker brown to black distally. The face is demarcated into a mask, with whitish-gray markings along the jaw and throat from the chin to the ears, while the dorsum of the head is brown with a black midline that is continuous for almost the entire length of the body. The ears are large and cup-shaped, gray dorsally with black borders and (usually) a small cream-colored patch on the region beneath (Louis *et al.*, 2006b).

Geographic Range

Southeastern Madagascar. This species is currently known from the Manombo Special Reserve, south of the Manampatrana River and north of the Mananara River. Additional survey work is required to determine the northern and southern boundaries of the range (Louis *et al.*, 2006b).

Natural History

This species is known to inhabit one of the few remaining, low-altitude coastal rain forests of the region (Louis *et al.*, 2006b). However, as of 2010, there had been no field studies of this species.

Conservation Status

There is insufficient information to determine the conservation status of *L. jamesorum*, the latest IUCN Red List assessment (2008) classified it as Data Deficient (DD). It is known to occur in one protected area, the Manombo Special Reserve (Louis *et al.* 2006b), though it is not present in the adjacent Agnalahaza Forest (S. E. Johnson, pers. comm.).

As of 2010, this species was not being kept in captivity (I. J. Porton, pers. comm.).

Where to See It

At present, the only place to see this species is in the Manombo Special Reserve.

Fig. 8.20: Manombo sportive lemur (*Lepilemur jamesorum*), Manombo Special Reserve (photo by R. Randrianampionona).

Lepilemur wrightae **Louis *et al.*, 2006**
Wright's Sportive Lemur

Other English: Kalambatritra Sportive Lemur
French: Lépilémur de Wright
German: Wright's Wieselmaki
Malagasy: Hataka, Trangalava, Kotrika, Fitiliky, Kotriana

Identification

Lepilemur wrightae is a large sportive lemur, notable for its sexual dimorphism, which is so far unique in this genus. The head-body length is 24–26 cm, the tail length is 25–26 cm, the total length is 49–52 cm, and the body weight is 950–1,100 g (Louis *et al.*, 2006b). In both sexes the dorsum is a diffuse, reddish-brown and gray color and the underside a lighter grayish-brown. The head of the female, however, is a sharply contrasting uniform gray, whereas in the male the head and upper body are similarly colored. Moreover, in some females there is a slight color change around the face that forms a mask-like appearance. The ears in both males and females have minimal to short fur and are lighter in color (Louis *et al.*, 2006b; Lei *et al.*, 2008).

Geographic Range

Southeastern Madagascar. This species is currently known only from Kalambatritra Special Reserve, west of the Ionaivo River, east of the Mangoky River, and north of the Mandrare River. Further studies need to be conducted to determine the limits of its distribution (Louis *et al.*, 2006b).

Natural History

As of 2010, this species had not been studied in the wild.

Conservation Status

There is insufficient information to determine the conservation status of *L. wrightae*, and the latest IUCN Red List assessment (2008) classified it as Data Deficient (DD). It is known to occur in one protected area, the Kalambatritra Special Reserve (Louis *et al.*, 2006b).

As of 2010, this species was not being kept in captivity (I. J. Porton, pers. comm.).

Where to See It

At present, the only place to see this species is in the Kalambatritra Special Reserve.

Fig. 8.21: Female Wright's sportive lemur (*Lepilemur wrightae*), Kalambatritra Special Reserve (photo by E. E. Louis Jr.). Note the contrasting grey head.

Lepilemur fleuretae Louis *et al.*, 2006
Andohahela Sportive Lemur

Other English: Fleurette's Sportive Lemur
French: Lépilémur du Andohahela, Lépilémur de Fleurette
German: Fleurette's Wieselmaki
Malagasy: Hataka, Trangalava, Kotrika, Fitiliky, Kotriana

Identification

Lepilemur fleuretae is a medium-sized sportive lemur with a head-body length of 24–26 cm, a tail length of 27–30 cm, a total length of 51–56 cm, and a weight of 800–980 g (Louis *et al.*, 2006b). The pelage is predominantly gray above, lighter brownish-gray below, with a grayish-brown mixture along the proximal portion of the extremities and some light brown along the lateral edges of the belly. The fur is noticeably lighter over the eyelids than on the rest of the face. A diffuse stripe runs along the midline, starting from the forehead and continuing approximately half-way down the back. The tail is reddish-gray proximally, becoming darker gray towards the tip (Louis *et al.*, 2006b).

Geographic Range

Far southeastern Madagascar. Currently, this species is known only from the rain forest region of Andohahela National Park, in the Manangotry Parcel between the Mandrare River in the west and the Manampanihy River in the north. Further work needs to be done to confirm the extent of the distribution, particularly north of Manangotry (Louis *et al.*, 2006b). Formerly, the sportive lemurs in this region were thought to be *L. microdon*.

Natural History

As of 2010, this species had not been studied in the wild.

Conservation Status

There is insufficient information to determine the conservation status of *L. fleuretae*, and the latest IUCN Red List assessment (2008) classified it as Data Deficient (DD). It is known to occur in one protected area (Andohahela National Park) (Louis *et al.*, 2006). It may occur in the Midongy du Sud National Park as well, but this remains to be confirmed (Louis *et al.*, 2006b).

As of 2010, this species was not being kept in captivity (I. J. Porton, pers. comm.).

Where to See It

At present, the only place to see this species is in the rain forest region of Andohahela National Park.

Lepilemuridae

Fig. 8.22: Andohahela sportive lemur (*Lepilemur fleuretae*), Manangotry Parcel, Andohahela National Park (photo by E. E. Louis Jr.).

Lepilemur hollandorum Ramaromilanto *et al.*, 2009
Mananara-Nord Sportive Lemur

Other English: Holland's Sportive Lemur
French: Lépilémur de Mananara-Nord
German: Mananara-Nord-Wieselmaki
Malagasy: Hataka, Trangalava, Kotrika, Fitiliky, Kotriana

Identification

Lepilemur hollandorum is a large sportive lemur with a head-body length of 29.3–33.7 cm, a tail length of 26.8–29.4 cm, a total length of 56–63 cm, and a body weight of about 1 kg (Ramaromilanto *et al.*, 2009). The pelage on the head, extending along the shoulders and down to the mid-back, is mottled reddish-gray, where it becomes a lighter grayish-brown down to the pygal region of the tail. The head also has a faint dark brown to black mid-dorsal stripe or inverted Y-shaped pattern, which progresses as far as the lower half of the back. The ventral coat is primarily light gray, with darker undertones. The tail is dark brown to black towards the distal end, and the hands and feet are grayish-brown. The face is generally gray, while the neck area close to the ears and chin are a lighter brown to blonde. The ears are protruding and fleshy.

Geographic Range

Northeastern Madagascar. This species is known only from the Mananara-Nord region, with the only confirmed reports so far coming from the Ivontaka-Sud and Verezanantsoro (Ambinanibeorana) parcels of the Mananara-Nord Biosphere Reserve. The northern and southern limits of the range are as yet undefined, though tentatively they are assumed to be the area south of the Fahambahy or Mananara River and north of the Simianona, Sandratsio, or Maningory rivers, respectively (Ramaromilanto *et al.*, 2009). Additional surveys are required to determine the full extent of the distribution (Ramaromilanto *et al.*, 2009).

Natural History

As of 2010, this species had not been studied in the wild.

Conservation Status

The conservation status of this newly-described species has yet to be assessed. It is known to occur in one protected area, the Mananara-Nord National Park (Ramaromilanto *et al.*, 2009).

As of 2010, this species was not being kept in captivity (I. J. Porton, pers. comm.).

Where to See It

At this time, the only place to look for this species is in Mananara-Nord National Park.

Fig. 8.23: Mananara-Nord sportive lemur (*Lepilemur hollandorum*), Mananara-Nord National Park (photo by E. E. Louis Jr.).

Lepilemur seali Louis *et al.*, 2006
Seal's Sportive Lemur

Other English: Anjanaharibe-Sud Sportive Lemur
French: Lépilémur de Seal
German: Seal's Wieselmaki
Malagasy: Tsitsihy (Makira)

Identification

Lepilemur seali is a medium-sized sportive lemur with a head-body length of 27 cm, a tail length of 26 cm, a total length of 53 cm, and a body weight of about 950 g (Louis *et al.*, 2006b; Lei *et al.*, 2008). The pelage is extremely long and thick, being uniformly light chocolate-brown to reddish-brown above and lighter brownish-gray below with cream-tipped hairs along the lateral border. The face is light brownish-gray, and a yellow to white collar is present on the neck. The hands and feet are a light grayish-brown, and the tail is a contrasting brownish-gray, occasionally with the hairs tipped with white (Louis *et al.*, 2006b).

Geographic Range

Northeastern Madagascar. This species is so far known only from the Anjanaharibe-Sud region, ranging south of the Antainambalana River at least as far as the Fananehana River and including the Makira region (Louis *et al.*, 2006b; Lei *et al.*, 2008; Craul *et al.*, 2008). Formerly, the sportive lemur from this area was thought to be *L. mustelinus*. The *Lepilemur* from Mananara-Nord (south of the Antainambalana River) was provisionally assigned to this form by Louis *et al.* (2006) but was later described as a separate species by Ramaromilanto *et al.* (2009). Additional surveys are needed to determine the southern and northern extent of the distribution (Louis *et al.*, 2006b; Ramaromilanto *et al.*, 2009).

Natural History

As of 2010, this species had not been studied in the wild.

Conservation Status

There is insufficient information to determine the conservation status of *L. seali*, and the latest IUCN Red List assessment (2008) classified it as Data Deficient (DD). It is known to occur in one protected area, the Anjanaharibe-Sud Special Reserve (Louis *et al.*, 2006b; Craul *et al.*, 2008). Recent studies in the Makira Forest determined that current levels of hunting of this species are unsustainable (Golden, 2005).

As of 2010, this species was not being kept in captivity (I. J. Porton, pers. comm.).

Where to See It

At this time, the only places to look for this species are in Anjanaharibe-Sud Special Reserve and in the Makira Forest, both relatively difficult to reach.

Lepilemuridae

Fig. 8.24: Seal's sportive lemur (*Lepilemur seali*), Anjanaharibe-Sud Special Reserve (photo by R. Randrianampionona).

Lepilemur scottorum Lei *et al.*, 2008
Masoala Sportive Lemur

Other English: Scott's Sportive Lemur
French: Lépilémur de Masoala, Lépilémur de Scott
German: Scott's Wieselmaki
Malagasy: Hataka, Trangalava, Kotrika, Fitiliky, Kotriana

Identification

Lepilemur scottorum is a medium-sized sportive lemur with a head-body length of 25–28 cm, a tail length of 25–29 cm, a total length of 57–64 cm, and a body weight of around 880 g (Lei *et al.*, 2008). The fur is long and thick, being uniformly reddish-brown above and below with the exception of a diffuse black stripe that extends midline along the dorsum, and ends in the middle of the body. The tail is reddish-brown at the base, turning progressively brownish-gray towards the tip, which is black. The face is whitish-gray, and the cheeks and eyebrows are white. The hands and feet are reddish-brown (Lei *et al.*, 2008).

Geographic Range

Northeastern Madagascar. This species is currently known only from Masoala National Park (Masiaposa Forest). Additional surveys are needed to determine the eastern and northern limits to its distribution (Lei *et al.*, 2008).

Natural History

As of 2010, this species had not been studied in the wild.

Conservation Status

The conservation status of this species has yet to be assessed. It is known to occur in one protected area; the Masoala National Park (Lei *et al.*, 2008).

As of 2010, this species was not being kept in captivity (I. J. Porton, pers. comm.).

Where to See It

At present the only known place to see this species is in the Masiaposa Forest of Masoala National Park.

Fig. 8.25: Masoala sportive lemur (*Lepilemur scottorum*), Masiaposa Forest, Masoala National Park (photo by E. E. Louis Jr.).

Lepilemur milanoii Louis *et al.*, 2006
Daraina Sportive Lemur

Other English: None
French: Lépilémur de Daraina
German: Daraina-Wieselmaki
Malagasy: Hataka, Trangalava, Kotrika, Fitiliky, Kotriana

Identification

Lepilemur milanoii is a small sportive lemur with a head-body length of 22–24 cm, a tail length of 25–26 cm, a total length of 47–50 cm, and a body weight of about 720 g (Louis *et al.*, 2006b). The pelage is notably long and thick, being generally reddish-brown on the back and grayish-white below. The head is reddish-brown dorsally but gray-brown on the face, forming a sort of mask. There is a diffuse, darker brown midline stripe on the crown, which continues down part of the back. The limbs are mainly gray (although the anterior portions of the thighs are reddish-brown), and the tail is uniformly reddish-brown (Louis *et al.*, 2006b).

Geographic Range

Northern Madagascar. This species is currently known from the Daraina region south of the Loky River, with an additional population occurring in the Analamerana Forest. It appears to be sympatric with *Lepilemur ankaranensis* in the Andrafiamena Classified Forest. Field studies are needed to determine how these two species share the same forests. This is the only area where two *Lepilemur* species evidently occur in sympatry (Louis *et al.*, 2006b).

Natural History

As of 2010, this species had not been studied in the wild.

Conservation Status

There is not enough information to determine the conservation status of *L. milanoii*, and the latest IUCN Red List assessment (2008) classified it as Data Deficient (DD). It is known to occur in Daraina in the newly-created Loky-Manambato Protected Area, and in the Andrafiamena Classified Forest, which is slated to become a national park in the near future (Louis *et al.*, 2006b).

As of 2010, this species was not being kept in captivity (I. J. Porton, pers. comm.).

Where to See It

This species can be found in the forests of Daraina (Loky-Manambato Protected Area) in the Bekoroaka Parcel, as well as in the Andrafiamena Classified Forest. However, differentiating it in the latter location from sympatric *L. ankaranensis* is quite difficult.

Lepilemuridae

Fig. 8.26: Daraina sportive lemur (*Lepilemur milanoii*), Daraina region, Loky-Manambato Protected Area (photo by E. E. Louis Jr.).

Lepilemur ankaranensis **Rumpler and Albignac, 1975**
Ankarana Sportive Lemur

Other English: Ankarana Weasel Lemur
French: Lépilémur d'Ankarana
German: Ankarana-Wieselmaki
Malagasy: Valiha

Identification

Lepilemur ankaranensis is one of the smaller sportive lemurs, with an average head-body length of 22 cm, a tail length of 27 cm, a total length of 49 cm, and a body weight of 750–790 g (Louis *et al.*, 2006b). The description that follows is based on specimens that had previously been assigned to *Lepilemur septentrionalis,* a species that evidently has a much more restricted range than previously believed (Ravoarimanana *et al.*, 2004; Rumpler, 2004). The overall color is a light grayish-brown above with a gray underside. There is often a dark median stripe extending from the crown of the head along the spine, as well as brownish tinges in the shoulder region. The tail is pale brown, darkening towards the tip. The ears are less prominent than those of other *Lepilemur* species.

This species might be confused in the field with *Phaner* or *Cheirogaleus* if only a fleeting glimpse of the animal is obtained, and also with *Avahi* even under good conditions. Its vertical posture, prominent ears, darker abdomen and leaping locomotion readily distinguish it from the smaller, more quadrupedal *Cheirogaleus*. *Phaner* has a distinctive fork-marked pattern on the forehead, a more elongated face, moves more rapidly and continuously, and produces distinctive, loud vocalizations. *Avahi* is similar in size and posture to *Lepilemur*, but has much smaller ears and distinct white patches on its thighs, and often huddles closely with other family members.

Geographic Range

Northern Madagascar. This species is found in the tropical dry lowland forests of Ankarana, Andrafiamena and Analamerana, and the tropical moist montane forests of Montagne d'Ambre, occurring from low elevations up to 1,500 m (Rumpler *et al.*, 2001; Ravoarimanana *et al.*, 2004; Rumpler, 2004). It appears to be sympatric with *L. milanoii* in the Andrafiamena Classified Forest, and fields studies are needed to determine how these two species co-exist there; the only place where two Lepilemur species live in the same forest (Louis *et al.*, 2006b).

Natural History

The natural history of *L. ankaranensis* remains relatively poorly studied. Information on its behavior and ecology can be drawn from studies on sportive lemur populations previously assigned to *L. septentrionalis*. Population densities have been estimated at 150–550 individuals/km² (Ratsirarson and Rumpler, 1988; Hawkins *et al.*, 1990), and

Fig. 8.27: Photos showing Ankarana sportive lemurs (*Lepilemur ankaranensis)* in different tree holes, Ankarana National Park (photos by R. A. Mittermeier).

Lepilemuridae

Fig. 8.28: Ankarana sportive lemur (*Lepilemur ankaranensis*), Andriafiamena Forest (photo by R. A. Mittermeier).

a typical range size seems to be about one hectare. Adults remain solitary during nightly bouts of foraging for leaves. Tree holes and vine tangles are preferred daytime shelters. The Madagascar ground boa (*Acrantophis madagascariensis*) is known to prey upon sportive lemurs in their sleeping sites.

Conservation Status

The most recent IUCN Red List assessment (2008) classified *L. ankaranesis* as Endangered (EN). The principal threats are forest destruction for charcoal production and hunting for food. Hunting has become more important in recent years, with the appearance of large numbers of itinerant sapphire miners in the Ankarana region. The species is found in two national parks (Ankarana and Montagne d'Ambre) and two special reserves (Analamerana and Fôret d'Ambre), as well as in the Andrafiamena Classified Forest, which is slated to become a national park.

Fig. 8.29: Ankarana sportive lemur (*Lepilemur ankaranensis*), Ankarana National Park (photo by R. A. Mittermeier).

As of 2010, this species was not being kept in captivity (I. J. Porton, pers. comm.).

Where to See It

This species is readily seen in both Montagne d'Ambre National Park (especially near the Station des Rousettes) and in Ankarana National Park, where it can be quite visible and vocal at certain times of the year. In the latter, it can be observed in the Canyon Forestier, the Campement des Anglais, and in forests near the Mahamasina entrance (Garbutt, 2007; R. A. Mittermeier, pers. obs.).

Lepilemur septentrionalis Rumpler and Albignac, 1975
Sahafary Sportive Lemur

Other English: Northern Sportive Lemur, Northern Weasel Lemur
French: Lépilémur du nord, Lépilémur du Sahafary, Lépilémur septentrional
German: Nördlicher Wieselmaki
Malagasy: Fitsidika, perhaps also Songiky and Mahiabeala

Identification

Lepilemur septentrionalis is a small sportive lemur with a head-body length of 18–19 cm, a tail length of 25 cm, a total length of 43–44 cm, and a body weight of 600–750 g (Louis *et al.*, 2006b). The overall color is a light grayish-brown. The underside is gray. There is often a dark median stripe extending from the crown to the midline of the dorsum. There are sometimes brownish tinges around the shoulders. The tail is pale brown, darkening towards the tip. The ears are less prominent than those of other *Lepilemur* species.

This species might be confused in the field with *Cheirogaleus* if only a fleeting glimpse of the animal is obtained. Its vertical posture, prominent ears, darker abdomen, and leaping locomotion readily distinguish it from the smaller, more quadrupedal *Cheirogaleus*.

Geographic Range

This species occurs in a handful of tiny, tropical dry forest fragments in extreme northeastern Madagascar, just to the south of Antsiranana (= Diégo-Suarez). It was formerly believed to inhabit both dry and humid forests from the Montagne d'Ambre region south to the Mahavavy River near Ambilobe in the west, and probably to the Fanambana River south of Vohémar in the east (Ratsirarson and Rumpler, 1988; Hawkins *et al.*, 1990; Mittermeier *et al.*, 1994; Ravaoarimanana *et al.*, 2004). However, with the recognition of *L. ankaranensis* as a distinct species, the range of *L. septentrionalis* was reduced to a handful of very small remnant forest patches near the villages of Madirobe and Ankarongana in the Sahafary region, and in the immediate vicinity of Andrahona, a small mountain rising out of the surrounding lowlands about 30 km south of Antsiranana and east of RN6 (Y. Rumpler, pers. comm.; R. A. Mittermeier, pers. obs.). As a result, it must be considered one of the most restricted and least protected lemurs in Madagascar, and probably the one closest to extinction.

Recent faunal surveys in the Montagne des Français, a calcareous massif of about 6,114 ha approximately 12 km south east of Antsiranana (= Diégo-Suarez), listed *L. septentrionalis* as one of the species occurring there (D'Cruze *et al.*, 2007; Sabel *et al.*, 2009), but we are not sure if it is actually *L. septentrionalis* or the more wide-ranging *L. ankaranensis*. This remains to be determined, and doing so should be a high priority.

Natural History

Data previously collected on the ecology and behavior of *Lepilemur* in far northern Madagascar would now refer to the more wide-ranging *L. ankaranensis*. Consequently this species, as now defined, has not been studied in the wild.

Conservation Status

Lepilemur septentrionalis is listed as Critically Endangered (CR) on the IUCN Red List (2008). Its population is unknown, but likely to be extremely small. The principal threats are habitat destruction for *Eucalyptus* plantations, collection of firewood, and charcoal production, and perhaps also hunting for food. Most of its habitat is already gone, and it does not occur in any official protected areas. What is more, it is uncertain whether any of the forest patches in which it still survives would be of sufficient size to warrant creation of a protected area.

Fig. 8.30: Sahafary sportive lemur (*Lepilemur septentrionalis*), Tsaratanana Forest, northwest of Ankarongana village (photo by R. A. Mittermeier).

Lepilemuridae

Fig. 8.31: Sahafary sportive lemur (*Lepilemur septentrionalis*), individual from the Analalava in the Sahafaky region (photo by E. E. Louis Jr.).

It was listed as one of the world's 25 Most endangered primates in 2008 (Ravaorimanana *et al.*, 2009). Total numbers are unknown but, taking into account its limited distribution in the forests of Sahafary, Andrahona and Andranomadiro, probably only about 100-150 individuals remain. Surveys of five areas in 2007 provided the following population estimates: 1) Area of Andrahona (forest patches and gallery forests of Andrahona, Analajanana, and Analanjavavy)—20 individuals in the entire area; 2) Area of Ankarakataova (forests of Ankarakataova Be and Ankarakataova kely)—none found; and 3) Area of Sahafary (degraded forest patches in Western Sahafary, Sahafary East, Sahafary North, Andravina, Sahandrano, Andranomadiro, and Analalava)—about 100 individuals (Ravaorimanana *et al.*, 2009). None of these areas are protected.

The combination of a very small range containing little and rapidly decreasing suitable habitat with high pressure from hunting makes this species especially threatened. A consortium of the *Association Européenne pour l'Etude et la Conservation des Lémuriens* (AEECL), the University Louis Pasteur of Strasbourg and the Fondation Nature et Decouverte supported the field work and the genetic study. Socio-economic studies are under way to determine the anthropogenic effect on the remaining population (Lernould, 2006).

The Andrahona Forest is considered a sacred forest, but it is tiny. Furthermore, during a recent visit (R. A. Mittermeier, pers. obs., August, 2005), it was found to be riddled with trails and in the process of being exploited for saplings for local construction. During a later visit, E. E. Louis Jr. and colleagues located eight animals, but again in very degraded habitat measuring only 400 m × 20 m in size.

This is clearly a species on the verge of extinction, and in need of special attention. This could include a last-ditch effort to save a piece of remaining habitat, with the Andrahona Forest perhaps presenting the best opportunity. Another option may be to undertake a captive breeding program, although members of the genus *Lepilemur* have always proven difficult to keep in zoos.

As indicated above, it is possible that the sportive lemur in Montagne des Français, a calcareous massif 12 km from Antsiranana (= Diego-Suarez), is *L. septentrionalis* (D'Cruze *et al.*, 2007; Sabel *et al.*, 2009). A survey and genetic study is urgently needed to determine if the species occurring there is in fact *L. septentrionalis*, and not the more wide-ranging *L. ankaranensis*. If it is, then the prospects for survival of *L. septentrionalis* in the wild would be considerably improved.

As of 2010, this species was not being kept in captivity (I. J. Porton, pers. comm.).

Where to See It

This lemur is very difficult to find in the wild. One individual was seen recently in a small forest patch (locally referred to as the Tsaratanana Forest) in the middle of *Eucalyptus* plantations 5.4 km to the northwest of the village of Ankarongana, which is along the road to Irodo on the coast (R. A. Mittermeier, pers. obs.). It may also occur in the very small area of forest at the edge and on top of the Andrahona outcrop, and perhaps in other tiny forest patches north of Madairobe. E. E. Louis Jr. and his team found it in the Analalava Forest, approximately 30 minutes by car south of the village of Sadjoavata. However, this animal is so difficult to see that it is not recommended for first-time visitors to Madagascar. In any case, the use of experienced guides and local villagers is essential.

Lepilemuridae

Lepilemur dorsalis Gray, 1871
Gray's Sportive Lemur

Other English: Back-striped Sportive Lemur, Gray-backed Sportive
Lemur
French: Lépilémur de Gray, Lépilemur à dos gris
German: Gray's Wieselmaki
Malagasy: Apongy, Fitsidika

Identification

Lepilemur dorsalis is a small sportive lemur with a head-body length of 23–26 cm, a tail
length 26–28 cm, a total length of 51–54 cm, and an average weight of 500–730 g (Louis *et*
al., 2006b). The ears are relatively short and rounded, the muzzle blunt, and the face dark
gray to brown. The dorsal coat, including the tail, is medium brown to gray-brown and
bisected by a darker brown median stripe. The ventral coat is a lighter gray-brown, paler
towards the throat.

This species might be confused with *Cheirogaleus medius* and *Avahi unicolor.* It can
be distinguished from *Cheirogaleus* by its larger size, vertically-oriented posture, and
clinging-leaping form of locomotion. It can usually be distinguished from *Avahi* by its more
prominent ears. *Avahi* also has larger, owl-like eyes, a woollier appearance, and distinctive
white patches on its thighs, and often huddles closely with other family members.

The precise taxonomy of the sportive lemurs of northwestern Madagascar, and their
relationship to each other, remain undetermined. Zinner *et al.* (2007) showed that the three
teams which described new *Lepilemur* species there in 2006 and 2007 (Andriaholinirina
et al., 2006a; Louis *et al.*, 2006b; Craul *et al.*, 2007) each had different concepts of *L.*
dorsalis, and that the validity of *Lepilemur tymerlachsonorum* vs. *Lepilemur mittermeieri*
in particular depends on which concept turns out to be correct. The type locality of *L.*
dorsalis ie either Mourountsang (= Anorantsangana, 13°55'S, 47°55'E) or Passandava
(= Ampasindava, about 13°40'S, 48°15'E). If the former, then *L. tymerlachsonorum* is a
synonym of *L. dorsalis* and *L. mittermeieri* is valid. The species found at Anorontsangana
is also found on Nosy Be (Zinner *et al.*, 2007). The name *Lepilemur grandidieri* (Forsyth
Major, 1894) was given to a species from this general area,
and this too may prove to be a senior synonym of one of the
species described in 2006/2007 (C. P. Groves, pers. comm.).

Geographic Range

Northwestern Madagascar. This species is found in the
Sambirano region, its distribution centering on the town of
Ambanja (Petter *et al.*, 1977; Tattersall, 1982). This used to
be considered to be the species on the island of Nosy Be as
well, but a separate species, *Lepilemur tymerlachsonorum*,
has now been described from that island.

Lepilemuridae

Natural History

Previous studies attributed to this animal were carried out on the island of Nosy Be. The Nosy Be sportive lemur is, however, now considered a distinct species, *Lepilemur tymerlachsonorum*.

Conservation Status

Having lost much of its former range due to taxonomic revisions (see *L. tymerlachsonorum*, *L. mittermeieri*, and *L. sahamalazensis*), we now know too little about the geographic range of *L. dorsalis* to determine its conservation status. The latest IUCN Red List assessment (2008) classified it as Data Deficient (DD). Although this species is often abundant where it is found, there are several threats to its survival. The main threat is habitat loss for rice and coffee cultivation, and illegal logging, but it is sometimes hunted for food as well. The only protected area where it is known for certain to occur is the Manongarivo Special Reserve (Nicoll and Langrand, 1989). It may also occur in the Tsaratanana Strict Nature Reserve, which is well within its range, but this remains to be confirmed.

As of 2010, this species was not being kept in captivity (I. J. Porton, pers. comm.).

Where to See It

The best place to see this species is in the Manongarivo Special Reserve, south of Ambanja. Unfortunately, this reserve is difficult to reach.

Fig. 8.32: Gray's sportive lemur (*Lepilemur dorsalis*), Antafondro (photo by E. E. Louis Jr.).

Lepilemuridae

Lepilemur tymerlachsonorum Louis *et al.*, 2006
Nosy Be Sportive Lemur

Other English: Nosy Be Weasel Lemur
French: Lépilémur de Nosy Be
German: Nosy-Be-Wieselmaki
Malagasy: Fitsidika, Apongy

Identification

Lepilemur tymerlachsonorum is a small to medium-sized species with a head-body length of 23 cm, a tail length of 25 cm, a total length of 48 cm, and a body weight of roughly 880 g (Louis *et al.*, 2006b). The dorsum is light brownish-gray, with the upper half of the back a light reddish-brown and the underside a light grayish-white. The anterior aspects of the thighs and edges of the extremities also have a light reddish-brown diffuse color. A dark brown to black midline stripe is present from the head to the lower half of the back, and the tail is a uniform light reddish-gray to brown. The face is gray and mask-like (Louis *et al.*, 2006b).

The taxonomy of the sportive lemurs in this part of Madagascar still remains to be clarified, especially the relationship between this species, *Lepilemur dorsalis*, and *Lepilemur mittermeieri*.

Geographic Range

Northwestern Madagascar. The Nosy Be sportive lemur, *Lepilemur tymerlachsonorum*, appears to be confined to the Lokobe region on the island of Nosy Be (Louis *et al.*, 2006b). This may or may not be the species that occurs on the island of Nosy Komba as well, but sportive lemurs have not been observed there in recent years.

Zinner *et al.* (2007) found that some specimens from the mainland were identical in mtDNA to the type of *L. tymerlachsonorum,* so there is some question as to whether or not this species is also on the mainland. The sportive lemurs found on Nosy Be were previously considered to be *Lepilemur dorsalis*.

Natural History

This species inhabits tropical moist lowland forests that are subject to a dry season each year. It appears to be more common in secondary forests. In dense primary forest it favors tree holes for daytime sleeping, but will seek out vegetation tangles in more open deciduous forest (Petter and Petter, 1971; Raxworthy and Rakotondraparany, 1988). It feeds on leaves, fruit and bark. Births occur from August through November, mothers typically producing a single young. Predators include the Madagascar Harrier-hawk (*Polyboroides radiatus*) and the Madagascar Buzzard (*Buteo brachypterus*).

Fig. 8.33: Nosy Be sportive lemur (*Lepilemur tymerlachsonorum*), Lokobe Strict Nature Reserve, island of Nosy Be (photo by R. A. Mittermeier).

Lepilemuridae

Fig. 8.34: Nosy Be sportive lemur (*Lepilemur tymerlachsonorum*), Lokobe Strict Nature Reserve, island of Nosy Be (photo by R. A. Mittermeier).

Conservation Status

We do not know enough to determine the conservation status of *L. tymerlachsonorum* and the latest IUCN Red List assessment (2008) classified it as Data Deficient (DD). It is known to occur in one protected area, the Lokobe Strict Nature Reserve on Nosy Be (Louis *et al.*, 2006b).

As of 2010, this species was not being kept in captivity (I. J. Porton, pers. comm.).

Where to See It

This species can easily be seen in the Lokobe Strict Nature Reserve on the island of Nosy Be. Several tours visit forests around this protected area, and local guides usually know the whereabouts of their daytime sleeping sites, which are only a few meters above the ground and where the animal is quite easy to observe. A particularly good site is Ampasipohy, where there are two comfortable beachfront lodges, with *Lepilemur* to be found in forest right behind them.

Lepilemuridae

Fig. 8.35: Nosy Be sportive lemur (*Lepilemur tymerlachsonorum*), Lokobe Strict Nature Reserve, island of Nosy Be (photo by J. Zaonarivelo).

Lepilemur mittermeieri Rabarivola *et al.*, 2006
Mittermeier's Sportive Lemur

Other English: None
French: Lépilémur de Mittermeier
German: Mittermeier's Wieselmaki
Malagasy: Apongy, Fitsidika

Identification

Lepilemur mittermeieri is a small sportive lemur with a head-body length of 27.1–29.2 cm, a tail length of 25.4–28.1 cm, a total length of 53.1–56.6 cm, and a body weight of 730 g (E. E. Louis Jr., unpubl. data). The dorsum is reddish-gray, with a dark brown to black midline stripe occasionally present on the top of the head. The tail is a uniform light reddish-gray to brown but darkens towards the tip. The face is gray and mask-like with whiter pelage under the eyes, extending under the mandible (Rabarivola *et al.*, 2006; E. E. Louis Jr., pers. obs.).

The taxonomy of the sportive lemurs in this part of Madagascar still remains to be clarified, especially the relationship between this species, *L. dorsalis*, and *L. tymerlachsonorum*.

Geographic Range

Northwestern Madagascar. This species was described from the Ampasindava Peninsula (Rabarivola *et al.*, 2006). Studies are now underway to determine if it ranges elsewhere. The sportive lemur in this area was formerly considered to be *L. dorsalis*.

Natural History

As of 2010, this species had not been studied in the wild.

Conservation Status

There is insufficient information to determine the conservation status of *L. mittermeieri*, so the latest IUCN Red List assessment (2008) classified it as Data Deficient (DD). It is not known for certain from any protected area, but it might occur in the northern part of the newly-created Sahamalaza-Iles Radama National Park (C. Schwitzer, pers. obs.).

As of 2010, this species was not being kept in captivity (I. J. Porton, pers. comm.).

Where to See It

This species can be seen on parts of the Ampasindava Peninsula. One site where it was recently observed (by R. A. Mittermeier) was in the Sorongono Forest at the northern tip of the peninsula, near the village of Amporaha. The Sorongono Forest is about a 15-minute boat ride from Amporaha, and right next to the Ambatomatavy Mountain (an important site that should be considered for protected area status).

Lepilemuridae

Fig. 8.36: Mittermeier's sportive lemur (*Lepilemur mittermeieri*). Photographs taken in the Sorongono Forest on the Ampasindava Peninsula, NW Madagascar (photos by R. A. Mittermeier).

Lepilemur sahamalazensis **Andriaholinirina *et al.*, 2006**
Sahamalaza Sportive Lemur

Other English: None
French: Lépilémur de Sahamalaza
German: Sahamalaza-Wieselmaki
Malagasy: Fitsidiky

Identification

Lepilemur sahamalazensis is a small sportive lemur with a head-body length of 19–24 cm, a tail length of about 24 cm, a total length of 44–48 cm, and a body weight of roughly 700 g (Andriaholinirina *et al.*, 2006; Louis *et al.*, 2006b). The pelage coloration is variable, possibly depending on the age of the individual. The upper body is predominantly reddish-brown with gray or creamy underparts. It has a reddish-brown to deep brown tail. There is a dark, diffuse dorsal stripe running from the top of the head to the lower back. The face is essentially gray, with the forehead and areas around the ears reddish-brown, sometimes with darker, diffuse patches (Andriaholinirina *et al.*, 2006).

Geographic Range

This species is evidently restricted to the Sahamalaza Peninsula and the adjacent mainland of coastal northwestern Madagascar. The biogeography of this area and the distribution pattern of the sympatric *Eulemur flavifrons* make it likely that the boundaries of the range of *L. sahamalazensis* are the Andranomalaza River in the north and the Maevarano River in the south. Field studies to determine the full extent of the species' distribution and that of the neighboring *Lepilemur mittermeieri* are under way (C. Schwitzer, pers. comm.).

Natural History

This species has recently been studied in the Ankarafa Forest on the Sahamalaza Peninsula (Ruperti, 2007). Although these animals are essentially nocturnal, at least 40% of the time in their daytime sleeping sites is spent either resting vigilantly or grooming. Sahamalaza sportive lemurs seem to rest less in disturbed forest areas with a lower density of large trees and vegetation tangles. Although tree holes are usually the favored sleeping sites of sportive lemurs, individuals of this species observed in tree holes were found to be significantly more active during the day than those that had been resting in vegetation tangles (Ruperti, 2007).

Conservation Status

There was not enough information to determine the conservation status of *L. sahamalazensis* in the latest IUCN Red List assessment (2008), so it was classified as Data Deficient (DD). However, since then the species has been provisionally assessed as Critically Endangered, with a formal proposal submitted to the IUCN. It was also placed on

Fig. 8.37: Sahamalaza sportive lemur (*Lepilemur sahamalazensis*), Sahamalaza Peninsula (photo by R. A. Mittermeier).

Lepilemuridae

Fig. 8.38: Sahamalaza sportive lemurs (*Lepilemur sahamalazensis*), taken in the Ankarafa Forest, Sahamalaza - Iles Radama National Park (above photo by C. Schwitzer, below by M. Seiler).

the list of the world's 25 Most Endangered Primates 2006–2008 (Olivieiri *et al.*, 2007b). It occurs in the southern part of the newly-created Sahamalaza-Iles Radama National Park, where it seems to be abundant in primary and older secondary forest. However, it probably has a very limited distribution, and the forest that it lives in is rapidly decreasing and extremely fragmented. Hunting pressure is high. Indeed, the threats that it faces are similar to those of the sympatric blue-eyed black lemur (*Eulemur flavifrons*), which is Critically Endangered (CR). A maximum of five *L. sahamalazensis* were found to inhabit one hectare of forest, with an average of 2.8 per hectare. Total population size was estimated to be no more than 3,000 individuals within the boundaries of the national park (Ruperti, 2007). Population densities tend to be higher in areas with more large trees, a more closed canopy, and a greater abundance of food plants, suitable sleeping holes and vegetation tangles. The presence of livestock reduces population numbers.

As of 2010, this species was not being kept in captivity (I. J. Porton, pers. comm.).

Where to See It

The best place to see this species is in remaining forest patches on the Sahamalaza Peninsula. For example, the Ankarafa Forest can be reached by a one-hour boat trip from Analalava to the small village of Marovato, and from there a hike of about two hours inland. The Sahamalaza Peninsula can also be reached by pirogue from Maromandia. Sahamalaza sportive lemurs can readily be found when they are active during the night but also during the day when they are in their tree holes.

Fig. 8.39: Sahamalaza sportive lemur (*Lepilemur sahamalazensis*), taken in the Ankarafa Forest, Sahamalaza - Iles Radama National Park (photo by C. Schwitzer).

Lepilemur grewcockorum **Louis** *et al.***, 2006**
Anjiamangirana Sportive Lemur

Other English: Grewcock's Sportive Lemur
French: Lépilémur d'Anjiamangirana, Lépilémur de Grewcock
German: Anjiamangirana Wieselmaki
Malagasy: Repahaka, Boenga, Boengy, Kitrontro, Kitanta

Identification

Lepilemur grewcockorum is a small sportive lemur with a head-body length of 25 cm, a tail length of 28–29 cm, a total length of 53–54 cm, and a weight of 780 g (Louis *et al.*, 2006b). The pelage is predominantly gray above and light gray to white below with chocolate-mottled fur on the shoulders and along the sides of the body. A dark stripe is present on the midline of the crown. In some individuals, it continues onto the back. The ears are quite conspicuous with short hairs on the dorsal surface so they look almost pink. The tail is usually entirely gray, but it can have a white tip of variable length (this characteristic is also found occasionally in *L. edwardsi* and *L. otto)*. The area around the maxilla and the dorsal surface of the snout is whitish-pink with whitish fur along the mandible that continues down the throat (Louis *et al.*, 2006b).

Geographic Range

Northwestern Madagascar. This species is currently known from the Anjiamangirana region, north of the Sofia River and south of the Maevarano River (Louis *et al.*, 2006b). The range also includes the Bongolava Massif. Formerly, the sportive lemurs found in these areas were considered to be *L. edwardsi*.

Craul *et al.* (2007) described *Lepilemur manasamody* from Ambongabe (15°19'38.3"S, 46°40'44.4"E) and Anjiamangirana, 15°09'24.6"S, 47°44'06.2"E) in the Province of Mahajanga. Zinner *et al.* (2007) pointed out that localities for this species and those for *L. grewcockorum* were only 2 km apart (the Anjiamangirana Classified Forest is the type locality for *L. grewcockorum*) and that there was no obvious biogeographical barrier between them. They suggested that *manasamody* was a junior synonym as a result. A molecular genetic analysis by Lei *et al.* (2008) subsequently confirmed this.

Natural History

As of 2010, this species had not been studied in the wild.

Conservation Status

There is too little information to determine the conservation status of *L. grewcockorum*, so the latest IUCN Red List assessment (2008) classified it as Data Deficient (DD). It occurs in the proposed 50,300-ha conservation area on the Bongolava Massif.

As of 2010, this species was not being kept in captivity (I. J. Porton, pers. comm.).

Where to See It

The best place to see this species is in the Anjiamangirana Classified Forest, which is south of the city of Antsohihy in the forest west of RN6.

Fig. 8.40: Anjiamangirana sportive lemur (*Lepilemur grewcockorum*), Anjiamangirana Classified Forest (photos by E. E. Louis Jr.).

Lepilemur otto Craul *et al.*, 2007
Ambodimahabibo Sportive Lemur

Other English: Otto's Sportive Lemur
French: Lépilémur d'Otto, Lépilémur d'Ambodimahabibo
German: Otto's Wieselmaki
Malagasy: Repahaka, Boenga, Boengy, Kitrontro, Kitanta

Identification

Lepilemur otto is a medium-sized sportive lemur, with a head-body length of 28.7–30 cm, a tail length of 24.8–27.4 cm, a total length of 53.5–57.4 cm, and a body weight of 853–872 g (E. E. Louis Jr., unpubl. data). The dorsal pelage, including the shoulders and upper and lower forelimbs, is predominantly gray-brown, while the underside is generally gray to creamy. A dark, diffuse line runs from the middle of the crown and down the back, sometimes as far as the rump. The tail is gray-brown to deep brown, sometimes with a white tip. The face and forehead are essentially gray (Craul *et al.*, 2007).

Geographic Range

Northwestern Madagascar. This species is so far known only from the type locality of Ambodimahabibo. Its range is limited by the Mahajamba River in the south and the Sofia River in the north. Surveys are now required in this heavily deforested area to obtain additional information about the location and viability of other remaining populations so that conservation measures can be proposed (Craul *et al.*, 2007).

Natural History

As of 2010, this species had not been studied in the wild.

Conservation Status

There is insufficient information to determine the conservation status of *L. otto* and the latest IUCN Red List assessment (2008) classified it as Data Deficient (DD). It is not known to occur in any protected area.

As of 2010, this species was not being kept in captivity (I. J. Porton, pers. comm.).

Where to See It

At present the only place to see this species is at the type locality of Ambodimahabibo.

Fig. 8.41: Ambodimahabibo sportive lemur (*Lepilemur otto*), Ambodimahabibo Classified Forest (photo by J. F. Ranaivoarisoa).

Lepilemur edwardsi (Forsyth Major, 1894)
Milne-Edwards' Sportive Lemur

Other English: Milne-Edwards' Weasel Lemur
French: Lépilémur de Milne-Edwards'
German: Milne-Edwards-Wieselmaki
Malagasy: Repahaka, Boenga, Boengy, Kitrontro, Kitanta

Identification

Lepilemur edwardsi is one of the larger sportive lemurs, with a head-body length of 26–29 cm, a tail length of 26–29 cm, and a total length of 52–58 cm (Louis *et al.*, 2006b; Garbutt, 2007). Adult body weight may reach 1.1 kg (Smith and Jungers, 1997; Louis *et al.*, 2006b). The dorsal coat, including the tail, is gray-brown, except at the tip. The shoulders, forelimbs and upper thighs are more chestnut-brown. Some individuals have a darker mid-dorsal stripe. The ventral coat is gray with creamy patches. The face is darkish gray to brown, and the ears are prominent.

This species is most likely to be confused with *Avahi occidentalis*, which is similar in size and posture, but *L. edwardsi* can be distinguished by its darker color, pointed face and more prominent ears. *Avahi* also has larger, owl-like eyes, a woollier appearance, and distinctive white patches on its thighs, and often huddles closely with other family members.

Geographic Range

Milne-Edwards' sportive lemur is found in the tropical dry lowland deciduous forests of western Madagascar (up to 450 m), from north of the Betsiboka River to the Bay of Loza and the Mahajamba River. This represents a much-reduced distribution compared to older accounts, but previous range descriptions were based on the incorrect assignment of a museum specimen (Zaramody *et al.*, 2005). This new assessment is supported by strong genetic evidence (Pastorini *et al.*, 2003; Louis *et al.*, 2006b; Craul *et al.*, 2007). Further study is needed north of Ankarafantsika National Park to determine the northern extent of the range of this species.

Natural History

Lepilemur edwardsi is common in most places where it is found. It has been studied in dry deciduous forests in Ankarafantsika National Park, where its population density has been estimated at 60 individuals/km² (Warren and Crompton, 1997a). Home ranges appear to be about one hectare in size, and are vigorously defended with loud vocalizations and displays of branch-shaking (Albignac, 1981a). Several individuals can be found sleeping in the same shelter during the day, but they tend to be solitary foragers during the night. As with other *Lepilemur* species leaves are a dietary mainstay, but fruit, flowers, and fleshy seeds are also eaten (Albignac, 1981b; Razanahoera-Rakotomalala, 1981; Ganzhorn, 1988; Warren and Crompton, 1997a, 1997b; Rasoloharijaona *et al.*, 2000; Thalmann, 2001). Ganzhorn (1993) found that this sportive lemur ate lower quality leaves than at other field sites, a difference in diet that he attributed to food competition with *Avahi*.

This lemur is most active in the first few hours after dusk, after which bouts of foraging are interspersed with periods of rest. Its most serious predator is the fossa (*Cryptoprocta ferox*).

Conservation Status

The most recent IUCN Red List assessment (2008) classified *L. edwardsi* as Vulnerable (VU). Threats include forest destruction, fires set to create new pasture for livestock, and, in some areas, hunting for food. The only protected area where this species occurs is Ankarafantsika National Park (Nicoll and Langrand, 1989). It may also be present in the forests surrounding the Anjajavy Hotel along the coast to the north of Mahajanga (= Majunga), but this remains to be confirmed.

As of 2010, this species was not being kept in captivity (I. J. Porton, pers. comm.).

Where to See It

This species is most readily seen at the Ampijoroa Station in Ankarafantsika National Park, along the main road from Antananarivo to Mahajanga (= Majunga). It is easily found at night by its eye-shine and vocalizations, and can often be found in tree holes during the day as well, at times only one or two meters above the ground.

Fig. 8.42: Milne-Edwards' sportive lemur (*Lepilemur edwardsi*) in a daytime sleeping site, Ampijoroa Station, Ankarafantsika National Park (photo by R. A. Mittermeier).

Lepilemuridae

Lepilemur aeeclis Andriaholinirina *et al.*, 2006
Antafia Sportive Lemur

Other English: AEECL's Sportive Lemur
French: Lépilémur d'Antafia
German: Antafia-Wieselmaki
Malagasy: Boengy

Identification

Lepilemur aeeclis is a medium-sized sportive lemur with a head-body length of 21–24 cm, a tail length of 24–25 cm, a total length of 45–49 cm, and a body weight of 600–860 g. Although outwardly similar to *Lepilemur ahmansonorum*, it is significantly larger. Pelage coloration is said to be very variable. However, some consistent characters are present. The back and tail are generally gray or reddish-gray, with the underside being either light or dark gray. The face is also gray (sometimes with a darker patch on the forehead), with darker colored stripes above the eyes that run upwards to join in the middle of the crown and continue on down the back as far as the tail. The ears are protruding and rounded (Louis *et al.*, 2006b; Andriaholinirina *et al.*, 2006a).

Geographic Range

Central-western coastal Madagascar. This species is found northeast of the Mahavavy du Sud River and south of the Betsiboka River. The southern extent of the range is unknown and needs further research (Andriaholinirina *et al.*, 2006a; Louis *et al.*, 2006b). Formerly, the sportive lemurs in this region were considered to be *L. edwardsi*.

Natural History

As of 2010, this species had not been studied in the wild.

Conservation Status

According to the most recent IUCN Red List assessment (2008), *L. aeeclis* is Data Deficient (DD). It is not known to occur in any protected area.

As of 2010, this species was not being kept in captivity (I. J. Porton, pers. comm.).

Where to See It

At present, the only place to see this species is in the Antrema Classified Forest near Katsepy, across the Betsiboka River from the city of Mahajanga (= Majunga).

Fig. 8.43: Antafia sportive lemur (*Lepilemur aeeclis*), Anjahamana Classified Forest (photo by E. E. Louis Jr.).

Lepilemur ahmansonorum Louis *et al.*, 2006
Tsiombikibo Sportive Lemur

Other English: Ahmanson's Sportive Lemur
French: Lépilémur d'Ahmanson, Lépilémur du Tsiombikibo
German: Tsiombikibo Wieselmaki
Malagasy: Boengy

Identification

Lepilemur ahmansonorum is a small sportive lemur with a head-body length of 24–30 cm, a tail length of 23–34 cm, a total length of 47–54 cm, and a body weight of 460–760 g (Louis *et al.*, 2006b). The coat is mainly dark gray, both above and on the underside, with diffuse reddish-brown on the dorsal surface of the extremities, especially distally. A vague black stripe may be present on the crown. The tail is a dark reddish-brown on the dorsal surface, and a light grayish-blonde below (Louis *et al.*, 2006b).

Geographic Range

Central-west Madagascar. This species is currently known only from the Tsiombikibo Classified Forest, southwest of the Mahavavy du Sud River, near the city of Mitsinjo. The southern extent of the range is unknown (especially relative to *Lepilemur randrianasoloi*), but is here rather arbitrarily taken as the Maningoza River (Louis *et al.*, 2006).

Natural History

As of 2010, this species had not been studied in the wild.

Conservation Status

There is too little information to determine the conservation status of *L. ahmansonorum* and the latest IUCN Red List assessment (2008) classified it as Data Deficient (DD).

As of 2010, this species was not being kept in captivity (I. J. Porton, pers. comm.).

Where to See It

At present, the only place to see this species is in the Tsiombikibo Classified Forest.

Lepilemuridae

Fig. 8.44: Tsiombikibo sportive lemur (*Lepilemur ahmansonorum*), Tsiombikibo Classified Forest (photo by E. E. Louis Jr.).

Lepilemur randrianasoloi Andriaholinirina *et al.*, 2006
Bemaraha Sportive Lemur

Other English: Randrianasolo's Sportive Lemur
French: Lépilémur de Randrianasolo
German: Randrianasolo's Wieselmaki
Malagasy: Boengy

Lepilemuridae

Identification

Lepilemur randrianasoloi is a small sportive lemur similar to *L. aeeclis* but slightly smaller, with a narrower, slightly longer head. These differences in head size are most pronounced in males (Andriaholinirina *et al.*, 2006a). The head-body length averages 28.7 cm, the tail 27.6 cm, the total length is 56 cm, and the body weight is 720–856 g (E. E. Louis Jr., unpubl. data). The overall pelage is light gray, with a mixture of reddish-brown and gray on the dorsal surface of the forearms, hindlimbs, shoulders, and back. The face is a lighter gray, producing a mask-like appearance. A darker line is present mid-dorsally on the head, and the tail is a lighter red than the rest of the body (Andriaholinirina *et al.*, 2006a).

Geographic Range

Central-western Madagascar. This species is currently known from the type locality, Andramasay, as well as the Tsingy de Bemaraha National Park and adjacent Strict Nature Reserve. It probably occurs throughout the entire area between the Tsiribihina River in the south and the Manambaho River in the north (Andriaholinirina *et al.*, 2006a; Louis *et al.*, 2006b), though more research is needed to confirm the limits of its distribution. Formerly, the sportive lemur in this region was considered to be *L. ruficaudatus*.

Natural History

As of 2010, this species had not been studied in the wild.

Conservation Status

We know too little to be able to determine the conservation status of *L. randrianasoloi*, and the latest IUCN Red List assessment (2008) classified it as Data Deficient (DD). It is present in two adjacent protected areas, the Tsingy de Bemaraha National Park and Tsingy de Bemaraha Strict Nature Reserve.

As of 2010, this species was not being kept in captivity (I. J. Porton, pers. comm.).

Where to See It

Lepilemur randrianasoloi is easily seen in both the Tsingy de Bemaraha National Park and the adjacent Strict Nature Reserve.

Lepilemuridae

Fig. 8.45: Bemaraha sportive lemur (*Lepilemur randrianasoloi*), Tsingy de Bemaraha National Park (photo by E. E. Louis Jr.).

Lepilemur ruficaudatus A. Grandidier, 1867
Red-tailed Sportive Lemur

Other English: Red-tailed Weasel Lemur
French: Lépilémur à queue rousse
German: Rotschwanz-Wieselmaki
Malagasy: Boengy

Identification

Lepilemur ruficaudatus is a medium-sized sportive lemur with a head-body length of 24–30 cm, a tail length of 24–28 cm, a total length of 48–58 cm, and a body weight of 760–950 g (Eaglen, 1986; Schmid and Ganzhorn, 1996; Ganzhorn, 2002; Zinner *et al.*, 2003; Louis *et al.*, 2006b; Garbutt, 2007). The dorsal coat is gray-brown, with reddish-chestnut tinges on the shoulders and forelimbs, similar to the color pattern of *Lepilemur microdon.* The tail is tinted red. The ventral coat is pale gray, and the throat is cream-colored. The ears are rounded and prominent.

This species occurs in sympatry with at least five other nocturnal lemurs in four genera: *Microcebus, Mirza, Cheirogaleus,* and *Phaner.* It can be distinguished from *Microcebus* and *Mirza* by its much larger size, and from *Cheirogaleus* by its vertical clinging and leaping posture and locomotion. *Phaner* is smaller, moves rapidly, and has the distinctive fork-marked pattern on its head.

Geographic Range

Southwestern Madagascar. This species inhabits subtropical and tropical lowland dry forests, from sea level to 900 m. In the past it was thought to range from the Onilahy River north as far as the Betsiboka River. However, a number of new species have recently been described from portions of this formerly wide range (Pastorini *et al.*, 2003; Andriaholinirina *et al.*, 2006a; Louis *et al.*, 2006b), so the precise limits of its distribution remain to be determined. At present it is known to occur in the Menabe-Antimena Reserve and in the Andranomena and Kasijy Special Reserves, between the Tsiribihina and Morondava rivers.

Natural History

Lepilemur ruficaudatus is still common in much of its range. Petter *et al.* (1971) estimated population densities of 180–350 individuals/km² in the Marosalaza forests. Hladik *et al.* (1980) described this sportive lemur as a leaf-eater, although it also eats fruits in season, especially *Diospyros.*
Home range sizes are at or below one hectare and do not differ between males and females (Zinner *et al.*, 2003). Adults are organized into pairs, but they rarely interact and spend very little time in close proximity to each other (Hilgartner *et al.*, 2008). They spend the day in tree holes and can often be seen sunbathing at the entrance. According to Ganzhorn (1993), *L. ruficaudatus* feeds on leaves of high nutritional value in the Kirindy Forest, where *Avahi occidentalis* is not sympatric with it. However, in areas where *Avahi* and

Fig. 8.46: Red-tailed sportive lemur (*Lepilemur ruficaudatus*), Ankarafantsika National Park (photo by J. Zaonarivelo).

Lepilemuridae

Fig. 8.47: Red-tailed sportive lemur (*Lepilemur ruficaudatus*), Kirindy forest (photo by C. Fichtel).

Lepilemur coexist, *Avahi* typically eats the higher quality leaves. Red-tailed sportive lemurs are preyed upon by the fossa and the Madagascar Harrier-hawk (Rasoloarison *et al.*, 1995; Schülke and Ostner, 2001). They can correctly categorize vocalizations of these two predators and exhibit corresponding adaptive–evasive behavior, but they do not have specific anti-predator alarm calls (Fichtel, 2007). This species has one of the lowest resting metabolic rates recorded for any mammalian species (Schmid and Ganzhorn, 1996).

Mating occurs from May to July, and a single infant is born in November (Hilgartner *et al.*, 2008). The infant is initially transported in the mother's mouth and "parked" on a branch or in a tree hole while she forages (Petter-Rousseaux, 1964). Infants are weaned at about 50 days, and fathers provide no infant care (Hilgartner *et al.*, 2008).

Conservation Status

There is not enough information to determine the conservation status of *L. ruficaudatus*, and the latest IUCN Red List assessment (2008) classified it as Data Deficient (DD). The principal threat to its survival is habitat loss due to expanding livestock populations, but it is also heavily hunted and captured for food throughout much of its range. The species occurs in the Menabe-Antimena Protected Area (especially the Kirindy Forest) and in the Andranomena and Kasijy Special Reserves (E. E. Louis Jr., pers. obs.).

As of 2010, this species was not being kept in captivity (I. J. Porton, pers. comm.).

Where to See It

The best place to see the red-tailed sportive lemur is the Kirindy Forest north of Morondava, where it is easily seen at night and sometimes during the day as well.

Lepilemuridae

Lepilemur hubbardorum Louis *et al.*, 2006
Zombitse Sportive Lemur

Other English: Hubbard's Sportive Lemur
French: Lépilémur de Zombitse, Lépilémur de Hubbard
German: Hubbard's Wieselmaki
Malagasy: Apongy, Fitsidika

Identification

*Lepilemur hubbardoru*m is a medium-sized sportive lemur with a head-body length of 23–24 cm, a tail length of 24 cm, a total length of 47–48 cm, and a weight of 990 g (Louis *et al.*, 2006b). The dorsal pelage is dark reddish-brown around the shoulders and upper back, gradually becoming a lighter reddish-white to gray towards the base of the tail and hips. The underside is entirely white, and the tail is uniformly blonde or reddish-blonde. The face is grayish-brown around the muzzle and eyes, with a reddish-brown dorsal surface crown, and the fur around the neck is lighter, forming a reddish-blonde collar. Two phenotypes have been observed, possibly the male and the female but this has yet to be confirmed (Louis *et al.*, 2006b).

Geographic Range

Southwestern Madagascar. Currently known only the area of the Zombitse–Vohibasia National Park, north of the Onilahy River and south of the Fiherena River (Louis *et al.*, 2006b). Formerly, the sportive lemurs there considered to be *Lepilemur ruficaudatus*. Additional surveys are needed to determine the northern, western and eastern boundaries of the range of this species.

Natural History

As of 2010, this species had not been studied in the wild.

Conservation Status

There is insufficient information to determine the conservation status of *L. hubbardorum*, so the latest IUCN Red List assessment (2008) classified it as Data Deficient (DD). It is known to occur in one protected area, Zombitse-Vohibasia National Park (Louis *et al.*, 2006b).

As of 2010, this species was not being kept in captivity (I. J. Porton, pers. comm.).

Where to See It

At present the only place to see this species is in Zombitse-Vohibasia National Park.

Lepilemuridae

Fig. 8.48: Zombitse sportive lemur (*Lepilemur hubbardorum*), Zombitse National Park (photo by I. Relanzón).

Lepilemuridae

Fig. 8.49: Zombitse sportive lemur (*Lempilemur hubbardorum*), Zombitse-Vohibasia National Park (photo by R. A. Mittermeier).

Fig. 8.50: A second individual of the Zombitse sportive lemur (*Lempilemur hubbardorum*) (photo by R. A. Mittermeier).

Lepilemur petteri Louis *et al.*, 2006
Petter's Sportive Lemur

Other English: None
French: Lépilémur de Petter
German: Petter's Wieselmaki
Malagasy: Apongy, Fitsidika

Lepilemuridae

Identification

Lepilemur petteri is a small southern *Lepilemur*, similar to *L. leucopus* but slightly larger. It has a head-body length of 23 cm, a tail length of 24 cm, a total length of 47 cm, and a body weight of roughly 630 g (Louis *et al.*, 2006b). The pelage is gray to grayish-brown above and whitish-gray below, with a diffuse brownish-gray on the anterior aspect of the thighs and along the dorsal midline. The face is gray with lighter circular patches around the eyes and under the chin, and the ears are trimmed in lighter fur, highlighting the dark brownish-gray inner lining (Louis *et al.*, 2006b).

Geographic Range

Southwestern Madagascar. This species is currently known only from the Beza-Mahafaly region, south of the Onilahy River and west of the Linta River. Further studies are needed to determine the northern extent of the species' distribution. In addition, studies should be conducted in the remaining forest regions around the Linta and Menarandra rivers to determine the range of both *L. petteri* and *Lepilemur leucopus* (see Louis *et al.*, 2006b). Formerly, the sportive lemur from the Beza-Mahafaly region was thought to be *L. leucopus*.

Natural History

Lepilemur petteri has been studied in the Beza-Mahafaly Special Reserve (Nash, 1998), where it occurs mainly in deciduous thicket or thorn scrub as well as in the limited gallery forest present there.

Conservation Status

There is insufficient information to determine the conservation status of *L. petteri*, so the latest IUCN Red List assessment (2008) classified it as Data Deficient (DD). It is known to occur in one protected area, the Beza-Mahafaly Special Reserve (Louis *et al.*, 2006b).

As of 2010, this species was not being kept in captivity (I. J. Porton, pers. comm.).

Where to See It

Thus far, the only places where this species can be seen is in the Beza-Mahafaly Special Reserve and in the nearby Classified Forest, 35 km northeast of Betioky Sud, about a five-hour drive from Toliara (= Tuléar) in a four-wheel-drive vehicle (Ratsirarson, 2003; Bradt, 2007).

Fig. 8.51: Petter's sportive lemur (*Lepilemur petteri*), Beza-Mahafaly Special Reserve (photo by R. Randrianampionona).

Lepilemur leucopus (Forsyth Major, 1894)
White-footed Sportive Lemur

Other English: White-footed Weasel Lemur
French: Lépilémur à pattes blanches
German: Weissfuss-Wieselmaki
Malagasy: Songiky

Lepilemuridae

Identification

Lepilemur leucopus is one of the smallest sportive lemurs, with a head-body length of 19–26 cm, a tail length of 22–26 cm, a total length of 41–52 cm, and a body weight of 500–700 g (Russell, 1977; Louis *et al.*, 2006b; Garbutt, 2007). The dorsal coat, including the head, is pale gray tending toward brown at the shoulders, upper forelimbs, and upper thighs, while the underside is grayish-white and often conspicuous along the flanks and around the base of the tail, even when the animal is clinging to a vertical support. The tail is grayish-brown. The face is grayish-brown, and the eyes are marked by whitish spectacles. The ears are relatively large, rounded and have whitish tufts at their bases.

This species is sympatric with *Microcebus* and *Cheirogaleus*. It is most likely to be confused with *Cheirogaleus*, but can usually be distinguished by its vertical clinging posture and tendency to leap from one support to another rather than moving quadrupedally along branches as dwarf lemurs do.

Geographic Range

The white-footed sportive lemur is found in spiny forest, gallery forest, and subtropical dry lowland forest (sea level to 300 m) in southern and southwestern Madagascar, from the spiny forest portion of Andohahela National Park in the eastern part of its range to the Onilahy River along the west coast (Petter *et al.*, 1977; Tattersall, 1982; Sussman and Richard, 1986; Louis *et al.*, 2006b).

Natural History

Lepilemur leucopus has been studied mainly in the gallery forest and spiny forest of the Berenty Private Reserve (Charles-Dominique and Hladik, 1971; Hladik and Charles-Dominique, 1974; Russell, 1977, 1980). Densities in both types of forest have been estimated at several hundred animals per square kilometer (Charles-Dominique and Hladik, 1971; Hladik and Charles-Dominique, 1974). Territories are small, much less than a hectare in size, and are defended by both males and females. The two sexes may sleep separately or together during the day, either in tree holes or liana tangles. In spiny bush forests, leaves of the spiny *Alluaudia procera* and *Alluaudia ascendens* trees are mainstays of the diet, with flowers providing supplementary food during the dry season. This is also the only lemur known to engage in cecotrophy (the ingestion of the extruded contents of its cecum, as practiced also by rabbits) to extract maximum nutrition from the food eaten (Charles-Dominique and Hladik, 1971).

Fig. 8.52: White-footed sportive lemur (*Lepilemur leucopus*), in a daytime sleeping site in the Berenty Private Reserve (photos by R. A. Mittermeier).

Conservation Status

There is insufficient information to determine the conservation status of *L. leucopus*, so the latest IUCN Red List assessment (2008) classified it as Data Deficient (DD). The principal threat is habitat destruction to clear land for pasture and the felling of trees for charcoal production. Protected areas in which it is known to occur include two national parks (the spiny desert portions of Andohahela and Tsimanampetsotsa) and the Berenty Private Reserve. Consideration should be given to the establishment of a new protected area toward the center of its range.

As of 2010, this species was not being kept in captivity (I. J. Porton, pers. comm.).

Where to See It

The easiest place to see *L. leucopus* is in the Berenty Private Reserve, where it occurs in the gallery forest and spiny bush, and can be quite common. It may also be observed in the spiny forest patches of Andohahela National Park.

Fig. 8.53: White-footed sportive lemur (*Lepilemur leucopus*) in an *Alluaudia* tree, Anjapolo parcel, Berenty Private Reserve (photo by R. A. Mittermeier).

Fig. 8.54: Another white-footed sportive lemur in spiny forest, Berenty Private Reserve (photo by R. A. Mittermeier).

Fig. 8.55: White-footed sportive lemur (*Lepilemur leucopus*) in an *Alluaudia* tree in the spiny forest of the Berenty Private Reserve (photo by R. A. Mittermeier).

Lemuridae

Fig. 9.1: Gray bamboo lemur (*Hapalemur griseus griseus*), Andasibe (photo by I. Relanzón).

CHAPTER 9

FAMILY LEMURIDAE Gray, 1821

The family Lemuridae consists of two main subgroupings that include the best known and most widespread of the lemurs. The genera *Lemur*, *Eulemur*, and *Varecia* all are considered "true lemurs" and have diets that are largely made up of fruits and leaves. The bamboo lemurs, which include the genera *Hapalemur* and *Prolemur*, specialize in eating bamboo although they take other food items as well.

Members of the Lemuridae range in weight from 700 g to 4.5 kg. With forelimbs slightly shorter than hindlimbs, they move largely quadrupedally along branches and will leap across gaps in the forest. Typically they live in groups and are active during the day, but all except the ruffed lemurs (*Varecia*) and the ring-tailed lemurs (*Lemur*) are also active a certain amount of time during the night, exhibiting an activity pattern referred to as *cathemeral* (Tattersall, 1987). The extent of this nocturnal activity remains poorly documented in many species, and represents a growing area of interest among primatologists (Curtis and Rasmussen, 2006; Donati *et al.*, 2007; Kappeler and Erkert, 2003).

Until the late 1980s, the genus *Lemur* was considered to include six species and to be closely related to the genus *Varecia*. However, both Simons and Rumpler (1988) and Groves and Eaglen (1988) suggested that the ring-tailed lemur, *Lemur catta*, had closer affinities to the bamboo lemurs, *Hapalemur*, and should therefore be distinguished from other members of the family. As a result, the other species were placed in the genus *Eulemur*, with only *L. catta* remaining in the genus *Lemur*.

More recently, Groves (2001) placed the former *Hapalemur simus* in its own genus, *Prolemur*, based on a suite of distinctive dental, chromosomal, and behavioral characteristics, and also because its retention in *Hapalemur* would have made the latter genus paraphyletic (since the sister genus to the *Hapalemur griseus* group is *Lemur*, not "*H.*" *simus*). We continue to follow this recommendation here, and recognize *Hapalemur* and *Prolemur* as distinct genera (Vuillaume-Randriamanantena *et al.*, 1985; Macedonia and Stanger, 1994; Stanger-Hall, 1997).

Hapalemur I. Geoffroy, 1851
Bamboo or Gentle Lemurs

Members of the genus *Hapalemur* are best known for a diet dominated by bamboo (Rand, 1935); an unusual ecological specialization among primates. All authorities agree in placing the bamboo lemurs in the family Lemuridae, although considerable uncertainty remains regarding their relationships to other genera in the family.

The genus *Hapalemur* can be readily distinguished from *Lemur*, *Eulemur*, and *Varecia* by features of the head, including its round shape, large face, short muzzle, and ears that are largely hidden by fur. All *Hapalemur* are medium to small, grayish animals, have moderately long hindlimbs, prefer vertical resting postures, and leap readily between closely-spaced vertical supports. They tend to be crepuscular in their habits. As in *Lemur*, brachial and antebrachial glands are present (Macedonia and Stanger, 1994).

Lemuridae

Hapalemur taxonomy, including phylogenetic relationships among members of this genus, is a source of continuing debate (Fausser *et al.*, 2002a, 2002b; Pastorini *et al.*, 2002a, 2002b; Rumpler *et al.*, 2002; Rabarivola *et al.*, 2007). Most authors over the past two decades recognized three species of bamboo lemur: *Hapalemur griseus* (with at least three subspecies), *H. aureus*, and *H. simus* (see Mittermeier *et al.*, 1994). Groves (2001) recently elevated three *Hapalemur griseus* subspecies to full species status as *H. griseus*, *H. alaotrensis* and *H. occidentalis*, and placed *Hapalemur simus* in its own genus, *Prolemur*. He did not, however, recognize the southern bamboo lemur, *Hapalemur* (*griseus*) *meridionalis* Warter *et al.*, 1987, which Fausser *et al.* (2002a, 2002b) believe is a full species. In this guide, we follow Groves (2001) in moving *H. simus* to the genus *Prolemur* and in elevating *H. g. griseus*, *H. g. alaotrensis* and *H. g. occidentalis* to full species, but also follow Fausser *et al.* (2002) in recognizing *H. meridionalis* as a full species.

In 2007, Rabarivola *et al.* described two new subspecies of *H. griseus* (*H. g. ranomafanensis* and *H. g. gilberti*). They were described as subspecies rather than as distinct species because available molecular data do not distinguish them. In total, therefore, we currently recognize five species and seven taxa in this genus: *H. griseus* (with three subspecies), *H. occidentalis*, *H. alaotrensis*, *H. meridionalis*, and *H. aureus*. However, it is clear that additional research is needed to clarify evolutionary, distributional, and taxonomic relationships in this genus, and also that there may still be new taxa to be discovered.

Fig. 9.2: Gray bamboo lemur (*Hapalemur griseus*), Ile des Lemuriens, Hotel Vakona, Andasibe (photo by R. A. Mittermeier).

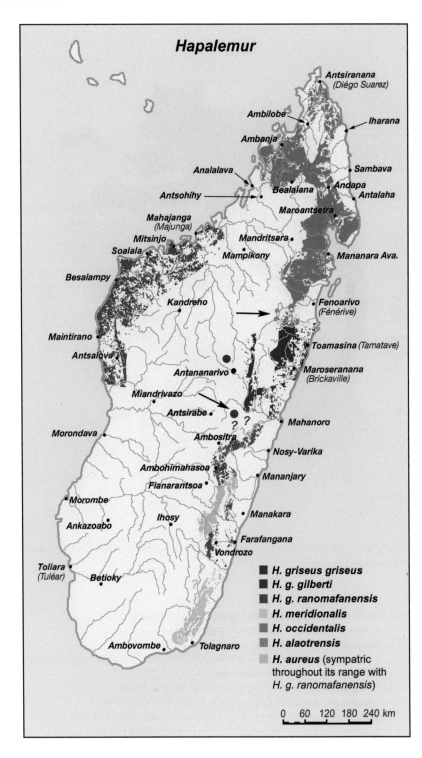

Hapalemur

Antsiranana
(Diégo Suarez)

Ambilobe

Iharana

Ambanja

Analalava

Sambava

Antsohihy

Bealalana

Andapa

Antalaha

Maroantsetra

Mahajanga
(Majunga)

Mitsinjo

Mandritsara

Soalala

Mampikony

Mananara Ava.

Besalampy

Kandreho

Fenoarivo
(Fénérive)

Maintirano

Toamasina (Tamatave)

Antsalova

Maroseranana
(Brickaville)

Antananarivo

Miandrivazo

Antsirabe

Mahanoro

? ?

Morondava

Ambositra

Nosy-Varika

Ambohimahasoa

Mananjary

Fianarantsoa

Morombe

Ihosy

Manakara

Ankazoabo

Farafangana

Vondrozo

Toliara
(Tuléar)

Betioky

■ **H. griseus griseus**
■ **H. g. gilberti**
■ **H. g. ranomafanensis**
   H. meridionalis
■ **H. occidentalis**
■ **H. alaotrensis**
   H. aureus (sympatric
   throughout its range with
   H. g. ranomafanensis)

Ambovombe

Tolagnaro

0   60   120   180   240 km

Lemuridae

Fig. 9.3: Distribution of *Hapalemur*.

P.Z.S.1870. Pl. LII.

J. Smit

J Smit lith.   M.& N Hanhart imp.

HAPALEMUR SIMUS.

Fig. 9.4: A hand-colored lithograph of *Prolemur simus* by J. Smit, published in the *Proceedings of the Zoological Society of London* in 1870.

Fig. 9.5: *Hapalemur* postural and behavioral drawings (next page):

   a. *Hapalemur griseus* in a vertical clinging rest posture
   b. *Hapalemur griseus* resting, braced between two trunks
   c. *Hapalemur griseus* sitting on a horizontal branch
   d. *Hapalemur aureus* descending a branch
   e. *Hapalemur aureus* reaching up to feed on bamboo shoots
   f. *Hapalemur griseus* looking around in a vertical clinging posture
   g. *Hapalemur aureus* using a vertical clinging posture to feed on bamboo
   h. *Hapalemur griseus* with an infant in a crouched sitting posture
   i. *Hapalemur griseus* with an infant in a crouched sitting posture (the adult's mouth
      is open in threat)

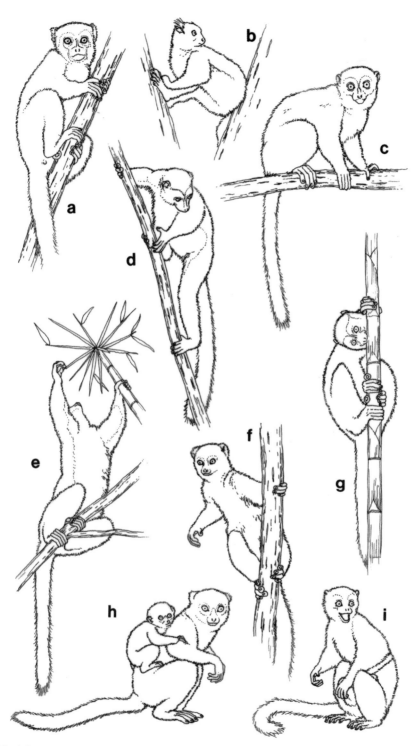

Fig. 9.5.

Lemuridae

**Gray Bamboo
Lemur**
*Hapalemur griseus
griseus*

**Beanamalao
Bamboo Lemur**
*Hapalemur
griseus gilberti*

**Ranomafana
Bamboo Lemur**
*Hapalemur
griseus
ranomafanensis*

**Southern Bamboo
Lemur**
Hapalemur meridionalis

Fig. 9.6.

Northern Bamboo Lemur
Hapalemur occidentalis

Lac Alaotra Bamboo Lemur
Hapalemur alaotrensis

Golden Bamboo Lemur
Hapalemur aureus

Fig. 9.7.

Hapalemur griseus griseus (Link, 1795)
Gray Bamboo Lemur

Other English: Eastern Gray Bamboo Lemur, Eastern Lesser
Bamboo Lemur, Gray Gentle Lemur
French: Petit Hapalémur gris
German: Östlicher Bambuslemur, Grauer Bambuslemur
Malagasy: Bokombolo, Kotrika, Kontè (Ambalarondra region)

Identification

Hapalemur griseus is the best known of the bamboo lemurs and also one of the smallest.
The nominate form has a head-body length of around 30 cm, a tail length of 37 cm, a total
length of 67 cm, and a weight of 700–850 g (Glander *et al.*, 1992; Terranova and Coffman,
1997; Rabarivola *et al.*, 2007; C. P. Groves, pers. comm.). The coat color ranges from
gray to olivaceous to rust-brown, and there are usually darker and more reddish patches
on the head and shoulders. The face is lighter colored. Males and females are not sexually
dimorphic.

Bamboo lemurs are easy to identify. They are different from members of the genus
Eulemur (the only other sympatric diurnal lemurs with which they might be confused) in
being considerably smaller and in having a shorter muzzle. They are also usually found in
or near stands of bamboo.

Geographic Range

Before recent taxonomic splitting of what was thought
to be the most widespread of the bamboo lemurs, the
presumed range of *Hapalemur griseus* extended through
all remaining tropical moist lowland and montane forests
in eastern Madagascar, from the latitude of Lake Alaotra in
the north to Ranomafana in the south, wherever bamboo is
present (Rabarivola *et al.*, 2007). However, the geographic
distributions of the different forms that make up this genus
have recently been revised by Rabarivola *et al.* (2007).
According to these authors the nominate form, *H. g. griseus*,
is now restricted to central-eastern Madagascar, roughly
from the Onibe River south to the Nesivolo River (which
separates it from *Hapalemur griseus gilberti*).

Natural History

Field studies have been carried out on this subspecies in
Analamazaotra. There, population density was estimated at
47–62 individuals/km² (Pollock, 1979b), and home range
size at 6–10 ha (Wright, 1986).

Conservation Status

The most recent IUCN Red List assessment (2008) classified *H. griseus griseus* as
Vulnerable (VU). However, this subspecies now has a smaller range than was believed at

Fig. 9.8: Gray bamboo lemur (*Hapalemur griseus griseus*), Lemurs' Park (lemurspark@ wanadoo.mg) (photo by R. A. Mittermeier).

Lemuridae

Fig. 9.9: Gray bamboo lemur (*Hapalemur griseus griseus*) in a patch of bamboo in the Analamazaotra Special Reserve, Andasibe (photo by R. A. Mittermeier).

the time of the 2006 Red List assessment and needs to be reassessed. It is known to occur in two special reserves (Analamazaotra and Mangerivola), as well as in the Betampona Strict Nature Reserve and Mantadia National Park (E. E. Louis Jr., pers. obs.).

As of 2010, there was a small captive population of around 16 individuals in Europe and North America listed as *Hapalemur griseus*. Unfortunately, these animals are of unknown origin and very possibly hybridized with other *Hapalemur* taxa (ISIS, 2009).

Where to See It

The best place to see *H. griseus griseus* on the tourist circuit is at Andasibe (= Périnet) (Analamazaotra Special Reserve and Mantadia National Park). In this area and elsewhere, it is most likely to be observed at dusk in stands of common bamboo. In Analamazaotra, a group is often seen in bamboo right next to an old warden's house near the fish ponds, in various bamboo stands on the trail into the indri viewing area, and sometimes even along the main road heading into Andasibe village.

Fig. 9.10: Gray bamboo lemur (*Hapalemur griseus griseus*), Ile des Lemuriens, Andasibe (photo by R. A. Mittermeier).

Lemuridae

Hapalemur griseus gilberti Rabarivola *et al.* 2007
Beanamalao Bamboo Lemur

Other English: Gilbert's Bamboo Lemur, Gilbert's Gentle Lemur
French: Hapalémur du Beanamalao, Hapalémur du Gilbert
German: Gilbert's Bambuslemur
Malagasy: Bokombolo, Kotrika

Identification

Hapalemur griseus gilberti is larger than *Hapalemur g. griseus*, *H. g. ranomafanensis* or *H. meridionalis*, averaging 967 g, although the actual head-body length is smaller, about 28 cm. The tail is about 35 cm long. Males and females are similar in size. The dorsal fur is gray-brown, while the underside is gray in its anterior part and reddish in the posterior. The tail is dark gray. The face has a dark gray ring encircling the eyes, which is gray above (Rabarivola *et al.*, 2007). The ear is shorter than that of *H. griseus griseus* or *H. meridionalis* (C. P. Groves, pers. comm.).

Bamboo lemurs are easy to identify. They are smaller and have shorter muzzles than do members of the genus *Eulemur* (the only other sympatric diurnal lemurs with which they might be confused). They are also usually in stands of bamboo.

Geographic Range

East-central Madagascar. Known only from the type locality of Beanamalao, and presumably a small area north of the Nesivolo River and south of the Mangoro and Onive Rivers (Rabarivola *et al.*, 2007). Further field studies are required to determine the exact extent of the distribution, and in particular the boundaries between it and the other two subspecies of *H. griseus*.

Natural History

As of 2010, this species had not been studied in the wild.

Conservation Status

There is not enough information to determine the conservation status of *H. g. gilberti*, so the latest IUCN Red List assessment (2008) classified it as Data Deficient (DD). It is not known to occur in any protected areas.

In 2010, some these bamboo lemurs were being kept at Tsimbazaza Zoo, Madagascar (E. E. Louis Jr., pers. obs.).

Where to See It

At present the only place where one can be sure to see this subspecies is at the type locality of Beanamalao.

Fig. 9.11: Beanamalao bamboo lemur (*Hapalemur griseus gilberti*).

Hapalemur griseus ranomafanensis Rabarivola *et al.* 2007
Ranomafana Bamboo Lemur

Other English: Ranomafana Gentle Lemur
French: Hapalémur du Ranomafana
German: Ranomafana-Bambuslemur
Malagasy: Bokombolo, Kotrika

Identification

Hapalemur griseus ranomafanensis is approximately the same size as *H. g. griseus*, with a head-body length of around 30 cm, a tail length 37 cm, a total length 67 cm, and a weight of 700–850 g (Glander *et al.*, 1992; Terranova and Coffman, 1997; Rabarivola *et al.*, 2007; C. P. Groves, pers. comm.). The upperparts are gray to olive-gray, while the face and underparts are lighter. The tail is gray. The fur around the eyes is a paler gray, and the ears are small and rounded (Rabarivola *et al.*, 2007). Males and females are similar in size.

Bamboo lemurs are easy to identify. They are smaller and have shorter muzzles than do members of the genus *Eulemur* (the only other sympatric diurnal lemurs with which they might be confused). They are also usually associated with stands of bamboo. In Ranomafana National Park this subspecies is sympatric with *H. aureus* and *Prolemur simus* (Wright, 1992; Sterling and Ramoroson, 1996; Goodman *et al.*, 2001). With a clear sighting, *H. griseus ranomafanensis* can be distinguished from *H. aureus* by its smaller size and lack of a golden-colored face, and from *Prolemur simus* by its much smaller size and the lack of prominent ear tufts.

Geographic Range

This subspecies evidently occurs in two, widely separated population pockets in east-central and west-central Madagascar, respectively. In the east, it is known from the eastern forests to the south of the Mangoro and Onive rivers (except Beanamalao, which is the type locality of *H. g. gilberti*) in the forests of Ranomafana and Kianjavato. In the west, it has been reported from the western forests of Tsingy de Bemaraha, probably as far as the Betsiboka River (Rabarivola *et al.*, 2007). Further field studies are required to determine the exact extent of the distribution of *H. g. ranomafanensis*, in particular the boundaries between it and neighboring forms of *Hapalemur*.

Natural History

This is the best-studied of the three *Hapalemur griseus* subspecies. Home range size has been estimated to be as much as 15 to 20 ha at Ranomafana (Wright, 1989; Overdorff *et al.*, 1999; Tan, 1999). Group size varies from two to seven, and groups can contain more than one breeding female (Pollock, 1986b; Tan, 1999). Territories are defended by scent-marking, vocal displays, and chasing. Both males and females are reported to disperse from their natal groups.

Lemuridae

Fig. 9.12: Ranomafana bamboo lemur (*Hapalemur griseus ranomafanensis*), Ranomafana National Park (photo by D. Haring/DLC).

Fig. 9.13: Another Ranomafana bamboo lemur (*Hapalemur griseus ranomafanensis*), Ranomafana National Park (photo by D. Haring/DLC).

Bamboo constitutes at least three-quarters of the diet, primarily new shoots and leaf bases to which these lemurs gain access by pulling new leaves from the end of a branch, biting the soft base, and discarding the tough leaf blade. Other food items include fig leaves, grass stems, young leaves, small fruits, flowers, and fungi (Wright, 1986; Overdorff et al., 1997; Tan, 1999).

The birth season is essentially October–January, following a gestation of 137–140 days (Petter and Peyriéras, 1970a; Pollock, 1986b; Wright, 1990; Tan, 2000). Single infants are the rule, and the inter-birth interval is typically one year. Infants are first carried in the mother's mouth, then on her back a few weeks after birth, and eventually she is able to "park" them for short periods while she forages (Tan, 2000).

Conservation Status

The conservation status of this subspecies has yet to be assessed. It is found in at least two protected areas (Ranomafana National Park and Tsingy de Bemaraha National Park) (Rabarivola et al., 2007).

As of 2010, several individuals were being kept at Tsimbazaza Zoo, Madagascar (E. E. Louis Jr., pers. obs.).

Where to See It

This subspecies can be seen in Ranomafana National Park, most likely at dusk in stands of common bamboo. Opportunities exist in areas of dense bamboo in the Tsingy de Bemaraha National Park as well.

Lemuridae

Hapalemur meridionalis Warter *et al.*, 1987
Southern Bamboo Lemur

Other English: Rusty-gray Bamboo Lemur, Southern Lesser
Bamboo Lemur, Southern Gentle Lemur
French: Hapalémur méridional
German: Südlicher Bambuslemur
Malagasy: Halo

Identification

Hapalemur meridionalis was first proposed as a subspecies of *H. griseus* by Warter *et al.* (1987), based on cytogenetic studies as well as differences in body size and coloration. It is similar in size to *Hapalemur griseus griseus* and *Hapalemur griseus gilberti*, with a total length of 65–68 cm and a body weight of 840–870 g (Rabarivola *et al.*, 2007; C. P. Groves, pers. comm.). Its coat color, however, is apparently darker and redder, the ears are longer, and the tail is shorter (Groves, 2001). Mutschler (2000) also found that the vocalizations of *Hapalemur meridionalis* distinguish it from *Hapalemur* populations to the north.

In Andringitra National Park, this species is sympatric with *Hapalemur aureus* and *Prolemur simus* (Wright, 1992; Sterling and Ramoroson, 1996; Goodman *et al.*, 2001). With a clear sighting, *H. meridionalis* can be distinguished from *H. aureus* by its smaller size and lack of a golden-colored face, and from *Prolemur simus* by its much smaller size and the lack of prominent ear tufts.

Geographic Range

This is the southernmost of the bamboo lemurs. The type locality is the forestry station of Mandena, approximately 10 km north of Tolagnaro (= Fort-Dauphin) in southern Madagascar (Warter and Tattersall, 1994). Rabarivola *et al.* (2007) recorded it also at Andohahela National Park. A cytogenetic study indicated that an animal from the Atsimo region was a hybrid between this species and *H. griseus ranomafanensis*. At present, *H. meridionalis* would appear to be found from Mandena and the Andohahela region extending north. However, it has yet to be determined how far north it occurs or where the hybrid zone begins and ends (Rabarivola *et al.*, 2007).

Natural History

The behavior and ecology of this species are poorly known. *Hapalemur meridionalis* was first found in degraded littoral forests dominated by *Ravenala madagascariensis* and *Pandanus*, and with only patchy stands of bamboo (Mutschler and Tan, 2003), but it is now known to occur in subtropical moist lowland and montane forests up to 1,600 m. It is believed to live in relatively small groups (T. Mutschler, pers. comm.).

Lemuridae

Fig. 9.14: Southern bamboo lemur (*Hapalemur meridionalis*), Mandena Conservation Zone (photo by I. Relanzón).

Conservation Status

The most recent IUCN Red List assessment (2008) classified *H. meridionalis* as Vulnerable (VU). The principal threat is habitat loss due to slash-and-burn agriculture, but also due to charcoal production, logging, and mining. The species is reported to occur in three national parks (Andohahela, Andringitra, and Midongy du Sud), three special reserves (Kalambatritra, Manombo, and Pic d' Ivohibe), and in the Mandena Conservation Zone (Feistner and Schmid, 1999; Rabarivola *et al.*, 2007; P. C. Wright, pers. comm.).

As of 2010, this species was not being kept in captivity (I. J. Porton, pers. comm.).

Where to See It

It is possible to see this species in the rain forest portion (Parcel 1) of Andohahela National Park, especially along the road to Col de Manangotry a few hours drive by car from Tolagnaro (= Fort-Dauphin). It can also be seen in the Mandena Conservation Zone and in the Jardin de Nampoana, approximately 20 minutes northeast of Tolagnaro. Visitors hoping to see it in this area can arrange for vehicles and hotels in Tolagnaro. Midongy du Sud National Park is another place to see *H. meridionalis*, but only the well-seasoned traveler should try this park, since the journey is difficult and can only be done during the drier months.

Lemuridae

Fig. 9.15: Southern bamboo lemur (*Hapalemur meridionalis*), Mandena Conservation Zone (photo by I. Relanzón).

Fig. 9.16: A bamboo lemur from Midongy du Sud National Park of uncertain identity (photo by J. Zaonarivelo).

Hapalemur occidentalis Rumpler, 1975
Northern Bamboo Lemur

Other English: Western Lesser Bamboo Lemur, Western Gentle
Lemur
French: Hapalémur occidental
German: Westlicher Bambuslemur
Malagasy: Bokombolo, Akomba-Valiha, Bekola, Kofiy,
Kitronytrony

Identification

Hapalemur occidentalis is similar in size to *Hapalemur griseus*, with a head-body
length of 27–28 cm, a tail length of 36–39 cm, and a total length of 55–67 cm. It appears to
show a noteworthy degree of sexual dimorphism in terms of weight, with males averaging
846 g, but females reaching 1,188 g (E. E. Louis Jr., unpubl. data). It is more uniformly
gray-brown in coat color than *H. griseus*, and its face is paler than other members of the
genus. Ear length is similar to *H. griseus* (Groves, 2001; C. P. Groves, pers. comm.). It
differs in diploid chromosome number (2n = 58) from *H. griseus* and *H. alaotrensis* (2n =
54) (Rabarivola *et al.*, 2007).

This species is unlikely to be confused with other diurnal lemurs in its range. It is
considerably smaller than any of the *Eulemur* species and is usually associated with stands
of bamboo.

Geographic Range

The northern bamboo lemur occurs in a number of
discontinuous pockets in western and northern Madagascar.
It is known from the forests of Ankarana and Analamerana
in the far north, the Sambirano region, the Ampasindava
Peninsula, and the Sahamalaza region (north of the
Andranomalaza River) in the northwest; the Tsiombikibo,
Baie de Baly, Tsingy de Namoroka and Bongolava regions
in the central-west between the Mahavavy and Tsiribihina
Rivers; Masoala, Maroansetra and Ile Roger (Aye-aye
Island) in the northeast; and as far south as Zahamena and
Marovohangy near Lake Alaotra (Tattersall, 1982; Hawkins
et al., 1990, 1998; Rakotoarison *et al.*, 1993; Curtis *et al.*,
1995; Rabarivola *et al.*, 2007; Y. Rumpler, pers. comm.; C.
Schwitzer, pers. obs.). Information on which forests may or
may not be contiguous remains to be determined.

Natural History

Little is known about the ecology and behavior of *H.
occidentalis*. It evidently has a preference for forests that contain bamboo or bamboo vines
(Petter and Peyriéras, 1970a; Tattersall, 1982). It has also been reported from degraded
habitats in the Sambirano River valley, as well as in patches of bamboo surrounded by
agricultural land (Mutschler, 2000). A survey conducted in the Manongarivo Special
Reserve found this species to be diurnal and its group size to be small, usually no more than
four individuals (Raxworthy and Rakotondraparany, 1988). However, in the Sambirano

region, Mutschler (2000) described it as being active mainly at night, and also reported observing a group of six individuals.

The birth season is roughly October–January, following a gestation of 137–140 days (Petter and Peyriéras, 1970a; Pollock, 1986b; Tan, 2000). Single infants are the rule, and the interbirth interval is typically one year. Infants are first carried from the mother's mouth, then on her back a few weeks after birth, and eventually she is able to "park" them for short periods of time while she forages (Tan, 2000).

Lemuridae

Fig. 9.17: Northern bamboo lemur (*Hapalemur occidentalis*) from Benavony, about 6 km south of Ambanja, northwestern Madagascar (photo by R. A. Mittermeier).

Lemuridae

Fig. 9.18: Northern bamboo lemur (*Hapalemur occidentalis*), Marojejy National Park, northeastern Madagascar (photo by E. E. Louis Jr.).

Conservation Status

The most recent IUCN Red List assessment (2008) classified *H. occidentalis* as Vulnerable (VU). The principal threat is habitat loss due to regular burning to create pasture for livestock, charcoal production, and mining. Recent studies in the Makira Forest documented the hunting of this species, but did not determine whether current levels were sustainable (Golden, 2005). Its presence is reported in eight national parks (Ankarana, Baie de Baly, Mananara-Nord, Marojejy, Masoala, Sahamalaza-Iles Radama, Tsingy de Namoroka, and Zahamena), two strict nature reserves (Tsaratanana and Zahamena), and eight special reserves (Ambatovaky, Analamerana, Anjanaharibe-Sud, Bemarivo, Kasijy, Maningoza, Manongarivo, and Marotandrano) (Nicoll and Langrand, 1989; Schmid and Smolker, 1998; Hawkins *et al.*, 1998; Thalmann *et al.*, 1999; Randrianarisoa *et al.*, 2001a, 2001b; C. P. Groves, pers. comm.; Rabarivola *et al.*, 2007; C. Schwitzer, pers. obs.). Recent surveys, however, did not encounter any animals in Analamerana or Ankarana, just in a single patch of unprotected forest in the corridor that connects these reserves (Banks, 2005). The *Hapalemur* at Tsingy de Bemaraha National Park, previously thought to be this species, is now thought to be *H. g. ranomafanensis* (see Rabarivola *et al.* 2007).

As of 2010, there was a small, non-breeding population of around 18 in various European zoos (C. Schwitzer, pers. obs.; I. J. Porton, pers. comm.).

Where to See It

This lemur is not easily seen and is apparently nowhere common. Garbutt (2007) and R. A. Mittermeier (pers. obs.) have seen *H. occidentalis* in forests along the Sambirano River Valley near the village of Benavony, southeast of Ambanja, and it has also been seen on Nosy Faly, peninsula approximately 30 km northeast of Ambanja. There are simple hotel accommodations in Ambanja and better accommodations at Ankify nearby. Sightings are also possible around Lac Bemamba and in the Manongarivo Special Reserve, but one might have to spend several days to ensure success. On the eastern side of its range, it can also be seen in the national parks of Marojejy and Masoala.

Lemuridae

Hapalemur alaotrensis Rumpler, 1975
Lac Alaotra Bamboo Lemur

Other English: Alaotran Bamboo Lemur, Lac Alaotra Gentle
Lemur
French: Hapalémur du Lac Alaotra
German: Lac Alaotra-Bambuslemur
Malagasy: Bandro

Identification

Hapalemur alaotrensis is larger than all other *Hapalemur* except for *H. aureus* (see
Vuillaume-Randriamanantena *et al.*, 1985). Head-body length and tail length are about
equal at 40 cm, and the average total length is 80 cm. Adult body weight ranges from
1.1–1.55 kg, with males usually slightly larger than females (Mutschler, 1999; Ralainasolo,
2004; Rabarivola *et al.*, 2007). The pelage is dense and woolly. It is gray-brown on the
dorsal coat, and the face and ventral coat are a lighter gray. The crown and nape are
chestnut-brown.

The species is not likely to be confused with other lemurs in the field since it is the
only diurnal lemur in its unusual reed bed habitat. The only other species reported to
be sympatric with it is a mouse lemur, which is much smaller and entirely nocturnal (J.
Ratsimbazafy, pers. obs.).

Geographic Range

The Alaotran bamboo lemur is known only from
the papyrus and reed beds surrounding Lac Alaotra,
Madagascar's largest lake, on the western edge of the
eastern rain forest region (Mutschler and Feistner, 1995).
There are two subpopulations, a small one in the northern
part of the lake around the Belempona Peninsula and a
larger one in the adjoining marshlands along the lake's
southwestern shores (Mutschler *et al.*, 2001). Its entire
range is evidently less than 9,000 ha, and it occurs only up
to elevations of 750 m.

Natural History

In its unique marshland habitat, this lemur feeds
principally on four food items: the pithy stems of
papyrus (*Cyperus madagascariensis*), tender shoots of
reeds (*Phragmites communis*), and two species of grass
(*Echinocochla crusgalli* and *Leersia hexandra*) (Mutschler,
1999).

Active mainly during daylight hours, *H. alaotrensis* also exhibits significant nocturnal
activity, a pattern referred to as cathemeral (Mutschler *et al.*, 1998). The typical mode of
locomotion is vertical clinging and leaping, and there are reports of it swimming (Petter
and Peyriéras, 1975).

Lemuridae

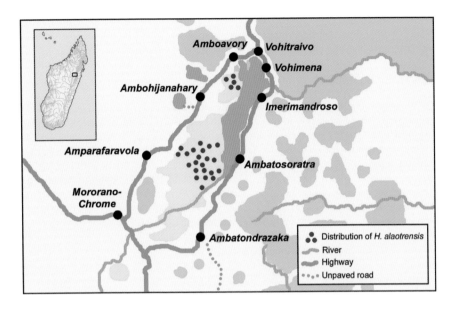

Fig. 9.19: Distribution of *Hapalemur alaotrensis*.

Fig. 9.20: Lac Alaotra bamboo lemur (*Hapalemur alaotrensis*), Andreba village, Lac Alaotra (photo by R. A. Mittermeier).

The Lac Alaotra bamboo lemur lives in family groups of up to a dozen members, and defends territories ranging in size from 1 to 8 ha (Nievergelt *et al.*, 1998; Razafindramahatra, 2004; J. Durbin, pers. comm.). Young are born from September through February and twins are common (Mutschler *et al.*, 2000). Groups may contain more than one breeding female.

Conservation Status

The most recent IUCN Red List assessment (2008) classified *H. alaotrensis* as Critically Endangered (CR). Conversion of marsh habitat to rice fields has been the most significant historical threat, to the point where little suitable land remains on which local farmers might cultivate this crop. Hunting for food and capture for pets have also reduced lemur numbers (Petter and Peyriéras, 1970a; Jolly *et al.*, 1984). Various methods of hunting and trapping are employed by local people. Direct pursuit by dogs is the most common, but they may also be captured by using a harpoon, a snare, a stick to knock them out or into the water, by burning their reed bed habitat, or just by chasing them down. Commercial drainage projects are a potential threat. Regular burning to increase cattle pasture, facilitate local fishing, and develop new rice fields in dry years reduces suitable lemur habitat and also promotes the invasion of exotic plant species that may choke the remaining marshes.

Population estimates for *H. alaotrensis* range from 2,500 to 5,000 individuals, representing a decline of approximately 30% in just over a decade (Ralainasolo, 2004; J. Ratsimbazafy, unpubl.). Thanks to efforts of Durrell, a new 42,478-ha protected area was created there in early 2007. This includes both a strict conservation area of 8,000 ha, and an adjacent 5,200-ha core zone of marsh where controlled activities (e.g., fishing) are permitted. In addition, public awareness campaigns continue to focus on the benefits of habitat conservation to the half million or more people who live by the lake. The benefits include erosion control, the biological filtering of agricultural pollutants, and flood prevention. Lac Alaotra is a 722,500-ha Ramsar wetland site, designated in 2003.

As of 2010 there was a small, self-sustaining population of around 66 individuals in various European zoos (I. J. Porton, pers. comm.). The captive population was first started by the Jersey Wildlife Preservation Trust (now Durrell) back in 1990, when the first wild animals were obtained, and is an excellent example of the role that captive breeding of an endangered species can play for conservation purposes.

Where to See It

The best way to see this cryptic and elusive lemur is to travel by pirogue through the reed beds of Lac Alaotra. When water levels are low, it can also be seen by walking in and around the reed beds, but it is helpful to have experienced guides familiar with the animal. The best starting points are Andreba on the eastern side of the lake or Andilana Atsimo on the western side. Both villages can be reached from Ambatondrazaka, the main town on the lake's south side. Ambatondrazaka offers simple hotel accommodation and can be reached in 40 minutes by plane or six to seven hours by car from Antananarivo.

Fig. 9.21: Lac Alaotra bamboo lemur (*Hapalemur alaotrensis*), Andreba village, Lac Alaotra (photo by R. A. Mittermeier).

Hapalemur aureus Meier *et al.*, 1987
Golden Bamboo Lemur

Other English: None
French: Hapalémur doré
German: Goldener Bambuslemur
Malagasy: Bokombolomena, Varibolomena

Identification

The golden bamboo lemur was first discovered in 1985, and was described two years later (Meier *et al.*, 1987). With an adult weight of approximately 1.3–1.7 kg, it is the largest member of the genus *Hapalemur*, since the greater bamboo lemur (formerly *H. simus*) has now been placed in its own genus, *Prolemur* (see Groves, 2001). Head-body length is about 34 cm and tail length about 41 cm, for an overall length of 70–80 cm. The dorsal coat is reddish-brown; darker on the shoulders, back, top of the head and tail. The tail also darkens toward the tip. The ventral coat, including the inner limbs, is a paler golden-brown. A pink nose contrasts with the dark muzzle, which is surrounded by a ring of gold-colored hair on the cheeks and around the eyes. The ears are tipped with golden-brown hairs, but are not tufted.

Hapalemur aureus is sympatric with *H. griseus ranomafanensis* in Ranomafana National Park, with *H. meridionalis* in Andringitra National Park, and with *Prolemur simus* in both of these protected areas. However, it can be readily distinguished from all of these taxa by its golden coloration, especially on the face. It is larger than the other two *Hapalemur* and smaller than *Prolemur*, and the lack of ear tufts also differentiates it from the latter. Molecular data support its inclusion in the genus *Hapalemur* (Pastorini *et al.*, 2002a, 2002b).

Geographic Range

Hapalemur aureus is known from tropical moist lowland and montane forests of southeastern Madagascar, at altitudes of 600–1,400 m (Arrigo-Nelson and Wright, 2004). It occurs in and around Ranomafana National Park, where it has been observed as far to the north as Miaranony, and also occurs at least as far south as Andringitra National Park and in the forest corridor that connects Ranomafana with Andringitra (Sterling and Ramaroson, 1996; Lehman and Wright, 2000; Goodman *et al.*, 2001; Arrigo-Nelson and Wright, 2004; Rakotondravony and Razafindramahatra, 2004; Irwin *et al.*, 2005). However, there has recently been an unconfirmed sighting of this species as far south as the Vevembe Forest (west of Vondrozo) (P. Rabeson, pers. comm.).

Natural History

The golden bamboo lemur is active during the day but has a distinct midday rest period. It lives in small groups of 3–4 individuals that maintain home ranges of up to 30 ha (Tan, 1999). At times, it can

Lemuridae

Fig. 9.22: Golden bamboo lemur (*Hapalemur aureus*), Ranomafana National Park (photo by I. Relanzón).

be quite vocal. Females give birth to a single young in November or December after a gestation of about 138 days. The young are born in an altricial state, and are kept safe in dense vegetation for the first two weeks of life (Mutschler and Tan, 2003).

Based on studies at Ranomafana National Park, as much as 90% of this lemur's diet consists of bamboo, principally giant bamboo (*Cathariostachys madagascariensis*), and the number of plant species it eats is quite low (Meier and Rumpler, 1987; Meier *et al.*, 1987; Mutschler and Tan, 2003). Young leaves and shoots are the plant parts most readily eaten. Glander *et al.* (1989) found astonishingly high levels of cyanide in the shoots of giant bamboo as well as in the blood and feces of the golden bamboo lemur, and suggest that similar levels in the diets of other mammals would be lethal. Presumably, this tolerance to dietary toxins allows *H. aureus* to live in sympatry with three other bamboo-eating lemurs, *H. meridionalis*, *H. g. ranomafanensis* and *Prolemur simus*, all of which appear to avoid either plant species or plant parts with such high cyanide levels (Wright, 1989).

Conservation Status

The IUCN Red List assessment of 2008 classified *H. aureus* as Endangered (EN). The principal threat to its survival is habitat loss due to slash-and-burn agriculture and the harvesting of bamboo for local use (e.g., building houses, carrying water, making baskets). Hunting for food can also be a threat in some areas. Known to occur in only two national parks (Andringitra and Ranomafana) and probably numbering less than 2,500 individuals, its distribution is patchy and it typically occurs at low population densities (Nicoll and Langrand, 1989; Sterling and Ramaroson, 1996). The Ranomafana / Andringitra forest corridor has been proposed as a conservation unit in conjunction with efforts to propagate and re-establish stands of bamboo species that serve as food for this species.

Fig. 9.23: Captive golden bamboo lemur (*Hapalemur aureus*) feeding on bamboo (photo by R. A. Mittermeier).

As of 2010, this species was not being kept in captivity (ISIS, 2009; E. E. Louis Jr., pers. comm.).

Where to See It

The golden bamboo lemur can be seen in Ranomafana National Park around the research station at Talatakely, but a visit of at least two or three days is recommended. The use of local guides to find this animal is essential.

Lemuridae

Fig. 9.24: Golden bamboo lemur (*Hapalemur aureus*), Ranomafana National Park (photo by R. A. Mittermeier).

Lemuridae

Fig. 9.25: Greater bamboo lemur (*Prolemur simus*), Ranomafana National Park (photo by I. Relanzón).

Prolemur (Gray, 1871)
Greater Bamboo Lemur

This genus contains a single species, *Prolemur simus*. Tattersall (1982) and other earlier authors had placed this animal in the genus *Hapalemur* as *Hapalemur simus*, but a recent taxonomic revision of the primates by Groves (2001) placed it in its own genus and resurrected the name *Prolemur* (Gray, 1871). It is still referred to as a bamboo lemur along with all members of the genus *Hapalemur*, and like other bamboo-eating lemurs has a broadened and shortened muzzle. However, it is much larger than any of the other species (Albrecht *et al.*, 1990), and has at least nine cranio-dental features that are distinctive (Vuillaume-Randriamanantena *et al.*, 1985). Genetic studies further support its separation from the other bamboo lemurs and suggest that the genus *Hapalemur* may, in fact, be more closely related to *Lemur* (Rumpler *et al.*, 1989; Macedonia and Stanger, 1994; Stanger-Hall, 1997).

Lemuridae

Fig. 9.26: Greater bamboo lemur (*Prolemur simus*) and infant, born December 18, 2007, at Talatakely, Ranomafana (photo by J. Jernvall).

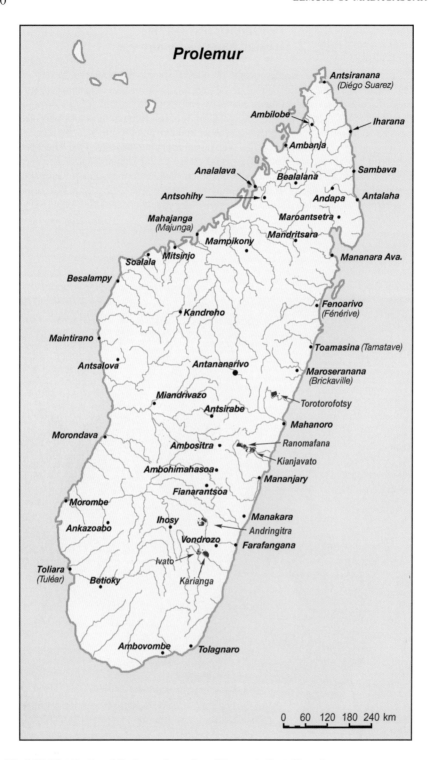

Fig. 9.27: Distribution of *Prolemur simus*. Localities are indicated in red.

**Greater Bamboo
Lemur**
Prolemur simus

**Greater Bamboo
Lemur (form from
Andringitra)**
Prolemur simus

Fig. 9.28.

Prolemur simus (Gray, 1871)
Greater Bamboo Lemur

Other English: Broad-nosed Bamboo Lemur, Broad-nosed Gentle
Lemur
French: Grand Hapalémur
German: Grosser Bambuslemur, Breitschnauzenmakiki
Malagasy: Varibolo, Varibolomavo (Ranomafana region), Godroka,
Godrogodroka (Torotorofotsy region), Tan-Tang (Bay of Antongil),
Bokombolobe, Reniben' ny Kotrika, Halogodro (Soanierana-
Ivongo), Varikovoka (Ambolomavo)

Identification

Prolemur simus is the largest of the bamboo lemurs and is so distinct that it has been
placed in its own genus. It has a head-body length of 40–42 cm, a tail length of 45–48
cm, a total length of 85–90 cm, and a weight of 2.2–2.5 kg (Meier *et al*., 1987; Kappeler,
1991). The dorsal coat, including the tail, is grayish-brown with a slight reddish tinge; the
head, neck, shoulders and upper arms tend to be more olive-brown. There is a rusty-brown
pygal patch. The ventral coat is a lighter creamy-brown. The muzzle is blunt and dark gray,
and the most distinctive feature of this species is its white ear tufts. There is no sexual
difference in body weight (Tan, 2000).

Garbutt (2007) mentions a population of *P. simus* discovered on the Andringitra
Massif which might be a distinct color morph, having uniformly a deep golden-red head,
upperparts, throat and underparts, but with a gray-tipped tail. The face and muzzle are dark.
Individuals in this area are also said to be different in having large and prominent ears that
lack the white tufts so visible in animals from the main population. The identity of this
population requires further investigation.

The greater bamboo lemur is sympatric with *Hapalemur griseus ranomafanensis* in
Ranomafana National Park, with *Hapalemur meridionalis* in Andringitra National Park,
and with *Hapalemur aureus* in both of these protected areas. It might be confused with
any of these bamboo lemurs or with *Eulemur rufifrons* if one does not get a clear look at
the animal. It is much larger than the *Hapalemur* species
and distinguishable from them by its prominent white ear
tufts and blunter, broader face. It also lacks the golden face
of *H. aureus*. The facial features and ear tufts of the greater
bamboo lemur also distinguish it from the sympatric *E.
rufifrons*, which is similar in size or slightly larger.

Geographic Range

Historical records and subfossil remains confirm
a previous widespread distribution that covered the
northern, northwestern, central and eastern portions of
Madagascar, including Ampasambazimba in the Itasy
Basin, the Grotte d'Andrafiabè on the Ankarana Massif,
the Grottes d'Anjohibè near Mahajanga, and the Tsingy
de Bemaraha (Schwarz, 1931; Godfrey and Vuillaume-
Randriamamantena, 1986; Wilson *et al*., 1988; Godfrey *et
al*., 1999, 2004b).

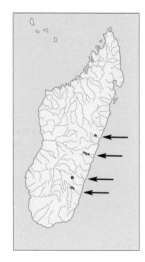

Fig. 9.29: Greater bamboo lemur (*Prolemur simus*), Ranomafana National Park (photo by I. Relanzón).

Until recently, documented populations were restricted to the south-central portion of the country's eastern rain forests at elevations of 200–1,100 m (Sterling and Ramaroson, 1996; Arrigo-Nelson and Wright, 2004), including Ranomafana and Andringitra National Parks, the corridor and isolated forests between and to the east of these localities (e.g., Ambolomavo, Ifanadiana, Kianjavato), and one locality (Evendra) southeast of Andringitra but north of the Manampatrana River (Meier and Rumpler, 1987; Wright *et al.*, 1987; Sterling and Ramaroson, 1996; Goodman *et al.*, 2001; Andriaholinirina *et al.*, 2003; Arrigo-Nelson and Wright, 2004; Irwin *et al.*, 2005).

While reports of large bamboo lemurs fitting this animal's description have been filtering in from various sites (Rakotosamimanana *et al.*, 2004; Schmid and Alonso, 2005), recent surveys have now confirmed its presence in the forests of Torotorofotsy, in the region of Andasibe-Mantadia (Dolch *et al.*, 2004, 2008).

Most commonly known as Varibolomavo in the Ranomafana region, and as Godrogodroka in the Torotorofotsy region, vernacular names for the species vary widely across its range. Under the vernacular names given above, we include Malagasy names for several localities from which its presence has not yet been confirmed, but where names for it apparently exist.

Natural History

As its common name implies, the greater bamboo lemur subsists predominantly on bamboo, but its diet includes at least seven plant species from three different families. The bamboo *Cathariostachys madagascariensis* can account for as much as 95% of the diet, including its shoots, young and mature leaves, and pith, so the presence of this plant is a strong determinant of the presence of *Prolemur* (Grassi, 1998, 2001; Tan, 1999, 2000). Other food items include flowers of the traveler's palm (*Ravenala madagascariensis*), fruits of *Artocarpus integrifolius*, *Ficus* spp. and *Dypsis* spp., and leaves of *Pennisteum clandestinum* (see Meier and Rumpler, 1987). When eating bamboo, this lemur strips the outside of the live stalk and tears apart the bamboo pole to get to the pith, an impressive accomplishment for such a small animal. Feeding in this manner leaves strong evidence of its presence. There are occasional reports from agricultural plantations where bamboo is prominent.

Observations of wild populations and animals in captivity suggest that *P. simus* is cathemeral, active during the day and at night throughout the year (Santini-Palka, 1994; Tan, 1999, 2000). It lives in polygamous groups of up to 28 animals that can occupy home ranges of 60 ha (Ranomafana; Tan, 1999, 2000) to several hundred ha (Torotorofotsy; R. Dolch, unpubl.). Ranges may overlap those of other sympatric bamboo lemur species (Sterling and Ramaroson, 1996; Tan, 1999, 2000).

Mating begins in May or June, with infants typically born in October and November after a gestation period of approximately 150 days (Mutschler and Tan, 2003). Females usually give birth to a single young each year. Unlike the sympatric bamboo lemurs, *H. meridionalis*, *H. g. ranomafanensis* and *H. aureus*, *P. simus* females do not "park" their infants while foraging.

Conservation Status

The 2008 IUCN Red List assessment classified *P. simus* as Critically Endangered (CR). It has been on the list of the World's 25 Most Endangered Primates, prepared every two

Lemuridae

Lemuridae

Fig. 9.30: Greater bamboo lemur (*Prolemur simus*), Torotorofotsy, near Andasibe (photo by R. Randrianampionona).

Lemuridae

Fig. 9.31: Greater bamboo lemur (*Prolemur simus*), Ranomafana National Park (photo by R. A. Mittermeier).

years by the IUCN/SSC Primate Specialist Group, the International Primatological Society, and Conservation International, since 2002.

Prolemur is threatened by slash-and-burn agriculture, mining, illegal logging, and the cutting of bamboo. It is also hunted for food, using slingshots, spears and snares (Meier, 1987; Meier and Rumpler, 1987; Wright *et al.*, 2008; E. E. Louis Jr., pers. obs.). Remnant populations now receive protection in the Andringitra and Ranomafana National Parks. A recent assessment of the species (Wright *et al.*, 2008, 2009) has shown that the species only occurs at 12 sites and now occupies only 1–4% of its former range. However, it is quite possible that future field surveys will turn up additional populations, as in the case of the Torotorofotsy population.

As of 2009, there were 15 individuals in six European collections, along with four in Parc Ivoloina, Madagascar (ISIS, 2009; E. E. Louis Jr., pers. obs.).

Where to See It

The best location for seeing this species is Ranomafana National Park, which also has populations of two other bamboo lemurs, *H. g. ranomafanensis* and *H. aureus*. Finding all three is possible but requires time and perseverance, as all are secretive. Use of a local guide is essential and greatly increases the likelihood of finding these animals, two of which are among the world's rarest and most endangered primates. The Agricultural Station of Kianjavato near Ranomafana is also an excellent site for this species. It is possible to see the Torotorofotsy population near Andasibe by taking a guide from the Association Mitsinjo. The Torotorofotsy animals are being studied by this local conservation organization, and you will have the chance to join the researchers as they track the animals.

Lemuridae

Fig. 9.32: Greater bamboo lemur (*Prolemur simus*), Talatakely, Ranomafana (photo by J. Jernvall).

Lemuridae

Fig. 9.33: Ring-tailed lemur (*Lemur catta*), Berenty Private Reserve (photo by R. A. Mittermeier).

Lemur Linnaeus, 1758
Ring-tailed Lemur

The ring-tailed lemur, *Lemur catta*, is the most widely recognized and best studied of all Madagascar prosimians. As aptly stated by primatologist Dr. Alison Jolly (2003, p. 1329), "*Lemur catta* is almost Madagascar's trademark, with its raccoon-like face mask, svelte gray fur, and, above all, the black-and-white ringed tail," and in fact it was chosen as the symbol of ANGAP, the National Association of Protected Areas in Madagascar (now Madagascar National Parks). The genus *Lemur* as originally proposed by Linnaeus (1758) contained the ring-tailed lemur and two non-lemurs: the slender loris (*Loris*), another prosimian, and the Philippine colugo (*Cynocephalus volans*), a member of the order Dermoptera and not a primate at all. Until the late 1980s, the genus included 12 species and subspecies, 11 of which have now been assigned to the genus *Eulemur*. Noting that *L. catta* appeared to show some affinities to *Hapalemur*, Simons and Rumpler (1988) and Groves and Eaglen (1988) proposed separating *Eulemur* as a distinct genus. This was not accepted by all authorities. Tattersall and Schwartz (1991), for example, reviewed the available evidence, and concluded that it was insufficient to determine degrees of relationship within the Lemuridae, argued against creating a new genus, and recommended a return to the genus *Lemur* containing all taxa currently assigned to *Lemur*, *Eulemur*, and *Varecia*. This argument was not widely accepted in the primatological community, which preferred to recognize *Eulemur* and *Varecia* as distinct genera, and this is the arrangement that we have followed (Mittermeier *et al.*, 1994, 2006, 2008c), and continue to follow here.

Lemuridae

Fig. 9.34: Ring-tailed lemurs (*Lemur catta*) basking in the morning sun, Berenty (photo by R. A. Mittermeier).

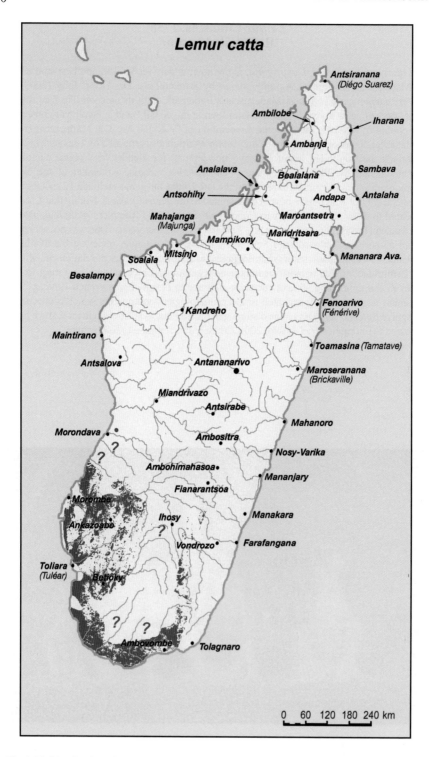

Fig. 9.35: Distribution of *Lemur catta*.

Ring-tailed Lemur
Lemur catta

Fig. 9.36: Illustration of *Lemur catta*.

THE MAUCAUCO.

Lemuridae

Fig. 9.37: Aquatint illustration of a ring-tailed lemur (*Lemur catta*) from Charles Catton's book *Animals Drawn from Nature*, published in London in 1788.

Fig. 9.38: *Lemur catta* **postural and behavioral drawings (next page):**
> **a.** *Lemur catta* **feeding on tamarind fruit**
> **b.** *Lemur catta* **in mid-leap**
> **c.** *Lemur catta* **male anointing its tail with scent from the antebrachial gland on the plantar surface of the wrist**
> **d.** *Lemur catta* **in mid-leap**
> **e.** *Lemur catta* **in mid-leap**
> **f.** *Lemur catta* **climbing in a tree**

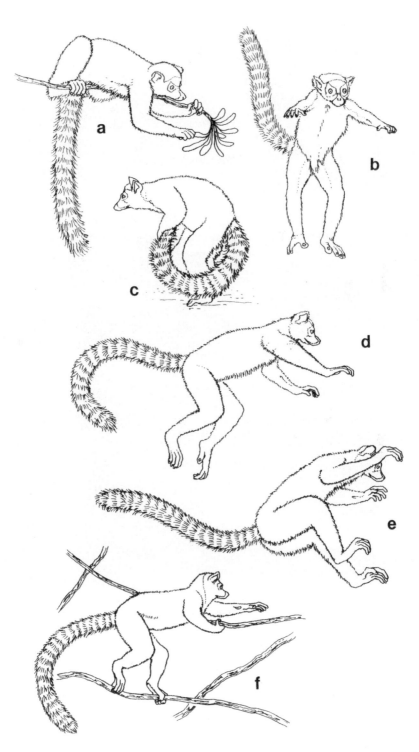

Fig. 9.38.

Lemuridae

Fig. 9.39: Ring-tailed lemurs (*Lemur catta*) walking down the road, Berenty Private Reserve (photo by R. A. Mittermeier). The ring-tail is the most terrestrial of the living lemurs.

Fig. 9.40: Lemur catta postural and behavioral drawings (next page):
>   a. *Lemur catta* examining scent on a branch at the group's range boundary
>   b. *Lemur catta* resting with an infant on its back
>   c. *Lemur catta* in seated "sun-worshipping" posture
>   d. *Lemur catta* descending a vertical tree trunk
>   e. *Lemur catta* scent-marking a tree using its perianal glands
>   f. *Lemur catta* with infant, walking on the ground

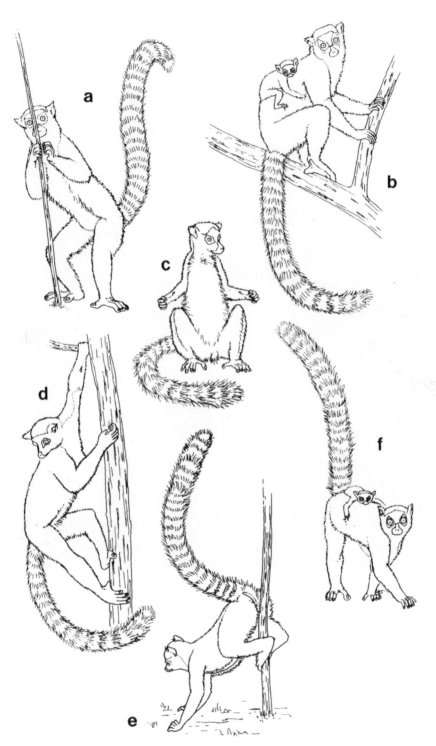

Fig. 9.40.

Fig. 9.41: Ring-tailed lemur (*Lemur catta*) nursing an infant, Berenty Private Reserve (photo by R. A. Mittermeier).

Fig. 9.42: *Lemur catta* postural and behavioral drawings (next page):

    a. *Lemur catta* running quadrupedally
    b. *Lemur catta* standing bipedally
    c. *Lemur catta* suckling
    d. *Lemur catta* with tail in characteristic "stink fight" position
    e. Close-up of face
    f. *Lemur catta* sitting on the ground
    g. *Lemur catta* group moving on the ground (note the characteristic tail postures)

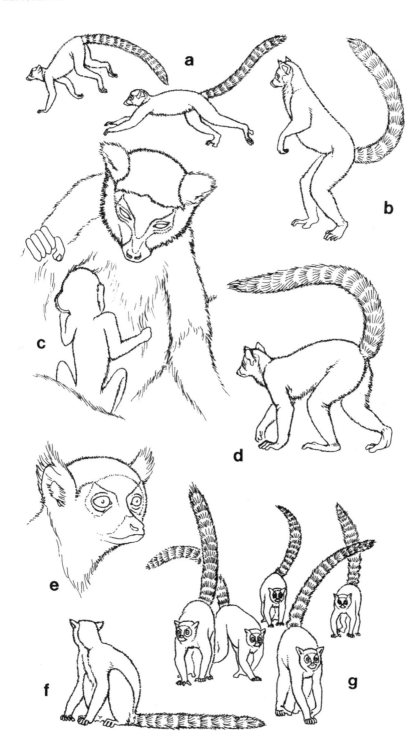

Fig. 9.42.

Lemur catta Linnaeus, 1758
Ring-tailed Lemur

Other English: None
French: Maki, Maki Mococo, Maque
German: Katta
Malagasy: Maky, Hira

Identification

Lemur catta is a relatively large, diurnal lemur, easily recognized by its black-and-white ringed tail. It is by far the most terrestrial of the lemurs. It has a head-body length of 39–46 cm, a tail length of 56–63 cm, a total length of 95–110 cm, and a mean weight of 2.2 kg (Sussman, 1991). The dorsal coat is gray to rosy-brown along the back, gray along the flanks, limbs and haunches, and darker gray on the crown and neck. The ventral coat is white to cream. The throat, cheeks, ears, and forehead are white. The muzzle is grayish and the nose is black. The eyes are circled by black, triangular rings. The tail is ringed with black-and-white transverse bands along its entire length, the tip being black. Both sexes possess small dark (antebrachial) glands on the palmar surface of the wrists (the trait that associates *Lemur* with *Hapalemur* more closely than with *Eulemur*), these being overlain by a spur in the males, and males also have larger (brachial) cutaneous glands on the medial aspects of the upper arms near the shoulders. This species is the best known of Madagascar's lemurs and cannot be confused with any other.

Geographic Range

The ring-tailed lemur is found in the tropical dry forests and spiny bush of southern and southwestern Madagascar, as far east as near Tolagnaro (= Fort-Dauphin), as far north as Belo-sur-Tsiribihina along the west coast, and inland to the mountains of Andrigitra on the southeastern plateau (Goodman and Langrand, 1996b; Yoder *et al.*, 1999). The (historical) northern limit extends all the way up to the Morondava River, and the species exists today in Kirindy Mitea at low densities. It is very patchily distributed throughout this large area, and population densities are highly variable (Sussman *et al.*, 2003).

Natural History

Lemur catta is the most intensively studied of all lemurs (Jolly and Pride, 1999; Sauther *et al.*, 1999; Jolly, 2003; Jolly *et al.*, 2006a). It inhabits many forest types throughout its range, including dry scrub and Didiereaceae forest, as well as deciduous and gallery forests. Population densities vary with habitat type, with highs of 100 individuals/km² in the dry forests of the Beza-Mahafaly Special Reserve and 250–600 individuals/km² in the gallery forests and secondary forests of the Berenty Private Reserve (Sussman, 1991; Sauther *et al.*, 1999; Koyama *et al.*, 2001; Jolly *et al.*, 2002).

Lemuridae

Fig. 9.43: Ring-tailed lemur (*Lemur catta*), Isalo National Park (photo by R. A. Mittermeier).

Lemuridae

Lemuridae

Fig. 9.44: Ring-tailed lemur mother and infant in spiny *Alluaudia*, **Berenty Private Reserve (photo by R. A. Mittermeier).**

Ring-tailed lemurs live in multi-male multi-female groups usually numbering 6–24 animals but groups of over 30 individuals are reported occasionally (Jolly, 2003). Home range size varies from 6 to 23 ha, and groups have been recorded maintaining the same home ranges for more than three decades (Budnitz and Dainis, 1975; Sussman, 1977; Jolly and Pride, 1999; Mertl-Milhollen, 2000). Females are dominant over males and remain in their natal groups (Jolly, 1966; Sussman, 1977; Kappeler, 1990a). Males become sexually mature at about three years, and some emigrate at this time (Jones, 1983; Sussman, 1992; Koyama *et al.*, 2002; Gould *et al.*, 2003). Females typically have multiple mates (Pereira and Weiss, 1991). Males compete for females in "jump fights," when they leap into the air, each opponent trying to slash the other with its upper canines and often inflicting significant wounds. Competition among females of different groups is high, the most aggressive animals typically facing off against each other and engaging in threatening behaviors, but rarely inflicting any physical damage. Within the group, however, female competition for dominance can result in serious wounds and the expulsion of inferior members (Vick and Pereira, 1989; Jolly *et al.*, 2000), as well as the possibility of eviction and range takeover (Ichino and Koyama, 2006).

Scent-marking is an important means of communication. Females demarcate the territory by marking branches with the vulva (Mertl-Milhollen, 2006; Palagi and Norscia, 2009). Males use wrist and shoulder glands to mark their tails, which they then wave at each other during ritual "stink fights." Males also use the spurs on their forearms to make small scars in tree trunks, which they then anoint with secretions from their scent glands (Kappeler, 1998).

Mating begins in mid-April and most young are born in September (Koyama, 1988; Koyama *et al.*, 2001). Males guard their mates after copulating. Some females may be in estrus several times, as late as the middle of August (T. Soma, pers. obs.). Females first give birth at three years of age, and most produce offspring annually; single births are the norm, but twins are born on occasion. The gestation period is 138–141 days in the Berenty population (S. Ichino and T. Soma, unpubl.). The young are precocious, transferring to their mother's back at one to two weeks old, and soon thereafter to the backs of other group members. Infant mortality is high. At Beza-Mahafaly, about half of all infants die in their first year and only about 40% reach maturity (Sussman, 1991). In the wild, the longest lifespan was recorded in Berenty, where a female reached 20 years of age (S. Ichino, unpubl.).

This is the most terrestrial of the lemurs (Sussman, 1974). In Andringitra National Park, where the species occurs above the line of seasonal frost, troops regularly move along rocky, barren terrain and take shelter at night in caves (Goodman and Langrand, 1996b). The diet consists of fruit, leaves, flowers, herbs, bark, and sap from close to three dozen different plant species (Simmen *et al.*, 2006a, 2006b). The kily tree (*Tamarindus indica*) is especially favored, with its fruit and leaves accounting for as much as 50% of all time spent feeding throughout the year in areas where it is present (Rasamimanana and Rafidinarivo, 1993; Sauther, 1993; Soma, 2006). Ring-tailed lemurs eat rotten wood, earth, insects, and small vertebrates, and they are also known to raid crops (Jolly, 1966; Budnitz and Dainis, 1975; Oda, 1996; Simmen *et al.*, 2003, 2006b).

In recent years, biologists and visitors to the Berenty Private Reserve have commented on the "ragged" condition of its ring-tailed lemurs. One explanation was that crowded conditions in the available habitat are having adverse effects on this population. Current studies, however, suggest that hair loss experienced by *Lemur catta* at Berenty is due to feeding on the leaves, fruit, and flowers of the introduced tree *Leucaena leucocephala*,

Lemuridae

which contains mimosine, an amino acid and known inhibitor of cell division in mammalian species (Crawford *et al.*, 2006; Jolly, 2009a, 2009b; B. Simmen, pers. comm.). As of early 2010, *Leucaena* had been removed almost entirely from Berenty, and the affected groups appear to be recovering. At Berenty, some ring-tailed lemur troops also eat and very much depend upon other introduced plants such as *Opuntia* sp. or *Azadirachla indica* (Simmen *et al.*, 2003; Pride, 2006; Soma, 2006), but the influence of these exotic foods on the health of the lemurs is not yet clear.

Ring-tailed lemurs sometimes fall prey to the fossa (*Cryptoprocta ferox*), introduced civet (*Viverricula indica*), Madagascar harrier-hawk (*Polyboroides radiatus*), Madagascar buzzard (*Buteo brachypterus*), Madagascar ground boa (*Acrantophis dumerelii*), and domestic cats and dogs (Goodman, 2003). An infant was reported to have been eaten by a hybrid *Eulemur* female in 2000 in Berenty (S. Pinkus, pers. obs.).

Conservation Status

The most recent IUCN Red List assessment (2008) classified *L. catta* as Near Threatened (NT). Habitat loss and hunting are the most significant threats. It has a strong preference for gallery forests, which are very limited in extent in southern Madagascar, and spiny forest, which continues to be destroyed to create pasture, for charcoal production, and for agriculture, especially corn plantations (Sussman *et al.*, 2003). The ring-tailed lemur is also hunted for food in certain areas, and frequently kept as a pet (O'Connor, 1987; Goodman and Raselimanana, 2003; Goodman *et al.*, 2004).

Fortunately, *L. catta* is found in a number of protected areas, including five national parks (Andohahela, Andringitra, Isalo, Tsimanampetsotsa, and Zombitse-Vohibasia), three special reserves (Beza-Mahafaly, Kalambatritra, and Pic d'Ivohibe), the Ambosary Sud and Berenty Private Reserves, the Anja Community Reserve, and in the Kirindy-Mitea National Park, just south of Morondava (Nicoll and Langrand, 1989; Sterling and Ramaroson, 1996; Goodman, 1999; Hawkins, 1999; Zinner *et al.*, 2001; Goodman and Raselimanana, 2003; P. Kappeler, pers. obs.). It does not occur in the Kirindy Forest Reserve, north of Morondava where the German Primate Center has its field research base. It has also been reported from the unprotected forests of Ankoba, Ankodida, Anjatsikolo, Anbatotsilongolongo, Bereny, Mahazoarivo, Masiabiby, and Mikea (Fenn *et al.*, 1999; Seddon *et al.*, 2000). It is important to note that many of the best remaining forest patches within the range of *L. catta*, and where it appears to occur at the highest densities, are found on sacred lands (Sussman *et al.*, 2003).

As of 2009, there were an estimated 2500, ring-tailed lemurs in zoos around the world, in addition to many more in smaller roadside collections, laboratories, and the pet trade. The species is not only the most common lemur in captivity, but indeed the most common of all captive primates (ISIS, 2009; I. J. Porton, pers. comm.).

Where to See It

This species can be seen in all the protected areas within its range, but is most easily observed in the Berenty Private Reserve, and in Andohahela National Park, Isalo National Park, and Zombitse-Vohibasia National Park.

Berenty is 2½–3 hour drive by car west of Tolagnaro (= Fort-Dauphin), and is the first stop on most tours to Madagascar. Habituated groups of ring-tailed lemurs and Verreaux's sifakas (*Propithecus verreauxi*) can be seen within minutes of arriving at the reserve. In Berenty, *L. catta* is seen mainly in gallery forest dominated by tamarind trees, but it can also be seen in patches of spiny forest on the grounds of the reserve.

An interesting site to view *L. catta* in Andohahela National Park is near the small village of Hazafotsy at the edge of the spiny forest portion of this protected area, about three to four hours by four-wheel drive vehicle from either Berenty or Tolagnaro (= Fort-Dauphin). This trip is a rewarding experience that takes the visitor through an attractive piece of

Lemuridae

Fig. 9.45: Ring-tailed lemur (*Lemur catta*), Berenty Private Reserve (photo by R. A. Mittermeier).

southern spiny forest that is lightly inhabited by scattered villages of the Tandroy, the traditional people of this region.

The sandstone cliffs and canyons of Isalo National Park are also a good site for ring-tailed lemurs, which are easily observed in the Canyon des Makis. In Andringitra National Park, ring-tails can be observed at Camp Catta and at a community conservation site called Anja on the main road from Ambalavao heading towards Toliara.

Lemuridae

Fig. 9.46: Ring-tailed lemur (*Lemur catta*), Isalo National Park (photo by R. A. Mittermeier).

Fig. 9.47: Ring-tailed lemur (*Lemur catta*), Berenty Private Reserve (photo by R. A. Mittermeier).

Lemuridae

Fig. 9.48: Brown lemur (*Eulemur fulvus*), Anjajavy, northwestern Madagascar (photo by R. A. Mittermeier).

Eulemur Simons and Rumpler, 1988
True Lemurs

The genus *Eulemur* is widespread in Madagascar and has been the subject of many field studies. When the first edition of this field guide was published in 1994, the genus was considered by most experts to contain five species: the brown lemurs (*Eulemur fulvus*) with six subspecies, the black lemurs (*Eulemur macaco*) with two subspecies, the crowned lemur (*Eulemur coronatus*), the red-bellied lemur (*Eulemur rubriventer*), and the mongoose lemur (*Eulemur mongoz*). Subsequently, Groves (2001) elevated all former *E. fulvus* subspecies (*albifrons, albocollaris, collaris, fulvus, rufus,* and *sanfordi*) to full species, maintained the two subspecies of *E. macaco* (*flavifrons* and *macaco*), and left the other three monotypic species, *E. mongoz, E. rubriventer* and *E. coronatus*, as they were.

In 2002, at an IUCN/SSC Conservation Breeding Specialist Group (CBSG) CAMP Workshop in Madagascar, lemur experts proposed acceptance of full species status for *Eulemur albocollaris, Eulemur collaris,* and *Eulemur sanfordi,* but recommended that *albifrons, fulvus* and *rufus* be maintained as subspecies of *E. fulvus* (CBSG, 2002). Although several recent genetic and field studies continue to support the status of the *E. fulvus* forms as subspecies (Djletati *et al.,* 1997; Wyner *et al.,* 1999b; Johnson and Wyner, 2000), we consider all members of the *fulvus* group to be distinct species, unless it can be shown that gene flow between populations is too high to suggest ongoing divergence—unlikely, since all are consistently different at least in pelage characteristics, and are becoming increasingly isolated from one another by forest fragmentation. This arrangement was also followed during the important Red-Listing Workshop for Malagasy mammals held in Antananarivo, Madagascar, in April, 2005 which involved many of the world's specialists on lemurs.

In this book we follow the taxonomy of Groves (2001) for the most part, recognizing 12 species of *Eulemur* overall. However, we also recognize *Eulemur cinereiceps* as the senior synonym for what has previously been called *E. albocollaris*; we elevate *E. macaco macaco* and *E. m. flavifrons* to full species; and we recognize the recent proposed split of *Eulemur rufus* and *Eulemur rufifrons* (Groves, 2006; Mittermeier *et al.,* 2008c; Groves and Roos, in prep.). Finally, as indicated in the first and second editions, we continue to consider the brown lemurs inhabiting the island of Mayotte in the Comoros to be nothing more than introduced populations of *E. fulvus* (Mittermeier *et al.,* 1994).

Members of this genus are found in almost all forested areas of Madagascar except the spiny forest region of the extreme south. Traits they share include medium body size, sexual dichromatism (notably indistinct in *E. fulvus*), quadrupedal locomotion, and diurnal behavior patterns coupled with significant nocturnal activity. Weights for *Eulemur* species range from just under 1 kg to about 2.5 kg (Glander *et al.,* 1992; Rasmussen, 1999). Those species living in drier forest formations of western Madagascar tend to be smaller and lighter in weight than conspecifics inhabiting eastern rain forests (Albrecht *et al.,* 1990; Gerson, 1999). The extreme of sexual dichromatism in this genus is observed in *E. macaco* and *E. flavifrons,* in which males are black and females are blond. Beyond coat color, however, true lemurs do not exhibit significant sexual dimorphism (Kappeler, 1990b). Males tend to scent mark with the anogenital region, the hands and the head, while females mark with urine and the anogenital region, often eliciting over-marking by males. In most species, males mark the females as well.

Eulemur species move quadrupedally through the trees, but also leap frequently when traveling and especially when agitated. All those that have been studied in the wild demonstrate cathemeral activity patterns—concentrating most bouts of activity during

Lemuridae

the day but also showing significant activity at night (Tattersall, 1987). This behavior has been documented most extensively in *E. mongoz* (Curtis *et al.*, 1999; Donati *et al.*, 1999; Rasmussen, 1999), but has been observed in other members of the genus as well (S. E. Johnson, pers. comm.).

The true lemurs are predominantly fruit-eaters, this food category typically constituting anywhere from 60% to more than 90% of the diet during certain seasons (Overdorff and Johnson, 2003). Significant dietary differences are reported, however, related to geographic regions and population densities. For example, *Eulemur* populations inhabiting drier western forests tend to use fewer food species than populations inhabiting eastern rain forests. *Eulemur* species also seem to be particularly susceptible to predation by the fossa (*Cryptoprocta ferox*) and diurnal raptors (Goodman, 2003).

Social structure within the genus is variable. Some species tend to form small, pair-bonded groups while others occur in larger, multi-male/multi-female groups that can number close to twenty individuals (Overdorff *et al.*, 1999; S. E. Johnson, pers. comm.). Evidence gathered to date suggests that female dominance is not characteristic of this genus, but is found only in a few species (Pereira *et al.*, 1990). Breeding is seasonal, mating periods usually lasting from two to six weeks, and gestation is approximately 120 days (Wright, 1999; Curtis *et al.*, 2000). Females typically carry their offspring on their abdomens and wean them at six to seven months of age (Overdorff and Johnson, 2003).

These lemurs are found in a wide variety of habitats and are quite adaptable, but are nonetheless threatened by deforestation and habitat fragmentation (Mittermeier *et al.*, 1992). Furthermore, hunting of lemurs for food, and (to a lesser extent) killing them as agricultural pests, is rapidly emerging as a much more serious threat than previously imagined. Live capture for pets also occurs more frequently with this genus than with any other lemurs, but is not nearly as significant as hunting for food, and is often a by-product of such hunting.

Lemuridae

Fig. 9.49: Male black lemur (*Eulemur macaco*), Ampangorina Village, Nosy Komba, one of Nosy Be's biggest tourist attractions (photo by R. A. Mittermeier).

Lemuridae

Fig. 9.50: A female and offspring mongoose lemur (*Eulemur mongoz*), Ankarafantsika (photo by S. M. McGuire).

Fig. 9.51: *Eulemur* postural and behavioral drawings (next page):
　　　　　a. *Eulemur fulvus* female and infant standing quadrupedally
　　　　　b. *Eulemur mongoz* female and infant sitting on a branch
　　　　　c. *Eulemur albifrons* male walking quadrupedally on a branch
　　　　　d. *Eulemur fulvus* female standing and feeding
　　　　　e. *Eulemur fulvus* female in a sitting posture
　　　　　f. *Eulemur rubriventer* male in a vertical clinging resting posture

Fig. 9.51.

P.Z.S.1871 Pl XVI.

J.Smid,lith.   M & N Hanhart imp.

LEMUR MONGOZ ♂ ET ♀

Fig. 9.52: Hand-colored lithograph of *Lemur mongoz* (now *Eulemur mongoz*) by J. Smit, from the *Proceedings of the Zoological Society of London*, 1871. The female is above, and the male below.

Fig. 9.53: *Eulemur* postural and behavioral drawings (next page):
    a. *Eulemur rufifrons* female climbing horizontally
    b. *Eulemur albifrons* female sitting in a tree fork
    c. *Eulemur macaco* alert male and female on a rock
    d. *Eulemur mongoz* male sitting in a tree fork
    e. *Eulemur fulvus* female grooming
    f. *Eulemur macaco* alert female standing on a branch
    g. *Eulemur macaco* male sitting on forked branches
    h. *Eulemur sanfordi* male resting with its tail over its shoulder
    i. *Eulemur albifrons* male sitting on a branch

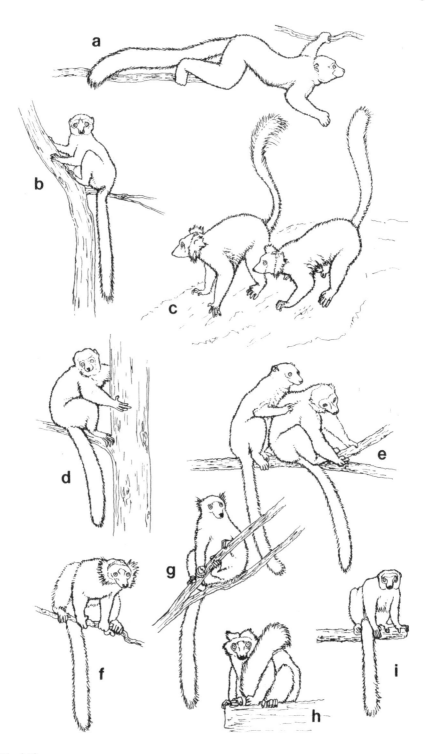

Fig. 9.53.

Fig. 9.54: *Eulemur mongoz* from Buffon's book *Histoire Naturelle, Generale et Particuliere* of 1783. The artist was Jacques de Seve.

Fig. 9.55: *Eulemur* postural and behavioral drawings (next page):
      a. *Eulemur fulvus* female leaping with an infant clinging to its waist
      b. *Eulemur macaco* male standing bipedally and looking around
      c. *Eulemur fulvus* female standing quadrupedally
      d. *Eulemur albifrons* female standing quadrupedally and feeding
      e. *Eulemur rufifrons* female with infant climbing on a vertical trunk

Fig. 9.55.

Lemuridae

Brown lemur
Eulemur fulvus

male

female

Rufous brown lemur
Eulemur rufus

male

female

Fig. 9.56.

**Red-fronted
brown lemur**
Eulemur rufifrons

female

male

**Red-collared
brown lemur**
Eulemur collaris

female

male

Lemuridae

Fig. 9.57.

Lemuridae

**White-collared
brown lemur**
*Eulemur
cinereiceps*

female

male

**White-fronted
brown lemur**
Eulemur albifrons

female

male

Fig. 9.58.

Sanford's brown lemur
Eulemur sanfordi

male

female

Black lemur
Eulemur macaco

male

female

Lemuridae

Fig. 9.59.

Lemuridae

Blue-eyed black lemur
Eulemur flavifrons

female

male

Mongoose lemur
Eulemur mongoz

female

male

Fig. 9.60.

Red-bellied lemur
Eulemur rubriventer

female

male

Crowned lemur
Eulemur coronatus

female

male

Fig. 9.61.

Lemuridae

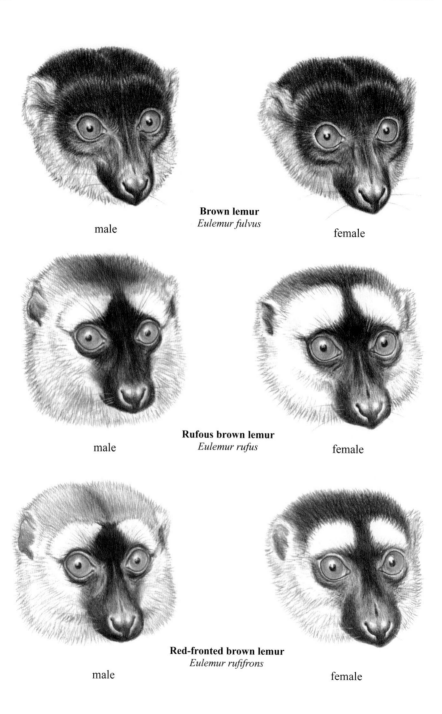

Brown lemur
Eulemur fulvus

male   female

Rufous brown lemur
Eulemur rufus

male   female

Red-fronted brown lemur
Eulemur rufifrons

male   female

Fig. 9.62.

male   female

Red-collared brown lemur
Eulemur collaris

male   female

White-collared brown lemur
Eulemur cinereiceps

male   female

White-fronted brown lemur
Eulemur albifrons

Lemuridae

Fig. 9.63.

Lemuridae

Sanford's brown lemur
Eulemur sanfordi

male   female

Black lemur
Eulemur macaco

male   female

Blue-eyed black lemur
Eulemur flavifrons

male   female

Fig. 9.64.

male **Mongoose lemur** female
Eulemur mongoz

male **Red-bellied lemur** female
Eulemur rubriventer

male **Crowned lemur** female
Eulemur coronatus

Lemuridae

Fig. 9.65.

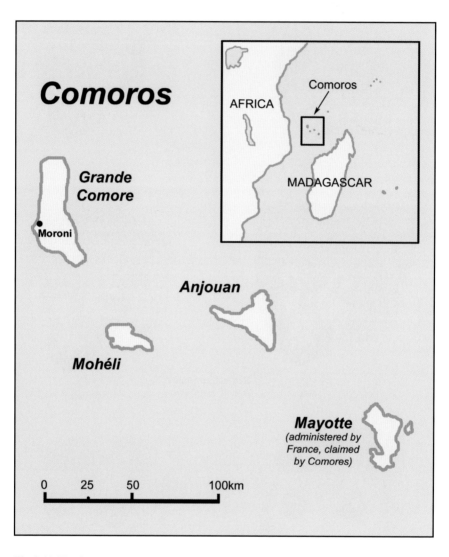

Fig. 9.66: The Comoros to the northwest of Madagascar. *Eulemur fulvus* occurs on the island of Mayotte, and *Eulemur mongoz* on Mohéli and Anjouan.

Fig. 9.67: Distribution of *Eulemur* species of the *fulvus* group.

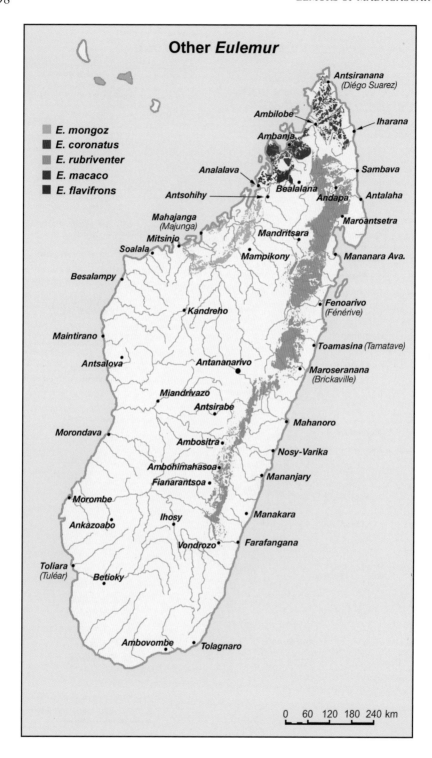

Fig. 9.68: Distribution of *Eulemur* species other than those in the *fulvus* group.

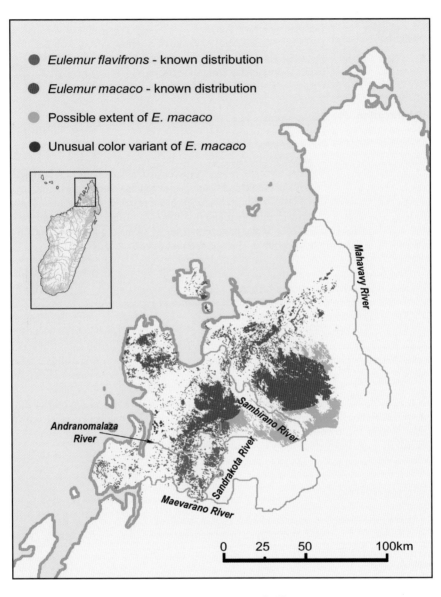

Fig. 9.69: Distribution of *Eulemur macaco* and *Eulemur flavifrons*.

Eulemur fulvus (É. Geoffroy, 1796)
Brown Lemur

Other English: Common Brown Lemur
French: Lémur brun
German: Brauner Maki
Malagasy: Varika, Varike, Varikosy, Akomba, Gidro, Dedrika
(between Mampikony and Port-Bergé), Varikafasin, (Andasibe
region), Varikamava (Andasibe region)
Comoros Islands: Komba Mainty

Identification

Eulemur fulvus is a medium-sized lemur with a head-body length of 43–50 cm, a tail length of 41–51 cm, an overall length of a little more than a meter, and a body weight of 1.7–2.1 kg (C. Schwitzer, pers. obs.). Males and females are similarly colored. The dorsal coat is brown to gray-brown and the ventral coat is paler, tending toward gray. The face, muzzle and crown are dark brown to almost black, the beard is lighter, and patches of light fur above the eyes are variable. Animals in the northern part of this lemur's range have large light patches over the eyes, while the eye patches of animals from more southerly populations may be barely discernible. The eyes are orange-red.

In the field, *E. fulvus* is most likely to be confused with the mongoose lemur (*Eulemur mongoz*) in the west and the red-bellied lemur (*E. rubriventer)* in the east, especially if only a fleeting glimpse of the animal is obtained. *Eulemur mongoz* tends to be grayer and exhibits sexually dimorphic coloration, as does *E. rubriventer*. Male red-bellied lemurs also have distinctive white "tear-drops" beneath their eyes, and females have white fur on the throat, chest and abdomen. *Eulemur fulvus* is usually more active and visible and moves in larger groups than these two species, which also facilitates distinguishing it from its congeners.

The population of this species on Mayotte shows many signs of being a hybrid swarm, composed mainly of *E. fulvus* founders but with features of a number of other brown lemur species (Mittermeier *et al.*, 2008c). Further genetic investigation on this population would be interesting, but we do not consider it to be taxonomically distinct.

Geographic Range

This species is found in western Madagascar north of the Betsiboka River, on the high plateau in scattered forest fragments, and in eastern Madagascar to the north of the Mangoro River as far as Tsaratanana, inland of the range of *Eulemur albifron*s. It is one of only two species to occur outside of Madagascar, being found on the island of Mayotte in the Comoros, where it was apparently introduced by our own species prior to European arrival. However, as noted above, the Mayotte population is not pure *Eulemur fulvus*.

The western populations can be divided into two sub-distributions, a southern one extending from the

Fig. 9.70: Male common brown lemur (*Eulemur fulvus*) at Anjajavy (photo by R. A. Mittermeier).

Betsiboka River and Ankarafantsika National Park north to the Maevarano River, and a northern one ranging from the Manongarivo Special Reserve to the Mahavavy du Nord River. Animals in the northern reaches of this range may also be found throughout the moister forests of the Sambirano region, as well as on the slopes of the Tsaratanana Massif, and they are very similar in coloration to the brown lemurs found on the island of Mayotte. In eastern Madagascar, *E. fulvus* is found northeast of Antananarivo and as far as the Ambatovaky Special Reserve. The distribution of *E. fulvus* in the northern part of its range and its relation to *E. albifrons* remain unclear, and additional surveys are needed.

Natural History

The brown lemur has been studied at Ankarafantsika by Harrington (1975), on the island of Mayotte by Tattersall (1977a), and at Andasibe (= Périnet) by Ganzhorn (1988). In Madagascar, groups vary in

Fig. 9.71: Male common brown lemur (*Eulemur fulvus*) from Lemur Island (photo by R. A. Mittermeier).

Fig. 9.72: Female common brown lemur (*Eulemur fulvus*), Anjajavy, northwestern Madagascar (photo by R. A. Mittermeier).

Lemuridae

size from 3 to 12, home ranges from 7 to 20 ha, and population densities are 40 to 60 individuals/km². Female dominance appears not to be a feature of this species (Pereira *et al.*, 1990).

The diet consists largely of fruits, young leaves, and flowers. Rasmussen (1999) found that *E. fulvus* sampled more than 100 plant species, but that only 15 of these made up the bulk of the diet. On Mayotte, Tattersall (1982) described considerable seasonal variation in diet, with fruit, leaves or flowers predominating in any one month. Ganzhorn (1988) also documented high levels of tannins and alkaloids in the diet. In terms of activity pattern, Rasmussen (1999) noted that the brown lemur remains diurnal throughout the year, but increases levels of nocturnal activity during the dry season.

Conservation Status

The 2008 IUCN Red List assessment of *E. fulvus* classified it as Vulnerable (VU). The principal threats are habitat loss due to slash-and-burn agriculture and hunting with firearms, blowguns, and traps. This species occurs in four national parks (Andringitra, Ankarafantsika, Mantadia, and Zahamena), two strict nature reserves (Tsaratanana and Zahamena), and seven special reserves (Ambatovaky, Ambohitantely, Analamazaotra, Bora, Mangerivola, Manongarivo, and Tampoketsa-Analamaitso) (Nicoll and Langrand, 1989; CBSG, 2002; Randriambinina *et al.*, 2003a, 2003c; E. E. Louis Jr., pers. obs.).

Fig. 9.73: Common brown lemur *(Eulemur fulvus)*, Anjajavy (photo by R. A. Mittermeier).

As of 2009, there were approximately 160 individuals in zoos around the world, though unfortunately many would appear to be of mixed or unknown origin (ISIS, 2009).

Where to See It

In eastern Madagascar, *E. fulvus* is easily seen at Andasibe (= Périnet), where it is one of the most common lemurs in both the Analamazaotra Special Reserve and Mantadia National Park. In western Madagascar, it is very easy to find at the Ampijoroa Forestry Station in Ankarafantsika National Park. The Anjajavy Hotel in northwestern Madagascar is also an excellent place to see this species, since it is found in the immediate vicinity of the hotel, and is completely habituated.

Eulemur rufus (Audebert, 1799)
Rufous Brown Lemur

Other English: Northern Red-fronted Lemur, Red-fronted Brown
Lemur
French: Lémur à front roux septentrional
German: Nördlicher Rotstirnmaki
Malagasy: Varika, Halo

Identification

Eulemur rufus is a relatively large lemur with a head-body length of 40–48 cm, a tail
length of 45–55 cm, an overall length of 85–103 cm, and a mean body weight of around
2 kg (Gerson, 1999). This species is sexually dichromatic. In males, coloration is dark
olive-gray with a deep brown tinge above and on the tail, and lighter below. The hands are
red. The crown is dark brick-red, the cheek beard golden-red, and the muzzle black with
an additional, broad, black midfacial stripe extending from the crown to the nose; the sides
of the latter as well as the spots above the eyes are creamy-white. In females, coloration
is gingery-red above with an orange underside and a short, golden-red cheek beard. The
crown is black, and there are large, gray-white eye and cheek spots (Groves, 2001, 2006).

There are no other members of the genus *Eulemur* throughout much of the range of the
species, although there is a small hybrid zone with *E. mongoz* in northwestern Madagascar
(Zaramody and Pastorini, 2001). The only species with which it is likely to be confused
(in captivity) is *E. rufifrons*, with which it was considered conspecific until quite recently
(Groves, 2006).

Geographic Range

The rufous brown lemur is found in tropical dry lowland
forests in west-central coastal Madagascar. It is patchily
distributed from the Mahavavy du Sud River south at least to
the Tsiribih.ina River. It may occur south of the Tsiribihina,
but this is questionable. The northernmost recorded locality
is Betsako, 15°35'S, 46°23'E; the southernmost, Beroboka,
19°58'S, 44°37'E (C. P. Groves, pers. comm.; C. Roos,
pers. obs.).

Natural History

Many studies of "*Eulemur rufus*" carried out in the past
(e.g., Sussman, 1974, 1975, 1977) are now attributed to *E.
rufifrons* (C. P. Groves, pers. comm.). *Eulemur rufus* itself
has not yet been the subject of a detailed behavioral or
ecological study.

Conservation Status

Very little is known of the conservation status of *E. rufus*, so the 2008 IUCN Red
List assessment classified it as Data Deficient (DD). It is found in three national parks
(Baie de Baly, Tsingy de Bemaraha, and Tsingy de Namoroka), the Tsingy de Bemaraha
Strict Nature Reserve, three special reserves (Bemarivo, Kasijy, and Maningoza), and in

Lemuridae

the Tsiombokibo Classified Forest (Nicoll and Langrand, 1989; Sterling and Ramaroson, 1996; Hawkins *et al.*, 1998; Hawkins, 1999; Thalmann *et al.*, 1999; Randrianarisoa *et al.*, 2001; Goodman and Raselimanana, 2003).

The numbers of this species in captivity are difficult to determine at this time, owing to taxonomic confusion with *E. rufifrons*. It is likely that most captive animals are *E. rufifrons*, but this remains to be verified.

Where to See It

The best place to see *E. rufus* is in the Tsingy de Bemaraha National Park, though it is also readily observed in Baie de Baly National Park. The Tsiombikibo Classified Forest near Mitsinjo is another possibility, although access can be difficult.

Fig. 9.74: Female rufous brown lemur (*Eulemur rufus*), Bay of Baly National Park in northwestern Madagascar (photo by R. A. Mittermeier).

Lemuridae

Eulemur rufifrons (Bennett, 1833)
Red-fronted Brown Lemur

Other English: Southern Red-fronted Brown Lemur
French: Lémur à front roux méridional
German: Südlicher Rotstirnmaki
Malagasy: Gidro, Halo, Varikamavo (east)

Identification

Eulemur rufifrons is a relatively large brown lemur with a head-body length of 40–48 cm, a tail length of 45–55 cm, an overall length of 85–103 cm, and a mean body weight of 2.2–2.3 kg (Glander *et al.*, 1992). This species is sexually dichromatic. In males the coloration is iron-gray above with a grayish-fawn underside; the crown is dark red and the tail black along part of its length. The digits are red. In females, the coloration is brownish olive-gray above with a whitish-red underside, a reddish head, and an orange-tipped tail. There is little gray above the eyes (Groves, 2001, 2006). All young are born with adult male coloration, the female infants undergoing a change into adult female coloration at 7–17 weeks (Barthold *et al.*, 2009).

This species may be confused with *Eulemur rubriventer* where the two are sympatric in the eastern rain forest. However, *E. rubriventer* can usually be distinguished by its redder coloration, the lack of white eyebrow patches, and by the prominent white tear-drop patches seen in males. A large hybridization zone with *E. cinereiceps* appears to be centered on the Iantara River (the headwaters of the Manampatra), near Andringitra National Park (Wyner *et al.*, 2002; Sterling and Ramarason, 1996; Delmore *et. al.*, 2009), and there is also an introduced population of this species (hybridized with *E. collaris*) inhabiting the Berenty Private Reserve in southern Madagascar. Finally, it can easily be confused with captive *E. rufus*, a species with which it was considered conspecific until quite recently.

Geographic Range

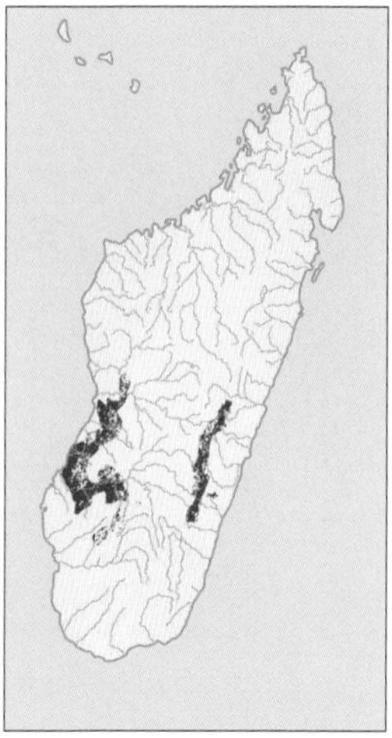

The red-fronted brown lemur is found on both sides of Madagascar, in the southeast and the southwest. It inhabits both tropical dry lowland forests (in the west) and tropical moist lowland to montane forests (in the east), up to elevations of 1,700 m (Petter *et al.*, 1977; Tattersall, 1982). In the southwest, it occurs patchily from the Tsiribihina River south to the region of the Onilahy River and the Andringitra Massif. In the east, it ranges from the Mangoro River and the Onive River in the north, with the southern limit probably being the Manampatrana River (which, for the most part, separates it from *E. cinereiceps*). Reports of its occurrence in the Kalambatritra Special Reserve are incorrect, since the species there is evidently *E. collaris* (Irwin *et al.*, 2001).

Natural History

This species has been studied in western Madagascar in the deciduous forests of Antserananomby and Tongobato

Fig. 9.75: Male red-fronted brown lemur (*Eulemur rufifrons*), Isalo National Park (photo by R. A. Mittermeier).

Lemuridae

(Sussman, 1974, 1975, 1977), in the Kirindy Forest (Donati *et al.*, 1999; Ostner and Kappeler, 1999), and in eastern Madagascar in Ranomafana National Park (Meyers, 1988; Overdorff, 1991; Johnson and Overdorff, 1999). These publications pre-date the recent recognition of *E. rufifrons* and *E. rufus* as separate species, and therefore refer to this species as *E. fulvus rufus*. The results of these and other studies demonstrate a very adaptable behavioral ecology. In the west, population density is reported to be very high and home ranges small, while in the east, population densities tend to be lower and home ranges as large as 100 ha. Group size is more consistent geographically, varying from 4–17 (with an average of nine) in the west and from 6–18 (with an average of eight) in the east.

Lemuridae

Fig. 9.76: Female red-fronted brown lemur (*Eulemur rufifrons*), Analabe, in the Menabe region (photo by R. A. Mittermeier).

Fig. 9.77: Female and male red-fronted brown lemur (*Eulemur rufifrons*), Isalo National Park (photo by R. A. Mittermeier).

Fig. 9.78: A male and female hybrids of *Eulemur rufifrons* and *Eulemur collaris,* Berenty Private Reserve (photos by R. A. Mittermeier).

Lemuridae

Fig. 9.79: Male and infant red-fronted brown lemurs (*Eulemur rufifrons*), Isalo National Park (photo by R. A. Mittermeier).

Dominance hierarchies are unknown in any populations, and rates of aggression appear very low.

The diet of some western populations is less diverse and much more folivorous than that of eastern populations, and includes a high proportion of leaves, pods, stems, flowers, bark, and sap of the *kily* tree (*Tamarindus indica*). At Kirindy, *E. rufifrons* includes substantial amounts of fruit in its diet, and is the sole seed disperser for a large number of tree species with large seeds (Ganzhorn *et al.*, 1999). The diet of eastern populations is dominated by fruit (Overdorff, 1993, 1996a, 1996b). Along with *E. rubriventer*, *E. rufifrons* feeds on flowers and nectar more often during in the warmer, wetter months of the year (Overdorff, 1992). Although largely diurnal, western populations of this lemur increase their nocturnal activity during the dry season (Donati *et al.*, 1999; Rasmussen, 1999; Kappeler and Erkert, 2003). Eastern populations are entirely cathemeral and active across a 24-hour period throughout the year (Overdorff and Rasmussen, 1995).

Reproduction is seasonal. In western populations, one male typically monopolizes the females of the group, while in the east several males may participate in reproductive pairings (Overdorff, 1998; Ostner and Kappeler, 1999). In the west, mating takes place in June, births occur in September and October, and the young are weaned by January (Sussman, 1977).

Conservation Status

Eulemur rufifrons was classified as Near Threatened (NT) in the 2008 IUCN Red List assessment. The principal threat to its survival is habitat loss due to slash-and-burn agriculture, burning for pasture, fuelwood gathering, and illegal logging. Hunting and trapping are also threats throughout its range—it is one of the most commonly hunted lemurs in all of Madagascar (E. E. Louis Jr., pers. obs.). It is found in four national parks (Andringitra, Isalo, Ranomafana, and Zombitse-Vohibasia), two special reserves (Andranomena, Pic d'Ivohibe), and in the Kirindy Forest (part of the Menabe-Antimena Protected Area) (Nicoll and Langrand, 1989; Sterling and Ramoroson, 1996; Hawkins *et al.*, 1998; Hawkins, 1999; Thalmann *et al.*, 1999; Goodman and Raselimanana, 2003; Sussman *et al.*, 2003).

The status of this species in captivity is difficult to determine at this time, owing to taxonomic confusion with *E. rufus*. However, both *E. rufus* and *E. rufifrons* are found in a number of collections worldwide.

Where to See It

An excellent place to see the red-fronted brown lemur in eastern Madagascar is Ranomafana National Park. April and May appear to be particularly good months for viewing, as Chinese guava (*Psidium* spp.) is in fruit and lemur groups tend to gather near the Belle Vue site (Garbutt, 2007), but the animal can be seen throughout the park. In the west, the Kirindy Forest north of Morondava offers the best opportunities for viewing this species. In addition, an introduced group that has hybridized with *Eulemur collaris* is easily seen in the Berenty Private Reserve in the far south. About eight captive animals, orphans from hunting in the Analabe Reserve in the Menabe forest, north of Morondava, escaped into Berenty during a hurricane in January 1975. The red-collared brown lemurs with which they hybridized were subsequently introduced gradually (a similar number of orphans obtained from the Forte-Dauphin market) up to 1985 (Jolly, 2004; p.30; pers. comm.).

Lemuridae

Eulemur albifrons (É. Geoffroy, 1796)
White-fronted Brown Lemur

Other English: White-fronted Lemur, White-headed Brown Lemur
French: Lémur à front blanc
German: Weisskopfmaki
Malagasy: Varika, Varikosy, Varikosa (Makira region), Alokosy

Identification

Eulemur albifrons is a medium-sized lemur with a head-body length of 39–42 cm, a tail length of 50–54 cm, an overall length of 89–96 cm, and a body weight of around 2 kg (C. Schwitzer, pers. obs.). This species is sexually dichromatic and its defining characteristics are largely restricted to the head of the male. It is also cranially the most distinct species of the *fulvus* group (C. P. Groves, pers. comm.). In males, the dorsal coat and tail are medium to dark brown, darkening and becoming redder moving front to rear. The ventral fur is pale gray, sometimes creamy-white on the throat and chest. The muzzle is black and contrasts with the thick white beard, bushy cheeks, and crown. The eyes are reddish-orange. In females, the dorsal fur is similar in color to that of the male and the ventral fur is gray. The face, muzzle, chest and shoulders are dark gray, as is the fur of the head, which contrasts sharply with the white head of the male. In both sexes the tail is darker than the dorsal coat. The male is easily distinguished from other *Eulemur* species by its distinctive white face. Although the other northern species, *E. sanfordi*, also has light colored ear tufts and a beard, the beard is much fuller in *E. albifrons*. Hybrids have been seen from north of Sambava. Females are sometimes difficult to distinguish from related species.

Geographic Range

This species is found in tropical moist lowland and montane rain forest (sea level to 1,600 m) in northeastern Madagascar, occurring from the Bemarivo River, near Sambava, south to the region of Mananara-Nord, including the Masoala Peninsula and the island of Nosy Mangabe, and possibly extending from Marojejy west into Tsaratanana. It formerly occurred in areas north of the present range, but apparently has been extirpated there. An isolated population is also found in the Betampona Strict Nature Reserve, which was likely introduced, and the Nosy Mangabe population may also be introduced (E. E. Louis Jr., pers. obs.). The distribution south of Mananara remains to be clarified as it appears to hybridize with *E. fulvus* over a wide area.

Natural History

The white-fronted brown lemur is believed to be cathemeral, active both day and night throughout the year (Rasmussen, 1999). Population density has been estimated at around 15 individuals/km² (Rakotondratsima and Kremen, 2001). Females are reported to feed more heavily on flowers than males during the dry season, when they also are more likely to give birth (Vasey, 1997a). Fecundity has been measured at 0.2–0.7 young per adult female per year, with most adult females producing offspring each year (Rakotondratsima and Kremen, 2001).

Lemuridae

Conservation Status

The 2008 IUCN Red List assessment (2008) classified *E. albifrons* as Vulnerable (VU). The principal threats are habitat loss due to slash-and-burn agriculture, logging, and mining. Hunting is also a major problem in some areas, and can be quite heavy. For example, recent studies in the Makira region have found that animals are taken with firearms and traps, that this is the most heavily hunted of all the lemurs, and that current levels of hunting are not sustainable (Golden, 2005). It is found in three national parks (Mananara-Nord, Marojejy, and Masoala) and two special reserves (Anjanaharibe-Sud and Nosy Mangabe), with an additional, introduced population in the Betampona Strict Nature Reserve (Mittermeier *et al.*, 1994; E. E. Louis Jr., pers. obs.).

As of 2009 there were approximately 150 white-fronted brown lemurs in zoos around the world (ISIS, 2009).

Where to See It

The white-fronted brown lemur can be seen in most forests throughout its range, but is difficult to observe for any length of time in regions where it is hunted. Perhaps the easiest place to observe it is on the island of Nosy Mangabe, about 5 km offshore in the Bay of Antongil, a site that can be reached by boat in about 20 minutes from Maroantsetra. Introduced animals are also easily seen on Ile Roger or Aye-aye Island, close to the town

Fig. 9.80: Male white-fronted brown lemur (*Eulemur albifrons*) on Aye-aye Island (= Ile Roger), near Mananara-Nord (photo by R. A. Mittermeier).

Lemuridae

Fig. 9.81: Male white-fronted brown lemur (*Eulemur albifrons*), Aye-aye Island, near Mananara-Nord (photo by R. A. Mittermeier).

of Mananara-Nord. Other places to observe wild populations include most sites in Masoala National Park, between camps 1 and 2 in Marojejy National Park, and near Befingotra in the Anjanaharibe-Sud Special Reserve (Garbutt, 2007). Finally, a free-ranging population also inhabits the Parc Zoologique d'Ivoloina, about 12 km northwest of Toamasina.

Fig. 9.82: Female white-fronted brown lemur (*Eulemur albifrons*) with infant on Aye-aye Island (= Ile Roger) near Mananara-Nord, northeastern Madagascar (photo by R. A. Mittermeier).

Fig. 9.83: A white-fronted brown lemur (*Eulemur albifrons*) in the 1860 book *Bilder-Atlas zur Wissenschaftlich-populären: Naturgeschichte der Säugethiere*, by Leopold Joseph Fitzinger (1802-1884).

Lemuridae

Eulemur sanfordi (Archbold, 1932)
Sanford's Brown Lemur

Other English: Sanford's Lemur
French: Lémur de Sanford
German: Sanford's Maki
Malagasy: Ankomba, Beharavoaka, Varika

Identification

Eulemur sanfordi is a medium-sized lemur with a head-body length of 38–40 cm, a tail length of 50–55 cm, an overall length of 88–95 cm, and a body weight of 1.8–1.9 kg (Terranova and Coffman, 1997). This species is sexually dichromatic. In males, the dorsal coat is brown, darker along the back and on the tail. The ventral coat is pale brownish-gray. Prominent ear tufts are the most notable feature of the male of this species, ranging from off-white to cream to slightly rufous, and complemented by a beard of similar color that gives the appearance of a mane. The nose, the muzzle, and the face are black. The top of the head is cream-colored to brown and always lighter than the dorsal coat. In females, the dorsal coat and tail are gray-brown, and the ventral coat is a paler gray. The face is also gray, as are the shoulders and the upper part of the back. Lighter patches are often found above the eyes. The female lacks the beard and ear tufts of the male. It is difficult to distinguish female Sanford's brown lemurs from female white-fronted brown lemurs, *E. albifrons*.

This species is sympatric with *E. coronatus* throughout its range, but the two can be easily distinguished. Both sexes of *E. coronatus* have the distinctive V-shaped orange marking above the forehead, and lack the distinctive white ear tufts and light beard of *E. sanfordi*.

Geographic Range

Sanford's brown lemur has a restricted range in northern Madagascar centered on the forests of Ankarana, Analamerana, and Montagne d'Ambre, with a disjunct population found in the Daraina region to the southeast. The Manambato River is the southern limit of its range, although hybrids with *E. albifrons* appear to occur between Vohémar and Sambava. This lemur is absent from very dry forests such as those of Cap d'Ambre, but it does occur in parts of the Montagne des Français near Antsiranana (= Diégo-Suarez).

Natural History

Sanford's brown lemur occurs in tropical moist and dry lowland and montane forests up to elevations of 1,400 m. It has been studied in the Ankarana Special Reserve and in Montagne d'Ambre National Park. In Ankarana, it appears to favor secondary forest, and is active both day and night (Wilson *et al.*, 1988, 1989; Fowler *et al.*, 1989; Freed, 1996). Groups are typically multi-male/multi-female. In Ankarana they may include up to 15 animals (Wilson *et al.*, 1989), significantly larger than those observed in Montagne

Lemuridae

Fig. 9.84: Male Sanford's brown lemur (*Eulemur sanfordi*) from Analamerana (photo by E. E. Louis Jr.).

d'Ambre, which range from three to nine animals (Freed, 1996). At Montagne d'Ambre, overlapping home ranges of close to 15 ha have been reported (Arbelot-Tracqui, 1983). In Analamerana, a population density of 3.5–5.4 individuals/km² has been reported by Banks (2005). Mating occurs in late May, and births usually take place in late September or early October after a gestation of about 120 days. There is no evidence of female dominance.

The diet of Sanford's brown lemur consists primarily of fruit, but includes other plant parts (buds, young leaves, flowers) according to seasonal availability, and also the occasional invertebrate (e.g., centipedes, millipedes and spiders). Flowers make up a greater portion of the diet during dry season months than they do during the rainy season (Freed, 1996). *Eulemur sanfordi* is also reported to associate with *E. coronatus* during the wet season, a time of greater food availability (Freed, 1996).

Conservation Status

The 2008 IUCN Red List assessment (2008) classified *E. sanfordi* as Endangered (EN). The principal threats are habitat loss due to logging and mining, as well as hunting. Nicoll

Fig. 9.85: Female Sanford's brown lemur (*Eulemur sanfordi*) in captivity at the Duke Lemur Center (photo by D. Haring/DLC).

and Langrand (1989) reported widespread poaching in Montagne d'Ambre, and Hawkins *et al.* (1990) reported the same for Analamerana. This species is also frequently kept as a pet in the Antsiranana region (O. Langrand, pers. obs.). It occurs in two national parks (Ankarana and Montagne d'Ambre) and in the Analamerana Special Reserve (Nicoll and Langrand, 1989), as well as in the forests of Daraina (the Loky-Manambato Protected Area) (Randrianarisoa *et al.*, 1999).

As of 2009, there were only six Sanford's brown lemurs reported in two zoological collections, both in the United States (ISIS, 2009).

Where to See It

Both the Montagne d'Ambre and Ankarana National Parks are good places to see Sanford's brown lemur. It often can be seen close to park headquarters and along the botanical trail of Petite Cascade in Montagne d'Ambre. In Ankarana, it is most easily observed in the Canyon Forestier and around the campsite at Campement des Anglais, but can be seen in other parts of the reserve as well (Garbutt, 2007).

Fig. 9.86: Male Sanford's brown lemur (*Eulemur sanfordi*) in captivity at the Duke Lemur Center (photo by D. Haring/DLC).

Eulemur cinereiceps (A. Grandidier and Milne-Edwards, 1890)
White-Collared Brown Lemur

Other English: Gray-headed Brown Lemur, White-collared Lemur
French: Lémur à collier blanc; Maki à fraise
German: Weisswangen-Halsbandmaki
Malagasy: Varika, Varika Mena (Manombo)

Identification

Eulemur cinereiceps is a medium-sized lemur with a head-body length of 39–40 cm, a tail length of 50–55 cm, an overall length of 89–95 cm, and a body weight of around 2.0–2.5 kg (Tattersall, 1982; Bradley *et al.*, 1997; Johnson *et al.*, 2005). This species is sexually dichromatic. In males, the dorsal coat is gray-brown, the tail and lower limbs slightly darker, and a dark brown stripe often runs along the spine. The ventral coat is a paler gray, as are the head and face. A dark gray crown turns lighter on the neck and shoulders. Both the cheeks and beard are white or light cream and bushy. Coloration of the males of this lemur is very similar to that of *E. collaris*, except that male *E. cinereiceps* have white beards rather than the rufous beards of *E. collaris*. Female *E. cinereiceps* are virtually indistinguishable from female *E. collaris*, the coat being reddish-brown above with lighter underparts. Their faces are uniformly slate-gray, with a short, reddish-brown beard that matches the coat color and is not bushy like that of the male (S. E. Johnson, pers. comm.). Genetic analyses show that these two taxa are distinct species (Djletati *et al.*, 1997; Wyner *et al.*, 1999b), as do field studies in apparent hybrid zones of *E. rufifrons* and *E. cinereiceps* (Sterling and Ramarason, 1996; Johnson and Wyner, 2000).

Lemur (recte *Eulemur*) *cinereiceps* was described by Grandidier and Milne-Edwards in 1890, and is illustrated in their monumental work on Madagascar. The specimen upon which this species was based was a female, hence the Latin name ("gray head"). Unfortunately, although the Grandidier plates are excellent, text was produced only for the Indriidae, not for the remaining lemurs. Schwarz (1931) assigned the *cinereiceps* name to two Paris museum specimens from two localities in southeastern Madagascar, Farafangana and Solohy. This animal remained in obscurity for a long time, until it was resurrected by Groves (1974). Unaware of this, Rumpler (1975) described the white-collared brown lemur as *Lemur albocollaris*, and this name, later changed to *Eulemur albocollaris*, has been used for this species for the better part of the last 35 years (including in the last two editions of this field guide). However, a recent survey by Johnson *et al.* (2008) found that the animals living in Farafangana and Solohy are in fact what has usually been referred to as *Eulemur albocollaris*. This evidence, added to that of Schwarz (1931), seems to confirm that Grandidier and Milne-Edwards' *cinereiceps* was based on females of the species named *albocollaris* by Rumpler (1975). Johnson *et al.* (2008) have reviewed the literature, and conclude that, according to Art. 23.9.1 of the International Code of Zoological Nomenclature, the senior synonym cannot be rejected in this instance, and that the correct name of the white-collared brown lemur is indeed *Eulemur cinereiceps* (C. P. Groves, pers. comm.). Consequently, we have adopted this name for the brown lemur species from this part of southeastern Madagascar, and no longer use the name *E. albocollaris*.

Lemuridae

Geographic Range

The white-collared brown lemur has the most restricted range of any *Eulemur* species. It occurs at low densities in a thin strip of tropical moist lowland forest (sea level to 500 m) in southeastern Madagascar from just above the Manampatrana River south to the Mananara River (Petter and Petter-Rousseaux, 1979; Tattersall, 1982), with a small, isolated population at Manombo and Agnalazaha on the coast south of Farafangana (Johnson and Overdorff, 1999; R. A. Mittermeier and J. Ratsimbazafy, pers. obs.). A hybrid zone with *E. rufifrons* appears to occur at the Iantara River (the headwaters of the Manampatra) near Andringitra National Park. Recent analyses of satellite imagery estimate that total habitat remaining within the range of this species is little more than 700 km² (Johnson and Wyner, 2000; Irwin *et al.*, 2005).

Natural History

Information regarding the natural history of this lemur comes largely from recent studies conducted in the forests of Vevembe. Johnson (2002) found it to be it is mainly frugivorous, its diet supplemented with leaves, flowers, and fungi.

Fig. 9.87: Male white-collared brown lemur (*Eulemur cinereiceps*), Manombo Special Reserve (photo by R. A. Mittermeier).

Lemuridae

Flowers are an especially important food item late in the dry season. *Eulemur cinereiceps* is cathemeral, remaining active both day and night throughout the year. Social groups also tend to be multi-male/multi-female and relatively large. They regularly exhibit fission/fusion. Female dominance has not been observed.

Conservation Status

Eulemur cinereiceps was classified as Endangered (EN) in the IUCN Red List assessment of 2008. However, a review by Johnson *et al.* (2009) has concluded that it is Critically Endangered (CR). It has an extremely small range, and a cyclone in 1997 reduced its population by about 50% (Ratsimbazafy *et al.*, 2002). What is more, it has apparently undergone hybridization with *E. rufifrons* in the northern part of its range, about 50% of its total distribution (K. Delmore, in prep.). Coastal populations have apparently undergone a significant genetic bottleneck. Effective population size (number of breeding individuals) falls well below total population estimates (R. Brenneman, E. E. Louis Jr. and S. E. Johnson, in prep.). In addition, preliminary evidence suggests heavy infestations of some parasites (e.g., pinworms) that could reduce fitness, particularly if degraded environmental conditions compromise immune response (S. Martin, in prep.).

Recognizing its critical status, *E. cinereiceps* has been listed as one of the world's 25 most endangered primates since 2004 (in 2004 and 2006 under the name *E. albocollaris*) (Johnson *et al.*, 2009).

The principal threats to its survival are habitat loss due to slash-and-burn agriculture and logging, and hunting with snares, shotguns, and slingshots. Apparently, it is easily baited and trapped during the fruiting season of the strawberry guava, *Psidium cattlianum* (J. Ratsimbazafy, pers. obs.). On the coast, the species numbers only in the low hundreds. It is found in the Manombo Special Reserve and also the Agnalazaha Forest, which is now being managed by the Missouri Botanical Garden. Unfortunately, this represents less than 5% of the remaining habitat within this species' range (Irwin *et al.*, 2005). *Eulemur cinereiceps* also occurs in two unprotected forests, Vevembe and Lambohazo, west of Vondrozo, both of which could be added to existing parks and reserves (Johnson and Overdorff, 1999). The population outside Andringitra National Park hybridizes with *E. rufifrons* (CBSG, 2002; Johnson, 2002). Expansion of the Manombo Special Reserve to include the neighboring classified forest is a high conservation priority, as is preservation of the existing, very interesting hybrid zone. A detailed search of remaining forests in the immediate Farafangana region is a high priority, since the protected areas in the broader region surrounding Farafangana all seem to harbor *E. cinereiceps*. Conservation International is presently initiating programs for the management of the Fandriana-Vondrozo forest corridor. This will be critical for the long-term survival of the white-collared brown lemur as the vast majority of populations are found within this corridor and few are presently protected.

As of 2009, there were approximately a dozen white-collared brown lemurs reported in four zoological collections (ISIS, 2009), but only one of these (Linton Zoo, UK) is keeping a breeding group (C. Schwitzer, pers. obs.).

Where to See It

The easiest place to see the white-collared brown lemur is the Manombo Special Reserve and the associated classified forest, about 30 km south of Farafangana on RN12 (Garbutt, 2007; J. Ratsimbazafy and R. A. Mittermeier, pers. obs.). A paved road leads visitors to the edge of the reserve, where guest bungalows are now available. The species can also be seen in the Agnalahaza Forest, 40 km south of Farafangana on RN12 and at a private reserve about 7 km inland to the west on a very rough dirt road. An alternative viewing site is the strip of forest just west of the town of Vondrozo on either side of RN27. Access to this site is a bit more difficult, especially during the wet season. Trips to these sites can be arranged through an Antananarivo-based tour operator or through hotels in Farafangana.

Fig. 9.88: Female (left) and male white-collared brown lemurs (*Eulemur cinereiceps*) in captivity in the Manombo forest (photo by I. Relanzón).

Lemuridae

Fig. 9.89: Top: A chromolithograph from Grandidier's 19th century book depicting *Eulemur cinereiceps*. Lower left: A captive female *E. cinereiceps* photographed in June, 2005 in Farafangana, southeastern Madagascar (photo by R. A. Mittermeier). Lower right: The type and paratype of *E. cinereiceps* in the Paris Museum (photos by C. P. Groves).

Lemuridae

Fig. 9.90: White-collared brown lemur (*Eulemur cinereiceps*) in captivity in the Manombo forest (photos by I. Relanzón).

Eulemur collaris (É. Geoffroy, 1812)
Red-collared Brown Lemur

Other English: Red-collared Lemur
French: Lémur à collier roux
German: Rotwangen-Halsbandmaki, Rotbartmaki
Malagasy: Varika

Identification

Eulemur collaris is a medium-sized lemur with a head-body length of 39–40 cm, a tail length of 50–55 cm, an overall length of 89–95 cm, and a body weight of 2.25–2.5 kg (Tattersall, 1982). This species is sexually dichromatic. In males, the dorsal coat is brownish-gray, the tail is darker, and there is also a dark stripe along the spine. The ventral coat is a paler gray. The muzzle, face and crown are dark gray to black. The creamy to rufous-brown cheeks and beard are thick and bushy, while the creamy to gray-colored eyebrow patches vary in their prominence. In females, the dorsal coat is browner or more rufous than that of the male. The ventral coat is a pale creamy-gray. The face and head are gray. The cheeks are rufous-brown, but less prominent than in the males. Both sexes have orange-red eyes.

The red-collared brown lemur is similar in coloration to *Eulemur cinereiceps*. Male *E. collaris* can be distinguished from male *E. cinereiceps* by their beards, those of the former being cream-colored or rufous while those of the latter are white. Female *E. collaris* are virtually indistinguishable from female *E. cinereiceps* (S. E. Johnson, pers. comm.). Recent genetic analyses support full species status for both taxa (Djletati *et al.*, 1997; Wyner *et al.*, 1999b).

Geographic Range

The red-collared brown lemur is found in tropical moist lowland and montane forests in southeastern Madagascar, from Tolagnaro (= Fort-Dauphin) north to the Mananara River. The western limits of its range are the forests of the Kalambatritra region, including the Kalambatritra Special Reserve. The Mananara River serves as a boundary between the ranges of *E. collaris* and *E. cinereiceps*, except for an isolated population at Midongy du Sud National Park (Irwin *et al.*, 2005) and another at Vohipaho, near Vangaindrano (S. E. Johnson, pers. comm.). There is also a small population in the Sainte-Luce Private Reserve.

Natural History

Very little information has been published regarding the natural history of this lemur. It is an inhabitant of moist tropical forest, and appears to be common where it occurs. Irwin *et al.* (2005) estimated a population density of 14 individuals/km². It is believed to be largely frugivorous and cathemeral, meaning that it is active both day and night throughout the year. Social groups tend to be multi-male/multi-female. Female dominance has not been observed (Donati, 2002; Bollen *et al.*, 2004).

Lemuridae

Fig. 9.91: Male red-collared brown lemur (*Eulemur collaris*), Midongy du Sud (photo by M. Andriantompohavana).

Fig. 9.92: Male red-collared brown lemur (*Eulemur collaris*), Mandena Conservation Zone (photo by I. Relanzón).

Conservation Status

The 2008 IUCN Red List assessment classified *E. collaris* as Vulnerable (VU). The principal threats are habitat loss due to slash-and-burn agriculture and charcoal

Fig. 9.93: Male red-collared brown lemurs (*Eulemur collaris*), Mandena Conservation Zone (photos by I. Relanzón).

Lemuridae

production, hunting for food, and capture to supply local pet trades (Raharivololona and Ranaivosoa, 2000). It occurs in the national parks of Andohahela and Midongy du Sud, in the Kalambatritra Special Reserve, and in the Sainte-Luce Private Reserve (Nicoll and Langrand, 1989; Mittermeier *et al.*, 1994; Wright and Porter, 2004; Irwin *et al.*, 2005). It is also found in the Mandena Conservation Zone, privately maintained by QIT Madagascar Minerals (QMM) (a partnership between the Government of Madagascar and Rio Tinto, in the development of an ilmenite mine near Fort-Dauphin). Six to eight orphan *E. collaris* that had been purchased in the Forte-Dauphin market were introduced into the Berenty Private Reserve over some years up to 1985. Other red-collared brown lemurs were introduced to the Kaleta Private Reserve nearby, and they also spread into Berenty. They hybridized with *E. rufifrons* which had been introduced previously (Jolly, 2004; p.30; pers.comm.).

As of 2009, there were 37 red-collared brown lemurs reported in zoological collections in Europe and North America (ISIS, 2009).

Where to See It

Eulemur collaris is most easily seen in the Mandena Conservation Zone, approximately 20 minutes east of Tolagnaro (= Fort-Dauphin), and in the Sainte-Luce Private Reserve, about three to four hours north of Tolagnaro along the coast. The Mandena Conservation Zone can be visited with the help of local tourist agencies or through contact with QIT Madagascar minerals in Tolagnaro. The Sainte-Luce Private Reserve is owned by M. Jean de Heaulme, the owner of Berenty, and arrangements to visit can be made through the Hotel le Dauphin in Tolagnaro. Another site is the rain forest portion (Parcel 1) of the Andohahela National Park, especially along the road to the Col de Manangotry. This area is a few hours drive by car from Tolagnaro and arrangements can also be made through all local tour operators.

Fig. 9.94: Red-collared brown lemurs (*Eulemur collaris*). Left: Two males. Right: a female with infant. Photographed in captivity at the Duke Lemur Center (photos by D. Haring/DLC).

Lemuridae

Eulemur macaco (Linnaeus, 1766)
Black Lemur

Other English: None
French: Lémur Macaco
German: Mohrenmaki
Malagasy: Ankomba, Akomba
Komba, Ankomba Joby

Identification

Eulemur macaco is a medium-sized lemur with a head-body length of 39–45 cm, a tail length of 51–65 cm, a total length of 90–110 cm, and a weight of 1.8–1.9 kg (Terranova and Coffman, 1997; C. Schwitzer, pers. obs.). This species is sexually dichromatic. In males, the dorsal coat varies from dark chocolate-brown to black. The ventral coat is similarly colored. The ears have prominent tufts of long black hair. In females, the dorsal coat varies from golden-brown to chestnut-brown, lighter on the flanks but darker on the tail. The ventral coat is typically creamy white on the abdomen grading to cinnamon on the chin, and this coloration may continue to just below the eyes and ear tufts. The face is gray to black, the crown a darker charcoal-gray, and the ears are tufted with long white hairs. The eyes of both sexes are yellow-orange to deep orange.

The black lemur hybridizes with *E. flavifrons* throughout a large part of the Manongarivo Special Reserve between Maromandia and Ambanja (Meyers *et al.*, 1989; Rabarivola *et al.*, 1991; Goodman and Schütz, 2000). Populations in the Sahamalaza-Iles Radama National Park, just north of the Andranomalaza River, differ in fur coloration and the prominence of ear tufts compared to populations in the northern part of the range (Schwitzer and Lork, 2004). *Eulemur macaco* (and hybrids) is sympatric with *E. fulvus* on the Galoka, Manongarivo, and Tsaratanana Massifs, and in the Ifasy and Ramena river valleys, and with *E. rubriventer* on the Tsaratanana Massif (Tattersall, 1976b, 1982; Andrews, 1989; Birkinshaw *et al.*, 2000; Goodman and Schütz, 2000). The black lemur can be distinguished from both of these congeners by its distinctive sexually dichromatic pelage and by the conspicuous ear tufts of both males and females.

Geographic Range

Northwestern Madagascar. The Mahavavy River is the northern limit of the range of *E. macaco*, and the Andranomalaza River forms part of the southern boundary. The eastern limit is poorly defined, but it likely occurs on the Tsaratanana Massif.

In the southern part of its range, it intergrades with *E. flavifrons* in and around the Manongarivo Special Reserve (Meyers *et al.*, 1989). It is found in the forests of the Ampasindava Peninsula, on the islands of Nosy Be and Nosy Komba, in the coastal forests northeast of Ambanja (including the peninsula leading to Nosy Faly), and it has been introduced to the small island of Nosy Tanikely, a local tourist attraction and dive-site (Koenders *et al.*, 1985a; Mittermeier *et al.*, 1994; Colquhoun, 1998b).

Lemuridae

Natural History

The black lemur inhabits tropical moist lowland and montane forests from sea level to 1,600 m in the Sambirano region. It is quite adaptable and has been reported from primary forest, secondary forest, forest-agriculture mosaics, and timber plantations (Groves and Eaglen, 1988; Andrews, 1989). It is considered cathemeral, being active day and night throughout the year (Andrews and Birkinshaw, 1998; Colquhoun, 1998a). Group size ranges from 2 to 15 animals, the median range being 7–10 (Petter, 1962a, 1962b; Colquhoun, 1993). During the birth season, intergroup agonistic interactions are most directly related to food access compared with the mating season (Bayart and Simmen, 2005). Females give birth to a single young, usually between September and November (Petter and Petter, 1971).

Fruits make up the bulk of its diet throughout the year, except for perhaps a month or so when leaves, seedpods, and nectar take on added significance and are also supplemented by fungi and invertebrates (Petter, 1962a, 1962b; Petter *et al.*, 1977; Andrews and Birkinshaw, 1998; Simmen *et al.*, 2007). Studies in Lokobe Strict Nature Reserve on Nosy Be and in the forests of the Ambato Massif suggest that the black lemur is a significant pollinator of the widespread traveler's palm (*Ravenala madagascariensis*) and the legume (*Parkia madagascariensis*); as it feeds on nectar (Birkinshaw and Colquhoun, 1998). At Lokobe, it

Fig. 9.95: Male (left) and female (right) black lemurs (*Eulemur macaco*) in forest at the edge of the Lokobe Strict Nature Reserve, behind the village of Ampasipohy (photos by R. A. Mittermeier).

also appears to be the sole seed disperser for many tree species (Birkinshaw, 1999a). In Anpasilkely Forest, black lemurs obtain 150–190 kcal from the daytime diet during the birth season, and some introduced plant species were preferred (Simmen *et al.*, 2007).

Conservation Status

The IUCN Red List assessment of 2008 classified *E. macaco* as Vulnerable (VU). The principal threats are habitat loss due to slash-and-burn agriculture, and to hunting (both for food and as a pest). Hunting with traps seems to kill females preferentially, as they tend to lead group travel. There is also a small, but persistent, trade in black lemurs as pets (I. Colquhoun, pers. comm.). This species occurs in one national park (Sahamalaza-Iles Radama), two strict nature reserve (Lokobe and Tsaratanana) and in the Manongarivo Special Reserve (Nicoll and Langrand, 1989; Schwitzer and Lork, 2004; Schwitzer, 2006). In Manongarivo it is reported to be the most common lemur, diurnal or nocturnal (Raxworthy and Rakotondraparany, 1988). The species is also protected on the island of Nosy Komba, where the local people consider it sacred and where it serves as a major tourist attraction.

As of 2009 there were an estimated 160 individuals in captivity worldwide (ISIS, 2009).

Where to See It

The best places to see the black lemur are on the islands of Nosy Be and Nosy Komba. On Nosy Komba, a largely degraded island, several groups of black lemurs come to a feeding site where tourists can offer them bananas sold by local villagers. The animals are habituated and will even sit on the visitor providing he or she remains calm. To see animals

Fig. 9.96: Black lemur (*Eulemur macaco*). Left: Male from the island of Nosy Be. Right: Female from the island of Nosy Komba near Nosy Be (photos by R. A. Mittermeier).

in more natural habitat, one can visit the Lokobe Strict Nature Reserve on Nosy Be, near the capital city of Hellville. Several enterprising villagers run tours to the edge of the reserve. They include an outrigger canoe ride, a walk in the forest (where the newly described Nosy Be sportive lemur, *Lepilemur tymerlachsonorum*, can readily be seen as well, even in the day), and a picnic. You can also overnight in two hotels on the Ampasipohy Beach, right at the edge of the reserve. Both of the sites described above are now on the regular tourist circuit and are a must for first-time visitors to Madagascar. A small population of introduced black lemurs on Nosy Tanikely near Nosy Komba is also easily observed.

Lemuridae

Fig. 9.97: Female black lemur (*Eulemur macaco*) in the forest at the edge of the Lokobe Strict Nature Reserve, behind the village of Ampasipohy (photo by R. A. Mittermeier).

Eulemur flavifrons (Gray, 1867)
Blue-eyed Black Lemur

Other English: Sclater's Lemur
Sclater's Black Lemur
French: Maki aux yeux turquoise
German: Sclater's Maki
Malagasy: Akomba, Akomba sy Manga Maso

Identification

Eulemur flavifrons is a medium-sized lemur with a head-body length of 39–45 cm, a tail length of 51–65 cm, a total length of 90–100 cm, and a weight of 1.8–1.9 kg (Terranova and Coffman, 1997; G. Randriatahina, pers. comm.). This species is sexually dichromatic. In males, the dorsal and ventral coats are black, the hairs sometimes tinged with brown, and a distinct ridge of hair on the forehead forms a noticeable crest. In contrast to *E. macaco,* with which it was long considered conspecific, there are no ear tufts. In females, the dorsal coat is reddish-tan to reddish-gray. The ventral coat is creamy-white to gray. The hands and feet are darker gray. The muzzle is slate-gray, the face lighter, and the crown rufous-tan. As with males, and again in contrast to female *E. macaco*, there are no ear tufts. The eyes of both sexes are blue to blue-gray, making this species one of the very few primates in the world that consistently has blue eyes, hence the common English name.

The taxonomic status of this lemur has been debated since it was first described in the late 1800s. Due to the lack of locality data for the few museum specimens collected, nothing was known of its status in the wild until its "rediscovery" in 1983 (Tattersall, 1982; Koenders *et al.*, 1985a). Subsequent genetic analysis indicated that it was distinct. It was at first separated as a subspecies (Fausser *et al.*, 2000), but we elevate it here to a full species (Mittermeier *et al.*, 2008c). The blue-eyed black lemur can only be confused with the black lemur, which is found just to its north and with which it is reported to hybridize in a large area of the Manongarivo Special Reserve. The lack of ear tufts in *E. flavifrons* and its striking blue-gray eyes readily distinguish it from *Eulemur macaco*.

Geographic Range

In November, 1983, the blue-eyed black lemur was "rediscovered" in northwestern Madagascar in forests north of Befotaka and south of Maromandia, just south of the Sambirano region. Subsequent expeditions established its presence on the Sahamalaza Peninsula. The Andranomalaza River is the northern boundary of its range, the Maevarano River the southern boundary, and the Sandrakota River the eastern boundary, although it is reported to occur to the northeast of the Andranomalaza River, east of the Manongarivo Special Reserve as well (Petter and Andriatsarafara, 1987; Rabarivola *et al.*, 1991; Andrianjakarivelo, 2004; Randriatahina and Rabarivola, 2004). A zone of hybridization or intergradation with *E. macaco* has been identified north of the Andranomalaza River in the Manongarivo mountains and the foothills of the southern Sambirano, including part of the Manongarivo

Lemuridae

Special Reserve (Meyers *et al.*, 1989; Rabarivola *et al.*, 1991; but see Schwitzer and Lork, 2004).

Natural History

Eulemur flavifrons inhabits more or less disturbed primary and secondary subtropical sub-humid forests, in a transition zone between the Sambirano region to the north and the western dry deciduous forests to the south. Its home range size and the way it uses its range differs between primary and secondary forest fragments, indicating that this species is somewhat able to adapt to different types of habitat. However, larger home ranges and

Fig. 9.98: Male blue-eyed black lemur (*Eulemur flavifrons*), Parc Tsimbazaza (photo by R. A. Mittermeier).

lower densities of *E. flavifrons* in secondary forest as compared to primary forest suggest that the former is less suitable habitat for the species (Schwitzer *et al.*, 2007a). During a 12-month study, *E. flavifrons* ate parts of 72 different plant species from 35 families; 52.3% of these were fruits, and 47.7% were leaves. The animals also fed on flowers, insects, insect excretions and fungi (Polowinsky and Schwitzer, 2009).

The blue-eyed black lemur has a bimodal activity pattern, with peaks during the morning and evening twilight. It has activity bouts during the day and night year-round. Nocturnal illumination and the proportion of illuminated lunar disk are positively associated with the amount of nocturnal activity. Total daily activity, as well as nocturnal activity, is higher in secondary forest than in primary forest (Schwitzer *et al.*, 2007b). At certain times of the year, this species may feed on large quantities of cicadas.

Conservation Status

The IUCN Red List assessment in 2008 classified *E. flavifrons* as Critically Endangered (CR). It is also considered one of the most threatened primates in the world, having been included on the 2008 list of the world's 25 Most Endangered Primates, drawn up every two years by the IUCN/SSC Primate Specialist Group, the International Primatological Society, and Conservation International (Schwitzer *et al.*, 2009). The principal threats to its survival are forest destruction due to slash-and-burn agriculture and selective logging, continued hunting and trapping, especially by the Tsimihety people in the eastern part of its distribution, and live capture for the local pet trade (C. Schwitzer, pers. comm.). Andrianjakarivelo (2004) found a density of up to 570 traps/km² in certain areas. Parts of the distribution area of *E. flavifrons* received official protected area status in 2007 as the Parc National Sahamalaza-Iles Radama, including the Sahamalaza Peninsula and some mainland forests to the north and east (Lernould, 2002; Schwitzer and Lork, 2004; Schwitzer *et al.*, 2006, 2009; C. Schwitzer, pers. obs.). The Sahamalaza Peninsula is also a UNESCO Biosphere Reserve.

As of 2010, there were about 75 individuals in captivity in Europe, North America and Madagascar (ISIS, 2009; I. J. Porton, pers. comm.).

Where to See It

The blue-eyed black lemur is most readily observed in remaining forest patches just south of Maromandia, on the main road from Antananarivo to Antsiranana (= Diégo-Suarez). It can also be seen in forest patches on the Sahamalaza Peninsula. The Ankarafa Forest on the Sahamalaza Peninsula can be reached by a one-hour boat trip from Analalava to the small village of Marovato, and from there there is a hike of about two hours inland. Analalava is served by a regular ferry from Antsohihy. The Sahamalaza Peninsula can also be reached by pirogue from Maromandia. In the beginning of 2008, a local guide association was in the process of being formed, and use of local guides is indeed essential to find this species. Given the difficulty of finding this lemur, it is strongly recommended that a trip be arranged through Antananarivo-based tour operators.

Lemuridae

Fig. 9.99: Male (above) and female (below) blue-eyed black lemur (*Eulemur flavifrons*), Sahamalaza, northwestern Madagascar (photos by R. A. Mittermeier). Note the blue eyes and lack of ear tufts, which distinguish this species from *Eulemur macaco*.

Eulemur coronatus (Gray, 1842)
Crowned Lemur

Other English: None
French: Lémur couronné
German: Kronenmaki
Malagasy: Ankomba, Ankomba Fiaka, Gidro

Identification

Eulemur coronatus is the smallest member of the genus, with a head-body length of 34–36 cm, a tail length of 41–49 cm, an overall length of 75–85 cm, and a body weight of 1.1–1.3 kg (Terranova and Coffman, 1997). This species is sexually dichromatic. In males the dorsal coat is gray-brown, becoming a richer chestnut-brown on the flanks and the limbs, and darker on the tail. The ventral coat is a paler, creamy-gray. Only the tip of the muzzle is black, the face and ears being pale gray to white. An orange-brown, forward-pointing, V-shaped crown runs from the eyebrows alongside the ears and onto the cheeks. There is a dark gray to black patch in the center of the crown. In females, the dorsal coat, flanks, limbs, tail, top of the head and cheeks are gray. The tail darkens toward the tip. The ventral coat, face and ears are a paler gray to creamy-white. The nose is black and the muzzle dark gray. The V-shaped crown is chestnut-orange, but is less prominent than in the male and does not curve around to the cheeks.

This species can be distinguished readily from Sanford's brown lemur (*Eulemur sanfordi*), the only other *Eulemur* species with which it is sympatric, by its V-shaped crown, as well as by the absence of the white face that is so characteristic of male *E. sanfordi*.

Geographic Range

The crowned lemur occurs in the tropical moist and dry lowland and mid-altitude forests of extreme northern Madagascar, from sea level to 1,400 m. As far as is known, it is the only lemur found on the Cap d'Ambre Peninsula, the most northerly point on the island. From there, its range extends south along the east bank of the Mahavavy River beyond Ambilobe. The eastern part of its range extends south along the Manambato River, south of Daraina, to just north of Sambava.

Natural History

Eulemur coronatus has been studied in the dry forests of Ankarana (Wilson *et al.*, 1989; Hawkins *et al.*, 1990) and Sakalava Bay (Arbelot-Traqui, 1983) and in the humid forests on Montagne d'Ambre (Arbelot-Traqui, 1983; Freed, 1996). Several estimates of population density have been made: 77 individuals/km² in the Analamerana Special Reserve; 104 individuals/km² in the humid forests of Montagne d'Ambre; and 221 individuals/km² (and even higher in small areas of selectively logged forest) in the Ankarana Special Reserve (Arbelot-Tracqui, 1983; Fowler *et al.*, 1989; Wilson *et al.*, 1989). A more recent study at Analamerana (Banks, 2005) yielded estimates of 21–25 individuals/km². Home range size is approximately 10–15 ha (Freed, 1996). This species is reported to inhabit all levels of the forest, but is most likely to be found in lianas, thick cover and terminal branches. It also readily descends to the ground to travel, or to eat fallen fruit or lick earth (Petter *et al.*, 1977). The crowned lemur lives in most patches of forests throughout its range, accepting more open, dry habitat than the sympatric *E. sanfordi*, which is restricted to humid or gallery forests. It can even be seen delicately moving through some of the knife-edged karst tsingys that occur within its range, especially in the Ankarana region.

Group size does not appear to differ significantly between habitat types, the average group being five or six and the maximum size about 15 individuals. Large multi-male/multi-female groups often split into foraging subgroups of two to four individuals. Mixed species associations with *E. sanfordi* are reported during the wet season months when food resources are more readily available. According to Freed (1996) this species is cathemeral, remaining active both day and night throughout the year.

Fruits make up the bulk of its diet, supplemented by young leaves, flowers, pollen and sometimes insects. Also, the crowned lemur tends to rely heavily on 10–20% of the nearly one hundred plant species it exploits, and feeds more on flowers during the dry season than at other times of the year. In Ankarana and Montagne d'Ambre mating occurs in late May and June, and births take place from mid-September through October. Gestation is 125 days (Kappeler, 1987). The crowned lemur is one of only three *Eulemur* species that show features of female dominance (Kappeler, 1993).

Conservation Status

The 2008 IUCN Red List assessment classified *E. coronatus* as Vulnerable (VU). The principal threats to its survival are habitat loss due to slash-and-burn agriculture, logging, and mining, as well as hunting and capture for the local pet trade, especially in the Antsiranana region (O. Langrand, pers. obs.). Hunting has recently emerged as a major threat in the Daraina area, where a number of animals were killed to serve a luxury restaurant trade in Sambava (Conservation International, 2010). The crowned lemur is found in two national parks (Ankarana and Montagne d'Ambre), two special reserves (Analamerana and Forêt d'Ambre) (Nicoll and Langrand, 1989), and in Daraina (Loky-Manambato Protected Area).

As of 2009, there were approximately 100 crowned lemurs in zoological collections worldwide (ISIS, 2009).

Where to See It

The best places to see crowned lemurs are in the Ankarana and Montagne d'Ambre national parks. In Ankarana, several groups have been habituated in the area of the Campement des Anglais and Lac Vert, and they are easily found elsewhere in the park as well. In Montagne d'Ambre they can be seen quite close to the main campsite, the Station Roussettes, and the viewpoint overlooking the Grand Cascade (Garbutt, 2007). The species is also common in Daraina and easy to see there, although they are not as evident as Tattersall's sifaka (*Propithecus tattersalli*).

Lemuridae

Lemuridae

Fig. 9.100: Male crowned lemur (*Eulemur coronatus*), Ankavanana, Analamerana Special Reserve (photo by R. Andriantompohavana).

Fig. 9.101: Female crowned lemur (*Eulemur coronatus*), Ankavanana, Analamerana Special Reserve (photo by R. Andriantompohavana).

Eulemur rubriventer (I. Geoffroy, 1850)
Red-bellied Lemur

Other English: None
French: Lémur à ventre rouge
German: Rotbauchmaki
Malagasy: Tongona, Barimaso, Tongo (Makira region), Halimena
(Mananara-Nord), Halomena (Soanierana-Ivonga), Soamiera,
Kirioka, Varikamena (Andasibe region)

Identification

Eulemur rubriventer is a medium-sized *Eulemur* with a head-body length of 35–40 cm, a tail length of 43–53 cm, a total length of 78–93 cm, and a weight of 1.6–2.4 kg (Glander *et al.*, 1992; Terranova and Coffman, 1997). This species is sexually dichromatic. In males, the dorsal coat is long, dense, and a deep chestnut-brown. The ventral coat is slightly lighter and more reddish. The tail is darker, shading to black like the muzzle, face and head. Conspicuous patches of white skin form characteristic "tear-drops" beneath the eyes. There is no bushy beard or ear tufts as in other *Eulemur* species, but the fur around the ears is particularly dense and gives the head a robust appearance. In females, the dorsal coat and tail color are similar to those of the male, but the ventral coat is a highly contrasting creamy-white that may extend all the way to the cheeks. Facial coloration is also similar to that of the male, except that the white patches beneath the eyes are reduced. The head appears less robust, as it lacks the long bushy cheek hairs of the male.

Over its relatively large range, the red-bellied lemur is sympatric with four other *Eulemur* species: *E. albifrons* in the northern part of its range, *E. fulvus* toward the middle of its range, and *E. rufifrons* and *E. cinereiceps* in the southern part. It can be distinguished from all of them by its dark luxurious coat and the male's conspicuous white eye patches. Males from the region of Andasibe (= Périnet) appear to have a more distinctive reddish belly compared to populations found farther south, such as in Ranomafana National Park (O. Langrand, pers. obs.).

Geographic Range

The range of *E. rubriventer* extends from northern Madagascar's Tsaratanana Massif south along the thin strip of eastern rain forest to the Pic d'Ivohibe Special Reserve and the Manampatrana River (Irwin *et al.*, 2005), although at one time it apparently reached as far as the Mananara River (Petter and Petter, 1971; Sterling and Ramaroson, 1996). It does not occur on the Masoala Peninsula. This species appears to be thinly distributed and restricted to intact forests, and is usually considerably rarer than other sympatric *Eulemur*. It occurs at altitudes of up to 2,400 m on the Tsaratanana Massif.

Natural History

The red-bellied lemur has been the subject of several field studies in Ranomafana National Park since the mid-1980s (Meier, 1987; Dague and Petter, 1988; Overdorff,

1988, 1991). Its activity pattern is cathemeral, animals being active both day and night throughout the year (Overdorff and Rasmussen, 1995). The diet consists principally of fruit, flowers, nectar, and leaves of more than 70 different plant species, including introduced species such as Chinese guava (*Psidium* spp.), and it is also considered a good seed disperser. Invertebrates may also be a significant part of the diet at certain times of the year.

Group size varies from two to 10 individuals, the typical group containing an adult pair and their offspring. Densities of approximately 5 individuals/km^2 have been recorded at Ranomafana (Irwin *et al.*, 2005). Home range size has been estimated at 12–15 ha. Groups travel and feed as single units throughout this home range, led primarily by females. Young are born in September and October, and they ride as often on the male as on the female for the first five weeks. After this time, females often reject the infants, while males may carry them up to the age of 100 days. Usually only one infant is born per year to each group, and mortality is approximately 50%.

Conservation Status

According to the most recent IUCN Red List assessment (2008), *E. rubriventer* is Vulnerable (VU). The principal threats to its survival are habitat loss due to slash-and-burn agriculture and illegal logging, and hunting, which can be heavy in certain areas. This species is found in five national parks (Andringitra, Mantadia, Marojejy, Ranomafana, and Zahamena), two strict nature reserves (Tsaratanana and Zahamena), and six special reserves (Ambatovaky, Analamazaotra, Anjanaharibe-Sud, Mangerivola, Marotandrano, and Pic d'Ivohibe) (Nicoll and Langrand, 1989; Schmid and Smolker, 1998).

As of 2009, there were approximately 165 individuals reported in zoological collections worldwide (ISIS, 2009).

Where to See It

The best place to see this species is in Ranomafana National Park, where it is common and where groups have been habituated along the main trail network. When the Chinese guava is in fruit (May and June), red-bellied lemurs are usually easy to find around the Belle Vue site feeding along with *E. rufifrons* (see Garbutt, 2007). This species also can be seen on occasion in the Analamazaotra Special Reserve, in Mantadia National Park, and in the Anjanaharibe-Sud Special Reserve in northeastern Madagascar, but it is quite rare in these reserves.

Lemuridae

Fig. 9.102: Male red-bellied lemur (*Eulemur rubriventer*), Marojejy National Park (photo by E. E. Louis Jr.).

Fig. 9.103: Female red-bellied lemur (*Eulemur rubriventer*), Analamazaotra Special Reserve, Andasibe (photo by R. A. Mittermeier).

Lemuridae

Eulemur mongoz (Linnaeus, 1766)
Mongoose Lemur

Other English: None
French: Lémur Mongoz
German: Mongozmaki
Malagasy: Dredrika, Gidro
Comoros Islands: Komba

Identification

Eulemur mongoz is a small member of the genus, with a head-body length of 30–35 cm, a tail length of 45–48 cm, an overall length of 75–83 cm, and a weight of 1.1–1.6 kg (Tattersall, 1982; Terranova and Coffman, 1995; Pastorini *et al.*, 1998). The species is sexually dichromatic. In males, the dorsal coat is gray-brown and darker at the tip of the tail. There is also a darker pygal patch. The back of the neck and shoulders are often a rufous brown. The ventral coat is a paler creamy-gray. The muzzle and face are gray. The rufous cheeks and beard are the most distinguishing features of the male. A triangular bald patch on the top of the head sometimes results from excessive rubbing during scent-marking. In females, the dorsal coat is gray and lighter than that of the male, but females share the darker tail and dark gray pygal patch, as well as a lighter, cream-colored abdomen. The muzzle is light gray, the face a darker, slate gray that is surrounded by a white bushy beard that extends to the ears and reaches down the throat and onto the forelimbs. The eyes are reddish-orange in both sexes.

North of the Betsiboka River this species is sympatric with the brown lemur, *E. fulvus*, which has a darker coat and is not sexually dichromatic. South of the Betsiboka River, *E. mongoz* is sympatric with the rufous brown lemur, *E. rufus*, with which it is unlikely to be confused, unless one gets only a fleeting glimpse of the animal. However, Zaramody and Pastorini (2001) report a small zone of hybridization between the two species. The mongoose lemur tends to be more cryptic in its behavior and lives in smaller groups than the other *Eulemur* species with which it is found.

In the Comoros, where this species also occurs, it is the only lemur on the islands of Mohéli and Anjouan, and cannot be confused with any other species.

Geographic Range

Eulemur mongoz is found in northwestern Madagascar. It is also one of only two lemur species found outside Madagascar, with populations occurring in the Comoros on the islands of Mohéli and Anjouan, where it was almost certainly introduced by our own species prior to European arrival. In Madagascar, it occurs in the region of Ambato-Boéni and Ankarafantsika, where the remaining forests are highly fragmented (Petter *et al.*, 1977; Tattersall, 1982). The northern limit of its distribution appears to be near Analalava on the Bay of Narindra. It is also found south and west of the Betsiboka River at Katsepy and on the shores of Lac Kinkony, on both sides of the Mahavavy River, and in the Tsiombikibo Classified Forest near Mitsinjo (Müller *et al.*, 2000).

Fig. 9.104: Female mongoose lemur (*Eulemur mongoz*), Anjahamena (photo by E. E. Louis Jr.).

Natural History

This species is found in tropical dry deciduous forests in western Madagascar and can also survive well in secondary forest (Petter, 1962a, 1962b; Tattersall, 1976a). It lives in small cohesive family units of an adult pair with one to four offspring (Curtis and Zaramody, 1999). Its activity pattern, variously described in earlier studies, is now understood to be cathemeral (Curtis *et al.*, 1999; Rasmussen, 1999). Fruit, flowers, nectar, leaves, and leaf petioles constitute the bulk of the diet, which may include relatively few species of plants (Tattersall and Sussman, 1975; Andriatsarafara, 1988; Curtis *et al.*, 1999). Mongoose lemurs have sometimes been observed intermingling with *E. fulvus* groups during feeding bouts (Harrington, 1978b), but usually keep to themselves and are much quieter than sympatric brown lemurs. The birth season appears to be around mid-October and it seems that females give birth each year (Tattersall, 1976a).

Conservation Status

In 2008, the IUCN Red List assessment classified *E. mongoz* as Vulnerable (VU). The principal threats are habitat loss due to slash-and-burn agriculture, burning to create pasture for cattle, charcoal production, and hunting for food. While previously under less threat on Anjouan and Mohéli, this species is increasingly seen as a crop pest, especially by an influx of Malagasy who do not adhere to local customs that have historically provided lemurs in the Comoros a greater degree of protection (Tattersall, 1998). The mongoose lemur occurs in just one protected area, Ankarafantsika National Park. Unprotected populations are found in the forests of Anjamena, Antrema (at Katsepy), Mariarano, and Tsiombikibo (near Mitsinjo).

Fig. 9.105: Male mongoose lemur (*Eulemur mongoz*), Anjahamena (photo by E. E. Louis Jr.).

As of 2009, there were 111 mongoose lemurs reported in zoological collections worldwide (ISIS, 2009).

Where to See It

The mongoose lemur is most readily seen at the Ampijoroa Forestry Station in Ankarafantsika National Park. The station is about a two-hour drive from Mahajanga along the main highway to Antananarivo, and there is now comfortable lodging available. Other potential viewing sites are in the Tsiombikibo Classified Forest northwest of Mitsinjo, around Lac Kamonjo approximately 90 km west of the Betsiboka estuary, and in the Anjamena Forest on the eastern bank of the Mahavavy River (Garbutt, 2007), but access to these sites is largely limited to the dry season. The species can also be seen at Katsepy, right across the Betsiboka River from Mahajanga, which is also an excellent site to see crowned sifaka (*Propithecus coronatus*).

Fig. 9.106: Male mongoose lemur (*Eulemur mongoz*), Lac Antsilomba, Ankarafantsika National Park, northwestern Madagascar (photo by R. A. Mittermeier).

Fig. 9.107: Female mongoose lemur (*Eulemur mongoz*), Lac Antsilomba, Ankarafantsika National Park, northwestern Madagascar (photo by R. A. Mittermeier).

Lemuridae

Lemuridae

Fig. 9.108: A black-and-white ruffed lemur (*Varecia variegata* spp.), Lemur Island, Hotel Vakona, Andasibe (photo by R. A. Mittermeier).

Varecia Gray, 1863
Ruffed Lemurs

Ruffed lemurs of the genus *Varecia* are the largest and most frugivorous members of the family Lemuridae. They are quadrupedal, largely diurnal, and highly vocal, and are found in the forests of eastern Madagascar from the Masoala Peninsula south to the Mananara River. These animals are clearly recognizable by their striking coloration and the luxuriance of their pelage, especially around the face. Identification is further aided by their characteristically long faces and their raucous loud call, making them difficult to confuse with any other lemurs.

The genus *Varecia* displays polygamous breeding behavior. It also has the shortest gestation period and produces the largest litters of the family Lemuridae (Vasey, 2007). Females have three pairs of mammae and reach maturity in less than two years, while males take three to four years to attain maturity (Foerg, 1982a). The mating season is May through July, with infants being born from September to November after a gestation of approximately 102 days (Rasmussen, 1985; Morland, 1990). Females commonly have litters of two or three infants that are kept in a nest for the first two weeks of life. Infants grow very rapidly, attaining roughly three-quarters of their adult weight by four months of age (Pereira *et al.*, 1987).

Ruffed lemurs were formerly included in the genus *Lemur*. Until recently experts only recognized a single species, *Varecia variegata*, with only two subspecies, the black-and-white ruffed lemur, *Varecia variegata variegata*, and the red ruffed lemur, *Varecia variegata rubra* (Tattersall, 1982; Mittermeier *et al.*, 1994). However, many color variations were known to occur within both previously recognized subspecies, as well as intermediates between them, and three names for black and white subspecies had actually been published earlier in the century: *variegata*, *editorum* and *subcincta* (Hill, 1953; Petter *et al.*, 1977). Groves (2001) and Vasey and Tattersall (2002) considered the black-and-white and red subspecies to be distinct species: *V. variegata* and *V. rubra*. Groves (2001) also recognized the three previously named subspecies of *variegata* (*variegata*, *editorum*, and *subcincta*), and noted at least two color morphs of *V. v. variegata* described by Petter *et al.* (1977) that did not appear to fit any of the named taxa. Recent genetic research supports some of these conclusions (C. Roos, pers. obs.; E. E. Louis Jr., pers. obs.; see also Wyner *et al.*, 1999a; Pastorini, 2000). Although we believe that there may still be changes in *Varecia* taxonomy in the future, we for now follow Groves in recognizing *Varecia variegata* and *Varecia rubra* as full species, and also in recognizing the three named subspecies of *Varecia variegata*: *Varecia variegata variegata*, *Varecia variegata editorum* and *Varecia variegata subcincta*. Some experts believe that all three of the black-and-white subspecies should be elevated to full species, whereas others feel that there is so much variation within populations that no subspecies are truly valid.

Fig. 9.109: Black-and-white ruffed lemur (*Varecia variegata* ssp.) displaying characteristic hindlimb suspensory posture, Lemur Island, Hotel Vakona, Andasibe (photo by R. A. Mittermeier). The color pattern in this invidual is intermediate between *V. v. editorum* and *V. v. variegata*.

Fig. 9.110: *Varecia* postural and behavioral drawings (next page):
> **a. *Varecia* standing quadrupedally on a rock**
> **b. *Varecia* female grooming young using the tooth comb**
> **c. *Varecia* employing a hindlimb suspensory posture and looking around**
> **d. *Varecia* using a hindlimb suspensory posture for feeding**
> **e. *Varecia* resting in the fork of a tree**
> **f. *Varecia* standing quadrupedally on a branch**
> **g. *Varecia* in a seated resting posture**
> **h. *Varecia* leaping from one tree branch to another**

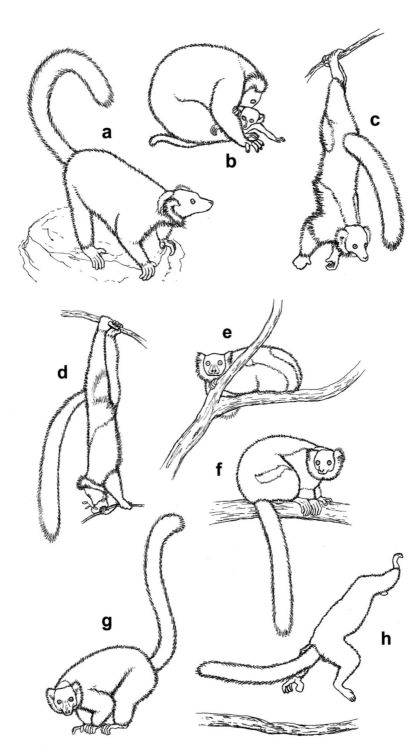

Fig. 9.110.

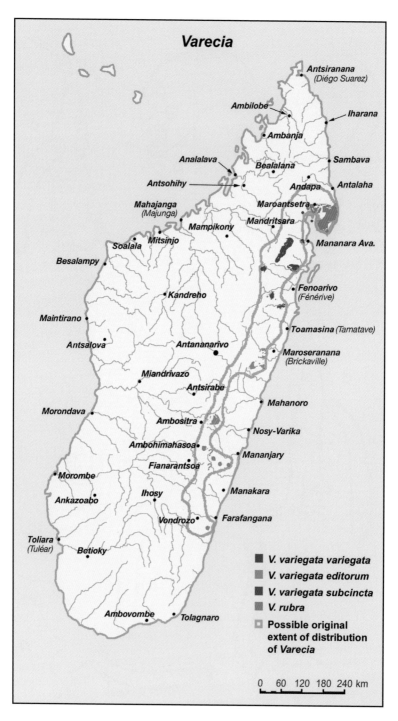

Fig. 9.111: Distribution of *Varecia*. The red and green question marks indicate the presence of *Varecia* subspecies, which, according to Vasey and Tattersall (2002), may be *V. variegata variegata* (red) and *V. variegata editorum* (green), but identity needs confirmation.

Variegated black-and-white ruffed lemur
Varecia variegata variegata

Southern black-and-white ruffed lemur
Varecia variegata editorum

Northern black-and-white ruffed lemur
Varecia variegata subcincta

Red ruffed lemur
Varecia rubra

Lemuridae

Fig. 9.112.

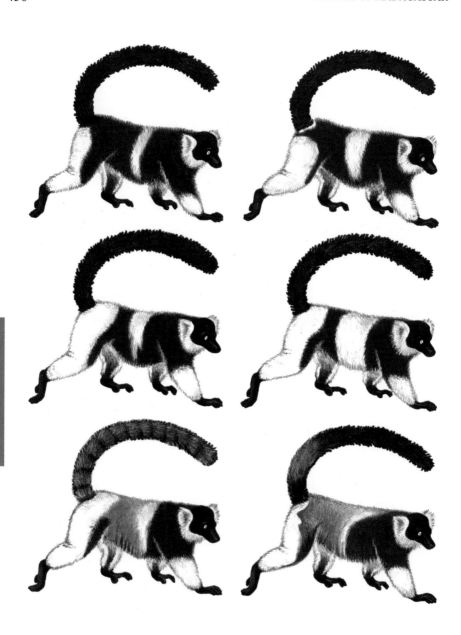

Varecia variegata subcincta

Fig. 9.113: Variation in the *subcincta* subspecies of the black-and-white ruffed lemur. Adapted from Ceska *et al.* (1992).

Varecia variegata subcincta

Fig. 9.114: More variation in the *subcincta* subspecies of the black-and-white ruffed lemur. Adapted from Ceska *et al*. (1992).

Varecia v. variegata   *Varecia v. editorum*

Fig. 9.115: Variation in the *variegata* subspecies of the black-and-white ruffed lemur. Adapted from Ceska *et al.* (1992).

Varecia rubra

Lemuridae

Fig. 9.116: Variation in the red ruffed lemur (*Varecia rubra*). Adapted from Ceska *et al.* (1992).

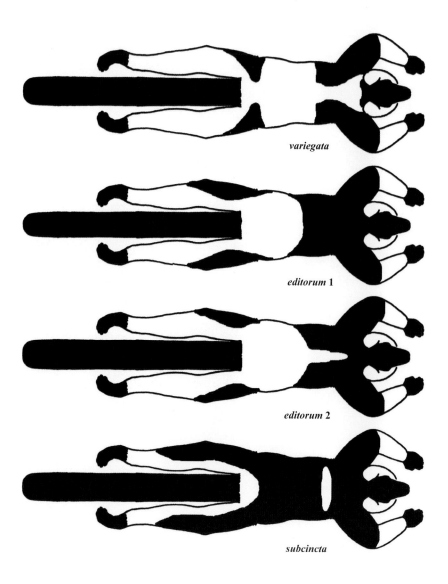

Lemuridae

Fig. 9.117: Illustrations showing variation in *Varecia variegata* subspecies according to Vasey and Tattersall (2002).

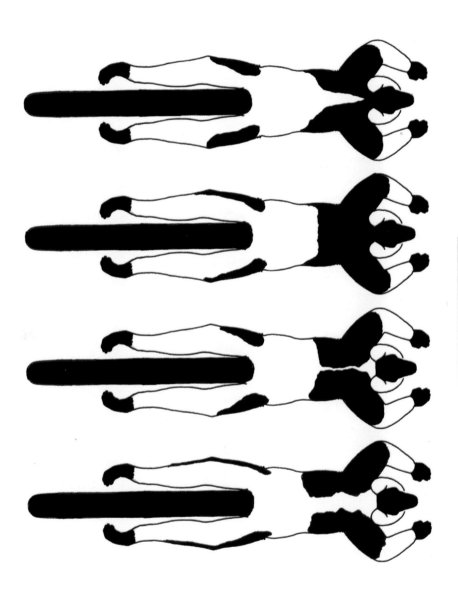

Fig. 9.118: Illustration showing variation in *Varecia variegata editorum*.

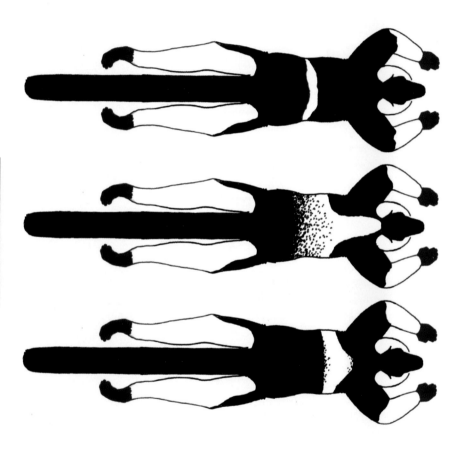

Fig. 9.119: Illustration showing variation in *Varecia variegata subcincta*.

Der Vari.

Fig. 9.120: Above: A black-and-white ruffed lemur from *Naturhistorische Abbildungen der Säugetiere* by Heinrich Rudolf Schinz, published in Zurich in 1840. Below: *Varecia* as depicted in Guerin-Meneville's book *Picturesque Dictionary of Natural History*, Paris, 1835.

Varecia variegata variegata (Kerr, 1792)
Variegated Black-and-White Ruffed Lemur

Other English: Pied Black-and-White Ruffed Lemur
French: Vari noir-et-blanc
German: Schwarz-weisser Vari
Malagasy: Vary, Varikandana, Varikandra, Varijatsy

Identification

Varecia variegata variegata is a large quadrupedal lemur with a head-body length of
43–57 cm, a tail length of 60–65 cm, a total length of 110–120 cm, and a weight of 3.1–
3.6 kg (Morland, 1991a; Britt, 1997; Terranova and Coffman, 1997; Balko, 1998; Vasey,
2003). As its common English name suggests, the coat of this animal is black and white.
The hair is black on the abdomen, tail, extremities, inner aspects of the limbs, forehead,
circum-orbital area, and top of the head. In contrast, the back, flanks, rump and most of the
hindlimbs are usually white. The shoulders are black and there is a thick white longitudinal
band in the center of the back, the latter distinguishing *V. v. variegata* from *V. v. editorum*.
This pattern may vary according to locality, and intermediate forms may exist. The coat is
exceptionally fluffy, the tail is long and bushy, and the ears are lavishly tufted, or "ruffed,"
with long, thick white hair. There is no difference between the sexes in size or coloration.

Geographic Range

The variegated black-and-white ruffed lemur inhabits
remnant tracts of tropical moist lowland and montane forests
(sea level to 1,300 m) in eastern Madagascar. The Anove
River (between Soanierana Ivongo and Mananara) is the
northern part of its range, while the southern part consists of
the region south of Mananjary as far as the Manampatrana
or Mananara Rivers (Vasey and Tattersall, 2002). This range
is now highly fragmented.

Natural History

Varecia v. variegata has been studied in Betampona (Britt,
1997, 2000; Britt *et al.*, 2003). Long-term field research
shows significant variation in home range size, group size
and territorial behavior. This lemur is highly frugivorous
and also feeds on nectar, seeds and leaves, according to
the season. Its locomotion is largely quadrupedal with
occasional bouts of leaping. Females usually give birth to
twins, which are left in a nest when young and afterwards
carried in the mother's mouth (Petter *et al.*, 1977). Ruffed lemurs are probably the only
primates that build nests exclusively for the birth and the first few days of infant-rearing
(Pereira *et al.*, 1987; Morland, 1990).

Conservation Status

According to the most recent IUCN Red List assessment (2008), *V. v. variegata*
is Critically Endangered (CR). The main threats are habitat loss due to slash-and-burn

Fig. 9.121: Variegated black-and-white ruffed lemur (*Varecia variegata variegata*), photographed in captivity on Lemur Island, Hotel Vakona, Andasibe (photo by R. A. Mittermeier).

agriculture, logging, and mining, but hunting is also a major factor and can be very heavy in certain areas. What is more, stochastic events such as cyclones can severely impact small populations (Balko, 1998; Ratsimbazafy, 2002). *Varecia v. variegata* is found in Zahamena National Park, two strict nature reserves (Betampona and Zahamena), and two special reserves (Ambatovaky and Marotandrano) (E. E. Louis Jr., pers. obs.). Individuals with the *variegata* coat pattern are also found in protected areas further south, well inside the range of *V. v. editorum*, with which the subspecies may overlap. This needs further investigation, but if there is actual sympatry, these subspecies will require recognition as full species. On the other hand, it may be that there is so much variation within this species that recognition of any subspecies is inappropriate. Final decisions on this issue cannot be made at this time.

Varecia v. variegata (unlike the other two *V. variegata* subspecies) is one of the most common lemurs in captivity (ISIS, 2009). However, although these animals do very well in zoos and breed readily there, the widespread problem of mixed or unknown ancestry greatly increases the likelihood of accidental inbreeding. In November, 1997, individuals of this subspecies that had been born and raised in U.S. zoological institutions were returned to Madagascar and released in the Betampona Strict Nature Reserve (Britt *et al.*, 2003). A study of this reintroduction effort is ongoing.

As of 2009, there were approximately 770 individuals reported in zoological collections worldwide (ISIS, 2009).

Where to See It

The easiest place to see this species in the wild is the Betampona Strict Nature Reserve, approximately 45 km north of Toamasina (=Tamatave). The reserve is somewhat difficult to reach because of the poor condition of the road, but it is the most accessible site for this subspecies. A permit from Madagascar National Parks is required.

Lemuridae

Fig. 9.122. Another captive variegated black-and-white ruffed lemur (*Varecia variegata variegata*), Lemur Island, Hotel Vakona, Andasibe (photo by R. A. Mittermeier).

Lemuridae

Varecia variegata editorum (Hill, 1953)
Southern Black-and-White Ruffed Lemur

Other English: Hill's Black-and-White Ruffed Lemur
French: Vari noir-et-blanc de Hill
German: Südlicher Schwarz-weisser Vari
Malagasy: Vary, Varikandana, Varikandra, Varijatsy

Identification

As with the other subspecies of *Varecia variegata*, this is a large quadrupedal lemur. Although no measurements have been published, it is safe to assume that they are similar to those of *V. v. variegata*. The fur of *V. v. editorum* is black and white. The abdomen, tail, extremities, inner aspects of the limbs, forehead, circum-orbital area, top of the head and anterior part of the back are black, whereas the posterior part of the back as well as the flanks, rump and outer aspects of the limbs are usually white. As in *V. v. variegata*, the coat is fluffy, the tail is long and bushy, and the ears are "ruffed" with long thick white hair. There is no difference in size or coloration between the sexes.

Geographic Range

This range of this subspecies extends from the forests of Mantadia National Park in the north to just south of Mananjary in the south. Its scientific name (*editorum* = "from the mountains") is somewhat misleading, as it inhabits lowland to mid-altitude rain forests (sea level to 1,300 m). The ranges of *V. v. editorum* and *V. v. variegata* appear to overlap, and intermediate forms may exist (Groves, 2001; Vasey and Tattersall, 2002), but so far, neither field surveys nor genetic studies have reliably confirmed this.

Recent surveys by Irwin *et al.* (2005) found that this subspecies is very patchily distributed, the result of its dependency on low- to mid-altitude primary forest and its susceptibility to hunting and trapping.

Natural History

The southern black-and-white ruffed lemur has been studied in Ranomafana National Park (White, 1991; Balko, 1998) and in the Manombo Special Reserve (Ratsimbazafy, 2002; Ralainasolo *et al.*, 2005). White (1991) found the diet to consist of 70.8% fruits, 11.1% leaves, 2.8% flowers, and 15.3% nectar. In addition, the animals occasionally exhibited geophagy—the eating of soil. The group that White (1991) observed lived in a 197-ha home range and was monogamous. Balko (1996) suggests that differences in the quality and distribution of food resources may influence the social organization of ruffed lemurs.

Lemuridae

Fig. 9.123: Southern black-and-white ruffed lemur (*Varecia variegata editorum*) on the Varijatsy trail heading towards Vatoharanana, Ranomafana National Park (photo by R. A. Mittermeier).

Conservation Status

The 2008 IUCN Red List assessment classified *V. v. editorum* as Critically Endangered (CR). The principal threat is habitat loss due to slash-and-burn agriculture, logging and mining, but hunting is also a major factor, and can be very heavy in certain areas.

Varecia v. editorum occurs naturally in two national parks (Mantadia and Ranomafana) and in the Manombo Special Reserve (Mittermeier *et al.*, 1994; Tombomiadana and Rakotondravony, 2000), as well as in the Anosibe an'ala Classified Forest and in the unprotected forests of Fandriana (proposed as a national park), Kianjavato, Lakia, Maromizaha, Tolongoina, and Vatovavy. However, since the distribution areas of *V. v. editorum* and *V. v. variegata* seem to overlap, some of the aforementioned localities might also hold populations of individuals with a *variegata* coat pattern. Past studies indicated its presence in Andringitra National Park (Nicoll and Langrand, 1989), but recent surveys have failed to find it there (Goodman and Rasolonandrasana, 2001; Irwin *et al.*, 2005). The original population in the Analamazaotra Special Reserve was extirpated by the 1980s, but it was successfully reintroduced in 2006 by E. E. Louis Jr. and a team of Malagasy researchers.

Lemuridae

Fig. 9.124: Young male southern black-and-white ruffed lemur (*Varecia variegata editorum*), Manombo Special Reserve (photo by R. A. Mittermeier).

Fig. 9.125: Young male southern black-and-white ruffed lemur (*Varecia variegata editorum*), Manombo Special Reserve (photo by R. A. Mittermeier).

As of 2009, there were no southern black-and-white ruffed lemurs reported in captiviy (ISIS, 2009).

Where to See It

Varecia v. editorum can be seen in Mantadia National Park, especially around km 15, although sightings are by no means guaranteed. It is also regularly observed at Kianjavato, not far from Vatovavy on the road to Mananjary. Finally, it is also once again to be found in Analamazaotra Special Reserve, thanks to the above-mentioned reintroduction.

Varecia variegata subcincta (A. Smith, 1833)
Northern Black-and-White Ruffed Lemur

Other English: White-belted Black-and-White Ruffed Lemur
French: Vari à ceinture
German: Gürtelvari
Malagasy: Vary, Varikandana, Varikandra, VarijatsyVarijatsy

Identification

As with the other subspecies of *Varecia variegata*, this is a large quadrupedal lemur with a body weight of 3.1–3.6 kg (Morland, 1991a). Although no measurements for this subspecies have been published, it is safe to assume that it is similar to *V. v. variegata*. The fur of *V. v. subcincta* is black and white with a distinct white belt around its otherwise black back. The abdomen, tail, extremities, inner aspects of the limbs, forehead, circum-orbital area, and top of the head are also black, whereas the outer aspects of the limbs as well as the base of the tail are white. As with *V. v. variegata*, the coat is fluffy, the tail is long and bushy, and the ears are "ruffed" with long thick white hair. The eyes can be yellow or amber-colored. There is no difference in size or coloration between the sexes.

Geographic Range

This is the northernmost of the *V. variegata* subspecies. Its range extends from the Antainambalana River (in the region of Maraontsetra) south to the Anove River (between Soanierana Ivongo and Mananara). The subspecies apparently once occurred as far south as the region of Toamasina as well, but has now disappeared from there (Vasey and Tattersall, 2002). All museum specimens examined by Groves (2001) were collected in the Maroantsetra region. This apparently is also the subspecies that was introduced to the island of Nosy Mangabe (Bay of Antongil) back in the 1930s (Kuhn, 1972). Its distribution is now very patchy and fragmented, and its population density generally low.

The confluence of the Vohimara and Antainambalana Rivers has been investigated as a possible contact or hybrid zone between this form and *Varecia rubra*, but results are inconclusive (Tattersall, 1982; Lindsay and Simons, 1986; Hekkala *et al.*, 2007; Vasey and Tattersall, 2002).

Natural History

A long-term study of *V. v. subcincta* was carried out on Nosy Mangabe by Morland (1990, 1991a, 1991b, 1993). On this island, the animal exhibits a "fission/fusion" social system, in which larger communities of up to 16 individuals split into smaller core-groups during times of the year when fruits are scarce, a behavior that may enhance foraging efficiency for each individual lemur. These core groups are not cohesive and continue to fission and fuse back together again. Although females usually give birth to twins, short-term data suggest that females do not always reproduce successfully every year, and that

Fig. 9.126: Northern black-and-white ruffed lemur (*Varecia variegata subcincta*), Lemur Island, Hotel Vakona, Andasibe (photo by R. A. Mittermeier).

a typical mother raises only one infant every second year. The diet consists mainly of ripe fruits, and it appears that only a small number of tree species are exploited.

Conservation Status

The most recent IUCN Red List assessment (2008) classified *V. v. subcincta* as Critically Endangered (CR). The principal threats are habitat loss due to slash-and-burn and commercial agriculture, logging and mining, but hunting is also a major factor since it can be very heavy in certain areas. Indeed, recent studies of villages in the Makira Forest have found that ruffed lemur meat is a desired food item and that current levels of hunting are unsustainable (Golden, 2005). This lemur occurs in the Mananara-Nord National Park, the Nosy Mangabe Special Reserve, and in the soon-to-be protected forests of Makira.

As of 2009, there was a small captive population, numbering individuals 38 in all, which were being actively managed in various European zoos (Schwitzer and Kaumanns, 2001b; ISIS, 2009).

Lemuridae

Fig. 9.127: Illustration of what is probably *V. v. subcincta*, from Edward Griffith's book *Quadrumana: General and Particular Descriptions of Monkeys and Lemurs*, London, 1821.

Where to See It

Varecia v. subcincta is most readily seen on the island of Nosy Mangabe, which can be reached easily by small boat from Maroantsetra, a trip of only about 30 minutes. Good camping facilities are available, but camping permits must be obtained from the local Madagascar National Parks office for overnight stays. A number of convenient tent platforms are provided. A motorized pirogue trip from Maroantsetra up the Antainambalana River may also be worthwhile, but finding this species on the mainland is much more difficult than on Nosy Mangabe. Excursions to Nosy Mangabe and longer trips can be arranged through the local Madagascar National Parks office, through local hotels (especially the Relais de Masoala), and with the Association des Guides de Maroantsetra.

This ruffed lemur is much more challenging to observe in the wild in Mananara-Nord National Park, as there is little infrastructure in place to facilitate visits. A permit is required from the UNESCO office in Mananara or from Madagascar National Parks in Antanambe. Access to the park is possible via a three-hour walk from Sandrakatsy, a small town served by taxi-brousse from Mananara. Once in the park, there are no good trails and this lemur is usually one of the most difficult to find. Use of a local guide is essential.

Fig. 9.128: Northern black-and-white ruffed lemur (*Varecia variegata subcincta*), Lemur Island, Hotel Vakona, Andasibe (photo by R. A. Mittermeier).

Lemuridae

Varecia rubra (É. Geoffroy, 1812)
Red Ruffed Lemur

Other English: None
French: Vari roux
German: Roter Vari
Malagasy: Varimena, Varignena, Varinaina (Makira region)

Identification

Varecia rubra is a large quadrupedal lemur with a head-body length of 50–55 cm, a tail length of 60–65 cm, a total length of 100–120 cm, and a weight of 3.3–3.6 kg (Vasey, 2003). The dominant coat color is a deep chestnut-red (but sometimes also red-orange or honey-blonde) that covers much of the dorsal body surface, as well as the legs, throat, cheeks and ear tufts (Vasey, 1997a). The ventral coat is black, as are the tail, insides of the limbs, feet, face, muzzle, and top of the head. In addition, there is a white patch on the neck, and small lighter-colored patches may also be present on the heels, digits and muzzle. Variations in color pattern are well known in this species, but do not appear to have a clear geographic pattern.

As with *Varecia variegata*, the red ruffed lemur is difficult to confuse with any other lemur. It is sympatric with the white-fronted brown lemur, *Eulemur albifrons*, but is larger, has the characteristic ear tufts, and lacks the striking white face. What is more, its raucous vocalizations are unmistakeable.

Geographic Range

The red ruffed lemur has a very restricted range, inhabiting only the remaining primary forests of the Masoala Peninsula and the region immediately north of the Bay of Antongil in northeastern Madagascar (Petter and Petter-Rousseaux, 1979; Tattersall, 1982). It once may have occurred as far north as Antalaha, but this is uncertain (Tattersall, 1977a). The Antainambalana River appears to separate *V. rubra* from *V. variegata subcincta*, but the western limit of the red ruffed lemur's range remains unclear. The confluence of the Vohimara and Antainambalana Rivers has been investigated as a possible contact or hybrid zone between these two forms, but results are inconclusive (Tattersall, 1982; Lindsay and Simons, 1986; Hekkala *et al.*, 2007; Vasey and Tattersall, 2002).

Natural History

Varecia rubra typically inhabits tropical moist lowland forest up to 1,200 m. It has been studied in the forests of Ambatonakolahy (Rigamonti, 1993) and Andranobe (Vasey, 1997a) on the Masoala Peninsula. It is diurnal, prefers tall forest, and is often observed in the crowns of large feeding trees. Population density has been variously estimated at 6 individuals/km² (Rakotondratsima and Kremen, 2001), 21–23 individuals/km² (Rigamonti, 1993), and 31–54 individuals/km² (Vasey, 1997b). Ruffed lemurs move quadrupedally through the

Lemuridae

canopy most of the time, leaping occasionally. Suspensory postures are common during feeding bouts (Vasey, 1999). These are the most frugivorous of Madagascar's primates, with as much as 75–90% of their diet consisting of fruit. Flowers, nectar, and leaves make up the balance. Females are reported to consume more low-fiber, high protein items (young leaves and flowers) prior to giving birth and during lactation, presumably to meet the higher energy demands of reproduction (Vasey, 2000a, 2002). At Andranobe, 132 different species from 36 plant families were eaten over the course of a year (Vasey, 2000b).

Reproduction varies considerably between years (Rakotondratsima and Kremen, 2001; Vasey, 2007). The mating season is May–July, with births occurring from September through early November after a gestation period of about 102 days. In captivity, litters range from one to five infants, but are usually two or three, each newborn weighing just under 100 g (Brockman *et al.*, 1987b; Schwitzer, 2003). In the wild, mean litter size of red ruffed lemurs is 2.11 (Vasey, 2007), while in captivity it is 2.22 (Rasmussen, 1985). Field observations indicate that this species is polygamous, and that multiple individuals participate in caring for the young (Vasey, 1997a, 2007). Social organization is described as fission/fusion; communities are usually multi-male/multi-female, and number 5–31 individuals. Home ranges cover 23–58 ha and appear to be defended (Rigamonti, 1993; Vasey, 2006). Scent-marking tends to take place during territorial battles and female greeting displays. This species' vocal repertoire is extensive and is employed in numerous contexts. The most characteristic vocalization is the very loud and raucous call, which appears to be used in territorial encounters and for purposes of intragroup spacing (Vasey, 2003).

Fig. 9.129: Red ruffed lemur (*Varecia rubra*) from the Masoala Peninsula (photo by E. E. Louis Jr.).

Lemuridae

Conservation Status

The 2008 IUCN Red List assessment (2008) classified *V. rubra* as Endangered (EN). The principal threats are habitat loss and hunting (Simons and Lindsay, 1987; Rigamonti, 1996; Vasey, 1996, 1997b). Due to its large size and evident need for tall primary forest, it is particularly susceptible to human encroachment and, sadly, hunting of this unique and important species still takes place. Needless to say, a major effort is needed to eliminate hunting of this important flagship species. Furthermore, because remaining populations are concentrated on the Masoala Peninsula, the red ruffed lemur may be threatened by the frequent cyclones (hurricanes) that hit this part of Madagascar. It is protected only in the Masoala National Park (Kremen, 1998).

Ironically, this species, with its very restricted range, was always considered more threatened than the more widely distributed black-and-white ruffed lemur. Whereas all three subspecies of *V. variegata* are now considered Critically Endangered, the most recent IUCN assessment places *V. rubra* in the Endangered category, in large part because of its presence in a major national park. However, this now needs to be reassessed. Masoala was the national park most impacted by the very rapid upsurge of illegal logging after the political events of early 2009, and this logging has continued well into 2010. It is highly likely that it is being accompanied by at least some hunting, which will almost certainly push *V. rubra* into the Critically Endangered category.

As of 2009, there were 590 red ruffed lemurs reported in captivity worldwide (ISIS, 2009). Such populations in American and European zoos represent a safeguard against extinction, but they are unfortunately very limited their genetic diversity (Schwitzer, 2003).

Fig. 9.130: Illustration of *Varecia rubra* from Edward Griffith's book *Quadrumana: General and Particular Descriptions of Monkeys and Lemurs,* London, 1821.

Where to See It

The only place to see red ruffed lemurs is on the Masoala Peninsula. Boat trips can be arranged from Maraontsetra to Ambanizana, Lohatrozona or Tampolo where there are several rustic but comfortable lodges. A nice package trip is to spend one night on Nosy Mangabe, which is quite close to the Masoala Peninsula, and then do a day visit to the Masoala to any of the previously mentioned sites. This species is relatively easy to find due to its loud vocalizations, which can often be heard from far away.

Fig. 9.131: Red ruffed lemur (*Varecia rubra*), Duke Lemur Center (photo by R. A. Mittermeier).

Indriidae

Fig. 10.1: Eastern woolly lemur (*Avahi laniger*), Andasibe (photo by R. A. Mittermeier).

CHAPTER 10

FAMILY INDRIIDAE Burnett, 1828

The family Indriidae contains three genera: *Avahi*, *Propithecus*, and *Indri*. The first one is small (roughly 1 kg) and nocturnal, the latter two are large (3–9 kg) and diurnal, and include the largest of all living lemurs, the indri (*Indri indri*) and the diademed sifaka (*Propithecus diadema*). All three genera are "vertical clingers and leapers," an unusual postural and locomotor complex among primates. This is characterized by resting postures in which the trunk of the body is held vertically on upright supports and locomotor behavior that involves leaps between vertical supports, sometimes quite spectacular and up to 10 m between trees. Suspensory postures are also a feature of this behavioral complex, especially when feeding and moving in peripheral branches and twigs of trees. Some species also regularly descend to the ground, where they jump bipedally, often with the arms held above the head. This amazing behavior, especially among the smaller sifakas (e.g., *Propithecus verreauxi*, *Propithecus coquereli*), has now become quite well known internationally, and is one of the highlights of a visit to Madagascar. All indriids have greatly elongated legs compared to their arms and trunks, and they are highly distinctive and difficult to confuse with other species. Indeed, they are among the most unusual of all primate families. The only real possibility of confusing any indriid with a member of another lemur family is at night, when *Avahi* might be mistaken for *Lepilemur* or possibly *Cheirogaleus*.

Avahi Jourdan, 1834
Woolly Lemurs

The genus *Avahi* contains the only nocturnal members of the family Indriidae. The common English name refers to the curly or woolly appearance of the dense fur, while the generic name is a transcription of the animal's high-pitched vocalization (Thalmann, 2003). Woolly lemurs are much smaller than the indri or any of the sifakas, usually weighing around 1 kg. Nonetheless, they are typical, thigh-powered vertical clingers and leapers, possessing hindlimbs proportionately longer than the trunk and forelimbs. Like the sifakas they have long tails, typically longer than their combined head and body length.

At a distance and at night, *Avahi* is often difficult to distinguish from species of *Lepilemur*, which are similar in size and also nocturnal. At reasonably close range, however, woolly lemurs are readily identified by the white patches on the backs of their thighs, which serve as highly visible identification marks when the animals assume their characteristic vertical resting posture. Indeed, this character is so distinctive that it has given rise to one of the most common names for woolly lemurs in Madagascar, "fotsife," which means "white leg." At first glance, *Avahi* may also be confused with *Cheirogaleus*, especially the larger eastern rain forest species. However, dwarf lemurs do not exhibit the vertical resting posture and are much smaller. Woolly lemurs also frequently rest closely huddled together in pairs or small family units of three or four, behavior rarely observed in the other similar-sized nocturnal genera.

Avahi was originally regarded as a single species, *Avahi laniger*, with an eastern and a western subspecies (Schwarz, 1931; Tattersall, 1982). Rumpler *et al.* (1990) subsequently elevated the subspecies to full species: *Avahi laniger* and *Avahi occidentalis*. Thalmann

Indriidae

and Geissmann (2000) later described a third species, *Avahi unicolor*, from the region of the Ampasindava Peninsula, and more recently a fourth, *Avahi cleesei*, from the Tsingy de Bemaraha region (Thalmann and Geissmann, 2005). These were followed by two more in 2006, when Zaramody *et al.* described *Avahi peyrierasi* and *Avahi meridionalis*, at the same time suggesting that *A. cleesei* may be a junior synonym of *A. occidentalis*. The validity of *A. cleesei* was subsequently reaffirmed by Andriantompohavana *et al.* (2007). Although *A. meridionalis* was originally described with two subspecies—*A. m. meridionalis* and *A. m. ramanantsoavanai*–Andriantompohavana *et al.* (2007) elevated both to full species. In 2007, Andriantompohavana *et al.* also described the new species *Avahi betsileo*. Lastly, Lei *et al.* (2008) described yet another, *Avahi mooreorum*, bringing the current number of described *Avahi* species to nine. However, there are strong indications that still more species of *Avahi* remain to be described, so we are not yet finished with this genus.

Indriidae

Fig. 10.2: Manombo woolly lemur (*Avahi ramanantsoavanai*), Manombo Special Reserve (photo by R. Randrianampionona).

Fig. 10.3: Distribution of the nine species of *Avahi* currently recognized.

Betourt et Faguet pinx.   Imp. Becquet à Paris.

Avahis laniger.

Fig. 10.4: *Avahi laniger* depicted in a plate from Alfred Grandidier's *Histoire Physique, Naturelle, et Politique de Madagascar*, **Vol. 9, Paris, 1875.**

Fig. 10.5: *Avahi* **postural and behavioral drawings (next page):**
> a. A group of *Avahi* huddled together in the characteristic sleeping posture
> b. *Avahi* infant "parked" on a branch by its mother
> c. *Avahi* in a supported sitting posture
> d. *Avahi* in a sitting posture
> e. *Avahi* mother and infant resting in the fork of a tree
> f. *Avahi* in the vertical clinging posture, showing the partly wound-up tail of an animal that has just been disturbed

Indriidae

Fig. 10.5.

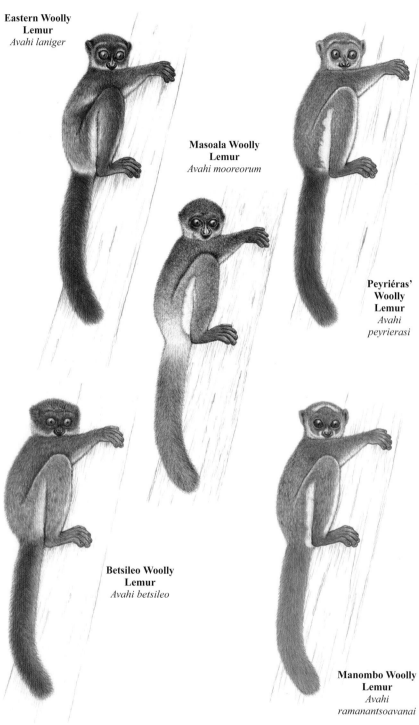

Eastern Woolly Lemur
Avahi laniger

Masoala Woolly Lemur
Avahi mooreorum

Peyriéras' Woolly Lemur
Avahi peyrierasi

Betsileo Woolly Lemur
Avahi betsileo

Manombo Woolly Lemur
Avahi ramanantsoavanai

Indriidae

Fig. 10.6.

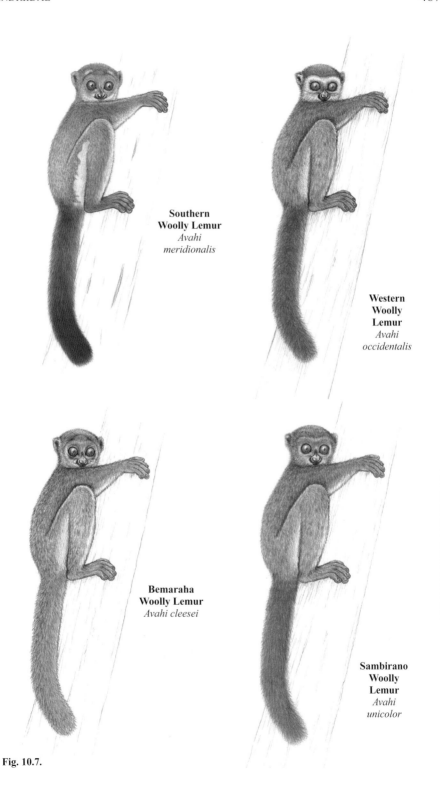

Southern Woolly Lemur
Avahi meridionalis

Western Woolly Lemur
Avahi occidentalis

Bemaraha Woolly Lemur
Avahi cleesei

Sambirano Woolly Lemur
Avahi unicolor

Fig. 10.7.

Indriidae

Avahi laniger (Gmelin, 1788)
Eastern Woolly Lemur

Other English: Eastern Avahi, Gmelin's Woolly Lemur
French: Avahi laineaux oriental
German: Östlicher Wollmaki
Malagasy: Fotsifé, Ampongy, Avahy, Fotsifaka

Identification

Avahi laniger has a head-body length of 27.7–32.2 cm, a tail length of 30.4–36.6 cm, a total length of 58.1–68.8 cm, and a weight of 1.0–1.4 kg (Glander *et al.*, 1992; Zaramody *et al.*, 2006; Andriantompohavana *et al.*, 2007; Lei *et al.*, 2008). This species is slightly larger and darker than *Avahi occidentalis*. It has dense short fur, tightly curled on the back. The dorsal coat is gray-brown to reddish, becoming paler towards the tail, which is a rusty-red. The chest and abdomen are gray. The face is brownish, with a lighter band or distinct patches above the eyes and lighter fur on the cheeks and throat. The ears are small and largely hidden by the thick fur.

The eastern woolly lemur is most likely to be confused with eastern rain forest species of *Lepilemur*, which also adopt a clinging posture when at rest, and, to a lesser extent, *Cheirogaleus*. *Avahi* can be distinguished from *Lepilemur* by its concealed ears and generally woollier appearance, its distinctive white thigh stripe, and by the fact that it is often seen huddled closely together with other group members, a behavior rarely observed in *Lepilemur*. *Cheirogaleus* is considerably smaller, does not employ the vertical clinging posture, is not a leaper (although it will occasionally jump from branch to branch), and has contrasting white underparts.

Geographic Range

Prior to the recent taxonomic splitting of this species, *A. laniger* was thought to range almost the entire length of Madagascar's eastern rain forests, from the Tolagnaro (= Fort-Dauphin) region in the extreme south to as far as the Ankarana Massif in the extreme north (Petter *et al.,* 1977; Tattersall, 1982; Fowler *et al.*, 1989; Hawkins *et al.*, 1990). With the description of a number of new species within this large area, it is now thought to range from the Bemarivo River in the north to the Nesivolo/Mangoro in the south (E. E. Louis Jr., pers. obs).

Natural History

Avahi laniger occurs in tropical moist lowland and montane forests, as well as secondary forest formations. Members of this genus typically eat flowers and fruits to a small extent, but the diet consists primarily of leaves, which provide a low level of nutrition for a primate of such small size (Ganzhorn *et al.*, 1985; Harcourt, 1991). Some biologists believe that this explains their relatively low level of activity, even during waking hours at night. During the day, woolly lemurs typically sleep in clumps of dense foliage, sometimes fairly close to the ground, and usually huddled together (Albignac, 1981b).

Indriidae

Fig. 10.8: Eastern woolly lemur (*Avahi laniger*), Anjanaharibe-Sud Special Reserve (photo by E. E. Louis Jr.).

Groups of up to five have been reported, and home ranges of 1–2 ha are aggressively defended (Albignac, 1981b; Razanahoera-Rakotomalala, 1981; Ganzhorn *et al.*, 1985). Longitudinal and genetic data are needed to better understand their social behavior. Research at the Analamazaotra Special Reserve provides estimates of densities reaching 72–100 individuals/km², and suggests a social organization based on monogamous pairs and their offspring (Ganzhorn, 1988).

Single births take place in August and September (Ganzhorn *et al.*, 1985). Infants initially cling to the mother's abdomen, but are eventually carried on her back (Ganzhorn 1988; Harcourt, 1988, 1991).

Conservation Status

The 2008 IUCN Red List assessment (2008) classified *A. laniger* as Least Concern (LC). However, we believe that this assessment needs reconsideration, especially given some of the recent hunting data that has emerged. It suffers mainly from habitat destruction due to logging and slash-and-burn agriculture, it is sometimes captured opportunistically at its daytime sleeping sites or in traps baited with fruit, and in some places it is pursued by hunters with slingshots (Mananara-Nord) or spears (Makira). *Avahi laniger* is reported from four national parks (Mananara-Nord, Mantadia, Marojejy and Zahamena), two strict nature reserves (Betampona and Zahamena) and five special reserves (Ambatovaky, Ambohitantely, Analamazaotra, Anjanaharibe-Sud, and Mangerivola) (Nicoll and Langrand, 1989; Sterling and Ramaroson, 1996; Schmid and Smolker, 1998; Britt *et al.*, 1999; CBSG, 2002; Andriantompohavana *et al.*, 2007; Lei *et al.*, 2008; J. U. Ganzhorn, pers. comm.; P. C. Wright, pers. comm.). It is unclear which woolly lemur is present in the Ankarana Special Reserve. For now, we tentatively assign the Ankarana population to *Avahi occidentalis*.

As of 2010, this species was not being kept in captivity (I. J. Porton, pers. comm.).

Where to See It

Although this species can be found in all of the protected areas listed above, perhaps the best place to see it on the tourist circuit is in Analamazaotra Special Reserve at Andasibe (= Périnet). A night walk along the road between the village of Andasibe and the entrance to the Analamazaotra Special Reserve will often produce several sightings, as well as views of other nocturnal lemurs. As with most other *Avahi* this nocturnal species can readily be observed during the day as well, especially with the assistance of knowledgeable local guides. Its sleeping sites are often just a few meters above the ground, and the animals usually remain there if not disturbed.

Indriidae

Fig. 10.9: Eastern woolly lemur (*Avahi laniger*), Andasibe (photo by R. A. Mittermeier).

Indriidae

Fig. 10.10: Family group of eastern woolly lemur (*Avahi laniger*), Andasibe (photo by R. A. Mittermeier).

Fig. 10.11: *Avahi laniger* depicted in *Histoire naturelle des Mammifères*, by Paul Gervais, Paris, 1854-1855.

Avahi mooreorum Lei *et al.*, 2008
Masoala Woolly Lemur

Other English: Moore's Woolly Lemur
French: Avahi de Moore, Avahi de Masoala
German: Masoala-Wollmaki, Moore's Wollmaki
Malagasy: Fotsifé, Ampongy, Avahy, Fotsifaka

Identification

Avahi mooreorum is slightly lighter than *A. laniger*, though slightly longer in body length. The head-body length is 28.4–33.0 cm, the tail is 29.4–37.2 cm, the total length is 57.8–70.3 cm, and the weight is roughly 920 g (Lei *et al.*, 2008). The overall pelage color is a mottled mixture of chocolate-brown and light brown on the dorsum, gradually lightening towards the base of the tail, which is distinctly cream-colored. A distinct whitish patch, characteristic of the genus, is present on the posterior surface of each hindlimb. The ventral surface, including the underside of the limbs, is gray, and the tail is reddish-brown. The head is darker than the back, and a face mask is apparent (though not as pronounced as in other eastern *Avahi* species). There is no noticeable eyebrow, but a whitish patch is present under each mandible. The ears are not readily seen, blending in as they do with the rest of the head (Andriantompohavana *et al.*, 2007; Lei *et al.*, 2008).

Geographic Range

Avahi mooreorum is currently known only from Masoala National Park in northeastern Madagascar. Further surveys are required to confirm the northern extent of this species within Masoala National Park and, possibly, in intervening forest fragments between Anjanaharibe-Sud Special Reserve (where *A. laniger* has been confirmed to occur) and the Masoala Peninsula (Lei *et al.*, 2008).

Natural History

As of 2010, this species had not been studied in the wild.

Conservation Status

The conservation status of this newly described species has not yet been assessed. It is known to occur in one protected area, Masoala National Park (Lei *et al.*, 2008).

As of 2010, this species was not being kept in captivity (I. J. Porton, pers. comm.).

Where to See It

At the present time the only place where one can see this species is in Masoala National Park.

Fig. 10.12: Masoala woolly lemur (*Avahi mooreorum*) from Masiaposa, Masoala National Park (photo by E. E. Louis Jr.).

Avahi peyrierasi Zaramody *et al.*, 2006
Peyriéras' Woolly Lemur

Other English: None
French: Avahi de Peyriéras
German: Peyriéras' Wollmaki
Malagasy: Fotsifé, Ampongy, Avahy, Fotsifaka

Identification

Avahi peyrierasi is a little smaller than *Avahi laniger*, with a head-body length of 26.1–31.7 cm, a tail of 28.5–34.4 cm, a total length of 54.7–66.6 cm, and a weight of 900 g–1.2 kg. The dorsal fur is gray-brown, with either a gray or a white underside and a red-brown tail. The outside of the thighs are gray-brown, and the insides are white. There are small white bands visible along the interior part of the legs, and in some cases along the upper part as well. In some individuals the face is completely encircled by a white border of fur, and white beards and cheeks are also present (Zaramody *et al.*, 2006).

Based on molecular sequence data, Andriantompohavana *et al.*, 2007 and Lei *et al.*, 2008 detected three "types" of *A. peyrierasi*. Their relationships or possible species status remains to be determined (E. E. Louis Jr., pers. obs.).

Geographic Range

Southeastern Madagascar. The precise limits of the distribution of this species, and in particular its relationship to *Avahi meridionalis* and *Avahi ramanantsoavanai* in the south, are as yet undetermined. It is currently known from south of the Mangoro/Nesivolo river systems in the forests of Manara, Vatoalatsaka, Sangalampona, Mahasoarivo and Ranomafana (Zaramody *et al.*, 2006). The southern extent of the range remains unclear (E. E. Louis Jr., pers. obs.).

Natural History

Population densities at Ranomafana tend to be higher in secondary forests and disturbed habitats (P. C. Wright, pers. comm.). Research conducted at Ranomafana National Park (P. C. Wright, pers. comm.) suggests that *A. peyrierasi* is a favored prey for raptors such as Henst's goshawk (*Accipiter henstii*).

Conservation Status

Very little is known of this species, so the 2008 IUCN Red List assessment classified it as Data Deficient (DD). It is known to occur in three national parks, Andringitra, Midongy du Sud and Ranomafana.

As of 2010, this species was not being kept in captivity (I. J. Porton, pers. comm.).

Indridae

Where to See It

Although *Avahi peyrierasi* can be found in the protected areas listed above, a good place to see it on the regular tourist circuit is in the Ranomafana National Park. Local guides frequently locate sleeping woolly lemurs in their daytime sleeping nests.

Fig. 10.13: Peyrieras' woolly lemur (*Avahi peyrierasi*), Ranomafana National Park (photo by E. E. Louis).

Fig. 10.14: This view of *Avahi peyrierasi* clearly shows the white thigh stripe, one of the best diagnostic features to identify woolly lemurs in the field (photo by E. E. Louis Jr.).

Indriidae

Fig. 10.15: Peyriéras' woolly lemur (*Avahi peyrierasi*), Ranomafana National Park (photo by E. E. Louis Jr.).

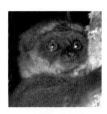

Avahi betsileo Andriantompohavana *et al.*, 2007
Betsileo Woolly Lemur

Other English: None
French: Avahi du Betsileo
German: Betsileo-Wollmaki
Malagasy: Fotsifé, Ampongy, Avahy, Fotsifaka

Identification

Avahi betsileo has a head-body length of 26–31.1 cm, a tail of 28.3–34.4 cm, a total length of 48–58.9 cm, and a weight of 900–1,200 g (Andriantompohavana *et al.*, 2007; Lei *et al.*, 2008). It differs significantly from other eastern woolly lemurs in having primarily light reddish-brown pelage on the upper body and on the dorsal surface of the extremities, with an underside that is dark gray towards the midline and diffusing to a light gray ventrolaterally. The tail is mainly reddish-brown and darker on the dorsal surface than on the ventral portion, which is a lighter reddish-blonde. There is a distinct facial mask, with grayish pelage under the mandible and diffuse, cream-colored eyebrow markings. The fur is thicker on the head than in other eastern *Avahi*, giving it a more rounded or oval-like apprearance (Andriantompohavana *et al.*, 2007).

Geographic Range

East-central Madagascar. This species is currently known only from the Bemosary Classified Forest (Fandriana), though the limits of the distribution may ultimately prove to extend from the Mangoro River in the north to the Mananjary River in the south (Andriantompohavana *et al.*, 2007).

Natural History

As of 2010, this species had not been studied in the wild.

Conservation Status

Very little is known of the Betsileo woolly lemur, so the 2008 IUCN Red List classified it as Data Deficient (DD). It is not known to occur in any protected areas.

As of 2010, this species was not being kept in captivity (I. J. Porton, pers. comm.).

Where to See It

At the present time the only place where one can be sure of seeing this species is in the Bemosary Classified Forest, a forest fragment located about one hour's walk from the village of Fandriana.

Indriidae

Fig. 10.16: Betsileo woolly lemur (*Avahi betsileo*), Fandriana Classified Forest (photo by J. Zaonarivelo).

Indriidae

Avahi ramanantsoavanai Zaramody *et al.*, 2006
Manombo Woolly Lemur

Other English: Ramanantsoavana's Woolly Lemur
French: Avahi de Manombo, Avahi de Ramanantsoavana
German: Manombo-Wollmaki, Ramanantsoavana's Wollmaki
Malagasy: Fotsifé, Ampongy, Avahy, Fotsifaka

Identification

Avahi ramanantsoavanai is slightly smaller than *Avahi laniger* and *Avahi peyrierasi*, with a head-body length of 24–31 cm, a tail of 33–40 cm, a total length of 54.6–68.9 cm, and a weight of 900–1,200 g (Zaramody *et al.*, 2006; Lei *et al.*, 2008). The dorsal fur is gray-brown and the ventrum is gray, the latter overtaking laterally from a white band on the posterior legs. The tail is red-brown. The facial mask differs slightly from that of *A. laniger* in that the fur of some individuals is lighter, while the outline of others may be more pronounced (Zaramody *et al.*, 2006).

Geographic Range

Southeastern Madagascar. This species is currently known only from the area of its type locality, the Manombo Special Reserve and Agnalahaza Forest. Further studies are required to determine its exact distribution, and especially the limits with regard to neighboring species (*A. peyrierasi* and *A. meridionalis*) (Zaramody *et al.*, 2006).

Natural History

As of 2010, this species had not been studied in the wild.

Conservation Status

The 2008 IUCN Red List assessment (2008) classified *A. ramanantsoavanai* as Data Deficient (DD). It is known to occur in one protected area (the Manombo Special Reserve) (Zaramody *et al.*, 2006; Andriantompohavana *et al.*, 2007).

As of 2010, this species was not being kept in captivity (I. J. Porton, pers. comm.).

Where to See It

At the present time, the only place where one can attempt to see this species is in the Manombo Special Reserve, south of Farafangana.

Indriidae

Fig. 10.17: Manombo woolly lemur (*Avahi ramanantsoavanai*), Manombo Special Reserve (photo by R. Randrianampionona).

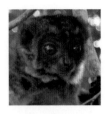

Avahi meridionalis Zaramody *et al.*, 2006
Southern Woolly Lemur

Other English: Southern Avahi
French: Avahi meridional
German: Südlicher Wollmaki
Malagasy: Fotsifé, Ampongy, Avahy, Fotsifaka

Identification

Avahi meridionalis is similar in size to *A. laniger* and *A. peyrierasi*, with a head-body length of 23–29 cm, a tail of 30–33 cm, a total length of 58.4–69.6 cm, and a weight of 950–1,400 g (Zaramody *et al.*, 2006; Lei *et al.*, 2008). The dorsal fur is gray-brown toning down to light gray distally, and the ventrum is gray. The tail is red-brown and darkens distally (Zaramody *et al.*, 2006).

Geographic Range

Southeastern Madagascar. The southernmost woolly lemur, this species is apparently restricted to Andohahela National Park and the area of Sainte-Luce (Zaramody *et al.*, 2006). Further studies are required to determine the exact distribution, and especially its limits in relation to neighboring species (*Avahi peyrierasi* and *Avahi ramanantsoavanai*).

Natural History

As of 2010, this species had not been studied in the wild.

Conservation Status

The 2008 IUCN Red List assessment (2008) classified *A. meridionalis* as Data Deficient (DD). It is known to occur in three protected areas (Andohahela National Park, the Sainte-Luce Private Reserve, and the Mandena Conservation Zone) (Zaramody *et al.*, 2006; Andriantompohavana *et al.*, 2007).

As of 2010, this species was not being kept in captivity (I. J. Porton, pers. comm.).

Where to See It

Our best recommendation for seeing this species is in the Mandena Conservation Zone (near Tolagnaro = Fort-Dauphin), although a nocturnal visit to the rain forest portion of Andohahela National Park may also produce results.

Indriidae

Fig. 10.18: Southern woolly lemur (*Avahi meridionalis*), Col de Manangotry, rain forest parcel of Andohahela National Park (photos by E. E. Louis Jr.).

Avahi occidentalis (Lorenz von Liburnau, 1898)
Western Woolly Lemur

Other English: Western Avahi
French: Avahi occidental
German: Westlicher Wollmaki
Malagasy: Fotsifé, Tsarafangitra

Identification

Avahi occidentalis is one of the smallest woolly lemurs and consequently among the smallest members of the family Indriidae. It has a head-body length of 26.9–30.3 cm, a tail length of 30.7–37.7 cm, a total length of 57.6–68.2 cm, and a weight of 800–1,100 g (Bauchot and Stephan, 1966; Thalmann and Geissmann, 2000; Thalmann, 2001; Zaramody *et al.* 2006; Lei *et al.*, 2008). It is lighter in color than *A. laniger*, with the dense, tightly curled fur of the back a light to medium gray, sometimes flecked with brown or olive, becoming paler towards the rear. Typically, the tail is gray as well, but can sometimes be reddish. The face, throat and cheeks are pale, not brown as in *A. laniger*.

Avahi occidentalis is most likely to be confused with the other species of western woolly lemurs, with *Lepilemur* and, to a lesser extent, with *Cheirogaleus medius*. It can be distinguished from *Avahi cleesei* and *Avahi unicolor* by its contrasting white facial mask and dark eye-rings (Thalmann and Geissmann, 2000). It is significantly larger than *Cheirogaleus* and quite different in its postural and locomotor behavior, and can usually be distinguished from *Lepilemur* by its less conspicuous ears, denser, curlier coat, and obvious white thigh patches. As with other woolly lemur species individuals frequently huddle together with other family members, a behavior very rare in other nocturnal species of comparable size.

Geographic Range

Northwestern Madagascar. According to Thalmann and Geissmann (2000), the core distribution of this species is to the north and east of the Betsiboka River as far as the Bay of Narinda, and this is also the species present in Ankarafantsika National Park. They believe that the isolated population much farther north in the Ankarana region may also be this species, but that, in between, *A. unicolor* inhabits both the Ampasindava Peninsula and the Sambirano region, including the Manongarivo Special Reserve (Schmid and Smolker, 1998; Sterling and McFadden, 2000; Thalmann and Geissmann, 2000).

Natural History

The western woolly lemur is found in tropical dry deciduous and secondary forests, sometimes at high densities. In the dry forests of Ankarafantsika groups of up to five individuals, typically consisting of an adult pair and immature offspring, occupy home ranges of 1–2 ha (Warren and Crompton, 1997a). Territorial defense appears to be less vigorous and vocal than in eastern rain forest *Avahi*,

Indriidae

with greater overlap between neighboring groups. Ganzhorn (1988) estimated population densities in Ankarafantsika at 67 individuals/km².

Young leaves and buds seem to be preferred food items, probably accounting for three-quarters of the dietary intake. More than 20 plant species have been documented as food items, many of which do not appear to be common in the surrounding forests (Albignac, 1981b; Razanahoera-Rakotomalala, 1981; Thalmann, 2001). Feeding bouts occur more toward the beginning and the end of the night, and individuals tend to be inactive in between.

Conservation Status

The 2008 IUCN Red List assessment classified *A. occidentalis* as Endangered (EN), based on its limited distribution, fragmented populations, and recent declines in habitat and overall numbers. It is threatened by forest destruction, mainly due to annual burning to create new cattle pasture, and is also hunted to some degree. It occurs in the Ankarafantsika National Park, the Bora Special Reserve, the Mariarano Classified Forest (Nicoll and Langrand, 1989; Randrianambinina *et al.*, 2003c; E. E. Louis Jr., pers. obs.), and perhaps in the Ankarana Special Reserve. Field surveys and genetic studies of *Avahi* populations at Ankarana are needed to determine the taxonomic and conservation status of woolly lemurs in that area.

As of 2010, this species was not being kept in captivity (I. J. Porton, pers. comm.).

Where to See It

Avahi occidentalis is abundant and easily seen at the Ampijoroa Forest Station in Ankarafantsika National Park, about a two-hour drive southeast of Mahajanga. It is visible there at night and also in its daytime sleeping sites, often only a meter or two above the ground. Other areas in which it occurs are less accessible and off the regular tourist circuit.

Indriidae

Fig. 10.19: Western woolly lemur (*Avahi occidentalis*), Mariarano Classified Forest (photo by E. E. Louis Jr.).

Fig. 10.20: Western woolly lemur (*Avahi occidentalis*), Mariarano Classified Forest (photo by E. E. Louis).

Avahi cleesei Thalmann and Geissmann, 2005
Bemaraha Woolly Lemur

Other English: Cleese's Woolly Lemur
French: Avahi de Cleese, Avahi du Bemaraha
German: Bemaraha-Wollmaki, Cleese's Wollmaki
Malagasy: Dadintsifaky

Identification

Avahi cleesei has a head-body length of 23–31 cm, a tail length of 32–36 cm, a total length of 55.2–67.5 cm, and a weight of 750–1,300 g (Thalmann and Geissmann, 2005; Zaramody *et al.*, 2006; Lei *et al.*, 2008). The face is slightly paler than the forehead and crown, and the triangular upward extension of the facial area onto the crown contrasts with the triangular downward extension of the crown into the facial area that is seen in *Avahi occidentalis* and *Avahi unicolor*. The fur of the forehead immediately above the face is blackish, forming a dark chevron pattern. The eyes are maroon and have black, hairless eyelids. The snout is black and hairless. Fur at the corners of the mouth is whitish. Head and body fur are brown-gray and woolly. The tail varies from brownish-gray to beige and is slightly reddish on the dorsal surface near its base. Fur of the ventral surface is thin and light gray. Characteristic white patches are found on the dorsal surface of the hindlimbs.

The Bemaraha woolly lemur is most likely to be confused with other western woolly lemurs, but it is not sympatric with them so this would not be a problem in the field. It differs from *Avahi occidentalis* by its lack of a white facial mask and dark eye-rings, and from both *Avahi occidentalis* and *Avahi unicolor* by the presence of a dark chevron on the forehead (Thalmann and Geissmann, 2000). It could be confused with *Lepilemur* and, to a lesser extent, *Cheirogaleus medius*. However, it is much larger than *Cheirogaleus* and quite different in its postural and locomotor behavior, and can usually be distinguished from *Lepilemur* by its less conspicuous ears, denser, curlier coat, and obvious white thigh patches.

Zaramody *et al.* (2006) suggested that *A. cleesei* could be a junior synonym of *A. occidentalis*. However, its validity as a species was reaffirmed by Andriantompohavana *et al.* (2007) and by Lei *et al.* (2008).

Geographic Range

This species is known only from the Tsingy de Bemaraha region of central-western Madagascar, north of the Manambolo River (Thalmann and Rakotoarison, 1994). Thalmann and Geissmann (2000) found it in the forests of Ankindrodro, Ankinjao, and Ambalarano. The northern limit of its range is unclear and there is no evidence of its occurrence between the Sambao and Mahavavy rivers (Thalmann *et al.*, 1999) or between the Mahavavy and Betsiboka rivers (Thalmann and Geissmann, 2000).

Indriidae

Natural History

Thalmann and Geissmann (2000) indicated that *Avahi* is generally rare in the Bemaraha region, where the forests it inhabits tend to have a high proportion of evergreen trees, and also reported that higher population densities seem to be found in disturbed habitats.

Conservation Status

The 2008 IUCN Red List assessment classified *A. cleesei* as Endangered (EN). It is known to occur in only two protected areas (the contiguous Tsingy de Bemaraha National Park and Strict Nature Reserve). It evidently has a restricted distribution, and is threatened by continued habitat loss.

As of 2010, this species was not being kept in captivity (I. J. Porton, pers. comm.).

Where to See It

At this time, the only places where this species may be seen are in the Tsingy de Bemaraha National Park and the adjacent Strict Nature Reserve, but it is not easy to find.

Fig. 10.21: Bemaraha woolly lemur (*Avahi cleesei*), Tsingy de Bemaraha (photo by E. E. Louis Jr.).

Indriidae

Avahi unicolor Thalmann and Geissmann, 2000
Sambirano Woolly Lemur

Other English: Sambirano Avahi, Unicolor Woolly Lemur
French: Avahi du Sambirano
German: Sambirano-Wollmaki
Malagasy: Fotsifé

Identification

Avahi unicolor is one of the smallest woolly lemurs and consequently among the smallest members of the family Indriidae. It has a head-body length of 23–31.0 cm, a tail length of 26.5–30.3 cm, a total length of 57.5–66.0 cm, and a weight of 700 g–1.0 kg (E. E. Louis Jr., pers. obs.). According to Thalmann and Geissmann (2000), the coat is woolly and the dorsal color is a sandy brownish-gray. The tail may be a darker grayish-brown or more reddish-brown, although the base of the tail tends to be lighter, even cream-colored. There is a triangular beige- or cream-colored pygal patch. The ventral coat is thinner than the dorsal coat and a lighter gray. The face is only slightly paler than the head and back, with short and straight hair, giving the impression of a facial ring or mask. The snout is hairless and black, the fur at the corners of the mouth whitish, and the eyes maroon.

In the field, *Avahi unicolor* is most likely to be confused with *Lepilemur* and, to a lesser extent, with *Cheirogaleus*, but it is not sympatric with other *Avahi*. It is significantly larger than *Cheirogaleus* and quite different in its postural and locomotor behavior, and can usually be distinguished from *Lepilemur* by its less conspicuous ears, denser, curlier coat, and obvious white thigh patches. It can be distinguished from *Avahi occidentalis* by the latter's distinct white facial mask and dark eye-rings, and from *Avahi cleesei*, which has a dark chevron pattern on its forehead (Thalmann and Geissmann, 2000).

Geographic Range

This species appears to be restricted to tropical moist lowland forests of the Sambirano region in northwestern Madagascar, including the Ampasindava Peninsula (Thalmann and Geissmann, 2000). Its presence on this peninsula was confirmed in August, 2003, when it was found in a forest about one hour from the village of Marotony (Baie de Kakamba; 13°35.690'S, 47°55.500'E) (U. Thalmann and A. Zaramody, pers. comm.). The northern extent of its distribution is possibly the Sambirano River and the southern limit either the Andranomalaza or Maevarano River. The woolly lemur reported from the western slopes of the Manongarivo Special Reserve by Raxworthy and Rakondroparany (1988) was originally thought to be *A. laniger*, but subsequently determined to be *A. unicolor*. This species is quite rare and difficult to find.

Natural History

Avahi unicolor is known only from a few individuals and has yet to be studied in the wild.

Fig. 10.22: Sambirano woolly lemur (*Avahi unicolor*), Antofondro Classified Forest (photo by E. E. Louis Jr.).

Conservation Status

Very little is known about this species, so the 2008 IUCN Red List assessment (2008) classified it as Data Deficient (DD). Habitat destruction for slash-and-burn agriculture and charcoal production are the principal threats to its survival. The degree to which it is hunted is not known. The only protected area in which *A. unicolor* occurs is the Manongarivo Special Reserve, where it is known only from the western slopes. A recent study indicated that it is also found in the Antofondro Classified Forest (Andriantompohavana *et al.*, 2007). Consideration should be given to establishing a protected area on the Ampasindava Peninsula, and to extending the boundaries of the Manongarivo Special Reserve eastward.

As of 2010, this species was not being kept in captivity (I. J. Porton, pers. comm.).

Where to See It

At this time we have little advice to offer those who wish to view this species in the wild, other than to visit the Manongarivo Special Reserve. However, this reserve is difficult to reach, and requires a four-wheel-drive vehicle, as well as permission obtained in advance from Madagascar National Parks in Antananarivo. As more information becomes available regarding its presence in protected areas and other points on the tourist circuit, it is likely that reliable observation sites will emerge. Those who wish to investigate the area could do so with the help of tour operators based in Antsiranana or Ambanja. Hotel accommodation is available in Ambanja and Ankify. Another possibility might be to access the Bay de Kakamba and the village of Marotony on the Ampasindava Peninsula by boat from Nosy Be. The latter is certainly not recommended for first time visitors to Madagascar though, as no tourist facilities are available.

Indriidae

Indriidae

Fig. 10.23: Diademed sifaka (*Propithecus diadema*), feeding on a banana, Lemur Island, Hotel Vakona, Andasibe (photos by R. A. Mittermeier).

Propithecus Bennett, 1832
Sifakas or Simponas

The sifakas or simponas, genus *Propithecus*, are large diurnal lemurs with long tails and legs relative to their trunk and arms. As with other members of the family Indriidae, they are classic "vertical clingers and leapers." At rest they prefer to cling to vertical tree trunks, legs flexed and knees held close to the abdomen. Movement is mainly by leaping, which begins with a rapid extension of the legs that propels the animal upward and outward to the next vertically-oriented support, a process that repeats itself from one support to the next. Suspensory postures are also a feature of this behavioral complex, especially when feeding and moving in peripheral branches and twigs of trees, or when playing. Some species also regularly descend to the ground, where they hop and bound bipedally, often with the arms held above the head. This comical behavior, especially among the smaller sifakas (e.g., *Propithecus verreauxi* and *Propithecus coquereli*) has now become quite well known, and seeing it is one of the highlights of a visit to Madagascar.

The name "sifaka" is derived from the characteristic threat behavior in which the animal issues an explosive, hiss-like "shee-faak" and jerks its head rapidly backwards, often several times in succession. This is characteristic of the smaller species such as *Propithecus verreauxi*, *P. deckenii*, *P. coronatus*, and *P. coquereli*, which are known by the name "sifaka" throughout their ranges, but it is not used in the larger species. Three of the larger sifakas, *P. diadema*, *P. edwardsi*, and *P. candidus* of eastern and northern Madagascar are usually called "simpona" by local people, the name apparently stemming from an alarm call that sounds like a very loud, forced sneeze. The only exception to the use of these two names comes from the northernmost part of Madagascar, where the very restricted Perrier's sifaka (*P. perrieri*) is known as "ankomba joby" or "radjako" and where Tattersall's sifaka (*P. tattersalli*) is known as "ankomba malandy."

The distribution of this genus is like a ring encircling Madagascar's periphery, although populations are by no means uniformly distributed or present everywhere. Some species (e.g., *P. diadema* and *P. verreauxi*) have quite large ranges, while several others (e.g., *P. candidus*, *P. perrieri*, and *P. coronatus*) are very restricted and have some of the smallest primate ranges on Earth.

Sifakas range in weight from about 3.0–8.5 kg, with males and females not differing significantly in size. Those inhabiting the eastern rain forests tend to be larger, live in smaller social groups that occupy larger home ranges, and occur at lower densities than sifaka populations of western and southern Madagascar (Richard, 2003).

When the first edition of this field guide was published in 1994, the genus *Propithecus* was considered to contain three species: *P. diadema* with four subspecies (*candidus*, *diadema*, *edwardsi*, and *perrieri*), *P. tattersalli* with no subspecies, and *P. verreauxi* with four subspecies (*coquereli*, *coronatus*, *deckenii*, and *verreauxi*) (Mittermeier *et al.*, 1994). Several recent studies have resulted in a number of changes, although there is by no means universal agreement on these. Groves (2001), for example, elevated all of the larger sifakas, as well as *P. verreauxi* and *P. coquereli*, to full species, and recognized *P. deckenii* as a species with two subspecies, *deckenii* and *coronatus*, based on geographic distribution. Thalmann and Rakotoarison (1994) presented evidence that the two supposed subspecies of *P. deckenii* should be regarded as different species. Groves and Helgen (2007), on the basis of an examination of craniodental characters, recognized all these taxa as full species, and raised questions about the status of *P. holomelas*, customarily regarded as a synonym of *P. edwardsi*. On the other hand, Pastorini *et al.* (2001b), on the basis of genetic studies, argued that *P. tattersalli* is more likely a subspecies of *P. coquereli*, and that *P. v. deckenii* and *P. v. coronatus* do not deserve subspecific rank. The results of yet another study (Mayor *et al.*, 2004) maintained *P. tattersalli* as a distinct species, along with *P. coquereli*, and elevated all previous *P. diadema* subspecies to full species as well.

A further wrinkle was provided by the discovery of a new sifaka population in the forests of Tsinjoarivo in east-central Madagascar, a little to the south of the capital of Antananarivo (Goodman and Schütz, 1999). This animal, called "sadabe" by local people, was initially regarded as a new subspecies of *P. diadema*, since it exhibited greater pelage variation than previously reported for this species. Later, Mayor *et al.* (2004) did not find sufficient genetic differences between known *P. diadema* populations to establish the Tsinjoarivo animal as a distinct taxon. Now, the animal has been assessed once again, and Y. Rumpler (pers. comm.) and colleagues have decided that it is in fact distinct, and plan on describing it as a new subspecies. Our observations indicate that this population is nothing more than a hybrid swarm (with animals exhibiting different characters, including at least one entirely black individual within a single group). Consequently, we do not recognize it as distinct at this time, although we do illustrate it with photographs taken in the Tsinjoarivo areas (Figs. 10.59 and 10.60).

We believe that it is essential to consider a combination of morphological data, genetic data, field studies, and information on geographic distributions in making final determinations on the taxonomic status of any group of species. After examining recent publications on this genus, adding field observations on known taxa (all of which have been seen in the wild by at least four authors of this book), and following a discussion of taxonomy at a IUCN Red List Workshop on Madagascar Mammals held in Antananarivo in April, 2005, we believe that the most appropriate approach is to recognize all nine *Propithecus* taxa as full species. These include two major groupings, the smaller species (*P. verreauxi, P. deckenii, P. coronatus, P. coquereli*) that weigh 3.0–4.5 kg and are found mainly in the south and west, with *P. tattersalli* as an outlier in the far north, and the larger species that weigh from 5.0–8.5 kg and are found mainly in the eastern rain forests (*P. edwardsi, P. diadema, P. candidus*), with *P. perrieri* as an outlier again in the dry forests of the far north. As indicated above, we withhold final judgement on the status of the Tsinjoarivo form of *P. diadema* pending publication by Rumpler and colleagues.

Indriidae

Fig. 10.24: Coquerel's sifaka (*Propithecus coquereli*), Anjajavy (photo by R. A. Mittermeier).

Fig. 10.25: Silky sifaka (*Propithecus candidus*), Marojejy National Park (photo by I. Relanzón).

Fig. 10.26: *Propithecus* postural and behavioral drawings (next page):
    a. *Propithecus verreauxi* in a suspensory feeding posture
    b. *Propithecus verreauxi* feeding
    c. *Propithecus verreauxi* leaping
    d. *Propithecus verreauxi* sitting in a tree fork
    e. *Propithecus verreauxi* in a suspensory posture

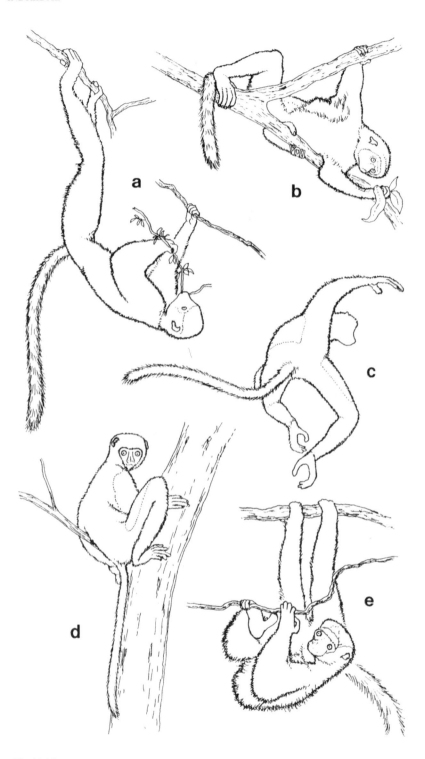

Fig. 10.26.

Madagascar.   Mammifères. Pl. 6.

Propithecus Coquereli.

Indriidae

Fig. 10.27: A lithographic plate of *Propithecus coquereli* from Alfred Grandidier's *Histoire Physique, Naturelle et Politique de Madagascar*, published in Paris in 1875.

Fig. 10.28: *Propithecus* postural and behavioral drawings (next page):
    a. *Propithecus coquereli* in the characteristic "chair" sitting posture
    b. *Propithecus verreauxi* resting on forked branches
    c. *Propithecus coquereli* in a suspensory resting posture
    d. *Propithecus verreauxi* female and infant sitting on a branch
    e. *Propithecus coquereli* female and infant resting in a vertical
      clinging posture

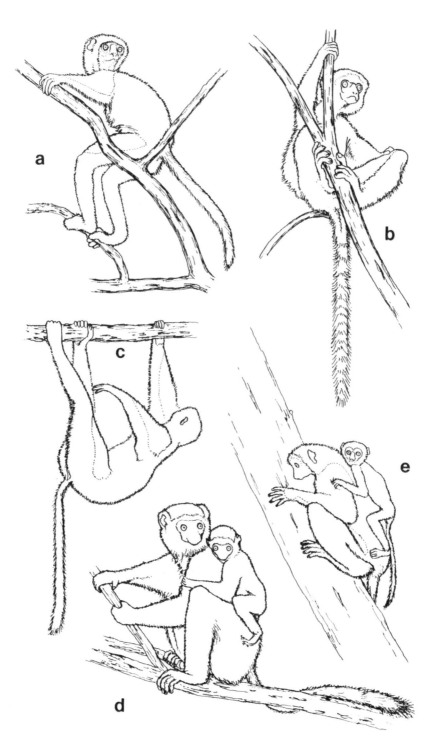

Fig. 10.28.

Indriidae

Fig. 10.29: Verreaux' sifaka (*Propithecus verreauxi*), "dancing" in the Berenty Private Reserve (photos by R. A. Mittermeier). This behavior is performed daily and has become one of the best highlights of a trip to Madagascar.

Fig. 10.30: *Propithecus* postural and behavioral drawings (next page):
      a. *Propithecus edwardsi* with an infant in a seated resting posture, using branches
        above as support
      b. *Propithecus edwardsi* with infant, about to leap from a vertical clinging position
      c. *Propithecus edwardsi* with infant in a vertical clinging resting posture
      d. *Propithecus edwardsi* in a seated resting posture

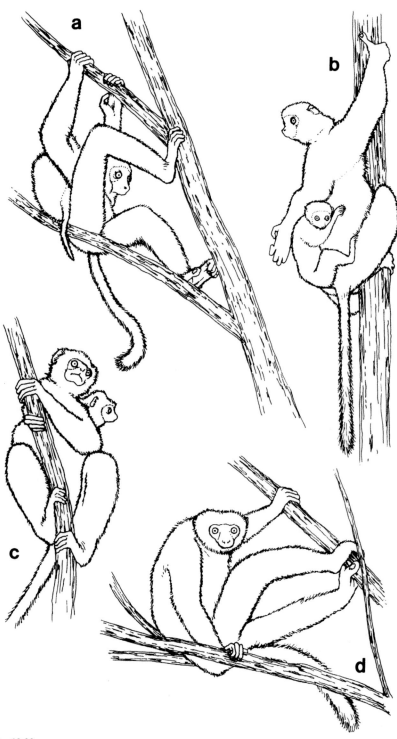

Fig. 10.30.

Fig. 10.31: Verreaux' sifaka (*Propithecus verreauxi*) leaping between two spiny *Alluaudia* trees in the Berenty Private Reserve. How the animal is able to do this without being impaled on the very sharp, closely-packed spines of these trees remains a mystery (photos by R. A. Mittermeier).

Fig. 10.32: *Propithecus* postural and behavioral drawings (next page):
       a. *Propithecus verreauxi* jumping from a tree to the ground
       b-g. *Propithecus verreauxi* using the characteristic bipedal hopping locomotion to
          cross the ground

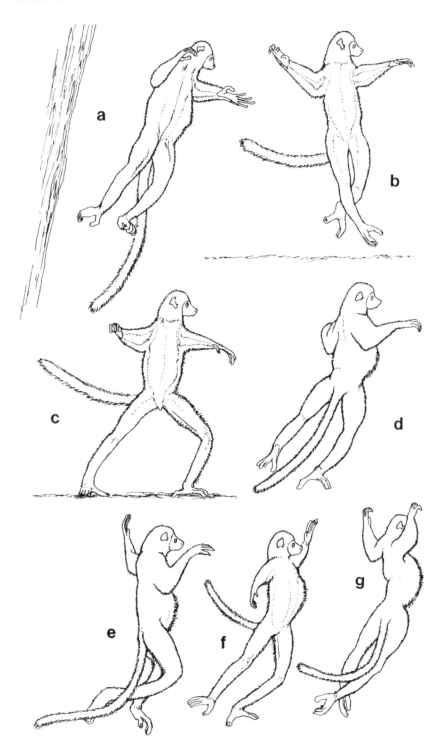

Fig. 10.32: *Propithecus* postural and behavioral drawings.

Indriidae

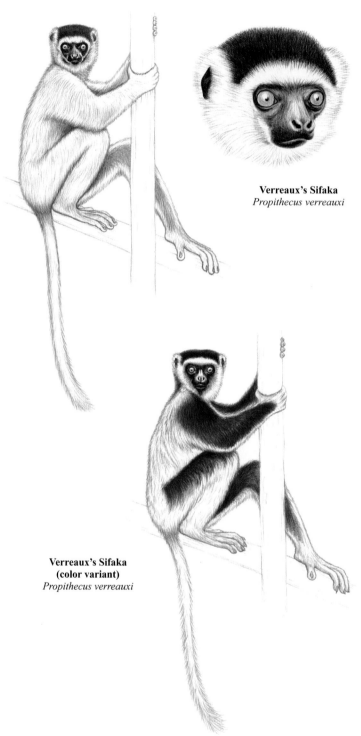

Verreaux's Sifaka
Propithecus verreauxi

**Verreaux's Sifaka
(color variant)**
Propithecus verreauxi

Indriidae

Fig. 10.33.

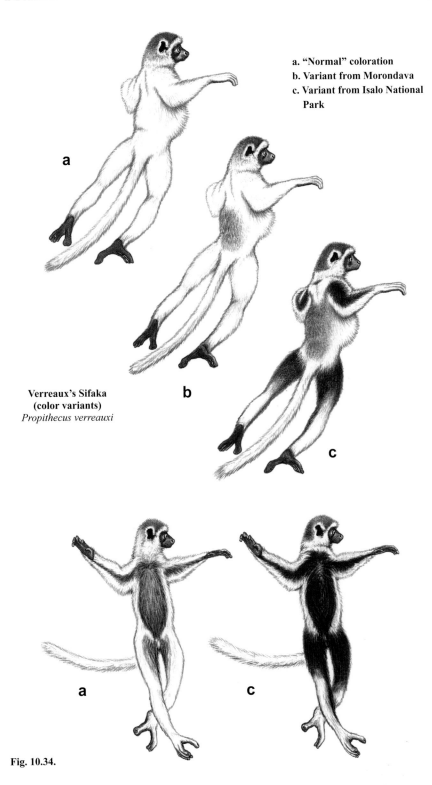

a. "Normal" coloration
b. Variant from Morondava
c. Variant from Isalo National Park

Verreaux's Sifaka (color variants)
Propithecus verreauxi

Fig. 10.34.

Indriidae

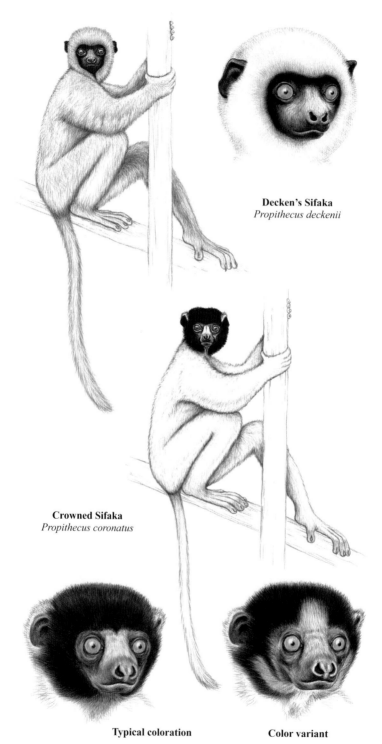

Decken's Sifaka
Propithecus deckenii

Crowned Sifaka
Propithecus coronatus

Typical coloration   **Color variant**

Fig. 10.35.

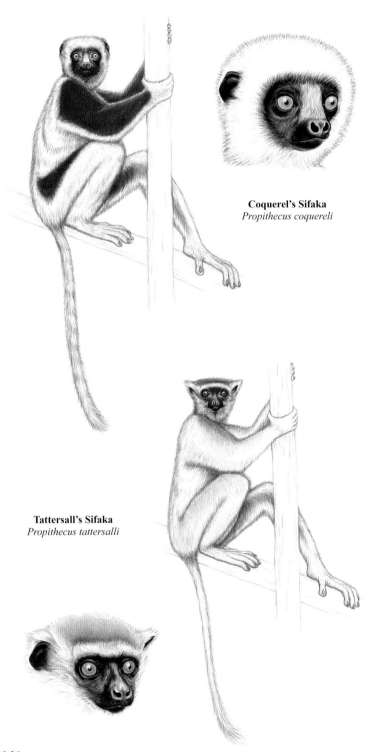

Coquerel's Sifaka
Propithecus coquereli

Tattersall's Sifaka
Propithecus tattersalli

Indriidae

Fig. 10.36.

Diademed Sifaka
Propithecus diadema

Indriidae

Milne-Edwards' Sifaka
Propithecus edwardsi

Fig. 10.37.

Facial
pigmentation
is variable.

Silky Sifaka
Propithecus candidus

Perrier's Sifaka
Propithecus perrieri

Fig. 10.38.

Diademed Sifaka
Propithecus diadema

Fig. 10.39: Color variants within a population of *Propithecus diadema* from the Tsinjoarivo region representing either a new subspecies or a hybrid population (from photographs by M. Irwin).

Diademed Sifaka
Propithecus diadema

Fig. 10.40: Color variants within a population of *Propithecus diadema* from the Tsinjoarivo region representing either a new subspecies or a hybrid population (from photographs by M. Irwin).

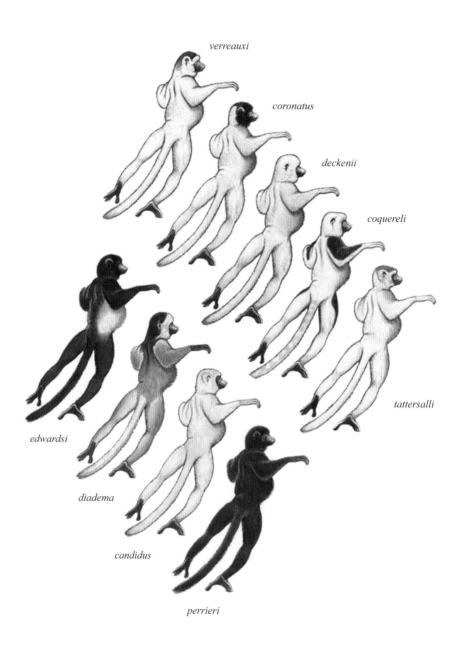

verreauxi

coronatus

deckenii

coquereli

tattersalli

edwardsi

diadema

candidus

perrieri

Fig. 10.41: Dorsal coloration of all nine sifaka species, plus the *Propithecus*.

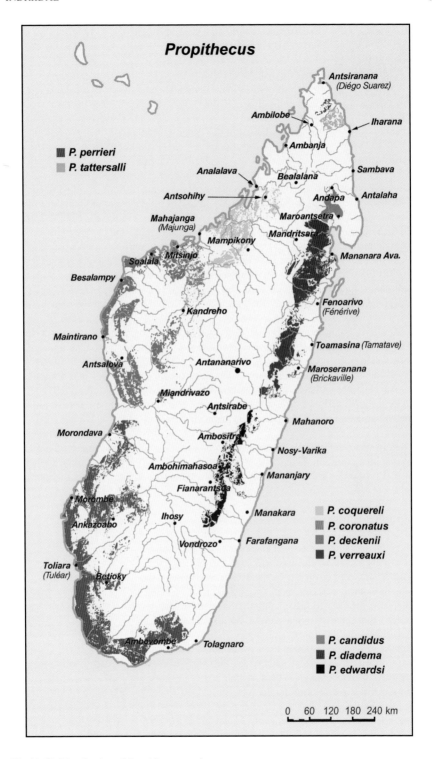

Fig. 10.42: Distribution of *Propithecus* species.

Propithecus verreauxi A. Grandidier, 1867
Verreaux's Sifaka

Other English: White Sifaka
French: Propithèque de Verreaux
German: Südlicher Kronensifaka, Südlicher Kappensifaka,
Verreaux's Sifaka
Malagasy: Sifaka, Sifaka-Bilany (Isalo area)

Identification

Propithecus verreauxi, one of the smaller sifakas, is a pale form from southern and southwestern Madagascar. It has a head-body length of 40–48 cm, a tail length of 50–60 cm, a total length of 90–110 cm, and a weight of 3.0–3.5 kg (Tattersall, 1982; Kappeler, 1991; Richard *et al.*, 2000, 2002). The pelage is long and thick, and the predominant coat color, including the tail, is white. This contrasts sharply with the black face, muzzle, hands and feet, the dark brown crown that extends down the nape of the neck in both sexes, and the reddish-brown patch found on the upper chest of males that is associated with their sternal glands. Fur on the ears is white and slightly tufted. Fur on the ventral surface is sparse, giving the abdomen a grayish appearance due to the underlying dark skin.

A distinctive color variant has been described and given the name *P. verreauxi majori* Rothschild, 1894, but most experts now consider it to be nothing more than a melanistic form of Verreaux's sifaka (Tattersall, 1982; Mittermeier *et al.*, 1994; Groves, 2001). This "*majori*" variant is also predominantly white, including the cheeks, ears and forehead, but has a chocolate-brown head cap, and is brownish to brownish-black on the chest, back, inside of the arms and legs, and tail, except for its white tip. It is almost always found in groups of normally colored *P. verreauxi* (F. Hawkins, pers. obs.).

Entirely white individuals are also occasionally observed in the midst of normally colored animals (e.g., in Berenty, R. A. Mittermeier, pers. obs.). Despite the variations of color that exist in this species, it is impossible to confuse it with any other lemur in its range.

Geographic Range

Southern and southwestern Madagascar. The Tsiribihina River is believed to be the northern limit of the range of Verreaux's sifaka in the west. In the southeast, it is found near to (just north of) Tolagnaro (= Fort-Dauphin) in the Nahampoana Private Reserve, although it was probably introduced there and is not a part of its historical range. Tolagnaro is in the rain forest zone where *P. verreauxi* does not otherwise occur. The range limit in the southeast is the transitional and spiny forest patches of the Mangatsiaka Parcel of Andohahela National Park, which is a 1–1½ hour drive from Tolagnaro. It is not found in the rain forest parcel of the park (Petter *et al.*, 1977; O'Connor *et al.*, 1986, 1987), and the eastern limit is the Tsimehaly Parcel in the Anosy Range (about 40 km west of Tolagnaro). Population densities vary in different forest types, but even very small forest patches can support sizeable populations.

Indriidae

Fig. 10.43: Verreaux's sifaka (*Propithecus verreauxi*), Mangatsiaka Parcel, Andohahela National Park (photo by E. E. Louis Jr.).

Indriidae

Fig. 10.44: *Propithecus verreauxi* sitting in an *Alluaudia* in the Berenty Private Reserve (photo by R. A. Mittermeier).

Natural History

Verreaux's sifaka is a diurnal lemur that typically inhabits tropical dry lowland and montane forest (from sea level to 1,300 m), including spiny bush, brush-and scrub thickets, and riparian forests (Sussman et al., 1987), but it is also known from humid forests at low altitudes (Rasoarimanana, 2005). It tends to live in small- to medium-sized multi-male groups that range from 2–14, but average 5–6 individuals (Jolly, 1966; Richard, 1974a, 1985). Females appear to be dominant over males. Home ranges may exceed 10 ha but are often very much smaller (Richard et al., 1993; Carrai and Lunardini, 1996, Raharivololona and Ranaivosoa, 2000). Core areas of overlapping home ranges are defended against neighboring sifaka groups (Benadi et al., 2008). Population densities have been estimated at 47 individuals/km^2 in the degraded forests of Belaoka, at 150–200 individuals/km^2 in Berenty (Jolly et al., 1982b; O'Connor, 1987), and at 400–500 individuals/km^2 at Antserananomby (Sussman, 1974).

The diet is seasonally variable but consists principally of leaves, fruit, and flowers. Leaves are the most important food item during the dry season and fruit during the wet season, at which time this sifaka also appears to use fewer plant species (Richard, 1977). Most seeds consumed are destroyed, meaning that this species is at least partly a seed predator (Ralisoamala, 1996). The survival of Verreaux's sifaka in Didiereaceae forest suggests that it does not need to drink and can survive severe drought (Jolly, 1966). Richard (1974b) suggested that water may be obtained during the dry season by eating the bark and cambium of *Operculicarya decaryi*.

The ability of this sifaka to leap from trunk to trunk of spiny, cactus-like plants of the family Didiereaceae, such as *Alluaudia ascendens* and *Alluaudia procera*, is one of the most spectacular wildlife phenomena to be observed in Madagascar. These tall thin plants are covered with very hard sharp spines, yet the sifakas are able to leap from one trunk to the next with apparently no concern and without sustaining any injuries. On the ground, Verreaux's sifaka moves bipedally, bounding on its hindlimbs, usually sideways, with its arms raised above its head. This is a very different spectacle from leaping between the spiny trunks of *Alluaudia*, but it is equally impressive and has become one of the best known and most appealing symbols of Madagascar's wildlife.

The age at which sexual maturity is reached varies with habitat. For example, in the spiny forests of Beza-Mahafaly, fewer than half the females have reproduced by six years of age (Richard et al., 2002), whereas at Berenty three-year-old females are routinely seen with newborns (Jolly, 1966). Breeding is seasonal. Mating occurs in January and February, with births occurring 162–170 days after conception (Richard, 2003). A single dominant male monopolizes paternity in each group in Kirindy (Kappeler and Schäffler, 2008), whereas paternity by extra-group males is common in the Beza-Mahafaly population (Lawler et al., 2003). Infants ride on their mother's belly until about three months of age, at which point they shift to her back. They are almost completely independent at six months (Jolly, 1966). These sifakas sometimes fall victim to the fossa (*Cryptoprocta ferox*) and the Madagascar harrier-hawk (*Polyboroides radiatus*) (Rasoloarison et al., 1995; Karpanty and Goodman, 1999); they have specific alarm calls for the latter (Fichtel and Kappeler, 2002). Individuals also occasionally fall prey to the large Madagascar ground boas (*Acrantophis madagascariensis*, *Acrantophis dumerili*) when they descend from the trees (L. A. de Roland, pers. comm.).

Conservation Status

The 2008 IUCN Red List assessment classified *P. verreauxi* as Vulnerable (VU). Despite its wide distribution, the two principal habitats upon which it depends—spiny forest and riparian or gallery forest—are under continual threat because of logging, slash-and-burn agriculture (especially for corn plantations) and charcoal and fuelwood production (Sussman and Richard, 1986). Although hunting of *P. verreauxi* is "fady" (taboo) to several of the tribes living within its range (e.g., Antandroy, Mahafaly), it is hunted by other tribes (e.g., Sakalava) and by immigrants to the region (Goodman and Raselimanana, 2003; Goodman *et al.*, 2004). In the Isalo region, this lemur is known as "sifaka-bilany" ("sifaka of the cooking pot") but it is unclear whether this is because of its popularity as a food item or because of the sooty black appearance of individuals from this part of the species' range (J. Ratsimbazafy, pers. obs.; P. C. Wright, pers. comm.).

Propithecus verreauxi occurs in four national parks (Andohahela, Isalo, Tsimanampetsotsa, and Vohibasia-Zombitse), two special reserves (Andranomena and Beza-Mahafaly), two private reserves (Analabe and Berenty), in the large new Menabe-Antimena Protected Area (which contains the Kirindy Forest), and in a number of unprotected classified forests and forest reserves (Nicoll and Langrand, 1989; Fenn *et al.*, 1999; Hawkins, 1999; Goodman and Raselimanana, 2003; Sussman *et al.*, 2003).

As of 2010, this species was not being kept in captivity (I. J. Porton, pers. comm.).

Where to See It

Not only is this lemur one of the most appealing and attractive animals in Madagascar, it is also one of the easiest to see. It is most readily observed in the Berenty Private Reserve west of Tolagnaro (= Fort-Dauphin), with sightings guaranteed even on a day trip. At Berenty, it is usually seen in gallery forests in the main part of the reserve, but can also be found in small patches of Didiereaceae bush adjacent to gallery forest, and even around the camp clearings. Indeed, several groups of this species "dance" across roads and through the lodge areas in Berenty every day, usually in the early morning or late afternoon.

A particularly interesting site to visit is the Anjapolo section of the Berenty Reserve, some 15 km from the main lodge area. There the animal can be see in a beautiful old stand of spiny forest, much more impressive than the spiny forest usually visited by tourists.

Two places to see Verreaux's sifaka in large impressive stands of Didiereaceae bush are at Mangaziaka and Ihazafotsy at the edge of Parcel 2 of Andohahela National Park, and in the region surrounding the Beza-Mahafaly Special Reserve some five to six hours by car east of Toliara (= Tuléar). It can also readily be seen in the Kirindy Forest north of Morondava, where there are several habituated groups, and it is now routinely seen in the forested canyons of Isalo National Park as well. Another good location is the Nahampoana Private Reserve, just north of Tolagnaro (= Fort-Dauphin) where it was probably introduced.

Indriidae

Fig. 10.45: Verreaux's sifaka (*Propithecus verreauxi*), Berenty Private Reserve (photo by R. A. Mittermeier).

Propithecus deckenii Peters, 1870
Decken's Sifaka

French: Propithèque de von der Decken
German: Von der Decken's Sifaka
Malagasy: Sifaka, Tsibahaka

Identification

Propithecus deckenii is a medium-sized, white sifaka from western Madagascar. It has a head-body length of 42–48 cm, a tail length of 50–60 cm, a total length of 92–110 cm, and a weight of 3.0–4.5 kg (Tattersall, 1982). The dorsal coat is creamy-white with tints varying from gold to pale brown on the neck, shoulders, back and limbs. The face is black, but usually with a patch of white fur running across it. Bony pockets on either side of the muzzle give this animal a rather blunt-nosed appearance, but not as extreme as in the crowned sifaka (*Propithecus coronatus*).

Decken's sifaka is easy to distinguish from other lemurs within its range except for *P. coronatus*, with which it may partially overlap in limited areas. *Propithecus coronatus* is also predominantly white, but has a distinctive dark brown to black hood, extending onto the shoulders. It has a very distinct and unusual bulbous nose.

Geographic Range

This sifaka is found in patches of highly fragmented deciduous forest in western Madagascar between the Mahavavy and Manambolo rivers (Petter *et al.*, 1977; Tattersall, 1982, 1986; Thalmann and Rakotoarison, 1994). The southern limit of its range does not extend to the Tsiribihina River, which marks the northern limit for *Propithecus verreauxi*. To the north, in the coastal forests that occur between the Mahavavy and Betsiboka rivers, the geographic separation between *P. deckenii* and *P. coronatus* appears clear. However, in the lower reaches of the Mahavavy River, populations of the two species apparently hybridize, and there are individuals with intermediate coloration on islands in the middle of the Mahavavy (Thalmann *et al.*, 2002). More confusing is the situation in forests of the Bongolava Massif, far inland and to the southeast, where animals with color patterns characteristic of both species have been observed (Petter and Peyriéras, 1972). Furthermore, according to recent surveys, populations representing both species can be found at a number of sites (Randrianarisoa *et al.*, 2001; Thalmann *et al.*, 2002).

Needless to say, the taxonomic status of these two forms and their relationship to one another require further investigation, especially in the field. However, for now, we continue to recognize them as distinct species.

Indriidae

Fig. 10.46: Decken's sifaka (*Propithecus deckenii*) in a forest between Lac Sariaka and Baly Village, Baie de Baly National Park (photo by R. A. Mittermeier).

Indriidae

Natural History

This species has not yet been studied in the wild. We know only that it is diurnal, inhabits dry deciduous forests, lives in groups of 6–10 individuals, and can survive in degraded habitat, sometimes even appearing in *Eucalyptus* trees in the middle of the town of Soalala (F. Hawkins, pers. obs.).

Conservation Status

The 2008 IUCN Red List assessment classified *P. deckenii* as Vulnerable (VU). Forests in its range are already highly fragmented, and continued habitat loss is the greatest threat to its survival. Forests are burned to provide pasture for livestock and cut for charcoal production. The animal itself is protected by a very strong taboo in much of its range, becoming very tame as a result, but if the taboo were to break down for whatever reason the species could disappear very rapidly.

Decken's sifaka occurs in three national parks (Baie de Baly, Tsingy de Bemaraha, and Tsingy de Namoroka), the Tsingy de Bemaraha Strict Nature Reserve, four special reserves (Ambohijanahary, Bemarivo, Kasijy, and Maningoza), and in at least one classified forest (Tsiombikibo) (Nicoll and Langrand, 1989; Hawkins *et al.*, 1998; Garbutt, 2007; Thalmann *et al.*, 1999, 2002; Randrianasoa *et al.*, 2000; J. Durbin, pers. comm.; E. E. Louis Jr., pers. obs.).

As of 2010, this species was not being kept in captivity (I. J. Porton, pers. comm.).

Where to See It

The best place to see this species in the wild is the Tsingy de Bemaraha National Park, where it can be observed easily along the main tourist routes. It can also be observed in the Tsiombikibo Classified Forest northwest of Mitsinjo, about four hour's drive from Katsepy (Garbutt, 2007), and in forests in and near Soalala and on both sides of the Baie de Baly.

Indriidae

Fig. 10.47: Juvenile Decken's sifaka (*Propithecus deckenii*), Tsiombikibo Classified Forest (photo by E. E. Louis Jr.).

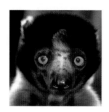

Propithecus coronatus Milne-Edwards, 1871
Crowned Sifaka

Other English: None
French: Propithèque couronné
German: Kronensifaka
Malagasy: Sifaka, Tsibahaka

Identification

Propithecus coronatus is a medium-sized, predominantly white sifaka from western Madagascar. It has a head-body length of 39–45 cm, a tail length of 48–57 cm, a total length of 87–102 cm, and a weight of 3.5–4.3 kg (Tattersall, 1982; Mittermeier *et al.*, 1994). The coat is creamy-white, which contrasts strongly with the chocolate-brown to black head, neck and throat. The muzzle is blunt and rounded, and even bulbous in form, and the face is naked and black. The bulbous nose is quite unusual and readily distinguishes this sifaka from all others. There is sometimes a patch of white fur across the bridge of the nose and slight white tufting around the ears. The body coat is variably tinted golden-yellow to golden-brown on the upper chest, shoulders and upper forelimbs. The hindlimbs and tail are white.

The crowned sifaka is easy to distinguish from most other lemurs in its range, but may be confused with Decken's sifaka (*Propithecus deckenii*) in areas where the ranges of the two species approach one another or even overlap. Both are predominantly white, but the dark head and bulbous nose of *P. coronatus* make it easy to tell the two apart. Forms intermediate between the two may also be seen.

Geographic Range

Kaudern (1915), who collected extensively in northwestern Madagascar early in the last century, described the limits of the crowned sifaka's distribution as the Mahavavy River to the southwest (separating it from *P. deckenii*) and the Betsiboka River to the northeast (separating it from *P. coquereli*). Petter *et al.* (1977) subsequently pointed out that hybridization between these two sifakas probably occurred along the upper reaches of the Mahavavy River. Collections made in the forests of Ambararatabe (to the west of the Mahavavy River) and sightings along the Bongolava Massif (west of Tsiroanomandidy) also appear to include individuals representing both species, as well as *P. verreauxi* (Petter and Peyriéras, 1972; Tattersall, 1986), but Thalmann *et al.* (2002) could not confirm earlier reports of the co-occurrence of this species with *P. deckenii* along the lower course of the Mahavavy. Reports of *P. coronatus* as far south as the Sakay River, as far to the east as Andanotongo, and to the southeast beyond Tsiroanomandidy suggest that

the distribution of this species is more complicated than originally believed (Tattersall, 1986). The most comprehensive surveys of the distribution of *P. coronatus* and *P. deckenii* have been compiled by Thalmann *et al.* (2002). In addition, Petter and Andriatsafara (1987) report that it was present in the Ambohitantely Special Reserve (on the high plateau) until perhaps midway through the last century, but it is now gone from this small, isolated locale.

Natural History

Field studies of the crowned sifaka have been few and short-term. It inhabits tropical dry lowland forests from sea level to 700 m, and also enters mangrove forests. At Anjamena, group size ranges from two to eight individuals and home ranges from 1.2–1.5 ha, with territories being defended aggressively against neighbors. The diet of this diurnal lemur consists largely of buds, unripe fruit and mature leaves (Curtis *et al.*, 1998).

Indriidae

Fig. 10.48: Crowned sifaka (*Propithecus coronatus*) photographed in Lemurs' Park outside Antananarivo (lemurspark@wanadoo.mg) (photo by R. A. Mittermeier).

Conservation Status

Propithecus coronatus was classified as Endangered (EN) in the 2008 IUCN Red List assessment. Habitat loss is the principal threat faced by this species. Forests in its range have declined dramatically in the last few decades, and they continue to be burned to provide pasture for livestock, and cut for charcoal production. There is also some live capture for the illegal pet trade (L. Dollar, pers. comm.).

There are reports that this species occurs in two special reserves (Ambohijanahary and Kasijy), but its status in these protected areas remains to be determined (Randrianarisoa *et al.*, 2001a, 2001b; Thalmann *et al.*, 2002). Efforts should be made to secure protection for the populations at Katsepy and Anjamena that have been the subject of brief studies and are also visited by tourists. Katsepy is considered a sacred site by some local people and is thus afforded a certain level of protection, and the Antrema Forest Station is the subject of a conservation program supported by Vincennes Zoo. A few classified forests within the crowned sifaka's range may also harbor viable populations and should be surveyed (Mittermeier *et al.*, 1994).

As of 2009 there were 17 individuals reported in captivity in Europe, with an additional two in the Lemurs' Park near Antananarivo, Madagascar (I. J. Porton, pers. comm.).

Where to See It

There are two very accessible sites for viewing the crowned sifaka. The first is the forest at Antrema below the lighthouse north of Katsepy, which can be readily reached by ferry (twice daily) or speedboat from Mahajanga (= Majunga). The comfortable and recently established Chez Chabaud Hotel is the only local accommodation. The proprietor is able to arrange transportation to and from the forests that harbor these animals, and they can sometimes also be seen in walks along the shore. A visit to Katsepy requires two days and a one-night stay, and can be arranged from Mahajanga. Katsepy is also a good site for the mongoose lemur (*Eulemur mongoz*), which is quite easy to see in this area.

An even more accessible site for viewing this species, as well as the crowned lemur (*Eulemur coronatus*), is in the nearby Belamboka-Bombetoka Forests. The area can be reached via Boanamary, which is 27 km to the west of RN4, and has basic, community-managed tourism facilities in Mataitromby. The animals are very easy to observe if you are

Fig. 10.49: Crowned sifaka (*Propithecus coronatus*), Lemurs' Park (photo by R. A. Mittermeier).

ready to walk 30 minutes. Fanamby is developing community-based ecotourism in the area and local guides are available (S. Wolhauser, pers. comm.).

The forests of Anjamena, on the east bank of the Mahavavy River, are also fairly easy to reach, and the prospects are good for viewing sifakas. Getting to and from the Mahavavy River delta requires expedition-level preparation and is now being offered by a small number of international tour operators, largely for the area's birdlife, but recent reports indicate that substantial numbers of lemurs are also observed during these trips.

Fig. 10.50: Crowned sifaka (*Propithecus coronatus*), Anjamena Classified Forest (photo by E. E. Louis Jr.).

Indriidae

Propithecus coquereli (A. Grandidier, 1867)
Coquerel's Sifaka

Other English: None
French: Propithèque de Coquerel
German: Coquerel's Sifaka
Malagasy: Sifaka, Tsibahaka

Identification

Propithecus coquereli is a medium-sized, predominantly white sifaka of northwestern Madagascar. It has a head-body length of 42–50 cm, a tail length of 50–60 cm, a total length of 93–110 cm, and a weight of 3.7–4.3 kg (Tattersall, 1982; Kappeler, 1991; Ravosa *et al.*, 1993). The pelage is dense. The dorsal coat color is mostly white, including the head and the tail. Prominent maroon patches cover the chest, the anterior and interior aspects of the forelimbs and hindlimbs, and sometimes the base of the back. The skin of the muzzle and face is bare and black, except for a white patch of fur extending across the bridge of the nose. The ears also are black, naked, and visible above the white fur of the head and cheeks. The eyes are yellow. It is impossible to confuse *P. coquereli* with any other lemur in its range.

Geographic Range

Coquerel's sifaka is found throughout the tropical dry lowland forests (up to 300 m) of northwestern Madagascar to the north and west of the Betsiboka River (Tattersall, 1982). Its most southerly occurrence is reportedly Ambato-Boéni, its northern limit is near Bealanana, and the eastern boundary of its range is near Antetemasy (just west of Befandriana Nord).

Natural History

This diurnal vertical clinger-and-leaper is most commonly found in mixed deciduous dry forests, and often in brush-and-scrub and secondary formations that are immediately adjacent to primary forest. In the forests of Ankarafantsika it is seen in groups of 3–10, using home ranges of 4–9 ha (Petter, 1962a, 1962b; Albignac, 1981a). Densities approaching 60 individuals/km² are estimated for this site (Ganzhorn, 1988). Coquerel's sifaka feeds mostly on young leaves, flowers, fruit, bark and dead wood in the wet season, and on mature leaves and buds in the dry season (Richard, 1974b). As many as 98 different plant species have been recorded in its diet (Richard, 1978a, 1978b).

Births are clustered in the months of June and July, and studies in captivity suggest a gestation period of 162 days (Richard, 1976, 1987). Infants cling to their mother's chest for the first month or so, and then transfer to her back. They become completely independent by about six months of age and reach adult size in one year.

Indriidae

Fig. 10.51: Coquerel's sifaka (*Propithecus coquereli*) with infant, Anjajavy (photo by R. A. Mittermeier).

As with other western sifaka species, *P. coquereli* regularly goes to the ground. Interestingly, its ground locomotion is somewhat different from that of *Propithecus verreauxi* further to the south. Whereas *P. verreauxi* usually bounds along the ground in a sideways position, *P. coquereli* leaps forward in a kangaroo-like fashion.

Indriidae

Fig. 10.52: Coquerel's sifaka (*Propithecus coquereli*), Anjajavy (photo by R. A. Mittermeier).

Conservation Status

The 2008 IUCN Red List assessment classified *P. coquereli* as Endangered (EN). Its restricted distribution makes this sifaka particularly susceptible to habitat loss and hunting. Slash-and-burn agriculture and annual burning to create new pasture for livestock are the principal causes of forest loss in northwestern Madagascar, but trees are also cut to produce charcoal. All of these practices threaten even officially protected areas. In some areas local traditions place taboos on hunting sifakas, but immigration to this region continues to change such long-held customs, and hunting of this species does take place (Nicoll and Langrand, 1989).

The only two protected areas in which *P. coquereli* is known to occur are the Ankarafantsika National Park and the Bora Special Reserve (Nicoll and Langrand, 1989; Randrianambinina *et al.*, 2003c). Unfortunately, hunting pressure on sifakas is significant in Ankarafantsika (Garcia and Goodman, 2003) and Bora has become seriously degraded. Populations of *P. coquereli* have also been reported from the forests of Anjiamangirana, Anjajavy, the Narinda Peninsula, and Mariarano, which should be considered for protected area status (N. Garbutt, pers. comm.; E. E. Louis Jr., pers. obs.).

As of 2010, there were 48 *P. coquereli* reported in various zoos in the United States, along with a few pairs in the Lemurs' Park near Antananarivo, Madagascar (I. J. Porton, pers. comm.; C. Schwitzer, pers. obs.).

Where to See It

The best place to see Coquerel's sifaka is at the Ampijoroa Forestry Station located right along the main road that runs through Ankarafantsika National Park. This site can be easily reached by car from Mahajanga (= Majunga) in about two hours, and a campsite and bungalows are available. Another excellent site where you can see this species is the forest around the Anjavavy Hotel, north of Mahajanga. There sifakas can be found every day right next to the hotel's bungalows, and they are fully habituated.

Fig. 10.53: Coquerel's sifaka (*Propithecus coquereli*) in Anjajavy (photo by R. A. Mittermeier). Note the distinctive areas of chocolate coloration that distinguish this species from its closest relatives.

Indriidae

Propithecus tattersalli Simons, 1988
Tattersall's Sifaka

Other English: Golden-crowned Sifaka
French: Propithèque de Tattersall
German: Tattersall's-Sifaka
Malagasy: Ankomba Malandy, Simpona

Identification

Propithecus tattersalli is similar in size to the southern and western dry forest sifakas. It has a head-body length of 45–47 cm, a tail length of 42–47 cm, a total length of 87–94 cm, and a weight of 3.4–3.6 kg (Meyers, 1993; Ravosa *et al.*, 1993; Lehman *et al.*, 2005a). The dorsal coat is creamy-white, with similar coloration on the chest, shoulders, upper arms, genital region and rump. The forearms and tops of the legs often are pale orange. The ears are prominent and black, sporting distinctive white tufts that give the head a triangular appearance. The face is bare and black, and the eyes are orange. The most useful characters in field identification are the golden cap and the protruding ear tufts. This species cannot be confused with any other lemur in its range.

Geographic Range

Tattersall's sifaka is quite restricted in range, being limited to forest patches in northeastern Madagascar between the Loky River in the north and the Manambato River in the south. Its range is centered on the town of Daraina and covers approximately 245,000 ha of human-altered degraded grasslands, dry scrub, agricultural land, gallery forests, littoral forests, and forest fragments (Meyers, 1993; Randrianarisoa *et al.*, 1999; Vargas *et al.*, 2002). It was first discovered in 1974, when Ian Tattersall sighted groups of animals north of Vohémar (Tattersall, 1982) and provisionally identified them as a variant of the silky sifaka (then *Propithecus diadema candidus*; Tattersall, 1982). More than a decade would pass before the species was finally described by science in 1988, when Elwyn Simons named it in honor of Tattersall (Simons, 1988).

Natural History

The forests in the range of this sifaka are highly fragmented, and isolated by extensive degraded grasslands. Most are deciduous formations similar in composition to transitional dry forests of western Madagascar, and this species occurs in them at altitudes up to 700 m (Meyers and Ratsirarson, 1989; Vargas *et al.*, 2002). Of 75 forest tracts identified by researchers, 45 were inhabited by sifakas. Groups range in size from 3–10, with an average of five, and occupy territories of 9–12 ha (Meyers, 1993). Recent population density estimates range from 10–23 individuals/km², and the total population is believed to be 6,000 to 10,000 animals (Meyers, 1996; Vargas *et al.* 2002).

This species is largely diurnal, though sometimes crepuscular during the rainy season, and sleeps at night in high emergent trees. Its diet consists of seeds, leaves, unripe fruits,

Indriidae

Fig. 10.54: Tattersall's sifaka (*Propithecus tattersalli*), Daraina (photo by R. A. Mittermeier).

and flowers, and may also include tree bark during the dry season. Mating occurs in late January. Newborn infants are commonly seen in July and August, and weaning typically in December (Meyers and Wright, 1993; D. Meyers, pers. comm.).

Conservation Status

The 2008 IUCN Red List assessment classified *P. tattersalli* as Endangered (EN). The major threats to its survival are slash-and-burn agriculture, uncontrolled grass fires, removal of trees and poles for housing and firewood, logging of precious hardwoods, gold mining, and some hunting. Now, however, hunting has perhaps become the most significant threat, especially by itinerant gold miners. Although gold miners were not observed to hunt this animal in 1995 during a period of intense mining activity (indeed, they even fed these animals every day in their camps near Daraina, R. A. Mittermeier, pers. obs.), more recent information indicates that these miners may have become a problem, at least in some areas.

A new conservation site to protect this species was declared in the Daraina region in June 2005, thanks largely to the efforts of Association Fanamby, a Malagasy non-governmental organization, and Conservation International. This 57,000-ha Loky-Manambato Protected Area is being managed by Association Fanamby in collaboration with the Ministry of Water and Forests (Association Fanamby, 1998; Vargas *et al.*, 2002).

As of 2010, this species was not being kept in captivity (I. J. Porton, pers. comm.).

Where to See It

This sifaka is most readily seen in forests south of the town of Antsahampano, between Daraina (about 10 km east) and the village of Andranotsimaty (Garbutt, 2007). There is basic accommodation at the headquarters of Association Fanamby, and trips to the area can be arranged by tour operators based in Antananarivo or Antsiranana (= Diégo-Suarez), or through Fanamby itself. However, it is best to go in the dry season, since the two-hour drive from Vohémar to Daraina in good conditions can turn into five or six hours during the rainy season.

Indriidae

Fig. 10.55: Golden-crowned or Tattersall's sifaka (*Propithecus tattersalli*), Daraina (photo by E. E. Louis Jr.).

Propithecus diadema Bennett, 1832
Diademed Sifaka

Other English: Diademed Simpona
French: Propithèque à diadème
German: Diademsifaka
Malagasy: Simpona, Simpony, Sadabe (Tsinjoarivo)

Identification

Propithecus diadema is the largest of the sifakas, and rivals the indri for the title of largest living lemur. It has a head-body length of 50–55 cm, a tail length of 44–50 cm, an overall length of 94–105 cm, and a weight of 6.0–8.5 kg (Glander *et al.*, 1992; Powzyk, 1996; Smith and Jungers, 1997; Lehman *et al.*, 2005a; K. Glander, pers. comm.). Comparing maximum weights for the largest diademed sifakas and the largest indris, it appears that the largest indris exceed the largest diademed sifakas in size by a kilogram or less, so these two species are quite similar in size. *Propithecus diadema* is also one of the most colorful and attractive of all the lemurs. Its coat is long and silky. The forehead, cheeks and throat are white, and a black crown may extend down the nape of the neck. The muzzle is short, the dark gray to black face is bare, and the eyes are reddish-brown. The shoulders and upper back are slate-gray, the lower back lightening to silver-gray. The flanks and tail are pale gray to white, and the base of the tail is often golden-yellow. The arms and legs are orange to yellow-gold, and the hands and feet are black. The ventral coat typically is white to pale gray. Males possess a large reddish-brown cutaneous gland in the middle of the throat, and a perianal patch of similar color is also believed to be glandular (Petter, 1962a). This large and distinctive sifaka cannot be confused with any other lemur.

Geographic Range

Despite the fact that the precise limits of its range are unknown, the diademed sifaka is believed to be the most widely distributed member of the genus *Propithecus*. It occurs in Madagascar's eastern rain forests from the Mangoro and Onive rivers north to the Mananara River, inhabiting forests from 200–1,600 m. Historically, its range extended farther north to the Antanambalaina River (Petter *et al.*, 1977; Petter and Petter-Rousseaux, 1979; Tattersall, 1982), but the species can no longer be found there (D. Meyers, pers. comm.). At the southern limit of its range there may be some hybridization between *P. diadema* and *Propithecus edwardsi* (Andriaholinirina *et al.*, 2004).

An unusual population of *P. diadema* can be found in the forests of Tsinjoarivo in south-central Madagascar, about a four-hour drive from Antananarivo. The Tsinjoarivo animals are quite variable in color, including even at least one all black individual, which indicates that they may represent a hybrid population between *P. diadema* and *P. edwardsi*. One preliminary genetic study (Mayor *et al.*, 2004) did not find sufficient evidence to warrant its recognition as a new taxon, whereas another more recent study indicated that it is in fact distinct (Y. Rumpler, pers. comm.). We await a final decision on this population, but in the meantime continue to include it within *P. diadema*. Illustrations of it are given in Figures 10.59 and 10.60).

Fig. 10.56: A male diademed sifaka (*Propithecus diadema*), Lemur Island, Hotel Vakona, Andasibe (photo by R. A. Mittermeier).

Indriidae

Natural History

This species has only once been studied for a significant period of time (Powzyk, 1996, 1997; Powzyk and Mowry, 2003). It is diurnal, appears to require intact rain forest, and lives in multi-male/multi-female groups of eight or more individuals that defend home ranges of 20–50 ha by means of scent-marking. The diet consists mainly of fruits, seeds, flowers and young leaves, their respective proportions varying according to seasonal abundance. The number of plant species used each day often reaches 25 or more, including

Fig. 10.57: Male diademed sifaka (*Propithecus diadema*) hopping on the ground, Lemur Island, Hotel Vakona, Andasibe (photos by R. A. Mittermeier).

Indriidae

fruits of two preferred species, the seeds of which contain significant levels of alkaloids. Compared to the sympatric, similar-sized *Indri indri*, *P. diadema* eats higher-energy foods and spends more time actively patrolling and defending its territories. The mean daily path length of 1,629 m for *P. diadema* can be compared to 774 m for *I. indri*.

Conservation Status

The 2008 IUCN Red List assessment classified *P. diadema* as Endangered (EN). The principal threat to its survival is habitat loss due to slash-and-burn agriculture, logging, and mining. However, it is also severely affected by hunting in many parts of the range, even in existing protected areas (Green and Sussman, 1990; Mittermeier *et al.*, 1992; Irwin and Ravelomanantsoa, 2004).

The diademed sifaka occurs in three national parks (Mananara-Nord, Mantadia, and Zahamena), two strict nature reserves (Betampona and Zahamena), three special reserves (Ambatovaky, Mangerivola, and Marotandrano) and in the recently-created Anjozorobe-Angavo Protected Area (Nicoll and Langrand, 1989; Britt *et al.*, 1999; CBSG, 2002; Powzyk and Mowry, 2003). It has also been successfully reintroduced into the Analamazaotra Special Reserve at Andasibe; it once occurred naturally in this area but was extirpated 30–40 years ago. The reintroduction was carried out by E. E. Louis Jr. and a team of Malagasy researchers in 2007 with animals rescued from the nearby Ambatovy mine site.

Additional populations have been identified in two classified forests (Andriantantely and Tsinjoarivo), the Marokitay Forest Reserve, and in the unprotected forests of Anosibe an'ala, Didy, Iofa, Maromiza and Sandranantitra (Lehman and Wright, 2000; Conservation International, 1999; Andriamasimanana *et al.*, 2001; Andriaholirina *et al.*, 2004; Garbutt, 2007). The Tsinjoarivo Classified Forest has been recommended as a new protected area, based on the presence of the unusual population of diademed sifakas found there.

As of 2010 only two individuals of this species were found in captivity, one in the Duke Lemur Center in Durham, North Carolina USA, and the other on Lemur Island, part of the Hotel Vakona in Andasibe, Madagascar (I. J. Porton, pers. comm.).

Where to See It

The diademed sifaka is rare, and difficult to see in the wild. However, in recent years the number of opportunities has increased, with the best place to see it now being

Propithecus diadema

Fig. 10.58: Illustration of a diademed sifaka from Volume 9 of Grandidier's monumental work on Madagascar.

Mantadia National Park. Local guides from the Association des Guides d'Andasibe have habituated several groups at km 15, and finding them is not difficult if accompanied by these experienced guides. This site is 15 km north of Andasibe (= Périnet) and can be included in a visit to see the indris at Analamazaotra. The trip can be arranged through any Madagascar tour operator, Madagascar National Parks, or the Association des Guides d'Andasibe.

Indriidae

Fig. 10.59: An unusual form of the diademed sifaka (*Propithecus diadema*) from the Tsinjoarivo region of central-eastern Madagascar (photo by R. A. Mittermeier).

It can now also be seen quite easily in the main indri viewing area in Analamazaotra, thanks to the above-mentioned reintroduction program, and in the new protected area of Anjozorobe-Ankavo, located on the high plateau, about a 90-minute drive from Antananarivo, and managed by Fanamby.

Indriidae

Fig. 10.60: Another individual of the unusual form diadema sifaka from the Tsinjoarivo region of central-eastern Madagascar (photo by M. Irwin).

Propithecus edwardsi A. Grandidier, 1871
Milne-Edwards' Sifaka

Other English: Milne-Edwards' Simpona
French: Propithèque de Milne-Edwards
German: Milne-Edwards' Diademsifaka
Malagasy: Simpona, Simpony

Identification

Propithecus edwardsi is a large dark sifaka. It has a head-body length of 42–52 cm, a tail length of 41–48 cm, a total length of 83–100 cm, and a weight of 5.0–6.5 kg (Glander *et al.*, 1992; Lehman *et al.*, 2005a). Its dorsal coat is dense and dark, varying from chocolate-brown to almost black on the head, upper body, limbs, and tail. Bilateral whitish patches of varying extent grade into the darker surrounding fur on the back and flanks, sometimes meeting along the spine. The ventral coat is equally dark, sometimes paler around the area of the chest, but less dense than the dorsal coat. The face is bare and the skin is dark gray to black, as are the ears that are barely discernible above the dark fur of the head. The eyes are orange-red. This species is very distinctive and cannot be confused with any other sympatric species.

In the past, some authors recognized another closely-related sifaka subspecies from the forests of Nandihizana, an animal described as *Propithecus diadema holomelas* Günther, 1875. It was all black in color except for a dark brown patch at the base of the tail. Tattersall (1986) regarded *P. d. holomelas* as nothing more than a color variant of *P. edwardsi* (formerly *P. d. edwardsi*). On the other hand, Groves and Helgen (2007) found that animals fitting the *holomelas* description were generally smaller in size, and preferred to keep the question of its validity open. Unfortunately, sifakas are now gone from this region and no similarly-colored animals have been found elsewhere, making it difficult to determine whether or not this animal is (or was) a distinct taxon.

Geographic Range

Milne-Edwards' sifaka is found in the rain forests of southeastern Madagascar. The Mangoro and Onive rivers are the northern limits of its present range and the Rienana River in Andringitra National Park is its southern limit. Its former range probably extended further south to the Manampatrana River (Tattersall, 1982), but populations in that region appear to have been extirpated. Andriaholinirina *et al.* (2004) found apparent intermediates between *P. diadema* and *P. edwardsi* at Anosiben 'Ifody, on the left bank of the upper Mangoro River, whereas typical *P. edwardsi* were observed further south along this river where it turns east towards the sea.

Natural History

Field studies of *P. edwardsi* have been carried out at Ranomafana National Park (Wright *et al.*, 1987, 1997; Wright, 1995, 1998; Hemingway, 1995, 1996). There it is found in primary and secondary forests at middle to high elevations (600–1,600 m). The typical group size is 3–9, and groups range over areas of 100–250 ha. Population density estimates are relatively low at 8 individuals/km². There are healthy populations south of Ranomafana National Park as well, but densities are also very low.

Indriidae

Fig. 10.61: Milne-Edwards' sifaka (*Propithecus edwardsi*), Ranomafana National Park (photo by R. A. Mittermeier).

Infants typically are born in June and July. They transfer from their mother's belly to her back after about three to four weeks, and ride comfortably there at about two months of age. Infant mortality has been calculated at almost 50% before the age of one year. Predation, especially by the fossa (*Cryptoprocta ferox*), is a significant cause of mortality, but some infant losses are also attributable to infanticide by unrelated male sifakas.

The diet consists mostly of leaves, fruit, seeds, and flowers, with approximately a dozen different plant species being sampled each day. However, dietary composition appears to vary significantly, not only from month to month but also from year to year (Hemingway, 1995, 1996).

Conservation Status

The 2008 IUCN Red List assessment classified *P. edwardsi* as Endangered (EN). Habitat destruction for slash-and-burn agriculture and also for logging and gold mining are the main threats, and sometimes take place even in protected areas. Hunting is also a problem, with shotguns, blowguns and slingshots used as weapons to bring down these animals (P. C. Wright, pers. comm.). This species is known to occur in two national parks (Andringitra and Ranomafana) (Nicoll and Langrand, 1989; Sterling and Ramarason, 1996). It may also occur in Andohahela National Park (O'Connor *et al.*, 1986, 1987), but

Indriidae

Fig. 10.62: Milne-Edwards' sifaka (*Propithecus edwardsi*), Ranomafana National Park (photo by R. A. Mittermeier). Note the presence of flies, which can be a problem for this species at certain times of the year.

this has not yet been verified (Feistner and Schmid, 1999). The Ranomafana National Park population is estimated at 4,500 and the total population for the species at 9,000 (P. C. Wright pers. comm.). Populations in unprotected forests north of Ranomafana include those near the villages of Kirisiasy, Marofotsy, Fandriana and Marolambo (Irwin *et al.*, 2000; Lehman and Wright, 2000; E. E. Louis Jr., pers. obs.). The forests of Marofotsy should be added to Ranomafana National Park. In addition, a number of forest reserves in eastern Fianarantsoa Province still harbor populations of *P. edwardsi* and these could be included in a conservation corridor linking Ranomafana and Andringitra National Parks (Mittermeier *et al.*, 1994; P. C. Wright, pers. comm.).

As of 2010, this species was not being kept in captivity (I. J. Porton, pers. comm.).

Where to See It

The best place to see this species is Ranomafana National Park, where it has been studied for several years and where a number of groups have been habituated. Finding it is relatively easy with the help of local guides, and virtually guaranteed if one devotes two days to the visit. Another excellent site is the forestry station of Ialatsara, 6 km north of Ambohimasoa on the main road from Antananarivo to Fianarantsoa. This site has a tented camp and several habituated sifaka groups that are readily observed.

Fig. 10.63: Milne-Edwards' sifaka (*Propithecus edwardsi*), Ranomafana National Park (photo by P. Oxford/naturepl.com).

Indriidae

Propithecus candidus A. Grandidier, 1871
Silky Sifaka

Other English: Silky Simpona
French: Propithèque soyeux
German: Seidensifaka
Malagasy: Simpona, Simpona fotsy, Simpony

Identification

Propithecus candidus is a large white sifaka from northeastern Madagascar. It has a head-body length of 48–54 cm, a tail length of 45–51 cm, a total length of 93–105 cm, and a weight of 5.0–6.0 kg (Lehman *et al.*, 2005a). Males and females are similar in size. The pelage is long and silky, which gives this species its common English name. It is a truly remarkable and attractive creature that looks more like a plush toy than a real animal. In some individuals, silver-gray tints may appear on the crown, back and limbs, and the pygal region (at the base of the tail) is sometimes yellow. The muzzle and face are bare, the skin a mix of pink and black, with some individuals having all pink and some all black faces. The tips of the naked black or pink ears protrude just beyond the white fur of the head and cheeks. This species does not occur with any other sifaka and cannot be confused with any other lemur within its range.

The silky sifaka may be the only member of its genus to show extreme individual variation in partial skin pigmentation loss, known as leucism. Although all infants are believed to be born with predominantly black faces, with age some individuals lose their pigmentation and show varying degrees of pink patches. The first western explorer to observe the silky sifaka (Alfred Grandidier, in 1871) believed that it was an albino subspecies of the diademed sifaka (*Propithecus diadema*). We now know that silky sifakas are not albinos. All individuals have some skin pigment, and photo-phobic individuals have never been observed (Milne-Edwards and Grandidier, 1875; Cousins, 2007).

Unlike *P. perrieri* and *P. edwardsi*, where adult males and females are difficult to distinguish, adult male and female *P. candidus* can be readily distinguished from one another by the color of the fur on the upper chest. Adult males have a large brown patch on their chest that results from scent-marking with the sternal-gular gland. As rates of male scent-marking increase during the mating season, the patch on the male's chest becomes larger and may even cover the entire front torso to the abdomen (Patel, 2006a).

Geographic Range

The silky sifaka has a very restricted range in northeastern Madagascar that includes the humid forest belt extending from Maroantsetra to the Andapa Basin and the Marojejy Massif (Tattersall, 1982). Most of the remaining population is found in the humid, mountainous forests in Marojejy National Park and Anjanaharibe-Sud Special Reserve. Currently, Marojejy is the northern limit of the species' distribution, although historic range maps suggest that it once occurred as far north as the Bemarivo River, near Sambava (Milne-Edwards and Grandidier, 1875). The

Fig. 10.64: Silky sifaka (*Propithecus candidus*), Marojejy National Park (photo by I. Relanzón).

Indriidae

Androranga River may be the northeastern range limit in the Tsaratanana Corridor, though further surveys are needed to confirm this. The Antainambalana River in the Makira Forest Protected Area is currently regarded as the southern limit (Patel and Andrianandrasana, 2008; Rasolofoson *et al.*, 2007a, 2007b; Wilmé and Callmander, 2006). The northeastern range limit of this species in Makira was only recently established, when a few groups were found in the Antohaka Lava Forest. Informal reports suggest that the unprotected Maherivaratra Forest, outside northeastern Makira, may also contain silky sifakas (E. R. Patel, pers. comm.).

Natural History

Propithecus candidus has been discussed in several survey reports (Safford *et al.*, 1989; Duckworth *et al.*, 1995; Sterling and McFadden, 2000), and two short-term studies (Kelley and Mayor, 2002; Queslin and Patel, 2008). A 14.5-month study was carried out by E. R. Patel in Marojejy National Park, including a detailed 12-month dietary study (E. R. Patel, pers. comm.). In Marojejy and in Anjaraharibe-Sud, animals are encountered in mountainous primary rain forest at altitudes between 700 and 1,900 m. They may sometimes be found in sclerophyllous forest, near their highest elevations. The southernmost silky sifakas in Makira adjacent to the Antainambalana River inhabit an unusual, low-elevation forest fragment at altitudes of 300 to 600 m. Despite its extreme rarity, this species has the greatest elevational range of any sifaka.

As with other eastern sifakas, *P. candidus* has a variable social structure, living in both pair-bonded and multi-male/multi-female groups of up to nine individuals. Home range size varies by site, ranging from 34 to 47 ha (Patel and Andrianandrasana, 2008).

Approximately 25% of the day is spent feeding and 44% resting, with 31% being devoted to other activities such as social behavior, travelling, and sleeping. Long bouts of terrestrial play involving adults are not uncommon (Patel, 2006b). Rates of aggression are low, and mainly occur during feeding. Females have feeding priority over males. Like other eastern sifakas, *P. candidus* is a folivorous seed predator that eats a very large variety of plant species. A recent 2-month study documented feeding from 76 species in 42 families (mainly trees, but many lianas and epiphytes as well). The most important plant families in the diet were Moraceae, Fabaceae, Myrtaceae, Clusiaceae, and Apocynaceae. Fruit from *Pachytrophe dimepate*, seeds from *Senna* sp., young leaves from *Plectaneia thouarsii*, and fruit from *Eugenia* spp. were the four foods most preferred, and

Fig. 10.65: Close-up of a silky sifaka (*Proptihecus candidus*) from the Anjanaharibe-Sud Special Reserve (photo by R. A. Mittermeier). Note the mottled face and muzzle, a feature common in some individuals of this species.

Indriidae

accounted for roughly 37% of total feeding time. Overall, 52% of feeding time was spent eating leaves, 34% fruit, and 11% seeds. Flowers and soil were eaten rarely (Queslin and Patel, 2008). Preliminary results from an ongoing, detailed 12-month dietary study suggest general similarity in diet with *P. diadema* and *P. edwardsi* (E. R. Patel, pers. comm.).

Mating is believed to occur on a single day each year in December or January, with infants born in June or July. Generally, females give birth to a single infant every two years; only occasionally in consecutive years (Patel, 2006b). Infants initially grasp the fur on their mother's belly, and about four weeks later begin to ride jockey-style on their mother's back. As is typical of *Propithecus*, all group members interact affiliatively with infants.

Fig. 10.66: Silky sifaka (*Propithecus candidus*), one of the most endangered primates of the world, Marojejy National Park (photo by I. Relanzón). Note the brown stain of the chest from the sebaceous gland found only in males.

Indriidae

Grooming is the most frequent form of non-maternal infant care, followed by playing and occasional carrying as well as nursing in a few remarkable instances (Patel, 2007a). Although in eastern sifakas generally both male and female group members disperse, female dispersal has not yet been observed in this particular species (E. R. Patel, pers. comm.).

The fossa (*Cryptoprocta ferox*) is the only documented predator of the silky sifaka, other than human beings (Patel, 2005). No aerial predation attempts by raptors have ever been observed, although these sifakas sometimes stare skyward and emit "aerial disturbance" roars in the presence of the Madagascar buzzard (*Buteo brachypterus*) (Patel *et al.*, 2003a). Acoustic analyses have revealed sex and individual differences in the structure of the silky sifaka *zzuss* vocalization (Patel *et al.*, 2005b, 2006). The adult vocal repertoire has seven different calls, a much smaller number than has been observed in *Lemur catta* and *Varecia* (Patel *et al.*, 2005c).

Eastern sifakas have several scent-marking glands that include a sebaceous chest gland only found in males, and mixed apocrine-sebaceous genital glands in both sexes. Sifakas, in contrast to *Eulemur*, do not allomark by directly scent-marking conspecifics. Females scent-mark trees by rubbing their genital glands against them in a rhythmic vertical motion. Males, for their part, scent-mark trees in several different ways, by rubbing them with their chest gland, with their genital glands, or with a combination of the two. Males routinely gouge trees with their toothcombs just prior to chest-marking, which leaves long-lasting visible marks (Patel and Girard-Buttoz, 2008). Both sexes often urinate while scent-marking. Although males scent-mark two or three times as often as females, female scent marks are responded to far more often and more quickly than male marks. Males commonly overmark a female's mark, followed by males overmarking the scent-marks of other males (Patel, 2006a; Patel and Girard-Buttoz, 2008; Ritchie and Patel, 2006).

Conservation Status

The IUCN Red List assessment of 2008 classified *P. candidus* as Critically Endangered (CR). This is one of the rarest and most endangered sifakas, and has been on the list of the world's 25 Most Endangered Primates (produced jointly by the IUCN/SSC Primate Specialist Group, the International Primatological Society, and Conservation International) since its inception in 2000 (Patel, 2009a). The world population is believed to be only a few hundred animals, and it is threatened by habitat destruction and hunting, even in protected areas. There is no local taboo or "fady" against eating this species, as exists for the indri in at least some parts of its range (Patel *et al.*, 2005). The situation has become even more severe since the political upheavals of early 2009. The majority of the silky sifakas occur in Marojejy National Park and Anjanaharibe-Sud Special Reserve. Marojejy was one of the first protected areas to be hit by a wave of illegal rosewood logging shortly after the coup that ousted President Marc Ravalomanana. It is very possible that hunting of this species accompanied these incursions, but this remains to be confirmed (Patel, 2007b; Patel, 2009).

A few groups have also been found in the Makira Forest Protected Area and in the Betaolana Corridor. Several unprotected forest fragments southeast of Marojejy, such as Andranomenabe and Maherivaratra, probably contain a few silky sifaka groups and require additional surveying. Efforts should be made to stop the hunting of sifaka in Marojejy and elsewhere.

Silky sifakas have never survived long in captivity, and there are none in zoos (I. J. Porton, pers. comm.).

Indriidae

Where to See It

This sifaka, rare and localized as it is, is relatively easy to see in Marojejy National Park. A visit of at least one night, and preferably two or three, is nevertheless required to find it. Comfortable bungalows and kitchen facilities are available at each of the three main camps. These can be reserved at park headquarters located on the main road between Andapa and Sambava. From the headquarters one drives in as far as the village of Mandena if road and bridge conditions permit, and from there it is about another 2.5-km walk to the park entrance itself and another 4.5 km to the first campsite, Camp Mantella. From there it is another 2 km to Camp Marojejia, which is the best location for finding the silky sifaka. This camp is situated in the transition from lowland to montane rain forest, and must be one of the most beautiful in Madagascar. A large, covered dining area is perched on a mountainside with views overlooking sheer rock outcrops and lush vegetation.

This species may also be seen in the northwest portion of the park in the direction of Doany, but this site remains far off the traditional tourist circuit and requires expedition-level preparations. Other remote locations are in the Befingotra Forest of the Anjanaharibe-Sud Specieal Reserve, as well as in the Andaparaty Forest of Makira.

Propithecus diadema (var. sericeus).

Fig. 10.67: Illustration of a silky sifaka from Volume 9 of Grandidier's multi-volume work on Madagascar.

Propithecus perrieri Lavauden, 1931
Perrier's Sifaka

Other English: None
French: Propithèque de Perrier
German: Schwarzer Diademsifaka, Perrier's Sifaka
Malagasy: Radjako, Ankomba Joby

Identification

   Propithecus perrieri is a medium-sized black sifaka from a very limited region of northern Madagascar. It has a head-body length of 43–47 cm, a tail length of 42–45 cm, a total length of 85–90 cm, and a weight of 4.3–5.0 kg (Lehman *et al.*, 2005a). The dorsal coat is dense, silky and black, while the ventral coat is shorter and tends to have a rosy-brown tint. The face is bare and black, the eyes are orange-red, and the ears, naked in some and furred in other individuals, are largely concealed (Tattersall, 1982; Mittermeier *et al.*, 1994). This species cannot be confused with any other lemur within its range and is not sympatric with any other sifaka.

Geographic Range

   Perrier's sifaka has a very restricted range in northern Madagascar that includes the Analamerana and Andrafiamena Massifs, and the eastern edge of the Ankarana forests (Petter *et al.*, 1977; Tattersall, 1982; Hawkins *et al.*, 1990; Rasoloharijaona *et al.*, 2005; M. Banks, pers. comm.; D. Meyers, pers. comm.).

Natural History

   This species is an inhabitant of tropical dry lowland forest at elevations less than 500 m. Groups range in size from 2 to 6 individuals and home ranges approach 30 ha (Meyers and Ratsirarson, 1988, 1989; Mayor and Lehman, 1999). Population density in the Analamerana Special Reserve is estimated at 3 individuals/km² (Banks, 2005). Leaves, both young and mature, fruits, stems and flowers compose the bulk of the diet, and at least a dozen different species of plants from nine families were identified as food sources during a very short study (Meyers and Ratsirarson, 1989). Unlike related species, Perrier's sifaka routinely descends from trees to cross open habitat and to drink water from riverbeds (Mayor and Lehman, 1999). The fossa (*Cryptoprocta ferox*) is an important predator of this species.

Conservation Status

   The 2008 IUCN Red List assessment classified *P. perrieri* as Critically Endangered (CR). It is one of the rarest and most endangered lemurs, and indeed one of the most endangered primates in the world. The total population could be as few as 500 and the effective breeding population only 125 individuals. The species is most abundant in semi-evergreen forests on sandstone that comprise only one quarter of its remaining habitat, and

Indriidae

Fig. 10.68: Perrier's sifaka (*Propithecus perrieri*), Analamerana Special Reserve (photo by R. A. Mittermeier).

these forests are also under the heaviest pressures from humans. Slash-and-burn agriculture is the greatest threat, and this is exacerbated by fires set to increase pasture, by logging, by cutting of trees for charcoal production, and by forest destruction by itinerant miners. Local hunting may be a problem as well, especially considering the tiny remaining population (Fowler *et al.*, 1989; Harcourt and Thornback, 1990; Mayor and Lehman, 1999).

The only protected area where Perrier's sifaka is found for certain is the Analamerana Special Reserve (Ganzhorn *et al.*, 1996/1997), but a small population may still occur in the eastern section of the Ankarana National Park, which is connected through a series of forest patches to populations at Andriafiamena and Analamerana. It has recently been seen in unprotected forest patches between Analamerana and Ankarana (D. Meyers, pers. comm.). It also occurs in the Andavakoera Classified Forest, but probably in very low numbers.

There is an urgent need for a full-time, long-term scientific presence in the Analamerana Special Reserve, as well as an expansion of this protected area to include the forests of Andriafiamena and a connection to Ankarana. Unfortunately, it appears that some logging is taking place in Andriafiamena, but Association Fanamby has been working to have this area protected. This effort should also include an education campaign in the region, as well as surveys in nearby forest patches to look for any other populations.

As of 2010, this species was not being kept in captivity (I. J. Porton, pers. comm.).

Where to See It

The best place to see Perrier's sifaka is the Analamerana Special Reserve, and especially in the Ankavanana (Antobiratsy and Ankavanana Forests), Analabe regions, and along the Bobankindro River, which bisects the reserve (E. E. Louis Jr., pers. obs.; R. A. Mittermeier, pers. obs.). Analamerana itself is not very difficult to reach, the turnoff being located about one hour south of Antsiranana (= Diégo-Suarez) on the main highway, and then another one-to-three hours depending on the final destination. However, once you turn off the secondary road driving conditions can be very poor, especially if there has recently been a heavy rain.

Excursions to the Analamerana Reserve can be arranged by local tour operators based in Antsirananana. They provide for overnight camping and will also arrange local guides and four-wheel-drive transportation. Camping overnight and using a local guide are essential, and it may be necessary to hike several hours to observe this sifaka. However, the reserve is rich in other lemurs as well, including both crowned lemurs (*Eulemur coronatus*) and Sanford's brown lemurs (*Eulemur sanfordi*), in addition to a number of nocturnal species.

Indridae

Indriidae

Fig. 10.69: Perrier's sifaka (*Propithecus perrieri*), Analamerana Special Reserve (photo by R. A. Mittermeier).

Indriidae

Fig. 10.70: Mother and infant indri photographed in the Anamalazaotra Special Reserve at Andasibe, August, 1984 (photo by R. A. Mittermeier).

Indri É. Geoffroy and G. Cuvier, 1796
Indri or Babakoto

The indri is the largest of the living lemurs, and one of the world's most spectacular flagship species. This delightful animal, which can be either black-and-white or almost entirely black, is distinguished from almost all other lemurs by its size and especially by its unique vestigial tail, the only living lemur with such a short tail. It is restricted to the northern half of the eastern rain forest region, lives in small, territorial family groups, and can reach quite high densities if not hunted by local people.

The name "indri" actually comes from the 18th century French naturalist Sonnerat, who recorded this term when his Malagasy guide pointed out an animal in the field. "Indri" is nothing more than a corruption of the Malagasy word "iry" or "ery," which simply means "there," meaning in this case "there it is." A common Malagasy name is "babakoto," which translates as "father of Koto" or "old man," and appears to be used interchangeably by the Malagasy to indicate respect for the elderly or to identify an "old fool."

The predominant fur color is black, contrasted in the darkest individuals by white patches on the crown, flanks, forelimbs and thighs, or any combination of these, and there appears to be considerable variation in pattern. In general, there is a tendency toward slightly lighter coloration in the southern part of the species' range, but the ears are always black, tufted and prominent. Groves (2001) recognizes a darker colored subspecies *I. indri indri* in the north as distinct from *I. indri variegatus* in the south. However, this differentiation into two subspecies is not supported by the genetic evidence and it does not appear to hold true in the field either, there being, for example, individuals with mixed color patterns in the Mananara region in the northern part of the range (Thalmann *et al.*, 1993). All indri young tend to be darkly colored during the first few months of their lives, the only white coloration on them being a small patch in the pygal region. The world's image of the indri comes largely from the black-and-white animals of the Analamazaotra Special Reserve at Andasibe (= Périnet), whose coloration looks like a primate version of a giant panda (*Ailuropoda melanoleuca*). However, it appears that this pied color pattern is less common than the largely or entirely black pattern found in most other places.

The indri is a folivore that subsists on a diet mostly of immature leaves, but also includes seeds, fruit and flowers. Its signature vocalization is a loud, drawn out, wailing territorial call that is one of the best known and most characteristic sounds of the Malagasy rain forest. It is heard most often during the morning hours, but can be given at any time of the day and can carry across the forest for several kilometers. It is much more frequently given in the warm rainy season than in the colder months. The adult pair in a family social group typically leads the chorus, and neighboring groups often call sequentially in response to one another.

The indri's tiny stump of a tail leads some Malagasy to believe it is related to a sacred ancestor (Powzyk and Thalmann, 2003). In some portions of its range, this belief supports local taboos against hunting the indri and helps to protect remaining populations where forest habitat is still largely intact. However, there is increasing evidence that this "fady" or taboo does not hold throughout its range, and that the animal may actually be heavily hunted in a number of areas (e.g., the Makira region, C. Golden, pers. comm.).

Indriidae

Fig. 10.71: Historical illustrations of the indri (*Indri indri*). (Top left) A plate from Shaw's *Mammalia* of 1800. (Top right) A chromolithograph from Forbes' *Handbook to the Primates* of 1896. (Lower left and lower right) Plates from Volume 9, the Indriidae, of Alfred Grandidier's *Histoire Physique, Naturelle, et Politique de Madagascar*, published in 1875.

Fig. 10.72: *Indri* postural and behavioral drawings (next page):
    a. *Indri* suspended by its arms, using a very simple arm-swinging locomotion
    b. *Indri* resting on a horizontal branch
    c-d. *Indri* leaping
    e. *Indri* feeding from a vertical clinging posture

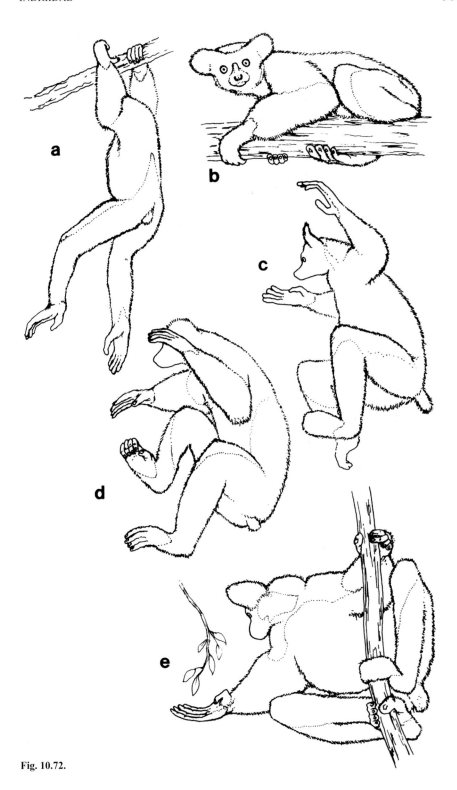

Fig. 10.72.

Fig. 10.73: Plate from *Dictionnaire pittoresque d'histoire naturelle et des phénomènes de la nature*, by Guérin-Méneville, Paris, 1833-1839.

Fig. 10.74: *Indri* **postural and behavioral drawings (next page):**
     a. Close-up of *Indri* **feeding on leaves**
     b. *Indri* **calling**
     c. *Indri* **looking up, about to leap from a vertical clinging posture**
     d. *Indri* **with infant resting in a vertical clinging posture**
     e. *Indri* **with infant resting in a sitting posture**

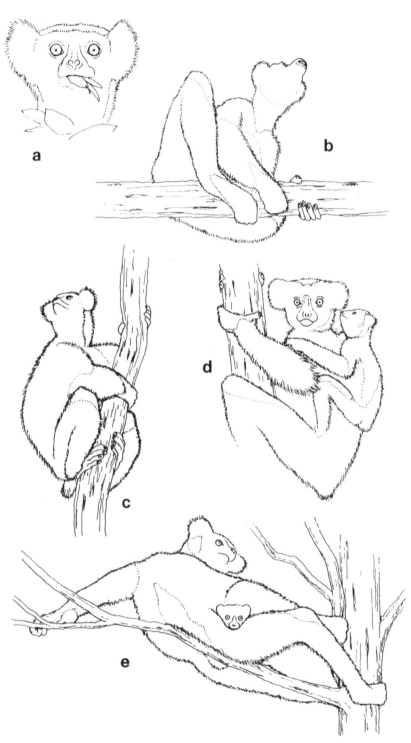

Fig. 10.74.

Fig. 10.75: Distribution of *Indri*.

Indri
Indri indri

Color variants of
Indri indri

Fig. 10.76.

Fig. 10.77: An illustration showing *Propithecus diadema* and *Indri indri* from *Das Buch Der Welt* published in Stuttgart, Germany in 1861.

L'Indri.

Publié par Pourrat F. a Paris.

Indriidae

Fig. 10.78: A hand-colored engraving of an indri (*Indri indri*) by R. Lesson, *Complements de Buffon*, published in Paris in 1838.

Indri indri (Gmelin, 1788)
Indri

Other English: None
French: Indri
German: Indri
Malagasy: Babakoto, Indry (Mananara), Endrina, Amboanala

Identification

Indri indri has a head-body length of 64–72 cm, a vestigial tail only 5 cm long, and a body weight that ranges from 6 kg to as much as 9.5 kg (Glander and Powzyk, 1998; Powzyk, 1997; E. E. Louis Jr., pers. obs.). The high end of the weight range makes it the largest of the living lemurs, but a big diademed sifaka (*Propithecus diadema*) approaches it in size. It is a typical vertical clinger and leaper, with long hind limbs compared to its trunk and forelimbs, and a preference for postures in which the trunk is held vertically. Coat color varies from predominantly black, contrasting with a white pygal patch and a broad, paler facial ring, to variegated black-and-white, the white areas corresponding to the occipital cap, a collar extending up to and beyond the ears, and the outer surfaces of the legs and lower arms (Groves, 2001). The ears are black, modestly tufted, and highly visible. The earliest indris to be described exhibited the darker color pattern, which is typical of museum specimens from Andapa and Maroantsetra, and has also been observed in wild populations from Anjanaharibe-Sud (Thalmann *et al.*, 1993; R. A. Mittermeier, pers. obs.), Makira (D. Meyers, pers. comm.), Ambatovaky, and Anjozorobe (F. Hawkins, pers. obs.).

The indri is readily located and identified by its eerie wailing song, and is unlikely to be mistaken for any other sympatric lemur (Powzyk and Thalmann, 2003). It is easily distinguished from the similar-sized, lighter-colored diademed sifaka, *Propithecus diadema*, by its prominent ears, long muzzle and vestigial tail, which contrasts strongly with the long tail of all *Propithecus* species. *Varecia variegata* also has a black-and-white color pattern but has a long tail, moves quadrupedally, and is smaller.

In the Analamazaotra Special Reserve and in the Anjozorobe-Angavo Protected Area, the male indri is slightly larger than the female, but there is no difference between the sexes in color pattern. Male and female indris can be distinguished, however, by their wailing song. Both sexes participate in the song in a coordinated manner but they differ in the presence or absence of note types, in the acoustic features of note types, and in the number of notes emitted (Giacoma *et al.*, 2010).

Geographic Range

Indri indri inhabits tropical moist lowland and montane forests of eastern Madagascar up to elevations of 1,800 m (Goodman and Ganzhorn, 2004a, 2004b). Its range extends from the Anosibe an'ala Classified Forest in the south to the Anjanaharibe-Sud Special Reserve in the north (Petter *et al.*, 1977; Tattersall, 1982; Powzyk and Thalmann, 2003). It does not occur on the Masoala Peninsula or in Marojejy National

Fig. 10.79: An indri (*Indri indri*) from the Analamazaotra Special Reserve at Andasibe (photo by R. A. Mittermeier). This is the well-known black-and-white form of the indri, typical of this region. However, darker and all black forms are prevalent in other parts of its range.

Park, despite the latter area being connected to forest less than 40 km away where the species is present. Subfossil evidence indicates that indri once occurred in the interior of Madagascar at least as far west as the Itasy Massif, southwest to Ampoza-Ankazoabo (Tattersall, 1982; Godfrey *et al.*, 1999) and north to the Ankarana Massif (Jungers *et al.*, 1995).

Natural History

The indri has been studied in the forests of Analamazaotra (Pollock, 1975a, 1975b, 1977, 1979a, 1979b, 1986a) and in the nearby Mantadia National Park (Powzyk, 1996, 1997; Powzyk and Mowry, 2003). In this region it lives in groups of 2–6 individuals, normally consisting of a monogamous adult pair, although changes in partners have been observed, and changes in group composition are quite frequent (V. Sorrentino, pers. obs.). Although groups in fragmented habitat have been reported to be larger than those in more extensive, undisturbed areas (Pollock, 1979a, 1979b; Powzyk, 1997), this is not always the case (V. Sorrentino, pers. comm.) The female appears to be the dominant member of the pair, normally feeding higher in the trees than the male, and having priority access to food sources. The diet consists primarily of immature leaves supplemented by flowers, fruit, seeds and bark, which vary in proportion according to season. Every day the indri descends to the ground to eat soil, which may help it detoxify seeds that it has eaten (Powzyk, 1997; Britt *et al.*, 2002; Powzyk and Thalmann, 2003). Although this behavior was once rarely seen by the tourist groups at Analamazaotra, it has become increasingly common in recent

Fig. 10.80: An indri (*Indri indri*) emitting its characteristic wailing call, one of the best known sounds of Madagascar's eastern rain forest, Analamazaotra Special Reserve at Andasibe (photo by R. A. Mittermeier).

Fig. 10.81: A black indri (*Indri indri*), Mananara-Nord National Park (photo by E. E. Louis Jr.). Although the indri is best known as a black-and-white animal, many populations, especially in the northern part of the range, are largely or entirely black.

years as the animals have become fully habituated to the daily tours (R. A. Mittermeier, pers. obs). Individuals at Analamazaotra and Anjozorobe also sometimes travel bipedally on the ground in the same way that Verreaux's sifakas (*Propithecus verreauxi)* do at Berenty (F. Hawkins, R. A. Mittermeier, pers. obs.). Home ranges average 18 ha in the fragmented forests of Analamazaotra, but can be as large as 40 ha in the more pristine forests of Mantadia, where day ranges of 300 to 800 m are common. Before dusk the group retires to a sleeping tree, bedding down at heights of 10–30 m, the female typically with her offspring and separated from the male by 2–50 m.

Spacing between groups may be conditioned by the famous loud morning calls, which are answered from as far as 3 km away. Indris call most during the austral summer, typically between 06:00 and 13:00 hours (and sometimes as early as 04:45 in the warmest months, R. A. Mittermeier, pers. obs.), with most activity occurring between 7:00 and 11:00 hours, and occasional bouts between 14:30 and 16:30 (Powzyk, 1997; Garbutt, 2007), but vocal activity sometimes lasts throughout the night (F. Hawkins, pers. obs.). These calling bouts appear to be effective in maintaining territorial spacing, and may help explain the relatively small degree of range overlap between neighboring groups. Moreover, acoustic-structural differences in the song of males and females can convey sex information that is potentially meaningful to the other group members or to other groups (Rendall *et al.* 2004; Norcross *et al.*, 1999; Giacoma *et al.,* 2010).

Females give birth every two to three years. Reproduction is highly seasonal, with the birth of a single offspring in May or June after a gestation period of 120–150 days. Infants ride on the mother's ventrum up to the age of four to five months, then transfer to the back. By eight months they are moving independently, but they stay close to the mother until well into their second year (Pollock, 1975a, 1975b). Reproductive maturity is reached between seven and nine years of age (Pollock, 1977a, 1977b). This slow reproductive rate means that indris, in theory, have more difficulty bouncing back from hunting pressure than smaller, more rapidly maturing species, and is a critical factor to take into account in designing conservation programs on their behalf.

Conservation Status

Indri indri was classified as Endangered (EN) in the 2008 IUCN Red List assessment. The principal threat to this species is habitat destruction for slash-and-burn agriculture, logging and fuelwood, with destruction of this kind occurring even in protected areas. However, contrary to what was believed in the past, hunting is also a major problem for the indri in certain areas. Although it was long thought to be protected by local "fady" (traditional taboos), these do not appear to be universal and it now appears that the indri is hunted even in some areas where taboos exist. In many places, these taboos are breaking down with cultural erosion and immigration, and local people often find ways to circumvent taboos even if they are still in place. For example, a person for whom eating the indri is forbidden may still hunt the animal to sell it to others, while those who may be forbidden to kill indri can still purchase them for food. Recent studies of villages in the Makira Forest indicate that indri were also hunted in the past for their skins (worn as clothing), that indri meat is prized and fetches a premium price, and that current levels of indri hunting are unsustainable (Golden, 2005). Given the enormous importance of this animal as a flagship species for conservation and as a symbol for Madagascar in general, special efforts should be made to put in place and strongly enforce a national ban on hunting.

The indri occurs in three national parks (Mananara-Nord, Mantadia and Zahamena), two strict nature reserves (Betampona and Zahamena), five special reserves (Ambatovaky,

Analamazaotra, Anjanaharibe-Sud, Mangerivola, and Marotandrano) and in the Anjozorobe-Angavo Protected Area (Nicoll and Langrand, 1989; Powzyk, 1997; Schmid and Smolker, 1998; Britt *et al.*, 1999; CBSG, 2002). The corridor between Mantadia and Zahamena has also been proposed as a new conservation site, and the Anosibe an'ala Classified Forest should be considered for the creation of a reserve as well. The indri also occurs in the Makira Forest, another proposed protected area, but hunting pressure there appears to be especially heavy (C. Golden, pers. comm.).

As of 2010, this species was not being kept in captivity (I. J. Porton, pers. comm.). Indeed, the indri is one of the few primate genera that has never been kept successfully in zoos, all previous attempts having failed after only a short period of time.

Fig. 10.82: Another black indri (*Indri indri*), this one a male from the Anjozorobe-Angavo Protected Area (photo by V. Sorrentino).

Indriidae

Where to See It

The classic site for viewing indri is the Analamazaotra Special Reserve at Andasibe (= Périnet). No trip to Madagascar is complete without a visit there to see this spectacular animal, surely one of the most attractive, appealing and unusual creatures in the Animal Kingdom. What is more, Andasibe is one of the most accessible sites in Madagascar, and can be easily reached by road from Antananarivo in two and a half hours. There are three lodges to choose from: the up-scale Vakona Hotel, the simple but comfortable Hotel Feon'ny Ala, and the quaint Mikalo Hotel, which also has a row of higher quality, recently-built chalets. Another hotel, Euphonia, is located along the main highway right before the turnoff to Andasibe, and is also a good place to stay. Employing a local guide makes finding the indri a virtual certainty. The local guides have organized themselves into three organizations, all of which can provide excellent service to visitors. The oldest is the Association des Guides d'Andasibe. The second is Association Mitsinjo, which operates its own private reserve right across the road from Analamazaotra, and the third, recently created, is the Association Tambatra. All three are a very positive force for conservation in this region.

An excellent site for seeing the black form of the indri is Anjozorobe-Ankavo, located on the high plateau about 90 minutes by car from Antananarivo. Association Fanamby has built a comfortable lodge there, and both black indri and diademed sifaka (*Propithecus diadema*) are easy to locate and observe.

Fig. 10.83: A black indri (*Indri indri*), Anjozorobe-Angavo Protected Area (photo by V. Sorrentino).

Indriidae

One of the best places to see indri in the northern part of its range is the Anjanaharibe-Sud Special Reserve, about 15 km southwest of Andapa. Unlike the Andasibe animals these are not yet habituated to human presence, so visitors should count on spending several days to ensure a sighting. They are also common in the Zahamena National Park and the Zahamena Strict Nature Reserve, but these areas are much more difficult to reach. The largest indris come from the Marotandrano Special Reserve, again an area that is very difficult to reach.

Fig. 10.84: A young female black indri (*Indri indri*), Anjozorobe-Angavo Protected Area (photo by V. Sorrentino).

Indriidae

Daubentoniidae

Fig. 11.1: Close-up of an aye-aye (*Daubentonia madagascariensis*), Duke Lemur Center (photo by R. A. Mittermeier). Note the prominent incisor teeth. The aye-aye is the only primate which, like rodents, has continuously-growing incisors.

CHAPTER 11

FAMILY DAUBENTONIIDAE Gray, 1863

Daubentonia É. Geoffroy, 1795
Aye-aye

The family Daubentoniidae has just one living species, the aye-aye (*Daubentonia madagascariensis*) and one extinct species (*Daubentonia robusta*). The living species is a very unusual nocturnal animal that differs from the other lemurs in many anatomical and behavioral specializations, among them its distinctive dental formula, the continually growing incisor teeth (which led to it being considered a rodent during part of the 19th century), the large ears that are almost certainly used to locate insect larvae in decayed wood, and the thin skeletal middle finger that is used to extract such prey. So unique is the aye-aye that it has proven difficult to determine which other lemurs are its closest relatives. Although it has been suggested that its affinities may lie with the indriids (Schwartz and Tattersall, 1985), all genetic studies (summarized in Quinn and Wilson, 2004) are in agreement that it is the sister-group to all other lemurs, to the extent that Groves (1989, 2001) and Roos *et al.* (2004) place it in the separate infraorder Chiromyiformes, distinct from the Lemuriformes.

Although only one living species of aye-aye is recognized, remains of a second, extinct species, *Daubentonia robusta*, are known from a few sites in southwestern Madagascar (Godfrey and Jungers, 2003b). The body weight of that animal is estimated at approximately 13 kg, four to five times heavier than the living species. However, despite its size, it may have fed upon similar structurally-defended resources (e.g., hard-coated seeds and wood-boring insect larvae; Sterling, 1994b), based upon the elongated incisors and post-cranial skeletal elements that have been found in subfossil remains. Teeth of *D. robusta* that appear to have been perforated for stringing and used as ornamentation also provide strong evidence that this species was hunted and possibly driven to extinction by humans (MacPhee and Raholimavo, 1988).

The aye-aye has the largest range of any living lemur. Although there have not yet been any studies of possible geographic differentiation among aye-aye populations in different parts of Madagascar, it would not be surprising to find some level of variation—especially given the extraordinary taxonomic diversity that exists in most other lemur genera (C. P. Groves, pers. comm.).

1. Haulaffe. (Psilodactylus)

Fig. 11.2: Hand-colored copper engraving of an aye-aye (*Daubentonia madagascariensis*) from Lorenz Oken's *Naturgeschichte für alle Stände*, published in Stuttgart, Germany, in 1843.

Fig. 11.3: *Daubentonia* postural and behavioral drawings (next page):
      a. Captive *Daubentonia* eating an egg using its long bony middle finger
      b. *Daubentonia* suckling an infant
      c. *Daubentonia* in an aggressive posture
      d. *Daubentonia* using its long incisor teeth to gnaw a hole in a branch
      e. *Daubentonia* listening and probing for grubs with its long, bony middle finger
        (note the position of the ears)
      f. *Daubentonia* grooming its long, bony middle finger

Daubentoniidae

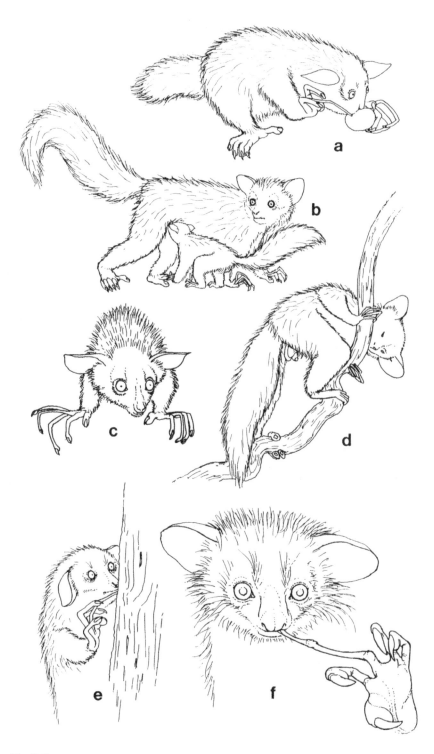

Fig. 11.3.

Fig. 11.4: Distribution of the aye-aye (*Daubentonia madagascariensis*).

Fig. 11.5: A colored engraving of the aye-aye (*Daubentonia madagascariensis*) from *Le Dictionnaire Universel d'Histoire Naturelle*, edited by A. C. V. D. d'Orbigny, published from 1839 to 1849.

Fig. 11.6: An illustration of the aye-aye (*Daubentonia madagascariensis*) from another 19th Century publication.

Aye-aye
Daubentonia
madagascariensis

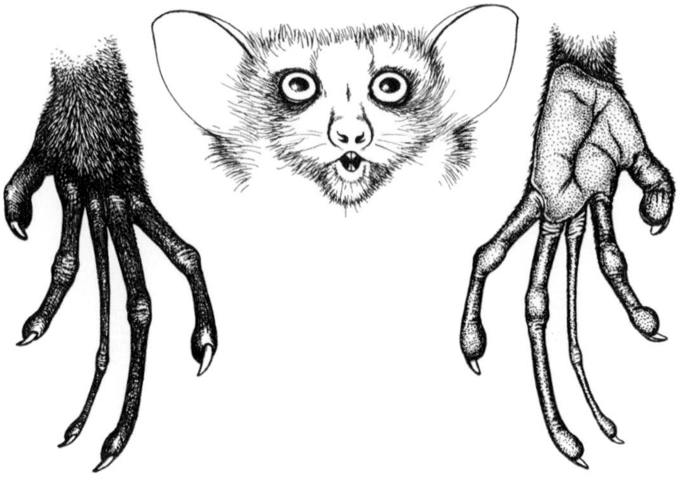

Fig. 11.7: Detailed views of the face, and dorsal (left) and ventral (right) surfaces of the left hand of *Daubentonia*. Note the slender, elongated third digit.

Daubentoniidae

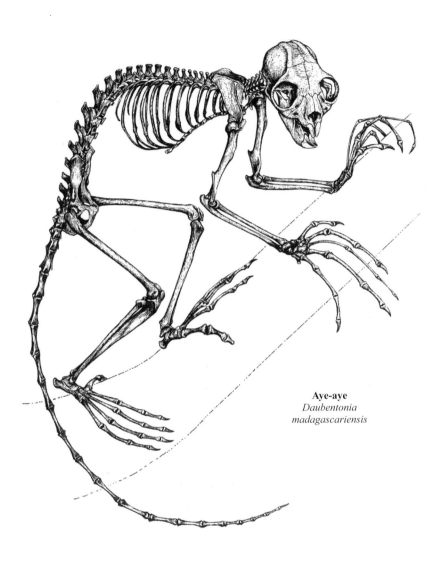

Aye-aye
*Daubentonia
madagascariensis*

Fig. 11.8: The skeleton of the most divergent of all primates.

Daubentonia madagascariensis (Gmelin, 1788)
Aye-aye

Other English: None
French: Aye-aye
German: Fingertier, Aye-aye
Malagasy: Hay-Hay, Ahay, Aiay, Bekapaky (Bemaraha),
Karakapaky (Namoroka), Fagnà (Marolambo)

Identification

The aye-aye (*Daubentonia madagascariensis*) is one of Madagascar's truly unique flagship species, and the most unusual and distinctive primate on Earth. A medium-sized lemur, with a head-body length of 30–37 cm, a tail length of 44–53 cm, a total length of 74–90 cm, and a body weight of 2.5–2.6 kg (Glander, 1994; Mittermeier *et al.*, 1994; Feistner and Sterling, 1995). The aye-aye is immediately recognizable by its prominent black, highly mobile ears, its long thin fingers and toes, and its long bushy tail. Its overall appearance is a dark grayish-brown. The dorsal coat, including that of the limbs, consists of a dense layer of short, off-white hairs overlaid by a longer, coarser layer of blackish-brown, white-tipped guard hairs, giving the animal a brindled appearance. The tail is darkly colored and its hairs are monochromatic. The ventral coat is similar to the dorsal coat in hair pattern, but not as dense, and turns whiter on the chest, throat and face. The muzzle is short and thinly haired, and the nose is pink. The elongated digits (save for the thumb) bear laterally-compressed, claw-like nails, and the third digit of the hand is particularly unusual, being skeletal in appearance. The incisors are large, rodent-like, and continuously-growing, the only primate with this feature. The mammae are inguinal.

It is very difficult to confuse the aye-aye with any other lemur, unless only the most superficial glimpse of this species is obtained in the forest at night. It is by far the largest fully nocturnal lemur, being more than double the size of *Avahi* and *Lepilemur*, and its large eyes shine back very brightly in a flashlight beam. Similarly-sized *Eulemur* species are sometimes active at night, and may briefly be thought to be aye-ayes. However, they usually move about in groups, do not have the strong eye-shine of the aye-aye, and will be quickly recognized for what they are; usually to the disappointment of the primate-watcher.

Geographic Range

Daubentonia madagascariensis was once believed to be very rare and primarily a denizen of Madagascar's eastern rain forests (Petter and Peyriéras, 1970b). However, since the 1980s it has been found in new localities in many different parts of the country (Sterling, 1994a). Recent confirmed sightings document the aye-aye's presence in the eastern forests from Ampanefana in the north to Andohahela National Park in the south, and in the western and northern forests from Montagne d'Ambre in the north to at least Tsingy de Bemaraha National Park in the south (Ganzhorn and Rabesoa, 1986a, 1986b; O'Connor *et al.*, 1986; Iwano *et al.*, 1991; Duckworth, 1993; Simons, 1993; Duckworth *et al.*, 1995; Sterling and Ramaroson, 1996; Schmid and Smolker, 1998; Sterling and Rakotoarison, 1998; Sterling and MacFadden, 2000; Sterling, 2003; Rahajanirina and

Fig. 11.9: A juvenile aye-aye (*Daubentonia madagascariensis*) on the island of Nosy Mangabe (photo by E. E. Louis Jr.).

Dollar, 2004). There are also two introduced island populations, one on Nosy Mangabe off the coast of northeastern Madagascar in the Bay of Antongil (according to Mittermeier *et al.* [1992], nine individuals introduced in 1966), and the other on "Aye-aye Island" (also called Ile Roger) at the edge of the town of Mananara-Nord, also in northeastern Madagascar (Petter, 1977; Bradt, 2007). Current opinion is that the aye-aye may be the most widely distributed of Madagascar's lemurs. Nonetheless, it is rare everywhere, and its numbers are believed to be declining with continued habitat loss and hunting.

Natural History

The aye-aye is quite adaptable and is known from a variety of habitats, including primary rain forest, deciduous forest, secondary forests, cultivated areas, dry scrub forest, coconut groves, and mangrove swamps (Sussman *et al.*, 1985; Harcourt and Thornback, 1990; Ancrenaz *et al.*, 1994; Andriamasimanana, 1994). Southern spiny forest seems to be the only habitat in which the species does not occur.

The presence of aye-aye in many areas appears to be determined largely by its primary food source, the seeds of *ramy* (*Canarium* spp.), but this is not always the case (Iwano *et al.*, 1991; Sterling, 1998). Other dietary staples include seeds of *Orania trispatha* and *Terminalia catappa*, beetle and moth larvae embedded in trees and bamboo, cankerous growths on *Intsia bijuga*, nectar from *Ravenala madagascariensis*, and a variety of crops such as coconuts, lychees, and mangos (Petter, 1977; Constable *et al.*, 1985; Sterling, 1993b, 1994b; Sterling *et al.*, 1994). Finger-tapping along the surface of branches and tree trunks helps an aye-aye locate hollow interiors and the insect larvae living in them (Erickson, 1998). It then uses its continuously growing incisors to gnaw through outer bark and its skeletal middle finger to extract the prey inside. This is sometimes done by rapidly vibrating the middle finger to extract the desired food item. Signs of aye-aye presence include holes gnawed in trees, dead wood and hard-shelled fruits.

The aye-aye spends up to 80% of the night traveling and feeding. During the day it sleeps in nests, tree forks or vine tangles (Petter and Petter, 1967; Petter, 1977). Nests may be occupied for a few days at a time and several individuals may use the same nest at different times. Males occupy much larger home ranges than females; 125–215 ha compared to 30–40 ha (Sterling, 1993). Interestingly enough, aye-ayes appear to spend more time moving on the ground than any other lemur except *Lemur catta* (Sussman, 1977; Sterling, 1993a).

Aye-ayes may not be as solitary as originally believed, with some studies suggesting foraging in tandem and differing relationships between animals of the same sex (Sterling and Richard, 1995). There does not appear to be a restricted mating season, and a single infant is produced once every two to three years (Petter and Peyriéras, 1970b).

Conservation Status

The 2008 IUCN Red List assessment classified *D. madagascariensis* as Near Threatened (NT), a status that we believe to be incorrect. Based on more recent evidence, we believe that it should now be placed back in the Endangered category. Once regarded as one of the world's most endangered mammals, the aye-aye has now been shown to be much more widespread than previously believed. Half a century ago, some experts thought it might even be extinct, until a population was discovered in the Ambato Mahambo Forest in eastern Madagascar in 1957, although that population ultimately vanished (Petter and Petter, 1967; Petter and Peyriéras, 1970b). In the mid-1960s, nine animals were trapped in coastal forests between Toamasina (= Tamatave) and Maroantsetra and introduced onto the island of Nosy Mangabe as a safety measure to prevent its extinction. Whether the species formerly existed on the island remains uncertain, but later expeditions confirmed that the animal had survived there and appeared to be reproducing (Bomford, 1976, 1981; Constable *et al.*, 1985), and this population still exists today.

Despite the aye-aye's wide distribution, it is still killed in some areas as a harbinger of evil and as a crop pest (e.g., coconuts, lychees). Habitat destruction also threatens it

Fig. 11.10: Lithograph of an aye-aye (*Daubentonia madagascariensis*) by Joseph Wolf, from Richard Owen's monograph *On the Aye-aye* (1862).

THE AYE-AYE (⅓ nat. size).

Fig. 11.11: A plate from Lydekker's *Royal Natural History*, London, 1893-1894.

throughout its range (Albignac, 1987; Harcourt and Thornback, 1990; Simons, 1993; Simons and Meyers, 2001; Koenig, 2005), with trees such as *Intsia bijugia* and *Canarium madagascariensis*, dietary staples for the aye-aye, being cut preferentially for the construction of boats, houses, and coffins (Pollock *et al.*, 1985; Iwano and Iwakawa, 1988). Recent evidence also indicates that it is hunted for food in some areas (e.g., Makira, C. Golden, pers. comm.).

Fig. 11.12: An aye-aye (*Daubentonia madagascariensis*) from Nosy Mangabe Special Reserve (photo by E. E. Louis Jr.).

Daubentonia madagascariensis is reported to occur in close to 30 protected areas, including 13 national parks (Andohahela, Andringitra, Mananara-Nord, Mantadia, Marojejy, Masoala, Midongy du Sud, Montagne d'Ambre, Ranomafana, Sahamalaza-Iles Radama, Tsingy de Bemaraha, Tsingy de Namoroka, and Zahamena), four strict nature reserves (Betampona, Tsaratanana, Tsingy de Bemaraha, and Zahamena), and 13 special reserves (Ambatovaky, Analamazaotra, Analamerana, Anjanaharibe-Sud, Ankarana, Bora, Forêt d'Ambre, Kalambatritra, Manombo, Manongarivo, Marotandrano, Nosy Mangabe, and Pic d'Ivohibe) (Nicoll and Langrand, 1989; Mittermeier *et al.*, 1994; Rakotoarison, 1995b; Sterling and Ramaroson, 1996; Schmid and Smolker, 1998; Britt *et al.*, 1999; Thalmann *et al.*, 1999; CBSG, 2002; Randriananbinina *et al.*, 2003c; Rahajanarina and Dollar, 2004; Schwitzer and Lork, 2004; N. Garbutt, pers. comm.; P. C. Wright, pers. comm.). In addition, the aye-aye has been sighted in the northeastern forests of Daraina (part of the newly-declared Loky-Manambato Protected Area) (Randrianarisoa *et al.*, 1999), as well as in the Anjiamangirana and Maroala Classified Forests (E. E. Louis Jr., pers. obs.). Although the aye-aye occurs in many protected areas, its presence is often based only on signs and infrequent sightings, so there is little understanding of population size and dynamics. There is an urgent need for a systematic census of this animal throughout its range, with the ultimate objective of developing a conservation action plan for the species.

As of 2010 there were approximately 50 aye-ayes in various zoological collections worldwide (ISIS, 2009).

Where to See It

Although seeing *Daubentonia* in the wild requires great patience and diligence, visitors to Madagascar now stand a fair chance of encountering this strange animal, once considered one of Nature's greatest rarities. Nonetheless, it is still one of the most desirable target species for the dedicated primate-watcher, and a sighting is by no means guaranteed. The easiest place to see it is on Ile Roger, or "Aye-aye Island," located just 2–3 km from the Mananara-Nord airstrip. Some 13 animals were introduced onto this 30-ha island over the course of seven years, and several animals are still to be found there. The island is mainly covered by an overgrown plantation that is being reclaimed by forest, but viewing conditions are excellent. The visitor can also see northern bamboo lemur (*Hapalemur occidentalis*) and white-fronted brown lemur (*Eulemur albifrons*) on the same trip. Good accommodation is available at Bungalows Aye-aye, located less than 100 m from the airstrip, and this facility can arrange visits to the island.

The next best chance is the island of Nosy Mangabe in the Bay of Antongil, which is easily reached by boat from Maroantsetra. There you have a good chance of seeing an aye-aye if you spend one or two nights on this small island, especially along the stretch of beach right in front of the campsite. Nosy Mangabe is included in several tour circuits, and camping facilities are available on the island.

Aye-ayes are occasionally sighted at several other tourist destinations, including the Analamazaotra Special Reserve at Andasibe, Montagne d'Ambre National Park, and Ranomafana National Park, but it is far more likely that visitors will only see signs of aye-aye, such as holes gnawed in tree bark, partially gnawed *ramy* nuts, or the occasional nest.

Fig. 11.13: An aye-aye (*Daubentonia madagascariensis*) in the Duke Lemur Center (photo by D. Haring).

Fig. 11.14: An aye-aye (*Daubentonia madagascariensis*) using its middle digit to extract food from a tree hole, Ile Roger (Aye-Aye Island), near Mananara-Nord, eastern Madagascar (photo by R. A. Mittermeier).

Fig. A.1: A view of Antananarivo from the Queen's Palace (photo by R. A. Mittermeier).

A number of cities, towns, and localities have several names, the French names that have wider use internationally and the Malagasy names that are official and are used by most of the populace. Although both French and Malagasy names are given in the text, for your convenience, we provide a partial listing here of those most commonly used.

FRENCH	MALAGASY
Tananarive	Antananarivo
Tamatave	Toamasina
Majunga	Mahajanga
Fort-Dauphin	Tolagnaro or Tolanaro
Diégo-Suarez	Antsiranana
Tuléar	Toliara
Périnet	Andasibe

APPENDIX A

MAPS OF MADAGASCAR

Fig. A.2: A topographic view of Madagascar, showing areas of forest along the coasts and the mostly deforested interior.

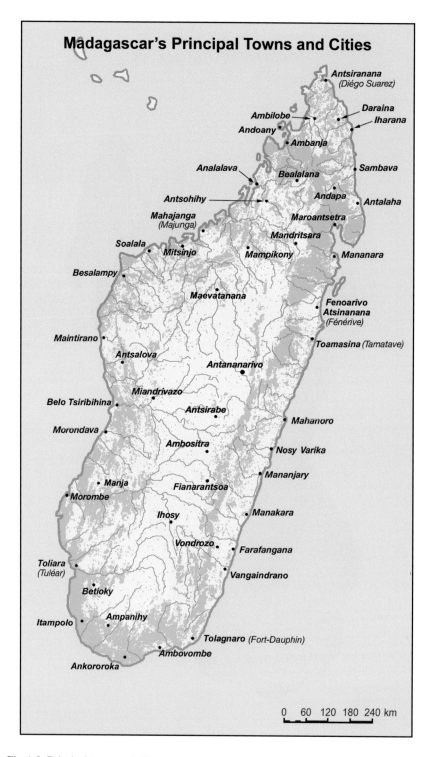

Fig. A.3: Principal towns and cities.

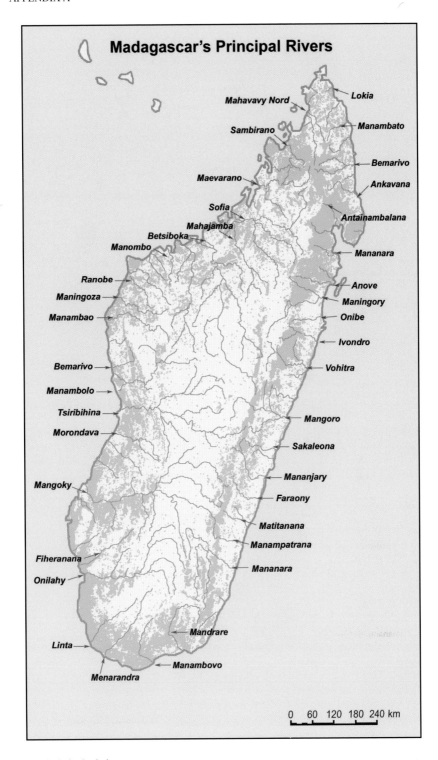

Fig. A.4: Principal rivers.

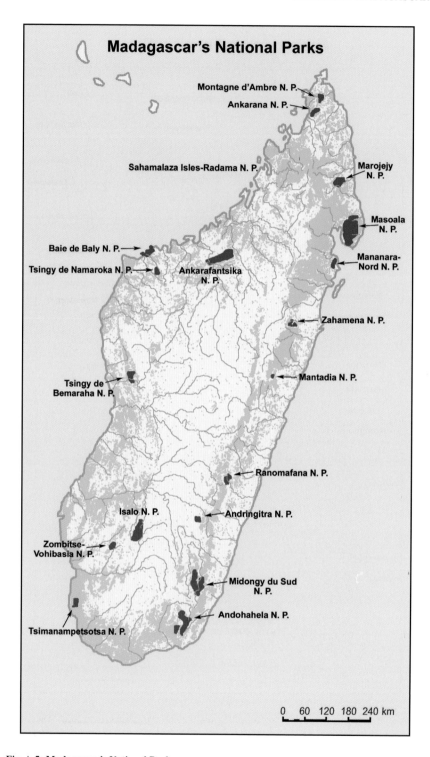

Fig. A.5: Madagascar's National Parks.

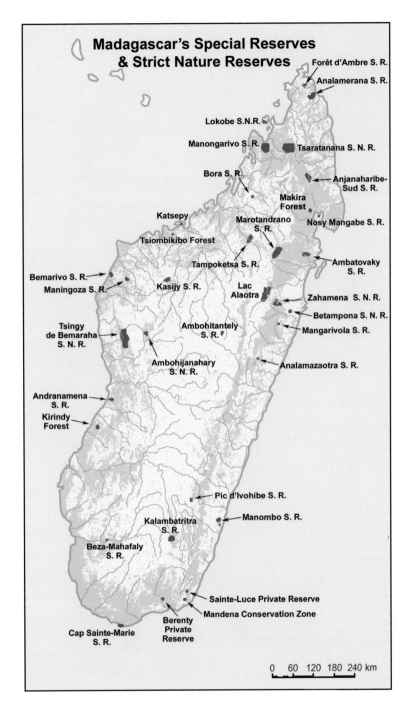

Fig. A.6: Madagascar's Special Reserves (S.R.) and Strict Nature Reserves (S.N.R.). These and the National Parks are managed by Madagascar National Parks (formerly A.N.G.A.P.). Also included in this map are four private areas, the Berenty Private Reserve, the Saint-Luce Private Reserve, the Mandena Conservation Zone, and the Kirindy Forest.

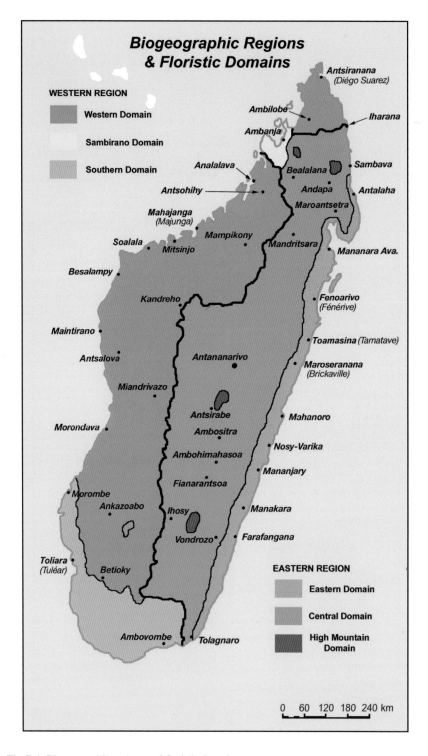

Fig. B.1: Biogeographic regions and floristic domains.

APPENDIX B

BIOGEOGRAPHIC REGIONS AND FLORISTIC DOMAINS OF MADAGASCAR

According to White (1983) in *The Vegetation of Africa*, Madagascar can be divided into two major biogeographic regions: Eastern and Western (Fig. B.1). The Eastern Region has four floristic domains: Eastern, Central, High Mountain, and Sambirano. The Western Region is divided into two domains: Western and Southern. Each domain is characterized by specific vegetation types (Guillaumet, 1984; Langrand, 1990).

Although these domains are the technical terms that are used for Madagascar's vegetation, one most often hears reference to the "Eastern Rain Forest Region," the "Western Dry Forest Region," the "Southern Spiny Forest," or "Southern Spiny Desert," and occasionally the "Sambirano Region" as well. We indicate below to which of White's regions each of these refer.

Eastern Region

Eastern Domain

Lowland rain forest, the natural vegetation between sea level and 800 m altitude, extends along the eastern coast of Madagascar from north of Sambava to Tolagnaro (= Fort-Dauphin). Average annual precipitation is between 2,000 and 3,000 mm and there is no dry season. The height of the evergreen canopy averages 20–30 m, with no emergent trees. This region is characterized by high species diversity and endemism. Eastern lowland forest is one of the most endangered vegetation types in Madagascar (only the much less extensive Sambirano and High Mountain Domains are more at risk), most of it having already been cleared. The largest remaining tracts are found in the northeastern and southeastern parts of the island. This and the eastern part of the Central Domain are the areas commonly referred to as the "Eastern Rain Forest Region" of Madagascar.

Central Domain

Forests of the Central Domain parallel those of the Eastern Domain and extend westward to Madagascar's central plateau above 800 m to altitudes of 1,300 m, and occasionally to 2,000 m. The average rainfall exceeds 1,500 mm and there is no dry season. Species diversity is as high as in the Eastern Domain; the level of endemism, however, is higher. The forest canopy is lower, between 20–25 m. Epiphytic vegetation is more plentiful and the herbaceous stratum is more developed. Most of the rain forest in the Central Domain has disappeared, but it remains Madagascar's most extensive biogeographic formation. The chief threats to what little remains in this region are slash-and-burn agriculture ("tavy") and exploitation for firewood.

High Mountain Domain

The High Mountain Domain is composed of five distinct components: Tsaratanana in the northwest, Marojejy in the northeast, Ankaratra in the central east, Andringitra in the central southeast, and Andohahela in the southeast. Forests of the High Mountain Domain

Fig. B.2: Lowland rain forest on Nosy Mangabe, part of the Eastern Domain (photo by R. A. Mittermeier).

grow at altitudes of 2,000–2,867 m. Rainfall is substantial throughout the year and there are marked diurnal and seasonal variations in temperature. Species diversity is lower here than in the Eastern and Central Domains, but species endemism is high. Fire is the chief threat to this vegetation type, although logging, especially for rosewood, has emerged as a significant threat in the past year as well, especially in Marojejy. The two largest intact blocks remaining are those at Marojejy and Tsaratanana.

Sambirano Domain

This domain consists of a small enclave of seasonal moist forest in the northwest. Together with the Tsaratanana Massif, it constitutes the northern end of Madagascar's central mountain range. Annual rainfall exceeds 2,000 mm. The Sambirano is characterized by high species diversity and endemism, and is a transition zone between Madagascar's Eastern and Western Regions. Forest canopy height is about 30 m, with some emergents. The chief threat to this vegetation type is land clearance for cultivation of rice.

Western Region

Western Domain

This is the area popularly referred to as the "Western Dry Forest Region" or the "Western Dry Deciduous Forest Region" of Madagascar. The vegetation of the Western Domain now consists of discontinuous patches of dry deciduous forests on the coastal plains and limestone plateau, ranging from sea level to 80 m. It covers the area from Antsiranana (= Diégo Suarez) in the north to Morombe in the southwest. Annual rainfall ranges from 500 to 2,000 mm, being lightest in the south and heaviest in the north. There is a marked dry season of almost seven months during which many trees in the canopy layer shed their leaves. The shrub layer is well developed and species diversity is comparable. This and the Eastern Domain are the most endangered forests in Madagascar. The principal threats to this type of vegetation are slash-and-burn cultivation, fire, and free-ranging livestock.

Southern Domain

The Southern Domain is characterized by deciduous thicket or thorn scrub. It runs southward from Morombe along the coast, covering much of the island's southern tip from sea level to 400 m. Rainfall in this region is sparse and irregular, ranging from 300 to 800 mm. The dry season is marked and very long. Forest height is low and the formations are usually impenetrable due to a high incidence of thorny vegetation. The Didiereaceae, a plant family endemic to the Southern Domain, and various species of *Euphorbia* are the dominant plant groups. Species diversity and levels of endemism are very high. This domain is popularly referred to as the "Southern Spiny Forest Region" of Madagascar.

The primary threats to the Southern Domain are collection of wood for charcoal and firewood, clearing of the natural vegetation (in particular for the production of corn), and the over-exploitation of the land by livestock, especially cattle and goats. Significant sections of this region have also been cleared in the past for sisal plantations. Finally, uncontrolled collection of ornamental and medicinal plants has also had a negative impact on some locally endemic species.

Fig. B.3: Spiny forest with a baobab (*Adansonia za*) at Hazafotsy, Andohahela National Park. Andohahela is unique in containing both Eastern and Southern Domain vegetation types, as well as significant transitional area (photo by R. A. Mittermeier).

Fig. B.4: One of the largest intact forest blocks of the High Mountain Domain is found in the region of Marojejy in northeastern Madagascar (photo by R. A. Mittermeier). Note the deforestation extending up to the borders of the national park.

Fig. B.5: Dry forest of the Montagne des Français near Antsiranana (= Diégo-Suarez), extreme northern Madagascar, Western Domain (photo by R. A. Mittermeier).

Fig. B.6: The world-renowned "Highway of the Baobabs", a.k.a. "Baobab Alley" near Morondava, an example of the Western Dry Decidious Forest (photo by R. A. Mittermeier).

Fig. B.7: Western dry deciduous forest in the wet season, Ankarafantsika National Park, at Ampijoroa (photo by R. A. Mittermeier).

Fig. B.8: Grove of *Alluaudia ascendens* in the Beza-Mahafaly region of southwestern Madagascar. These plants are members of the family Didiereaceae, which is endemic to the Southern Domain (photo by R. A. Mittermeier).

Fig. B.9: Clouds over the rain forest parcel of the Andohahela National Park, with the transitional forest of Tsimelahy (Parcel B) in the foreground, southeastern Madagascar (photo by R. A. Mittermeier).

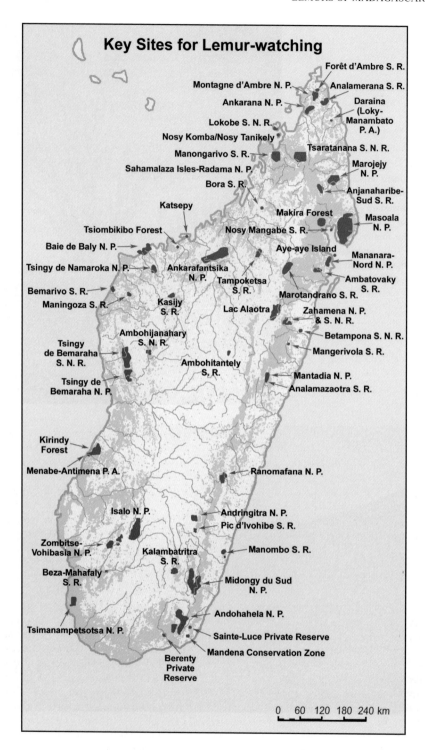

Fig. C.1: Key sites for lemur-watching.

APPENDIX C

KEY LEMUR-WATCHING SITES IN MADAGASCAR

In the "Where to See It" section for each species account, we have provided recommendations as to the best sites for seeing each lemur species and subspecies in the wild. In this appendix, we describe the majority of these sites in a little more detail. This is intended to give the reader information on how to reach a specific destination, the variety of lemurs that he or she might expect to see, and what facilities, accommodations, and services are likely to be available. For more information related to government national parks, strict nature reserves, and special reserves, we recommend you consult the Madagascar National Parks website (<www.parcs-madagascar.com>).

In this section, we also indicate priority sites for visitors to Madagascar. Those with three asterisks (***) are considered a must for the first-time lemur-watcher. Those with two asterisks (**) are also appropriate for those newcomers to Madagascar who have a bit more time, and who want to quickly increase the size of their lemur life-lists. Those sites with a single asterisk (*) are important for particular, very restricted-range species, but are more difficult to reach. Those sites without any asterisks are for the hardy adventurer who may already have a long lemur life-list, and who wants to get way off the beaten track to see new and rarely-visited places.

Sites are listed here in alphabetical order.

Ambanja*

The town of Ambanja is in northwestern Madagascar about 265 km south of Antsiranana along RN6, the popular tourist route to Nosy Be. Secondary forests near Ambanja offer opportunities to view the northern giant mouse lemur (*Mirza zaza*), which appears to be especially abundant in abandoned cashew orchards. The northern bamboo lemur (*Hapalemur occidentalis*) can also be be encountered in forests along the Sambirano River valley near the village of Benavony, southeast of Ambanja, and on the Nosy Faly Peninsula, approximately 30 km northeast of Ambanja. The Sambirano fork-marked lemur (*Phaner parienti*) can be seen in this region as well, sometimes even along the main roads at night. There are simple hotels in Ambanja and better ones, such as the Hotel Dauphin Bleu, about 25 km to the west in Ankify.

Ambatovaky Special Reserve

This special reserve covers some 60,050 ha of lowland forest, and is the largest special reserve in the country. Access is difficult and may require expedition-level preparation. What is more, there are no hotels nearby so visitors should be self-sufficient and prepared to camp. A large and varied selection of eastern rain forest taxa have been reported from this site. Among these are mouse lemurs (an unknown species of *Microcebus*), Masoala fork-marked lemur (*Phaner furcifer*), northern bamboo lemur (*Hapalemur occidentalis*), brown lemur (*Eulemur fulvus*), red-bellied lemur (*Eulemur rubriventer*), variegated black-and-white ruffed lemur (*Varecia variegata variegata*), eastern woolly lemur (*Avahi laniger*), diademed sifaka (*Propithecus diadema*), indri (*Indri indri*), and aye-aye (*Daubentonia madagascariensis*). The nearest town of any size is Soanoerana-Ivongo, which can be reached by car from Toamasina. Due to the difficulty of access, lack of tourist facilities, and various taboos which hold sway here, visitors are advised to arrange travel through an experienced Antananarivo-based ground operator.

Ambohijanahary Special Reserve

This small reserve (24,750 ha, between 800 and 1,600 m above sea level) is located in west-central Madagascar near Bongolava, between Tsiroanomandidy and Maintirano. The nearest airport is Tsiroanomandidy, a town best known for its large cattle market. The reserve provides an opportunity to see Decken's sifaka (*Propithecus diadema*) and possibly crowned sifaka (*Propithecus coronatus*), but there are presently no facilities for visitors. Trips should be organized through an Antananarivo-based tour operator, especially since there is a danger of cattle-rustlers in the area.

Ambohitantely Special Reserve

Located in east-central Madagascar on the high central plateau, about 130 km (2–3 hours by car) from Antananarivo, this reserve is easily accessed by way of RN4. Camping is possible, and there are basic hotels in the small nearby city of Ankazobe (30 km). Species that have been reported here include an as-yet unidentified form of mouse lemur (*Microcebus*), gray bamboo lemur (*Hapalemur griseus griseus*), brown lemur (*Eulemur fulvus*), and eastern woolly lemur (*Avahi laniger*). The crowned sifaka (*Propithecus coronatus*) was formerly found here as well, but was extirpated in the 1960s.

Andasibe (= Périnet): Analamazaotra Special Reserve, and Mantadia National Park ***

The Analamazaotra Special Reserve is one of the most frequently visited sites in the country, one of the easiest to reach, and one of the best places to observe lemurs in Madagascar, and indeed one of the best primate-watching sites in the world. It is located right next to the village of Andasibe, which is also sometimes referred to as Périnet (actually the name of the train station). Andasibe is about 145 km east of Antananarivo on RN2 (one of Madagascar's better roads and the highway to the eastern coastal port of Toamasina), and can be reached in 2½ to 4 hours by car, depending on traffic and stops along the way. There are various hotels in Andasibe, suitable for all budgets. A few are particularly worth mentioning; the upscale Vakona Hotel, the charming Feon'ny Ala Hotel (which has the advantage of being situated right next to the forest in which the principal indri tourist groups live), and the Mikalo Hotel, an extension of the historic old train station hotel, the Hotel de la Gare, which used to be the only place to stay prior to the 1980s. Another hotel, Euphon, is located along the main highway right before the turnoff to Andasibe, and is also a good place to stay.

Analamazaotra consists of mid-altitude montane rain forest at 900–1,250 m, but covers a mere 810 ha. However, it is immediately adjacent to the much larger Mantadia National Park and several other important forests, such as Maromizaha. An overnight stay at this site is an absolute must for the first time visitor to Madagascar, since it is the single best place in the country for seeing the indri (*Indri indri*). Two indri groups in the surrounding forest have been habituated to the presence of tourists and are easily found with the help of local guides. The Association des Guides d'Andasibe is composed of approximately 30 people from the village of Andasibe. They are excellent naturalists and can show visitors a wide variety of wildlife in a very short period of time. Guides are easily located at the entrance to the park or can be contacted through one of the hotels. The new Association Mitsinjo also has guides, as well as its own reserve in the Station Forestière d'Analamazaotra right across the street from the Analamazaotra Special Reserve. The Mitsinjo Reserve has the advantage of allowing night walks, which are sometimes prohibited in government protected areas. However, night walks along the road between the main highway and

Fig. C.2: Bungalows at the Feon'ny Ala Hotel, Andasibe. Habituated indris can sometimes be seen from the bungalows, and they are heard calling almost every morning (photo by W. R. Konstant).

Fig. C.3: Aerial view of the Feon'ny Ala Hotel in Andasibe. The forest of the Analamazaotra Special Reserve begins at the bottom of this photo (photo by R. A. Mittermeier).

Fig. C.4: Eastern rain forest habitat of the indri, Analamazaotra Special Reserve, Andasibe (photo by R. A. Mittermeier). Note the traveler's palm (*Ravenala madagascariensis*) in the foreground.

Andasibe are allowed at any time, and can be quite productive. A third guide association, Tambatra, was created recently and can also provide services. In all, there are almost a hundred guides from Andasibe working in this area.

In addition to the indri, the following lemurs are also relatively easy to observe at Analamazaotra: Goodman's mouse lemur (*Microcebus lehilahytsara*), Crossley's dwarf lemur (*Cheirogaleus crossleyi*), weasel sportive lemur (*Lepilemur mustelinus*), brown lemur (*Eulemur fulvus*), gray bamboo lemur (*Hapalemur griseus griseus*), and eastern woolly lemur (*Avahi laniger*), as well as recently re-introduced diademed sifaka (*Propithecus diadema*) and sometimes southern black-and-white ruffed lemur (*Varecia variegata editorum*), also a recent re-introduction. The sifakas are now quite easy to see in the same area as the two habituated indri groups, but the ruffed lemurs are more difficult. There is also a possibility of seeing the red-bellied lemur (*Eulemur rubriventer*) and the aye-aye (*Daubentonia madagascariensis*), although sightings of these species are much more infrequent. Finally, the rare hairy-eared dwarf lemur (*Allocebus trichotis*) is known to occur in the reserve, but is difficult to find. If this species is of interest, be sure to ask for a guide who knows where to look for it.

First time visitors to Madagascar should try to spend at least two nights in Andasibe, and should also go to the nearby Mantadia National Park, where it is now easy to see the diademed sifaka (*Propithecus diadema*) and possibly also southern black-and-white ruffed lemur (*Varecia variegata editorum*). Both of these species occur in Mantadia, and are regularly seen at km 15. In other words, with a little bit of luck and perseverance, one can see 8 to 11 different lemurs at this one site—a good start to any lemur-watching tour of Madagascar. Note that the smaller nocturnal species are much more difficult to find in the colder austral winter (June–August), so if seeing these is a priority it is better to visit during the warmer months (November–February). At present, nocturnal walks are conducted only along the road to Andasibe or in Station Forestière d' Analamazaotra, administered by Association Mitsinjo. However, we hope that Madagascar National Parks will reopen its parks and reserves to nocturnal visits in the near future.

In Mantadia, most excursions into the forest start at km 15, where there are several good trails. Birdwatching is also exceptionally good at Mantadia, especially in September and October when the ground-rollers (*Brachypteracias*) are visible, and butterfly and orchid enthusiasts can expect to find a great diversity of species as well. However, most facilities in Andasibe are heavily booked during these two months, so it is important to reserve early.

Analamerana Special Reserve **

This special reserve, covering 34,700 ha of forest between sea-level and 650 m, is located 100 km southwest of Antsiranana (= Diégo Suarez) in far northern Madagascar. Access by car up to Anivorano Ava is quite easy along RN6, but from there to the reserve requires a 4×4 vehicle. There are no facilities in the reserve, so visitors must be prepared to camp. The nearest facilities are in Ankarana National Park, located about 50 km further south along RN6, or in Antsiranana. The usual target species for lemur-watchers visiting the reserve is Perrier's sifaka (*Propithecus perrieri*), since this is the best place for seeing this very range-restricted animal. Other species that might be seen here include the Tavaratra mouse lemur (*Microcebus tavaratra*), the Montagne d' Ambre fork-marked lemur (*Phaner electromontis*), the Ankarana sportive lemur (*Lepilemur ankaranensis*), the northern bamboo lemur (*Hapalemur occidentalis*), Sanford's brown lemur (*Eulemur sanfordi*), the crowned lemur (*Eulemur coronatus*), and possibly the aye-aye (*Daubentonia madagascariensis*). It is essential to take along an experienced guide, or you will run the

Fig. C.5: Triangle palms (*Dypsis decaryi*) in the transitional parcel of Andohahela National Park. This species is found only in this parcel, and is an excellent example of a very restricted-range Malagasy endemic (photo by R. A. Mittermeier).

Fig. C.6: Transitional forest at Tsimelahy, Andohahela National Park (photo by O. Langrand).

risk of seeing little or nothing, and even getting lost. Visits to the reserve can be arranged by Le King de la Piste, a local ground operator based in Antsiranana, by Domaine de Fontenay, a lodge near Joffreville, or by an Antananarivo-based tour operator.

Andohahela National Park ***

Andohahela National Park is in extreme southeastern Madagsacar, and is composed of three non-contiguous parcels situated along the flanks of the Anosyennes Mountains. The park has excellent trails and camping facilities. Malio, the rain forest portion (Parcel 1), is a good place to see the red-collared brown lemur (*Eulemur collaris*) and the southern bamboo lemur (*Hapalemur meridionalis*) during daytime hours, especially along the road to Col de Manangotry. It is also the only place to see the Andohahela sportive lemur (*Lepilemur fleuretae*), and a number of other species have been reported as well, including an unknown mouse lemur (*Microcebus*), Milne-Edwards' sifaka (*Propithecus edwardsi*), aye-aye (*Daubentonia madagascariensis*), and possible even some form of fork-marked lemur (*Phaner*), but these need to be confirmed. This area is a few hours drive by car from Tolagnaro (= Fort-Dauphin) and arrangements can be made through all local tour operators.

Ring-tailed lemurs (*Lemur catta*) and Verreaux's sifaka (*Propithecus verreauxi*) can also be seen in the day in Ihazofotsy, the spiny forest portion of Andohahela (Parcel 2). Night hikes in this part of the park offer visitors the opportunity to view gray mouse lemur (*Microcebus murinus*), gray-brown mouse lemur (*Microcebus griseorufus*), fat-tailed dwarf lemur (*Cheirogaleus medius*), and white-footed sportive lemur (*Lepilemur leucopus*). Ihazofotsy can be reached by four-wheel drive vehicle either from Berenty or Tolagnaro (= Fort-Dauphin) in about three or four hours. The trip is a rewarding experience that takes the visitor through an attractive piece of southern spiny forest, lightly inhabited by scattered villages of the Antandroy (the traditional people of this region), but the road is very rough.

There is also an excellent trail through the transitional forest of Parcel 3 at Tsimelahy, located 8 km to the north of the main road to Amboasary (the route taken to go to Berenty). Although there are surprisingly few lemurs along this trail, it is a superb piece of transitional forest that includes baobabs (*Adansonia* spp.), *Pachypodium* spp., *Alluaudia* spp., and the triangle palm (*Dypsis decaryi*), a very distinctive species that is grown horticulturally in many parts of the world but is actually endemic to this very small transition zone. Botanically, this is one of the most interesting walks in the entire southern region of Madagascar, and it can be visited in two or three hours. The road is rough, but always passable with a four-wheel drive vehicle.

Andrafiamena

The Andrafiamena sandstone ridge is located between the Ankarana and Analamerana protected areas, two hours' drive from Diégo-Suarez. The Ampatsona Forest in Andrafiamena is home to a population of the Critically Endangered Perrier's sifaka (*Propithecus perrieri*); however, if one wants to see this species in the wild for the first time, it is easier to do so in Analamerana. Other species to be found in the Andrafiamena ridge forest include Tavaratra mouse lemur (*Microcebus tavaratra*), northern bamboo lemur (*Hapalemur occidentalis*), crowned lemur (*Eulemur coronatus*), Sanford's brown lemur (*Eulemur sanfordi*), and aye-aye (*Daubentonia madagascariensis*). Both the Ankarana sportive lemur (*Lepilemur ankaranensis*) and Daraina sportive lemur (*Lepilemur milanoii*) are apparently sympatric as well, but differentiating the two in the field is difficult. The best access is from Anjakely village, along 12 km of four-wheel-drive road south of Marotaolana (4 km southwest of the town of Anivorano-Nord). Association Fanamby is working to establish formal protected areas in the Andrafiamena forests, and neighboring Ambohipiraka-Andavakoera forest.

Andranomena Special Reserve

Covering some 6,420 ha, this special reserve is roughly 30 km north of Morondava and can be reached by car using the road to Belo-sur-Tsiribihina. Indeed, one passes through this reserve on the way to Kirindy, which is in fact a much better place for lemur-watching. Species in Andranomena include the gray mouse lemur (*Microcebus murinus*) and possibly Madame Berthe's mouse lemur (*Microcebus berthae*), Coquerel's giant mouse lemur (*Mirza coquereli*), the fat-tailed dwarf lemur (*Cheirogaleus medius*), the pale fork-marked lemur (*Phaner pallescens*), the red-tailed sportive lemur (*Lepilemur ruficaudatus*), the red-fronted brown lemur (*Eulemur rufifrons*), and Verreaux's sifaka (*Propithecus verreauxi*). Unfortunately, the reserve has been impacted by illegal logging and slash-and-burn agriculture, and there are no amenities for visitors.

Andringitra National Park *

Located 30 km east of Ambalavao in southeastern Madagascar, Andringitra is only accessible by way of a seasonal road that requires a four-wheel-drive vehicle. It is one of the most important montane areas in the country, and presents considerable altitudinal variation, from lowland rain forest to high-altitude forest and grassland amid spectacular granitic outcrops reaching 2,650 m. It is also one of the richest areas for lemurs in all Madagascar. Species known to occur here include rufous mouse lemur (*Microcebus rufus*), greater dwarf lemur (*Cheirogaleus major*), small-toothed sportive lemur (*Lepilemur microdon*), southern bamboo lemur (*Hapalemur meridionalis*), golden bamboo lemur (*Hapalemur aureus*), greater bamboo lemur (*Prolemur simus*), ring-tailed lemur (*Lemur catta*), brown lemur (*Eulemur fulvus*), red-fronted brown lemur (*Eulemur rufifrons*), red-bellied lemur (*Eulemur rubriventer*), Peyriéras' woolly lemur (*Avahi peyrierasi*), Milne-Edwards' sifaka (*Propithecus edwardsi*), and aye-aye (*Daubentonia madagascariensis*). The Critically Endangered southern black-and-white ruffed lemur (*Varecia variegata editorum*) formerly occurred here as well, but has not been reported in recent years. Camping is possible in the park and there is one permanent tented camp, Camp Catta, that is in the foothills on the western side of the massif, near Tsaranoro. Simple hotels, such as Les Bougainvilliers Hotel, are also found in Ambalavao.

Anjajavy ***

Located on a remote peninsula south of Analalava, the privately-run Anjajavy Hotel protects a 450-ha area of dry deciduous forest, limestone outcrops, and mangroves. Brown lemur (*Eulemur fulvus*) and Coquerel's sifaka (*Propithecus coquereli*) are common and enter the bungalow area and the hotel gardens every day. On guided night walks visitors can expect to see *Lepilemur*, *Cheirogaleus*, and at least one and perhaps two species of *Microcebus*. None of these nocturnal lemurs have yet been identified with certainty, meaning that some of them could be undescribed species. Also of note at Anjajavy is an underground cave where one can see two skulls of the extinct giant lemur, *Palaeopropithecus*, in the exact location in which they were found, along with a third now under lock-and-key in the lodge itself. This is the only site that we know of in Madagascar where one can actually see an extinct fossil lemur *in situ*. Anjavavy is one of the most upscale lodges in all of Madagascar and may be beyond the budget of many visitors, but it is well worth a visit.

Fig. C.7: An aerial view of the bungalows of the Anjajavy Hotel, with the tract of Western Dry Deciduous Forest protected by the hotel behind them (photo by R. A. Mittermeier).

Anjamena

The forests of Anjamena are located along the banks of the Mahavavy River, southwest of Katsepy in northwestern Madagascar. These forests offer visitors an opportunity to see the mongoose lemur (*Eulemur mongoz*) and crowned sifaka (*Propithecus coronatus*), but access is limited to the dry season and virtually impossible during January or February. Getting to and from the Mahavavy River Delta requires expedition-level preparation, but well-organized trips are now being offered by a small number of international tour operators, largely for the area's birdlife. Recent reports indicate that substantial numbers of lemurs are also observed during these trips.

Anjanaharibe-Sud Special Reserve *

The Anjanaharibe-Sud Special Reserve is located in northeastern Madagascar about 15 km south of Andapa. Among the diurnal lemurs one can expect to see there are the white-fronted brown lemur (*Eulemur albifrons*), particularly in the forests of Befingotra, the silky sifaka (*Propithecus candidus*), and a population of black indri (*Indri indri*). However, it requires a good two- to four-hour hike into the reserve to reach areas where the latter two species are likely to be seen. Anjanaharibe-Sud is also thus far the only place where one can see two newly-described nocturnal forms, Mittermeier's mouse lemur (*Microcebus mittermeieri*) and Seal's sportive lemur (*Lepilemur seali*). Other species that may be seen in the reserve include hairy-eared dwarf lemur (*Allocebus trichotis*), greater dwarf lemur (*Cheirogaleus major*), northern bamboo lemur (*Hapalemur occidentalis*), red-bellied lemur (*Eulemur rubriventer*), eastern woolly lemur (*Avahi laniger*), and aye-aye (*Daubentonia madagascariensis*). Visits can be arranged through Antananarivo-based tour operators, and useful information can be obtained through the website <www.marojejy.com>.

Anjiamangirana Classified Forest

Located in northwestern Madagascar, this forest is the only confirmed location for the Anjiamangirana sportive lemur (*Lepilemur grewcockorum*), and is a possible site for Ambarijeby mouse lemur (*Microcebus danfossi*). Unfortunately, information on access is not available at this time.

Anjozorobe-Angavo Protected Area ***

Located 85 km north of Antananarivo, or about two hours by car, the Anjozorobe-Angavo forest corridor was recently incorporated into a 53,000-ha Protected Area. It is ideal for seeing black indri (*Indri indri*) and diademed sifaka (*Propithecus diadema*), as well as other species such as Goodman's mouse lemur (*Microcebus lehilahytsara*). There are two comfortable lodges some 10 km from Anjozorobe town, Saha Forest Camp in Andreba, which offers a unique view to the forests and lemurs, and the Mananara Lodge, located in Amboasary An' ala.

The Saha Forest Camp at Anjozorobe-Angavo is managed by the Malagasy non-governmental organization, Association Fanamby, and has 10 comfortable bungalows right next to a primary forest. There is also a restaurant that serves various dishes cooked with local produce. More information can be found at <www.sahaforestcamp.org>.

Ankarafantsika National Park ***

Ankarafantsika National Park is located in northwestern Madagascar, about 115 km, or two-hours' drive, from the port city of Mahajanga (= Majunga) along RN4 to Antananarivo. Excursions to Ankarafantsika are easily arranged through hotels in Mahajanga or through Antananarivo-based tour operators. The Ampijoroa campsite has been upgraded recently

Fig. C.8: Aerial view of a section of the forest at Anjozorobe (photo by O. Langrand).

Fig. C.9: Western dry deciduous forest on the sandy plateau, Ampijoroa, Ankarafantsika Nature Reserve (photo by R. A. Mittermeier).

and now contains the locally managed Gîte d' Ampijoroa with comfortable rooms and a restaurant. In addition, more upscale chalets have recently opened at Lac Ravelobe right across the road. A local group (Association Pygargue) offers simple meals to visitors in an open-air restaurant.

The three diurnal lemurs that are readily seen at Ankarafantsika are the brown lemur (*Eulemur fulvus*), the mongoose lemur (*Eulemur mongoz*), and Coquerel's sifaka (*Propithecus coquereli*). Five nocturnal lemurs are also regularly observed during night walks, including the golden-brown mouse lemur (*Microcebus ravelobensis*), the gray mouse lemur (*Microcebus murinus*), and the fat-tailed dwarf lemur (*Cheirogaleus medius*). Both Milne-Edwards' sportive lemur (*Lepilemur edwardsi*) and western woolly lemur (*Avahi occidentalis*) can be seen both at night and in their daytime sleeping sites just a few meters above the ground.

Ankarafantsika, and especially the Ampijoroa area, is one of the best sites for first-time visitors to Madagascar. Accommodations are good and lemur-watching is easy. With a little bit of luck one can see all eight lemur species in an afternoon, an evening, and a morning. The mongoose lemur can sometimes be elusive, but only because it is very quiet, and it is important to have a knowledgeable guide to distinguish the two mouse lemur species which can easily be confused by beginning lemur-watchers. What is more, this is really the only site where one is likely to see *Microcebus ravelobensis*.

The Ampijoroa area within Ankarafantsika is also the site of the world's most important captive breeding project for endangered Madagascar turtles and tortoises, including the ploughshare tortoise or angonoka (*Asterochelys yniphora*), the flat-tailed tortoise or kapidolo (*Pyxis planicauda*), and the Madagascar big-headed sideneck turtle or rere (*Erymnochelys madagascariensis*). The ploughshare tortoise is one of the most critically endangered tortoises in the world, and this is presently the only breeding site for it outside its natural range.

Ankarana National Park ***

Ankarana National Park is located in northern Madagascar approximately 108 km south of Antsiranana (= Diégo-Suarez), from which excursions can be organized through some hotels and local tour operators. There are basic campsites available, and very simple accommodations at the Mahamasina entrance along RN6, including Chez Goulam and Chez Aurélien. By far the best site for camping is the Campement des Anglais, located in a forested canyon (Canyon Forestier) accessible from the west by four-wheel-drive vehicle in the dry season and by hiking from Mahamasina all year round. For those who prefer not to camp or stay in very rustic bungalows, there are simple yet comfortable hotels in nearby Ambilobe, about 45-minute drive from Mahamasina, including the Hotel National or Hotel Chez Diana. Closer to the park, the highly-regarded Relais d' Ankarana offers more upscale accommodation. It can be booked through either a local or Antananarivo-based tour operator. The Domaine de Fontenay Hotel in Joffreville can also arrange day excursions into the eastern part of the park year-round.

The Canyon Forestier, Campement des Anglais, and forests near the Mahamasina entrance offer the best opportunities for seeing Sanford's brown lemur (*Eulemur sanfordi*), the crowned lemur (*Eulemur coronatus*), and the nocturnal Ankarana sportive lemur (*Lepilemur ankaranensis*), which is also easily found in its daytime sleeping sites. In addition, several groups of crowned lemurs (*Eulemur coronatus*) have been habituated near the Campement des Anglais and Lac Vert, and they are easily found elsewhere in the reserve

Fig. C.10: Part of an extensive and spectacular tsingy formation at the western edge of Ankarana National Park (photo by R. A. Mittermeier).

as well. Ankarana is also the best place for seeing the Tavaratra mouse lemur (*Microcebus tavaratra*), where it lives sympatrically with an as-yet-undescribed grayish form of mouse lemur (*Microcebus*), and it is also very good for the fat-tailed dwarf lemur (*Cheirogaleus medius*) and the Montagne d' Ambre fork-marked lemur (*Phaner electromontis*). The northern bamboo lemur (*Hapalemur occidentalis*) has also been reported from Ankarana, but is much more difficult to find.

Aye-aye Island (= Ile Roger) **

This small island is located in northeastern Madagascar, just a couple of kilometers from the airstrip for the town of Mananara-Nord. At this time, it is the best place in the country for seeing the elusive aye-aye (*Daubentonia madagascariensis*) in a natural setting. Several aye-aye were introduced there years ago by the owner of the island, Monsieur Roger, and seeing at least one is almost guaranteed during a nocturnal visit. The island is basically an old overgrown plantation with various stages of secondary forest, but it is quite good for seeing lemurs. Also present are bamboo lemurs (*Hapalemur* sp.) and the white-fronted brown lemur (*Eulemur albifrons*). Comfortable bungalow accommodations are available at the Aye-aye Hotel in Mananara-Nord, situated conveniently about 100 m from the edge of the airstrip. Note that, as of 2009, Air Madagascar no longer operates scheduled flights to Mananara, so it is necessary to either charter a flight or travel by means of a motorized boat transfer arranged by hotels, such as Relais du Masoala in Maroantsetra.

Baie de Baly National Park *

This national park is located about 150 km southeast of Majajanga (= Majunga) in western coastal Madagascar, and can be reached by four-wheel-drive vehicle or by charter flight to Soalala, which is the town adjacent to the park. It is best known as the only remaining natural habitat for the Critically Endangered ploughshare tortoise (*Asterochelys yniphora*), the largest of the four endemic tortoises found in Madagascar and the most restricted in range. Lemur species that may be seen here include gray mouse lemur (*Microcebus murinus*), fat-tailed dwarf lemur (*Cheirogaleus medius*), northern bamboo lemur (*Hapalemur occidentalis*), rufous brown lemur (*Eulemur rufus*), and Decken's sifaka (*Propithecus deckenii*). Peters' mouse lemur (*Microcebus myoxinus*) may possibly occur here as well, but this remains to be determined. There are no accommodations either in the park or in Soalala, so it is therefore necessary to bring camping equipment, and highly advisable to organize your trip through a local operator.

The Bemarivo Special Reserve, located a little further down the coast, features essentially the same selection of lemur species. This park is one of the best places to see the rufous brown lemur (*Eulemur rufus*), recently resurrected and separated as a distinct species from the more wide-ranging red-fronted brown lemur (*Eulemur rufifrons*).

Bemosary Classified Forest

Located in central-eastern Madagascar, the Bemosary Classified Forest is currently the only place where one has a reasonable chance of seeing the Betsileo woolly lemur (*Avahi betsileo*), which was first described in 2007. The forest fragment where this species occurs is located about one hour (by foot) from the village of Fandriana. However, a visit to this site is best left to seasoned lemur-watchers with several trips to Madagascar under their belt.

Benavony *

The village of Benavony is located 5 km from Ambanja and 31 km from Ankify in northwestern Madagascar. Forests and plantations immediately behind the village are excellent for both the northern giant mouse lemur (*Mirza zaza*) and the western bamboo lemur (*Hapalemur occidentalis*), and local villagers are very accommodating in taking visitors out into the forest. There are basic accommodations in Ambanja and two good hotels at Ankify.

Berenty Private Reserve ***

The Berenty Private Reserve is one of the best known tourist destinations in Madagascar. Established in 1936 as a reserve on a sisal plantation, it opened for tourism in 1980 and is still operated by the de Heaulme family, the original owners. Berenty is located approximately 82 km west of the airport at Tolagnaro (= Fort-Dauphin) and just north of Amboasary. The drive from Tolagnaro takes about three hours without stops (owing to the poor condition of the road). However, it is best to schedule a full day for this trip because the scenery and the attractions along the way make this one of the most interesting stretches of road in Madagascar.

You start in the southern extreme of the eastern rain forest region in the land of the Antanosy people and drive through their small villages and markets, with a stop at a tomb site that has appeared in *National Geographic* (actually a monument, since the Antanosy bury their dead elsewhere). From there, you continue on through the transition zone between eastern rain forest and spiny forest, and have the option of diverting into the Tsimelahy region of Parcel III of Andohahela National Park. The small reception area for Tsimelahy is located some 8 km from the main highway on a very rough but passable dirt road. There is a well-laid out trail at Tsimilahy in a very picturesque spot that mixes

Fig. C.11: Entrance to the gallery forest of the Berenty Private Reserve in southern Madagascar, landscaped with plants of the surrounding spiny desert (photo by W. R. Konstant).

Fig. C.12: Tourists watching ring-tailed lemurs (*Lemur catta*), Berenty Private Reserve (photo by R. A. Mittermeier).

Fig. C.13: Southern Spiny desert mainly with *Alluaudia procera* and *Alluaudia ascendens*, Berenty Private Reserve (photo by R. A. Mittermeier).

elements of the spiny forest with several species endemic to the transition zone itself. The best known of these endemics is the famous triangle palm (*Dypsis decaryi*), a beautiful tree that is now grown horticulturally around the world, but is naturally found only in this tiny area.

Tsimelahy is best described as a natural botanical garden, and definitely worth a visit. From there, you return to the main road and continue on into the land of Antandroy, the true spiny forest. Along the road are still to be found some expanses of intact spiny forest dominated by the magnificent *Alluaudia* plants of the Didiereaceae family, and you also pass several villages of the Tandroy people, who live in this very inhospitable environment. The Tandroy still cut spiny forest for charcoal, but a Japanese non-governmental organization (Southern Cross) has been working with local communities on alternatives, including replanting of *Alluaudia,* creating a small handicraft industry, and primary education. Visitors should stop at the village of Andranomainty, where one can buy simple but charming little wood carvings of lemurs, chameleons, and other animals, and at Antrehatreha, where residents sell model planes and helicopters made from local materials. Finally, at about 60 km from the Tolagnaro (= Fort-Dauphin) airport, you arrive at the region of the Amboasary-Sud sisal plantations, a vast expanse of these Mexican plants that were introduced in the first half of the 20th century. You pass through the village of Ambosary-Sud, turn north off the main road, and drive about 10 km through the plantations to Berenty.

For those wishing to fly in by charter, there is also a small airstrip on the grounds of the plantation. If you can afford this option, we recommend flying first to Tolagnaro (= Fort-Dauphin) and doing the above route in one direction, then flying out from Berenty once your visit is over to avoid retracing your steps.

Berenty has large populations of ring-tailed lemurs (*Lemur catta*) and Verrreaux's sifaka (*Propithecus verreauxi*), which are very evident and usually in or near the parking lot, greeting visitors upon arrival. There is also an introduced population of hybrid red-fronted brown lemurs (*Eulemur rufifrons*) × red-collared brown lemurs (*Eulemur collaris*), the offspring of small groups of these two species that were introduced in the 1970s and 1980s. The introduced lemurs surely compete with the native species, probably to the detriment at least of the ring-tails, but they are there to stay. Three nocturnal species are also present. The white-footed sportive lemur (*Lepilemur leucopus*) is common and readily seen, even in the daytime in its sleeping sites. Research has also indicated that there are two mouse lemurs at Berenty, the gray (*Microcebus murinus*) in the gallery forests and the gray-brown (*Microcebus griseorufus*) in the adjacent spiny forest patches. Both are commonly seen in the warmer months.

The Berenty Reserve is situated along the Mandrare River and covers approximately 250 ha of gallery forest dominated by large tamarind trees (*Tamarindus indica*) and adjoining spiny forest, dominated by *Alluaudia procera* and *Alluaudia ascendens*. These patches of natural habitat are in the middle of the sisal plantation that was established in 1930.

Research on the ring-tails at Berenty has been going on for nearly 50 years, led by Dr. Alison Jolly and her colleagues and involving numerous other researchers. A number of publications by Dr. Jolly are readily available. The most recent of these is a fascinating book entitled *Lords and Lemurs.* It focuses both on the history of Berenty and on the behavior and ecology of the lemurs, and is highly recommended. Over the last 30 years, Berenty has probably been the most visited and most filmed of all sites in Madagascar.

Bungalows are available for overnight stays, and there is also a good restaurant on the premises. Berenty is accessible all year round, but September and October are the favored months for observing baby lemurs, while December through March is the best time to see native reptiles. Temperatures in the austral summer can be quite hot and nights in the austral winter can be quite cool, so dress accordingly. You will also need to be sure to book well in advance since this is one of most heavily visited sites in the country, especially in the peak season.

Although most visitors go only to the gallery forest and to a small, adjacent patch of spiny forest in the immediate vicinity of the bungalows, we also recommend excursions to several other forest patches in the area. These include the gallery forest of Bealokoa and the magnificent spiny forest patch at Anjapolo, located just 15 km from the headquarters of the reserve and still part of Berenty. The forest at Anjapolo is rich in *Didierea trolli*, an impressive species of Didiereaceae not found in the more frequented spiny forest patches in the main part of Berenty.

Berenty is a must for first-time visitors, and often the first stop on any inaugural trip to Madagascar. Although sometimes crowded in the high season, it is still a delightful place and one where the lemur-watcher can immediately add four or five species to a lemur life-list. The reserve is also excellent for birdwatching, and has what must be the most accessible roosting site for the Madagascar flying fox (*Pteropus rufus*) in the entire country. It is also a good staging point for excursions to other parts of the southern extreme of the country, notably Cap Sainte Marie and Faux Cap which are well worth a visit.

Betampona Strict Nature Reserve *

This small reserve, located 60 km northeast of Toamasina (= Tamatave), protects a region of low-altitude rain forest that is rich in biodiversity. It is home to at least nine lemur species, one of which, Simmons' mouse lemur (*Microcebus simmonsi*), is best seen here. Others definitely known to occur are the greater dwarf lemur (*Cheirogaleus major*), the weasel sportive lemur (*Lepilemur mustelinus*), the variegated black-and-white ruffed lemur (*Varecia variegata variegata*), the diademed sifaka (*Propithecus diadema*), indri (*Indri indri*), and the aye-aye (*Daubentonia madagascariensis*). There is also an introduced population of white-fronted brown lemur (*Eulemur albifrons*), and there are reports of greater dwarf lemur (*Cheirogaleus major*) and gray bamboo lemur (*Hapalemur griseus griseus*) as well. Unfortunately there are no accommodations nearby, and reaching this reserve by vehicle may be difficult since bridges are frequently washed away by tropical storms. In addition, only researchers with a permit are allowed to enter the reserve, so this must be requested from Madagascar National Parks.

Beza-Mahafaly Special Reserve *

The Beza-Mahafaly Special Reserve, like the Berenty Private Reserve, is made up of small patches of gallery forest (100 ha) and spiny forest (480 ha), and has been a key research site for the last quarter century. It is south of the Onilahy River about 35 km northeast of the village of Betioky-Sud, which itself is about five hours drive on RN10 from Toliara (= Tuléar). Both the RN10 and the dirt track to Beza-Mahafaly are in poor condition and require four-wheel-drive vehicles. Visitors should count on spending a day getting in and another day getting out. There are no hotels next to the reserve, but camping in the vicinity is possible.

Fig. C.14: Grove of *Alluaudia ascendens* in the Beza-Mahafaly region of southwestern Madagascar (photo by R. A. Mittermeier).

Lemurs that can be seen in Beza-Mahafaly are the same as those in Berenty, including the ring-tailed lemur (*Lemur catta*), Verreaux's sifaka (*Propithecus verreauxi*), the fat-tailed dwarf lemur (*Cheirogaleus medius*), the gray-brown mouse lemur (*Microcebus griseorufus*), and the gray mouse lemur (*Microcebus murinus*). Although the habitat in Beza-Mahafaly is similar to that of Berenty, Beza-Mahafaly is the only known site where one is sure to see the recently-described Petter's sportive lemur (*Lepilemur petteri*). What is more, the region as a whole is much more remote and worth the adventure of getting there.

Bongolava Classified Forest

Located in northwestern Madagascar near Port Berge, this is the only relatively large forest fragment left between the Mahajamba and Sofia Rivers and currently the only place where one can see the Bongolava mouse lemur (*Microcebus bongolavensis*). There are no amenities available in this area.

Bora Special Reserve

This small 4,800-ha patch of transitional forest between the Eastern and Western Domains is about 35 km from the town of Antsohihy in the northwest. The reserve is sadly lacking in infrastructure to protect the interesting lemur species found there, which include the newly-described Ambarijeby mouse lemur (*Microcebus danfossi*), as well as brown lemur (*Eulemur fulvus*), western woolly lemur (*Avahi occidentalis*), Coquerel's sifaka (*Propithecus coquereli*), and aye-aye (*Daubentonia madagascariensis*). As a result of the lack of protection, the forest has been severely degraded by illegal logging and charcoal production, and the animals are difficult to find. Indeed, in recent years, there has even been talk of de-gazetting Bora, which would be most unfortunate. There are no accommodations next to the reserve, but simple hotels such as the Biaina III or the Vatolampy Annexe can be found in Antsohihy.

Daraina (Loky-Manambato Protected Area) **

The town of Daraina is in northeastern Madagascar, two to five hours north of Vohémar depending on weather and road conditions. The surrounding patches of dry forest are best known for their large populations of Tattersall's sifaka (*Propithecus tattersalli*), but are also home to the fat-tailed dwarf lemur (*Cheirogaleus medius*), the Daraina sportive lemur (*Lepilemur milanoii*), the crowned lemur (*Eulemur coronatus*), and Sanford's brown lemur (*Eulemur sanfordi*). There is also an as-yet unidentified species of *Phaner*, which may be new to science, and the aye-aye (*Daubentonia madagascariensis*) have also been reported.

Daraina is now the core area of the newly-created, 57,000 ha Loky-Manambato Protected Area, which is managed by the Malagasy non-governmental organization, Association Fanamby. Fanamby has developed tourist facilities, known as "Camp Tattersall," at the edge of the Andranotsinaty Forest. These facilities include large, comfortable tents equipped with mattresses and a private bathroom, and Tattersall's sifaka may be found very near the campsite. Visits can be arranged either through Fanamby or through a number of tour companies in Antsiranana (= Diégo-Suarez).

Fandriana Classified Forest

Located in central-eastern Madagascar, Fandriana is home to a population of the Critically Endangered southern black-and-white ruffed lemur (*Varecia variegata editorum*), and is at

Fig. C.15: The remaining forests of Daraina exist as a fragile patchwork amid degraded grassland (photo by R. A. Mittermeier).

present the only known place to see the Betsileo sportive lemur (*Lepilemur betsileo*). This important area of forest has recently been proposed as a national park, but it has no tourist accommodations available at this time.

Isalo National Park

Isalo National Park is in south-central Madagascar, and can be reached by vehicle from Toliara (= Tuléar) in about three hours using RN7. Its sandstone cliffs and canyons are home to groups of ring-tailed lemurs (*Lemur catta*), red-fronted brown lemurs (*Eulemur rufifrons*), and Verreaux's sifakas (*Propithecus verreauxi*), all of which can be observed in the canyon near Ranohira. Ring-tails can also be seen at Camp Catta, near Andringitra National Park just east of Ambalavao, and at a community conservation site called Anjaha on the main road from Ambalavao heading towards Toliara. Other species reported from Isalo include gray mouse lemur (*Microcebus murinus*) and red-tailed sportive lemur (*Lepilemur ruficaudatus*), while a population of Coquerel's giant mouse lemur (*Mirza coquereli*) can be found in the Analalava Forest block just adjacent to the park. Isalo is one of the most heavily visited sites in the country and good accommodation of various levels are available in the park, the best of which are the Relais de la Reine, Le Jardin du Roy and the Satrana Lodge. Although the scenery is very attractive and worth seeing, this park is not a high priority for lemurs.

Fig. C.16: The Canyon des Makis (Lemur Canyon), Isalo National Park (photo by R. A. Mittermeier).

Kalambatritra Special Reserve *

Located in the southeast some 50 km east of Betroka, the very important Kalambatritra Special Reserve nevertheless remains poorly known. Access by car is difficult between Ihosy and Betroka, and very difficult between Betroka and the reserve. There are no accommodations available either in the reserve itself or nearby. However, this forest includes vegetation from both the Eastern Domain and the Southern Domain, and is the only site currently known for the recently-described Wright's sportive lemur (*Lepilemur wrightae*), one of the most distinctive members of the genus. Other lemurs occurring there include southern bamboo lemur (*Hapalemur meridionalis*), ring-tailed lemur (*Lemur catta*), red-collared brown lemur (*Eulemur collaris*), and aye-aye (*Daubentonia madagascariensis*).

Kasijy Special Reserve

This small reserve in west-central Madagascar covers roughly 19,800 ha, of which only a small portion is actually forest. Access is a major problem since the road system is almost non-existent between the reserve and Ambato Boeny, and what does exist is not maintained. Furthermore, there are no accommodations in the vicinity of the reserve. Nevertheless, it does offer opportunities to see the gray mouse lemur (*Microcebus murinus*), the red-tailed sportive lemur (*Lepilemur ruficaudatus*), the northern bamboo lemur (*Hapalemur occidentalis*), the rufous brown lemur (*Eulemur rufus*), Decken's sifaka (*Propithecus deckenii*), and possibly the crowned sifaka (*Propithecus coronatus*).

Katsepy–Belemboka Forests **

The town of Katsepy is located right across the Betsiboka River from Mahajanga (= Majunga) in northwestern Madagascar. The nearby forests of Antrema, north of Katsepy and below the lighthouse, offer excellent opportunities for seeing the mongoose lemur (*Eulemur mongoz*) and the crowned sifaka (*Propithecus coronatus*). This area is readily accessible by ferry (twice daily) or by speedboat from Mahajanga. The comfortable Chez Chabaud Hotel is the only local accommodation. The proprietor can arrange transportation to and from the forests that harbor these animals, and they can sometimes be seen right near the hotel in forest patches along the river. A visit to Katsepy requires an overnight stay, which can be arranged from Mahajanga. It is the only easily accessible place to see the crowned sifaka (*Propithecus coronatus*).

Nearby, Fanamby is currently working to achieve protected area status for the Belemboka-Bombetoka Forests, another site for *Propithecus coronatus* and *Eulemur mongoz*. The area can be reached via Boanamary, 27 km to the west of RN4, and has basic, community-managed tourism facilities in Mataitromby. A visit to the Belemboka Forests and the Bombetoky mangroves (using a patrol boat) can be arranged by Fanamby.

The Belemboka Forest is much more accessible than the Anjamena forests for several reasons. First is the availability of a boat to cross the Betsiboka River, second the presence of local guides, and third the ease with which one can see the sifakas. Reaching the forest requires a 30-minute walk, as opposed to a 1–3-hour drive from Katsepy to Anjamena. Fanamby is currently developing community-based ecotourism in the area.

Kirindy Forest ***

This site in central-western Madagascar is also known as the Swiss Forest, La Forêt des Suisses, or Kirindy-Nord, and is part of a former 12,500-ha Swiss forestry concession located northeast of Morondava. Tourists can reach the Kirindy forests from Morondava via the regular taxi-brousse service (which drops you off on the main road, a 5-km hike from the camp), or by renting a car through any of the Morondava hotels such as Palissandre Cote Ouest, Chez Maggie, or the Baobab Hotel. An overnight stay can be combined with a visit to the famous Highway of the Baobabs, or to the spectacular Tsingy de Bemaraha National Park. The Highway of the Baobabs is only 15 km from the Morondava Airport, and you have to pass through it to get to Kirindy, which is about 60 km north. If one wants to continue on to the Tsingy de Bemaraha, it is about a 10-hour drive from Morondava.

A tourist camp was constructed in Kirindy in 1996 by the Centre National de Formation, d' Etudes, et de Recherches en Environnment et de Foresterie or C.N.F.E.R.E.F. (formerly C.F.P.F.), and the bungalows and restaurant there were renovated and expanded in 2007. Accommodations are basic but comfortable, and the location is ideal. Reservations to stay can be made either by email or telephone. The German Primate Centre (DPZ) has operated a research station in Kirindy since 1993. With luck, you may run into some of the scientists, who are based right next to the tourist area. Kirindy Forest and the adjacent Ambadira Forest form part of the core area of the new Menabe-Antimena Protected Area in this region.

During daylight hours, visitors to Kirindy can expect to see red-fronted brown lemur (*Eulemur rufifrons*) and Verreaux's sifaka (*Propithecus verreauxi*), but the real value of Kirindy is in its nocturnal species. With six species in all, this site has one of the highest densities of nocturnal primates in the world, and is a must for the lemur-watcher. The prize here is Madame Berthe's mouse lemur (*Microcebus berthae*), for which Kirindy is by far the best site, but gray mouse lemur (*Microcebus murinus*), fat-tailed dwarf lemur (*Cheirogaleus medius*), Coquerel's giant mouse lemur (*Mirza coquereli*), pale fork-marked lemur (*Phaner pallescens*), and red-tailed sportive lemur (*Lepilemur ruficaudatus*) can all be seen during night walks in the area. Kirindy is particularly good for *Phaner*, but *Mirza* has become difficult to see in recent years. The other species are virtually guaranteed if you visit in the wet season, and take along one of the local guides.

Kirindy is the best place to see the endemic giant jumping rat (*Hypogeomys antimena*), a highly threatened rodent found only in this region, and the very rare kapidolo tortoise (*Pyxis arachnoides*), although the latter can only be seen after a rain in the months of December and January. It is also by far the best site in Madagascar for seeing the fossa (*Cryptoprocta ferox*), the country's largest carnivore. Over the past few years, fossa have even started to regularly visit the camp area itself.

In addition to the Kirindy Forest, one can also make a stop at the Marofandilia Forest, which is en route and located between the highway of the Baobabs and Kirindy. Also part of the Menabe-Antimena protected area, Marofandilia is a good place to view various species of lemur and features a camp inside the forest, "Camp Amoureux." The latter is composed of five spacious tents on platforms, each with a bed and private bathroom. Visits can be arranged either through Fanamby or through several tour companies in Antananarivo and Morondava.

Lac Alaotra **

Lac Alaotra is Madagascar's largest lake and also its most important rice-growing area. It is located in central-eastern Madagascar, just west of Zahamena National Park. It is

Fig. C.17: An aerial view of Lac Alaotra, Madagascar's largest lake (photo by W. R. Konstant).

the only place to see the Critically Endangered Lac Alaotra bamboo lemur (*Hapalemur alaotrensis*), which is endemic to the immediate vicinity of the lake, and occupies one of the most unusual niches of any primate.

The best starting points for lemur-watching excursions are Andreba on the eastern side of the lake or Andilana Atsimo on the western side. Both villages can be reached from Ambatondrazaka, the main town on the lake's south side. Ambatondrazaka offers simple hotel accommodations and can be reached in 40 minutes by plane or six hours by car from Antananarivo.

Bamboo lemurs can be found either by paddling a pirogue through the reed beds in the early morning, or, when water levels are low, by walking in and around the reed beds on dry land. However, it is essential to have an experienced local guide who is familiar with the behavior of this lemur, since it is a cryptic species and not easy to find. The village of Andreba has a marsh reserve where local guides can help find it, and there is a simple but well-run camp in Andreba as well.

The most important field work on this species has been carried out by Durrell, and a new, 42,478-ha protected area was created there in late 2006, covering the lake and surrounding marsh and with various use zones for the local people. Lac Alaotra is also a 722,500-ha Ramsar wetland site, designated in 2003.

Lokobe Strict Nature Reserve ***

Located on the island of Nosy Be in northwestern Madagascar, the Lokobe Strict Nature Reserve protects the only large block of intact forest remaining on this tourist island. It is easily accessible and close to the capital of Hellville, and can actually be seen from

Fig. C.18: On the left, the Lokobe Strict Nature Reserve Reserve and in the background the nearby island of Nosy Komba, seen from Mont Passot on Nosy Be (photo by R. A. Mittermeier).

Hellville itself. Several tours visit forests around this reserve, and local guides usually know the whereabouts of black lemurs (*Eulemur macaco*) and daytime sleeping sites for Nosy Be sportive lemurs (*Lepilemur tymerlachsonorum*), both of which are quite easy to observe. This is also the only place where one can see the Nosy Be mouse lemur (*Microcebus mamiratra*).

Several enterprising villagers run tours to the edge of the reserve. One that is easy access starts at the village of Ambatozavavy, a few kilometers from Hellville, goes 20–30 minutes by outrigger canoe to the village of Ampasipohy, and from there into the forest a few minutes away. An overnight stay at one of the two hotels at Ampasipohy is highly recommended. One is called the Paradisa-Kely and the other the Jungle Lodge, and both are quite comfortable and located right on the beach.

Makira Forest

The Makira Forest is one of the largest remaining blocks of forest in Madagascar and is located in the northeastern part of the island, southwest of Maroantsetra. Maroantsetra can be reached by commercial flight, and a good hotel, le Relais du Masoala, is available there. Access to the forest is by foot starting a few kilometers southwest of the town. Based on existing records, the lemur fauna here is remarkable and includes Anjiahely mouse lemur (*Microcebus macarthurii*), Masoala fork-marked lemur (*Phaner furcifer*), Seal's sportive lemur (*Lepilemur seali*), northern bamboo lemur (*Hapalemur occidentalis*), white-fronted brown lemur (*Eulemur albifrons*), northern black-and-white ruffed lemur (*Varecia variegata subcincta*), eastern woolly lemur (*Avahi laniger*), silky sifaka (*Propithecus candidus*), indri (*Indri indri*), and aye-aye (*Daubentonia madagascariensis*). Sibree's dwarf lemur (*Cheirogaleus sibreei*) has been reported from Makira but its occurrence there is not certain. The dwarf lemur there may be an as-yet-undescribed species. Unfortunately, there is heavy hunting pressure in this region, and it is actually quite difficult to find lemurs in Makira. Officially, the forest is under temporary government protection while awaiting final conservation status. However, given the difficulty of access and the hunting problem, we do not recommend it to first-time visitors to the country.

Mananara-Nord National Park

Mananara-Nord National Park is in eastern Madagascar south of Makira. It has a rich lemur fauna, including an undescribed form of mouse lemur (*Microcebus*), the hairy-eared dwarf lemur (*Allocebus trichotis*), the greater dwarf lemur (*Cheirogaleus major*), the Masoala fork-marked lemur (*Phaner furcifer*), the northern bamboo lemur (*Hapalemur occidentalis*), the white-fronted brown lemur (*Eulemur albifrons*), the northern black-and-white ruffed lemur (*Varecia variegata subcincta*), the eastern woolly lemur (*Avahi laniger*), the diademed sifaka (*Propithecus diadema*), indri (*Indri indri*), and the aye-aye (*Daubentonia madagascariensis*). The *Lepilemur* found there is now considered to be a new species; *Lepilemur hollandorum*. Unfortunately, there are no good trails, and there is little infrastructure, considerable deforestation, and hunting in this park. A permit is required to enter and can be obtained from the UNESCO office in Mananara, from Madagascar National Parks in Antananarivo, or the nearby town of Antanambe. Access requires a three-hour walk from Sandrakatsy, a small town served by taxi-brousse from Mananara. As with Makira, we do not recommend this park for first-time visitors to Madagascar.

Mandena Conservation Zone *

The forests of Mandena are in southeastern Madagascar, about a 20-minute drive northeast of Tolagnaro (= Fort-Dauphin). Visits can be arranged with the help of local tourist agencies or through contact with the mining company QMM in Tolagnaro. During the daylight hours, you can find the red-collared brown lemur (*Eulemur collaris*) and the southern bamboo lemur (*Hapalemur meridionalis*). At night, you can see the gray mouse lemur (*Microcebus murinus*) as well as two species of *Cheirogaleus*, the greater dwarf lemur (*Cheirogaleus major*) and the fat-tailed dwarf lemur (*Cheirogaleus medius*).

Mangerivola Special Reserve

Located in central-eastern Madagascar, about 50 km from Toamasina (= Tamatave), this special reserve covers some 13,000 ha. It is accessible only by foot, and has no accommodations nearby. Species that may be seen here include the brown lemur (*Eulemur fulvus*), the red-bellied lemur (*Eulemur rubriventer*), eastern woolly lemur (*Avahi laniger*), the diademed sifaka (*Propithecus diadema*), and indri (*Indri indri*). Sightings of the greater dwarf lemur (*Cheirogaleus major*) and the gray bamboo lemur (*Hapalemur griseus griseus*) are possible as well. As is the case for a number of other remote eastern rain forest reserves, we do not recommend this one for a first-time visitor to the country.

Maningoza Special Reserve

This special reserve is in central-western Madagascar and covers about 7,900 ha of deciduous dry forest. Although accessible from Besalampy and Morondava, this is only possible during the dry season and by means of a four-wheel-drive vehicle. There are no accommodations nearby. Species that may be seen here include the gray mouse lemur (*Microcebus murinus*), the fat-tailed dwarf lemur (*Cheirogaleus medius*), the northern bamboo lemur (*Hapalemur occidentalis*), the red-fronted brown lemur (*Eulemur rufifrons*), and Decken's sifaka (*Propithecus deckenii*).

Manombo Special Reserve and Classified Forest / Agnalahaza Forest **

The Manombo Special Reserve and Classified Forest is in southeastern Madagascar, south of the town of Farafangana. Although infrequently visited, it is the easiest place to see the Critically Endangered southern black-and-white ruffed lemur (*Varecia variegata editorum*) and the Endangered white-collared brown lemur (*Eulemur cinereiceps*). The Manombo Special Reserve covers some 5,000 ha, of which perhaps 3,000 ha is still forest, while the adjoining Classified Forest covers some 10,000 ha, of which about 7,000 ha is forest. It is hoped that the latter will soon be gazetted as a reserve as well.

Manombo can be reached by traveling about 30 km south of Farafangana to the village of Manombo on the excellent RN12. There are then several access routes to the forest, either on foot or on dirt tracks requiring a four-wheel-drive vehicle. One of the best sites is about 7 km in from the asphalt road, heading east. A visit requires permission from Madagascar National Parks, and arrangements can be made through one of the local hotels, especially the Austral Hotel and Les Cocotiers. Use of a guide is essential, as it is not easy to find the best sites for these animals. Durrell (formerly, the Durrell Wildlife Conservation Trust) also maintains a research presence in this area.

Aside from the two species already mentioned, which are among the real prizes of a lemur-watching expedition to Madagascar, one can also see several others at Manombo.

Fig. C.19: Manombo Special Reserve, about 30 km south of Farafangana (photo by R. A. Mittermeier).

These include an undescribed species of mouse lemur (*Microcebus*) and two newly-described species that are only found in this region; the Manombo sportive lemur (*Lepilemur jamesorum*) and the Manombo woolly lemur (*Avahi ramanantsoavanai*). Greater dwarf lemur (*Cheirogaleus major*) and southern bamboo lemur (*Hapalemur meridionalis*) are also present, and you can see signs of aye-aye (*Daubentonia madagascariensis*) as well.

The Agnalahaza Forest (formerly the Mahabo Forest Reserve) is close to Manombo, and is located 40 km along the main highway south of Farafangana, then 5–7 km in on a dirt track. It covers 1,500 ha and is covered in littoral forest, an increasingly rare formation in Madagascar, including some 600 ha of wooded swamp and stands of traveler's palm (*Ravenala madagasariensis*). The Missouri Botanical Garden carry out research there, and has already discovered 10 new plant species. Several groups of the white-collared brown lemur (*Eulemur cinereiceps*) occur in this forest, but *Lepilemur*, *Varecia* and *Daubentonia* appear to be absent. Arrangements can be made as for Manombo, and use of a guide is essential.

Manongarivo Special Reserve

The Manongarivo Special Reserve is in the Sambirano region of northwestern Madagascar. It can be reached by four-wheel-drive vehicle from Ambanja, about 60 km to the south, and it is best to contact an Antsiranana (= Diégo-Suarez) or Nosy Be-based tour operator to arrange such a trip. A permit is required from Madagascar National Parks in order to enter the reserve. There are several hotels in Ambanja and two very good ones in Ankify, but these are a good distance away from the reserve. Manongarivo is the best place to see the Sambirano mouse lemur (*Microebus sambiranensis*) and the Sambirano

Fig. C.20: Forest at the edge of the Manongarivo Special Reserve (photo by R. A. Mittermeier).

woolly lemur (*Avahi unicolor*), but both are quite difficult to find. Other species present include the Sambirano fork-marked lemur (*Phaner parienti*), Gray's sportive lemur (*Lepilemur dorsalis*), the northern giant mouse lemur (*Mirza zaza*), northern bamboo lemur (*Hapalemur occidentalis*), the black lemur (*Eulemur macaco*), the brown lemur (*Eulemur fulvus*), and perhaps the aye-aye (*Daubentonia madagascariensis*). This reserve is hard to reach and is not recommended for first-time visitors to Madagascar.

Mantadia National Park ***

See above, under Andasibe.

Marojejy National Park ***

Marojejy National Park is in northeastern Madagascar between the towns of Andapa and Sambava. It is the best place to see the silky sifaka (*Propithecus candidus*), one of the country's most endangered species, and is also quite good for white-fronted brown lemur (*Eulemur albifrons*) and northern bamboo lemur (*Hapalemur occidentalis*). Eight other species are reported from the park, including an unidentifed species of mouse lemur (possibly *Microcebus mittermeieri*), hairy-eared dwarf lemur (*Allocebus trichotis*), greater dwarf lemur (*Cheirogaleus major*), eastern fork-marked lemur (*Phaner furcifer*), Seal's sportive lemur (*Lepilemur seali*), red-bellied lemur (*Eulemur rubriventer*), eastern woolly lemur (*Avahi laniger*), and aye-aye (*Daubentonia madagascariensis*), but these are more difficult to find given the steep terrain. In any case, the real prize is the silky sifaka, and a visit of at least one night to Camp Marojejia (formerly known as Camp 2), and preferably two or three nights, is required to find this species. The latter may also be seen in the northwest portion of the park in the direction of Doany, but this site remains far off the traditional tourist circuit and requires expedition-level preparations. Even more remote locations for it are to be found in the Befingotra Forest of the Anjanaharibe-Sud Special Reserve, as well as in the Andaparaty Forest in Makira.

Park headquarters, with its newly-built information center, is located about 66 km from Sambava, along the main Andapa-Sambava road. From the headquarters, one drives in as far as the village of Mandena if road and bridge conditions permit. From there, it is another 2.5 km to the picnic area just inside the park entrance itself and another 4.5 km to the first campsite, Camp Mantella, where northern bamboo lemurs (*Hapalemur occidentalis*) can often be seen. From there it is another 2 km to Camp Marojejia, which is the best location for finding the silky sifaka. This camp is situated in the transition from lowland to montane rain forest, and must surely be one of the most beautiful in Madagascar. A large, covered dining area is perched on a mountainside with views overlooking sheer rock outcrops and lush vegetation. Continuing up the main summit trail another 2 km you find Camp Simpona, the highest-altitude camp in the park at 1,250 m elevation. The hike to this third camp is very steep, but well worth the effort since silky sifakas are occasionally seen near the bungalows in this unique montane habitat, and the views are truly magnificent. An additional 2 km of steep walking is needed in order to reach the summit of the Marojejy massif which, at 2,132 m, is one of the country's highest yet most accessible mountain peaks.

Marojejy is perhaps the only national park in Madagascar featuring comfortable bungalows as well as kitchen and toilet facilities deep in primary rain forest. These accommodations are available at each of the three main camps, and can be rented at very low cost at park headquarters, where guides, cooks, and porters can also be hired. For visitors with their own tents, reduced rates are available for using the basic tent sites at each of the three main camps.

Fig. C.21: A sign advertising Marojejy National Park, "the Sacred Mountain" (photo by R. A. Mittermeier).

Sadly, this park was subjected to illegal logging for rosewood in early to mid-2009, and was closed for a brief period. However, it reopened in May, 2009, and all facilities are intact and available for use. There is no reason not to visit this unique and spectacular park, which is one of Madagascar's real gems.

Marotandrano Special Reserve

Marotandrano Special Reserve is in north-central Madagascar near Mandritsara, and covers some 42,000 ha of rain forest. Access to the reserve is possible from Mandritsare by means of a four-wheel-drive vehicle, but only during the dry season. Basic accommodations can be found in Mandritsara, but staying in the reserve itself requires camping. Species that may be seen here include hairy-eared dwarf lemur (*Allocebus trichotis*), northern bamboo lemur (*Hapalemur occidentalis*), red-bellied lemur (*Eulemur rubriventer*), variegated black-and-white ruffed lemur (*Varecia variegata variegata*), diademaed sifaka (*Propithecus diadema*), indri (*Indri indri*), and possibly aye-aye (*Daubentonia madagascariensis*).

Masoala National Park ***

Madagascar's largest national park (240,000 ha), Masoala is in the northeastern part of the country on the Masoala Peninsula. A visit to this remote area is a must for any naturalist interested in Madagascar, but it requires both time and organization. Quality lodging is available on the mainland at Maraontsetra (which can be reached by regular flights from Antananarivo and Toamasina), notably in the excellent Relais du Masoala Ecolodge, and boat trips to the Masoala Peninsula can be arranged through hotels in Maraontsetra or through an Antananarivo-based tour operator. Accommodations are now available on the peninsula as well, at Andranobe, Ambanizana, Lohatrozona, and Tampolo.

Fig. C.22: Pristine forest in the interior of the Masoala Peninsula. Masoala is now under heavy pressure from illegal logging (photo by R. A. Mittermeier).

A rewarding package trip is to spend one night on the island of Nosy Mangabe, which is quite close to the peninsula, and then do a one- to three-day visit to Masoala to any of the above mentioned sites. The highlight of your visit will be a sighting of the red ruffed lemur (*Varecia rubra*), which is endemic to the peninsula and relatively easy to find due to its loud vocalizations. The white-fronted brown lemur (*Eulemur albifrons*) is common, and the northern bamboo lemur (*Hapalemur occidentalis*) can also be seen. Night hikes in the forests near the Lohatrozona campsite offer the opportunity to see the Masoala fork-marked lemur (*Phaner furcifer*), the Masoala sportive lemur (*Lepilemur scottorum*), and the Masoala woolly lemur (*Avahi mooreorum*), the latter two also endemic to the peninsula. Other species reported in the park include an undescribed form of mouse lemur (*Microcebus*), hairy-eared dwarf lemur (*Allocebus trichotis*), greater dwarf lemur (*Cheirogaleus major*), and aye-aye (*Daubentonia madagascariensis*).

As with Marojejy, this park suffered illegal logging in 2009, but we are not yet sure to what extent this has impacted tourism. Be sure to check with tour operators and with Madagascar National Parks upon arrival in Antananarivo.

Menabe-Antimena Protected Area

See above (under Kirindy).

Midongy du Sud–Befotaka National Park

Midongy du Sud–Befotaka National Park in southeastern Madagascar provides opportunities to view several lemur species, though only the well-seasoned traveler should attempt this journey and then only during the drier months. Species that may be found here are an undescribed form of mouse lemur (*Microcebus*), greater dwarf lemur (*Cheirogaleus major*), southern bamboo lemur (*Hapalemur meridionalis*), red-collared brown lemur

Fig. C.23: A view of the Western Dry Deciduous Forest along the coast in the Menabe-Antimena region (photo by R. A. Mittermeier).

(*Eulemur collaris*), Peyriéras' woolly lemur (*Avahi peyrierasi*), aye-aye (*Daubentonia madagascariensis*), and perhaps Andohahela sportive lemur (*Lepilemur fleuretae*).

Montagne d'Ambre ***

The Montagne d'Ambre forest complex, including the Montagne d'Ambre National Park and the Forêt d'Ambre Special Reserve, is easily reached by car from Antsiranana (= Diégo-Suarez), a trip that takes 45 minutes to one hour. A four-wheel-drive vehicle is needed for the portion between Ambohitra (= Joffreville) and the park entrance, especially after a heavy rainfall. There are now two excellent lodges at Montagne d'Ambre, the Nature Lodge and Domaine de Fontenay (which also has a 300-ha private reserve where night walks can be quite productive). Daylight hikes close to the main campsite near the forestry station (Les Roussettes) and to the viewpoint overlooking the Grand Cascade will usually result in sightings of crowned lemur (*Eulemur coronatus*) and Sanford's brown lemur (*Eulemur sanfordi*). Night hikes near Les Roussettes and in the botanical garden of the Montagne d'Ambre National Park, though unfortunately not available at the moment (owing to the closure of all parks to nocturnal visits), provide excellent opportunities to observe the Montagne d'Ambre mouse lemur (*Microcebus arnholdi*), the greater dwarf lemur (*Cheirogaleus major*), the Montagne d'Ambre fork-marked lemur (*Phaner electromontis*), the Ankarana sportive lemur (*Lepilemur ankaranensis*), and possibly aye-aye (*Daubentonia madagascariensis*). This park is also one of the best places in Madagascar to see endemic carnivores, including the ring-tailed mongoose (*Galidia elegans*) and perhaps even the very rare falanouc (*Eupleres goudotii*).

Nosy Komba and Nosy Tanikely ***

The small island of Nosy Komba, near Nosy Be in northwestern Madagascar, is a good place to see the black lemur (*Eulemur macaco*). The island consists mainly of secondary forest and scrub, but several groups of very habituated black lemurs come every day to a

Fig. C.24: Entry sign for black lemur feeding area on the island of Nosy Komba (photo by R. A. Mittermeier).

Fig. C.25: The Grande Cascade in Montagne d'Ambre National Park, northern Madagascar (photo by O. Langrand).

feeding site where tourists can offer them bananas sold by local villagers. Day tours are available from most of the hotels on Nosy Be. There are two small but excellent lodges on the wooded side of the island, the Jardin Vanille and the Tsara Komba, where visitors can spend the night. Semi-wild black lemur populations can also be seen around these lodges.

The small island of Nosy Tanikely, a short distance from Nosy Komba and part of the Nosy Be tourist circuit, has an introduced population of the black lemur (*Eulemur macaco*). It is not worth a special visit for the lemurs, since they are much better seen in Lokobe or Nosy Komba. However, if one happens to be on this island for diving, the principal attraction, a short walk up the hill will usually provide some lemur sightings.

Nosy Mangabe Special Reserve ***

The island of Nosy Mangabe is located in the Bay of Antongil along Madagascar's northeastern coast, about 5 km offshore from Maroantsetra. The island can be reached by boat, a ride that takes only 20–30 minutes. Stays at the well maintained but basic campsite can be arranged through lodges in Maraontsetra, such as the Relais du Masoala, or through an Antananarivo-based tour operator.

Naturally-regenerated lowland rain forest covers the 520-ha island, which was heavily logged about two centuries ago. Nosy Mangabe is home to two diurnal lemur species, the white-fronted brown lemur (*Eulemur albifrons*) and the northern black-and-white ruffed lemur (*Varecia variegata subcincta*), and both are quite easy to see. Three nocturnal lemurs also inhabit the island; an as-yet unidentified form of mouse lemur (*Microcebus*), the greater dwarf lemur (*Cheirogaleus major*), and the aye-aye (*Daubentonia madagascariensis*), which was introduced to Nosy Mangabe in the late 1960s. Although sightings of the aye-

Fig. C.26: Aerial view of the island of Nosy Mangabe, Bay of Antongil, northeastern Madagascar (photo by R. A. Mittermeier).

aye are by no means guaranteed, this is one of the best places in the country to see this elusive creature. Although there is often a lot of human activity along the beach next to the campsite, the beach trail between the campsite and a fisherman's camp a short distance away is nonetheless the most likely place to find them. Alternatively, ask the local guide if a *ramy* tree is in fruit, since this is one of the aye-aye's favorite foods. A climb to the lighthouse at the top of the island is also recommended, both for the view and for lemurs that can be found along the way.

Nosy Mangabe is also a delightful setting, a tropical island "paradise" at its best. In addition to the lemurs, it is excellent for a variety of reptiles and amphibians, and serves as a base from which to see migrating humpback whales from July to late September. Day trips from the island to the Masoala Peninsula are also possible.

Pic d' Ivohibe Special Reserve

This small reserve of 3,450 ha is located south of Andringitra National Park in southeastern Madagascar. It can be reached from Ihosy by means of a four-wheel-drive vehicle, though the journey can be challenging if the bridges along the way have not been repaired from damage sustained in the region's frequent tropical storms. Species to be seen here include rufous mouse lemur (*Microcebus rufus*), greater dwarf lemur (*Cheirogaleus major*), southern bamboo lemur (*Hapalemur meridionalis*), ring-tailed lemur (*Lemur catta*), red-fronted brown lemur (*Eulemur rufifrons*), red-bellied lemur (*Eulemur rubriventer*), and possibly aye-aye (*Daubentonia madagascariensis*).

"PK 32" and Ifaty

The forest called "PK 32" is near Ifaty, about one hour north of Toliara (= Tuléar) in southwestern Madagascar. It is best known to birdwatchers who come to see local endemics such as the subdesert mesite (*Monias benschi*), the long-tailed ground-roller (*Uratelornis chimaera*), and the running coua (*Coua cursor*). It is also one of the best places to see the gray-brown mouse lemur (*Microcebus griseorufus*). High-end hotels such as Les Dunes or Le Paradisier cater to more demanding tourists, while the Plage, Vovotelo and Le Baobab Hotels are suitable for those traveling on a more modest budget. Night walks in the forest can be arranged from many of the hotels in the Ifaty-Mangily region along the coast, and information on availability of local guides can be found in hotels such as the Mora Mora and the Lakana Vezo in Ifaty.

Ranomafana National Park ***

Ranomafana is located in southeastern Madagascar, and is one of the premier lemur-watching sites in the country. It also has one of Madagascar's most sophisticated research stations. It is particularly important for bamboo lemurs, of which three types can be seen within the park's boundaries. In fact one form, the golden bamboo lemur (*Hapalemur aureus*) was first discovered there in 1986. The greater bamboo lemur (*Prolemur simus*), one of the world's most endangered primates, is also present but down to vey low numbers. The smaller, recently-described Ranomafana bamboo lemur (*Hapalemur griseus ranomafanensis*) is more abundant and is most likely to be observed at dusk in stands of common bamboo. Finding all three forms is possible, but requires perseverance, the use of local guides, and at least a couple of days in the forest.

Fig. C.27: River by the entrance to Ranomafana National Park (photo by R. A. Mittermeier).

Many other lemur species are found in Ranomafana as well. Groups of red-bellied lemurs (*Eulemur rubiventer*), for instance, have been habituated along the main trail network and are easy to find, in contrast to most other sites where this species is usually quite rare. This is especially true when Chinese guava is in fruit (April–June), at which time they can be seen around Belle Vue along with red-fronted brown lemurs (*Eulemur rufifrons*). This is also one of the best places to find Milne-Edwards' sifaka (*Propithecus edwardsi*), which can be seen at several locations within the park including the Vohiparara region. The southern black-and-white ruffed lemur (*Varecia variegata editorum*) occurs in Ranomafana as well but finding this species usually requires a few hours of hiking from the Talakately Research Station to reach the more distant forests where they live. Night walks at Ranomafana, meanwhile, offer good opportunities to view several nocturnal lemurs, including rufous mouse lemur (*Microcebus rufus*), greater dwarf lemur (*Cheirogaleus major*), Peyriéras' woolly lemur (*Avahi peyrierasi*), and small-toothed sportive lemur (*Lepilemur microdon*), which is most likely to be observed in the park's Vohiparara region. Aye-aye (*Daubentonia madagascariensis*) are also present, but as always difficult to find.

Ranomafana is also a very popular destination for birdwatchers, who come especially to see the brown mesite (*Mesitornis unicolor*) and Pollen's vanga (*Xenopirostris polleni*). There are now a number of hotels available in the Ranomafana area, the two best being the Centrest Sejour and the Domaine Nature Lodge, which are near the park entrance. In the village of Ranomafana itself there are several other more modest accommodations such as the Setam Lodge. Guides are mandatory, and necessary if one wants to find all lemur species present in the park. They are highly skilled and will contribute significantly towards making your visit a success.

Ranomafana National Park can be reached from Antananarivo by car in about seven hours. It can also be reached by car from Fianarantsoa, which is accessible by a weekly commercial flight from the capital. From there, the 50-km drive to Ranomafana takes about an hour. The main highway is fine, and the RN25 is now paved all the way to the park.

Sahamalaza-Iles Radama National Park

The newly-created Sahamalaza-Iles Radama National Park in northwestern Madagascar is the best place to see the blue-eyed black lemur (*Eulemur flavifrons*), as well as the recently-described Sahamalaza sportive lemur (*Lepilemur sahamalazensis*). Other species to be found in the southern part of the park include the northern giant mouse lemur (*Mirza zaza*) and an as-yet-unidentified form of dwarf lemur (*Cheirogaleus*), while in the northern mainland part visitors may see black lemur (*Eulemur macaco*) and possibly Mittermeier's sportive lemur (*Lepilemur mittermeieri*). Also reported within the park's boundaries are northern bamboo lemur (*Hapalemur occidentalis*) and aye-aye (*Daubentonia madagascariensis*), but, as always, the latter is quite difficult to find.

The Ankarafa Forest in Sahamalaza can be reached by a one-hour boat trip from Analalava, a beautiful seaside resort with basic accommodation (e.g., Hotel Malibu, Hotel Narindra). From Analalava, one proceeds to the small village of Marovato, and from there it is a two-hour hike inland. Analalava is served regularly by ferry and bush taxi from Antsohihy, and boats can be arranged locally. However, use of an Antananarivo or Antsiranana-based tour operator and guide is essential. The Sahamalaza Peninsula can also be reached by pirogue from Maromandia. A local guide association was in the process of being formed in 2008.

Sainte-Luce Private Reserve **

The Sainte-Luce Private Reserve is in southeastern Madagascar north of Tolagnaro (= Fort-Dauphin). It consists of a small tract of coastal forest, and is a good site for seeing the red-collared brown lemur (*Eulemur collaris*) in the *Pandanus*-dominated forest right along the ocean. Sightings of fat-tailed dwarf lemur (*Cheirogaleus medius*) and southern woolly lemur (*Avahi meridionalis*) are possible as well. The reserve belongs to the de Heaulme family, the owners of Berenty, and arrangements to visit can be made through the Hotel Le Dauphin in Tolagnaro.

Tsaratanana Strict Nature Reserve

This large, isolated reserve in northwestern Madagascar provides protection for an important altitudinal gradient of rain forest that culminates at 2,876 m, the highest point in the country. Access is from Ambanja on the west coast, where simple hotels can be found. Visitors need a permit from Madagascar National Parks to enter, and getting there entails expedition-level preparation since this protected area is isolated and remote. A reasonable level of fitness is also necessary. Species to be found here include greater dwarf lemur (*Cheirogaleus major*), pale fork-marked lemur (*Phaner pallescens*), Gray's sportive lemur (*Lepilemur dorsalis*), northern bamboo lemur (*Hapalemur occidentalis*), black lemur (*Eulemur macaco*), brown lemur (*Eulemur fulvus*), red-bellied lemur (*Eulemur rubriventer*), and aye-aye (*Daubentonia madagascariensis*). The newly-described Margot Marsh's mouse lemur (*Microcebus margotmarshae*) may perhaps occur there as well as at higher elevations, though this has yet to be confirmed. This reserve is not recommended for first-time visitors to Madagascar, and mounting an expedition there can be quite costly.

Tsimanampetsotsa National Park

Tsimanampetsotsa National Park is in southwestern Madagascar, about a two-hour drive from Anakao (a coastal tourist location with good seaside hotels) or a 45-minute boat ride south of Toliara (= Tuléar). A visit to this protected area can be arranged by hotels in Anakao, such as the Prince Anakao, Anakao Resort, Safari Vezo, Chez Diégo, or De l'Autre Côté de la Lune. The Domaine d' Ambola, situated near the park, can be booked through an Antananarivo-based tour operator. Although mainly a site for flamingos and other waterfowl, as well as the rare carnivore, Grandidier's mongoose (*Galidictis grandidieri*), there is also a good selection of lemurs to be seen. The Mahafaly Plateau, with its dense covering of xeric vegetation, is home to the gray-brown mouse lemur (*Microcebus griseorufus*), fat-tailed dwarf lemur (*Cheirogaleus medius*), white-footed sportive lemur (*Lepilemur leucopus*), ring-tailed lemur (*Lemur catta*), and Verreaux's sifaka (*Propithecus verreauxi*).

Tsingy de Bemaraha National Park and Strict Nature Reserve ***

The Tsingy de Bemaraha National Park and adjoining Strict Nature Reserve are in southwestern Madagascar, and are best known for their amazing knife-like karst outcrops, or tsingys. This park was also Madagascar's first UNESCO World Heritage Site. The forests surrounding these strange formations are particularly good for Decken's sifaka (*Propithecus deckenii*) and rufous brown lemur (*Eulemur rufus*), and there is a chance of seeing the elusive Ranomafana bamboo lemur (*Hapalemur griseus ranomafanensis*) in stands of bamboo. This is also the only place where one can see Bemaraha woolly lemur (*Avahi cleesei*) and Bemaraha sportive lemur (*Lepilemur randrianasoloi*), and probably the best site for Peters' mouse lemur (*Microcebus myoxinus*). Other species that may be

Fig. C.28: Walkway through the tsingy formations in the Tsingy de Bemaraha National Park (photo by R. A. Mittermeier).

Fig. C.29: The spectacular karst formations, known locally as "tsingy", in the Tsingy de Bemaraha National Park (photo by R. A. Mittermeier).

encountered there include another as-yet unidentified form of *Microcebus*, Coquerel's giant mouse lemur (*Mirza coquereli*), pale fork-marked lemur (*Phaner pallescens*), and possibly the aye-aye (*Daubentonia madagascariensis*). Excursions can be arranged through the Hotel Chez Maggie in Morondava or through most Antananarivo-based tour operators. In addition, there are now two lodges in nearby Bemaraha, the Orchidée de Bemaraha and L'Olympe du Bemaraha. Simple campsites along the Manambolo River, such as Camp Croco, offer alternative accommodations in the form of small tents.

Tsingy de Namoroka National Park

Located in central-western Madagascar, the Tsingy de Namoroka is one of the three protected areas in Madagascar featuring the unusual karst formations known as tsingys. Lemur species known to occur here include gray mouse lemur (*Microcebus murinus*), northern giant mouse lemur (*Mirza zaza*), fat-tailed dwarf lemur (*Cheirogaleus medius*), pale fork-marked lemur (*Phaner pallescens*), northern bamboo lemur (*Hapalemur occidentalis*), rufous brown lemur (*Eulemur rufus*), Decken's sifaka (*Propithecus deckenii*), and possibly aye-aye (*Daubentonia madagascariensis*). Although this area is interesting for its tsingys, it is more difficult to reach than the other two, similarly-featured protected areas, and it is not a high priority for lemur-watching.

Tsiombikibo Forest *

The Tsiombikibo Forest is located northwest of Mitsinjo in western Madagascar. It is presently the only site where one can see the recently-described Tsiombikibo sportive lemur (*Lepilemur ahmansonorum*), and is also a good site for the mongoose lemur (*Eulemur mongoz*) and Decken's sifaka (*Propithecus deckenii*). Populations of rufous brown lemur

(*Eulemur rufus*) and northern bamboo lemur (*Hapalemur occidentalis*) occur here as well. The road from Katsepy, the only access, is closed during the rainy season (November–May), so visits are only practical during the dry season. Visitors need to be self-sufficient as there are currently no amenities. Engaging the services of an Antananarivo-based tour operator is highly recommended.

Vohimana

This 800-ha rain forest is part of the Mantadia-Vohidrazana forest block, and ranges in altitude from 700–1,040 m. Vohimana features many of the lemur species found in Analamazaotra Special Reserve and Mantadia National Park, including Goodman's mouse lemur (*Microcebus lehilahytsara*), Crossley's dwarf lemur (*Cheirogaleus crossleyi*), weasel sportive lemur (*Lepilemur mustelinus*), gray bamboo lemur (*Hapalemur g. griseus*), indri (*Indri indri*) and diademed sifaka (*Propithecus diadema*). Simple accommodations are situated on a steep gorge. The site is also excellent for reptiles and frogs.

Zahamena National Park and Strict Nature Reserve

The Zahamena National Park and the adjacent Zahamena Strict Nature Reserve are in the central-eastern part of the island. Access is difficult, and is normally undertaken by way of Ambatondrazaka to the west of the park. It takes about six hours by car from Antananarivo to Ambatondrazaka, and then two more hours to cover the 70 km to Antanadava. A four-wheel-drive vehicle is necessary for this last stretch of the journey. Ambatondrazaka offers some basic hotels, but you have to camp if you want to stay in the park itself. Access from the east of the park is exclusively by foot from Vavatenina, an 8-hour trek up Madagascar's steep eastern escarpment to the highly-degraded northeastern corner. Those who have permission to enter the Strict Nature Reserve can head south from Vavatenina (by motorcycle) to Miarinarivo, proceeding from there on a vigorous, two-day walk to the strictly protected lowland rain forests of the southeastern corner.

The forest in this region is spectacular, and species known to occur here include Simmon's mouse lemur (*Microcebus simmonsi*), hairy-eared dwarf lemur (*Allocebus trichotis*), Crossley's dwarf lemur (*Cheirogaleus crossleyi*), Masoala fork-marked lemur (*Phaner furcifer*), weasel sportive lemur (*Lepilemur mustelinus*), northern bamboo lemur (*Hapalemur occidentalis*), brown lemur (*Eulemur fulvus*), red-bellied lemur (*Eulemur rubriventer*), variegated black-and-white ruffed lemur (*Varecia variegata variegata*), eastern woolly lemur (*Avahi laniger*), diademed sifaka (*Propithecus diadema*), indri (*Indri indri*), and aye-aye (*Daubentonia madagascariensis*).

It should be noted that there is a high risk of malaria in Zahamena, so it is necessary to take precautions. Given the difficulty of access, Zahamena is not recommended for first-time visitors to Madagascar.

Zombitse-Vohibasia National Park *

This park is in southwestern Madagascar 145–150 km northeast of Toliara (= Tuléar), from which it can be reached by car in about two hours along an excellent road. Otherwise it may be reached from Isalo, 85–90 km to the southwest, using a portion of RN7 that has been recently renovated. Zombitse-Vohibasia is currently the only area for seeing the newly-described Zombitse sportive lemur (*Lepilemur hubbardorum*), which can easily be found even during the day as it peers out from daytime sleeping sites. Diurnal ring-tailed lemur (*Lemur catta*), red-fronted brown lemur (*Eulemur rufifrons*) and Verreaux's sifaka

Fig. C.30: View of the Zombitse section of the Zombitse-Vohibasia National Park (photo by R. A. Mittermeier).

(*Propithecus verreauxi*) also occur in the park, although it is by no means the best site for any of these species. Night hikes offer opportunities to see gray mouse lemur (*Microcebus murinus*), fat-tailed dwarf lemur (*Cheirogaleus medius*), and Coquerel's giant mouse lemur (*Mirza coquereli*), in addition to the Zombitse sportive lemur, and a fork-marked lemur that is probably *Phaner pallescens* but possibly a new species. There are very basic hotels located in Sakaraha about 12 km from the park, and camping is also possible. A visit to Zombitse-Vohibasia can be combined with a visit to Isalo National Park, since the two are only about an hour apart by car. The Zombitse section of the park is perfectly safe and located right along the highway. The more distant Vohibasia section is sometimes off limits for security reasons due to its use by cattle rustlers.

Captive Facilities for Lemurs in Madagascar

Parc Botanique et Zoologique de Tsimbazaza

Madagascar's national zoo, the Parc Botanique et Zoologique de Tsimbazaza (PBZT) was originally founded in 1925 by the French colonial government. It was intended to be a botanical garden for collecting and breeding local plant species, and for introducing "interesting foreign plants" to the island. Some cages with native animal species were later added at the request of the Muséum national d'Histoire naturelle in Paris. In 1960, the park was integrated into the French Office de la Recherche Scientifique et Technique d'Outre-mer (ORSTOM). In 1974, it was nationalized, and today is under the Ministry of Higher Education. The artificial lake in the center of the park was constructed in 1815 by King Radama I, who needed a place for his soldiers to bathe. It is now a breeding colony for a wild population of cattle egrets.

Fig. C.31: View of the new Nocturnal Lemur House and the old lemur cages, Parc Tsimbazaza (photo by R. A. Mittermeier).

Fig. C.32: Lemur cages at the Parc Botanique et Zoologique de Tsimbazaza (photo by R. A. Mittermeier).

Today, the PBZT is home to a variety of endemic Malagasy mammal, bird and reptile species, along with a few exotics such as ostriches, golden pheasants, and Aldabra tortoises. It also still houses an important collection of native plants, and offers a plant identification service for researchers. Lemurs are represented mostly by members of the Lemuridae (*Eulemur*, *Lemur*, *Hapalemur*, and *Varecia*), with a relatively new nocturnal house also featuring aye-ayes (*Daubentonia madagascariensis*) and various species of mouse lemur (*Microcebus*). The park keeps and breeds several highly threatened lemurs that can be challenging to see in the wild (e.g., *Varecia variegata* and *Eulemur flavifrons*). Most are kept in basic cages, though some have recently been renovated with the help of international donors, most notably the Henry Doorly Zoo in Omaha, Nebraska, USA. Some species are also kept on small islands in one of the lakes in the park.

Attached to the PBZT is a small natural history museum that houses interesting lemur specimens, including reconstructed skeletons of several of the extinct giant lemurs. At the time of writing, this museum was closed for renovation, and we are not certain when it will reopen. There is also a library on the park grounds that has a substantial collection of books and journals on the natural history of Madagascar, but it is not open to the general public.

The park is centrally located in Antananarivo, and open every day from 9:00 am to 5:00 pm. Entry for non-nationals is 10.000 ariary, or about US$5.00. Guides are available at the main entrance for a fee to be negotiated, but are not really necessary. The address of PBZT is Rue Fernand Kasanga, Tsimbazaza, Antananarivo 101 (phone: +261 20 22 311 49, +261 20 22 310 14, +261 20 22 337 56; email: <pbzt@bow.dts.mg>).

Croc Farm Parc Zoologique

Croc Farm is a private park owned by Reptel, a company that farms Nile crocodiles (*Crocodylus niloticus*) for leather production. The company, founded by Daniel Bessaguet and Jean Christophe Peyre in 1988, moved into its current premises in Ivato (about five minutes from Antananarivo's Ivato International Airport) in 1993. In 1994, they opened parts of their crocodile breeding farm to the public, and over the years added various lemur species and other Malagasy fauna to their live collection. The 3-ha park now claims to show more than 80 animal species, including seven different lemurs, fossa (*Cryptoprocta ferox*), parrots, tortoises and other reptiles, and amphibians. The amphibians and some of the smaller reptiles are housed in a small, very nice vivarium building. The largest part of the park is of course devoted to the breeding of Nile crocodiles. Some 200 large adults live in an artificial lake, and they are fed for the public at 1.00 p.m. on Wednesdays, Fridays and Sundays. Hundreds of other juveniles and young adults of varying sizes are also on view.

Croc Farm is open year-round (except January 1, June 26 and December 25) from 9:00 a.m. to 5:00 p.m., and admission is 10,000 ariary (about US$5.00). More information can be found at <www.reptel-mada.com>, and the park can be contacted at +261 (0)20 22 03071/00715, or at +261 (0)34 14 30010/30020.

Lemurs' Park

Lemurs' Park is a private, 5-ha site located 22 km southwest of Antananarivo along the RN1 (towards Ampefy), between the villages of Fenoarivo and Imerintsiatosika. It was founded about 10 years ago by Laurent Amouric and Maxime Allorge (grandson of Pierre Boiteau, Founding Director of the Parc Botanique et Zoologique de Tsimbazaza in Antananarivo), with the goal of showing lemurs to the public and eventually reintroducing captive-born lemurs back into the wild. The park, bordered on one side by the Katsaoka

River, is currently home to nine species of lemur, most of which are free-ranging in the pine forest and bamboo vegetation of the site. Notable species include two groups of Coquerel's sifakas (*Propithecus coquereli*), crowned sifaka (*Propithecus coronatus*), a single diademed sifaka (*P. diadema*), and a group of variegated black-and-white ruffed lemurs (*Varecia variegata variegata*). In addition, there are radiated tortoises, chameleons, and other reptiles. The park is successfully breeding Coquerel's sifakas, with several having been born since 2007.

Lemurs' Park is open year-round from 9:00 a.m. until 5:00 p.m. (last entry at 4:30 p.m.), and can be visited without prior booking. However, if you would like a full meal in the park's restaurant, this needs to be booked 48 hours in advance. Note that the restaurant and gift shop are closed on Mondays between January and April. The entrance fee of 15,000 ariary or about US$7.50 (8,000 for children 4-12; under 4 is free) includes a compulsory guided tour.

The easiest way to get to Lemurs' Park is by using the park's own minibus ("navette"), which needs to be reserved (+261 (0)33 11 252 59, <lemurspark@gmail.com>, <lemurspark@moov.mg>). It departs twice daily, at 9.00 a.m. and 2.00 p.m., from outside the Glacier restaurant in the center of Antananarivo (Analakely). The price of 25,000 ariary, or about US$12.50, per person includes transportation and entry to the park. More information can be found at <www.lemurspark.com>.

Ivoloina Parc Zoologique ***

Parc Ivoloina is a 282 ha forestry station that also includes a small zoo of about 4 ha. It is located 12 km north of Toamasina (= Tamatave) and is operated by the Madagascar Fauna Group (MFG), a consortium of North American and European zoos, under a long-term agreement with the Malagasy government. The zoo was reopened to the public by the MFG in 1990 after a cyclone had destroyed it four years earlier. It receives about 14,000 visitors annually, 70% of which are Malagasy.

Parc Ivoloina currently houses more than 100 lemurs of 10 different species, several of which are breeding. Species of note include greater bamboo lemur (*Prolemur simus*), blue-eyed black lemur (*Eulemur flavifrons*), and variegated black-and-white ruffed lemur (*Varecia variegata variegata*). The park also has aye-ayes (*Daubentonia madagascariensis*), and nocturnal visits can be arranged to see them when they are active. Five lemur species can also be seen in the forest surrounding the park, some of them, such as crowned lemur (*Eulemur coronatus*) having been introduced. The zoo has several bird, reptile, and amphibian species as well. MFG staff teach sustainable agriculture to visitors in their model station, and there is a conservation education center for school groups.

The park is open daily from 9:00 am to 5:00 pm, and entry for non-nationals is 10,000 ariary, or about US$5.00 (4,000 ariary for children aged 5–12). Guided tours can be arranged for 10,000 ariary. Meals can be arranged for groups, and there is a small souvenir shop that sells postcards and t-shirts. The park also has a conference room that seats 100 people, as well as a laboratory and a dormitory. Camping is possible near the lake for 4,000 ariary per night, but you need to bring your own tent. The postal address of Parc Ivoloina is Madagascar Fauna Group, BP 442 Toamasina 501 (phone office +261 (0)53 308 42, Parc Ivoloina Zoo +261 (0)53 931 68, Training Centre +261 (0)53 985 61).

APPENDIX D

PRIMATE-WATCHING AND PRIMATE LIFE-LISTING

With the publication of this new book, the latest in our Tropical Field Guide series, we would like to continue to promote the hobby/sport of *primate-watching*, and its associated activity, *primate life-listing*. Needless to say, the idea for this derives from birdwatching, which is one of the most popular hobbies in North America, Europe, and Australia, and increasingly in the world as a whole. Birdwatching has been with us for a long time, and its popularity appears to be growing. What is more, it is facilitated by an ever-increasing number of guidebooks covering a large portion of our planet, by increasingly sophisticated equipment, and, in this age of the Internet, by more and more websites connecting birders around the world. Indeed, wild bird feeding alone is said to be second only to gardening as a hobby, and its increasing popularity and connectivity is making it even more of a subculture than it has been in the past.

Birdwatching has brought with it a wide variety of merchandise, including books and magazines, DVDs, videos, bird-listing software, a trivia game (*The Great North American Birdwatching Trivia Game*), and even something called a "birdPod" (a device similar to an iPod, but with bird sounds instead of music), not to mention the required binoculars, cameras, and camping equipment that come in an endless variety of forms. All of this has been good for conservation, stimulating awareness of and love for birds, and providing many ecotourism-based economic opportunities for communities living in or near bird habitats—from the richest of the developed countries to the poorest in the developing world. This hobby has become a multi-billion dollar industry, with at least some of the benefits accruing to the bird-rich countries of the tropics. To give some idea of the scale of what already exists and the kinds of sites that are being visited, we provide some American examples in the Boxes 1 and 2:

(Sources: <www.gwf.org/birdbucks.htm> and
<www.library.fws.gov/Pubs/birding_natsurvey06.pdf>).

Inspired by the success and impact of birdwatching and bird life-listing, we decided about six years ago to launch *primate-watching* and *primate life-listing* as a formally recognized activity. There are in fact quite a few of us primate-watchers around already, and some of us have been active for nearly four decades. But we have not yet given ourselves a name, we do not have a website, and we do not have listing software. What is more, we have not yet recognized ourselves as a unique group, a clan or tribe if you like, within the global community of nature-lovers. What is more, we (with a handful of exceptions) have not yet begun to compete with one another—an essential ingredient in any hobby or sport. In addition, by comparison with what exists for birds, we have very little in the way of good published material to identify primates, such as country or region-wide field guides and other visual and auditory aids.

Fortunately, however, this is changing. We tried to stimulate it in 1994 with the first edition of this book on lemurs, have since published several other titles on primates, and have still more in preparation. In addition, a number of other authors have produced very useful primate guides, including ones on Central Africa, Brazil, French Guiana, Indonesia, India, and Vietnam, and primate information of variable quality can also be found in a number of other regional or national guidebooks on mammals.

Mittermeier and Rylands have launched a series of Pocket Identification Guides, which are small, very convenient folding guides to identify animals from a particular region. Thirteen of these have already been published, most of them on primates, and including four on lemurs, with a fifth and sixth to appear shortly based on this new guide.

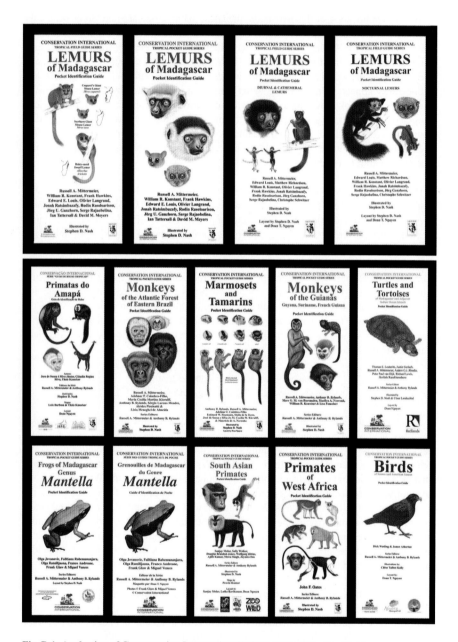

Fig. D.1: A selection of Conservation International's Pocket Identification Guides.

Consequently, although we are still way behind the birders in terms of the number of quality publications to help us identify what we are seeing and still do not have primate-specific software or a website, we are getting better. And we are just getting started.

The following two boxes provide examples of the scale of the interest and the economics of the business that surrounds bird-watching as a hobby, pastime and sport in the United States.

Box 1
The Impact of Birding in the United States

A report released in 2009 by the U.S. Fish and Wildlife Service shows that, as of 2006, 48 million people in the United States 16 years of age or older were birdwatchers. This number represents roughly 20 percent of the population. Backyard birdwatching was the most common activity reported (42 million people), but 20 million considered themselves birdwatchers away from their home. The report also shows that the higher the income and education level, the more likely a person is to be a birdwatcher.

The economics of birdwatching are also very interesting. Birdwatchers spend money on a wide variety of goods and services, from travel-related expenses (e.g., food, lodging, transport) to equipment (e.g., binoculars, cameras, camping gear). These travel and equipment expenditures, totaling some $36 billion in 2006, generated $82 billion in total industry output across the United States. These same expenditures helped to create, in that year alone, approximately 671,000 jobs and generated $28 billion in employment income. Finally, the tax revenues derived from birdwatching-related recreational spending in 2006 amounted to $6 billion at the state level, and $4 billion federally.

(Source: International Migratory Bird Day Organizers Packet, "*Sharing Your Passion for Birds*.")

Box 2
Examples of Specific Birdwatching Sites

The effect of dollars spent by ecotourists in and around birdwatching sites is "multiplied" as tourist dollars become profits, then local wages, then consumer income once again. In some regions, this cumulative effect may approach five-to-one. Consider the following examples.

Cape May, New Jersey: More than 100,000 birders visit this area annually, providing a cumulative impact of nearly $10 million.

High Island, Texas: In 1992, more than 6,000 birders visited this small Gulf Coast town. They spent $2.5 million directly in the community, and generated a total regional economic impact of about $6 million.

Chincoteague National Wildlife Refuge, Virginia: The economic impact to the local community by wildlife viewers in 1994 was nearly $10 million.

Hawk Mountain Sanctuary, Pennsylvania: More than 50,000 visitors each year contribute more than $4 million to the local economy.

Grand Island, Nebraska: At least 80,000 avitourists annually visit this rural community on the Platte River; they spend more than $15 million, and provide to the region a cumulative "roll-over" benefit of nearly $40 million.

Point Pelee, Ontario: Another migration "hot-spot" that attracts more than 57,000 birders each year, who spend almost $4 million in the area.

Arizona: A University of Arizona study revealed that two birding "hot-spots" in southwestern Arizona attracted 38,000 avitourists in 1991, who in turn spent $1.6 million and generated $2.7 million in local economic impact, sustaining 56 local jobs.

Ottawa National Wildlife Refuge, Ohio: More than $5 million was spent by birdwatchers visiting this refuge in 1993.

(Source: International Migratory Bird Day Organizers Packet, "*Sharing Your Passion for Birds*.")

Why should we bother? Well, first of all, because primate-watching and primate life-listing is fun. We who are as passionate about these animals as the birders are about theirs really enjoy seeing monkeys, apes, lemurs, lorises, galagos, pottos and tarsiers in their natural environments, and we want more of you to get excited about these animals as well. First and foremost, we want to stimulate awareness of primates through such activity. Second, primates are found mainly in tropical rain forests and are the most visible mammals in these forests. As such, they have been and continue to be excellent flagships for these dwindling habitats and have contributed greatly to tropical rain forest conservation over the past 30–40 years. Furthermore, we need more primate-based ecotourism to provide economic alternatives to the communities living in close proximity to the habitats in which primates live. These communities need to benefit economically from the presence of primate populations. To ensure that this happens, we need to go and see these creatures in their natural environments, interact with the communities upon whose survival they ultimately depend, share our excitement and enthusiasm, and, after all is said and done, make a contribution to the local economy. In many places, this may be the only effective tool at our disposal to ensure the survival of "Critically Endangered" and "Endangered" primates, and it needs to happen now.

Fig. D.2: Tourist photographing Crossley's dwarf lemur (*Cheirogaleus crossleyi*) feeding on the sap of a traveller's palm (*Ravenala madagascariensis*) right next to the restaurant of the Feon' ny Ala Hotel, Andasibe (photo by R. A. Mittermeier).

To be sure, some primate ecotourism already exists: mountain gorillas (and increasingly the lowland gorillas) in Central Africa; rehabilitated orangutans in Sumatra and Borneo; certain macaques and some other species at sacred sites in China, India, and Southeast Asia; Neotropical monkeys in parks and reserves in Central and South America; and, of course, the wonderful lemurs of Madagascar in the many sites described in this book.

Unfortunately, primate ecotourism has not always been done as well or as carefully as we might like, and we need to improve it wherever the quality is poor or even detrimental to primate survival. However, we need to recognize that it is here to stay, and we simply have to get it done in the most appropriate manner possible—promoting the conservation of tropical forests, the well-being of local communities, and the economies of the countries where primates occur, and of course, the survival of the primates themselves. In any case, we have only started to scratch the surface of the potential that exists for primate-watching, and to demonstrate at a much higher level the economic benefits that it can provide.

Fig. D.3: Russ Mittermeier and friend (photo by C. G. Mittermeier).

To further stimulate your interest in lemurs and to launch you on your primate-watching and primate life-listing career, we provide you not just with this comprehensive guidebook but also with a checklist of lemurs at the back of this book. Use it to jumpstart your own list on your trip to Madagascar. What is more, we provide the Madagascar life-list of one primate-watcher, Russ Mittermeier, who has seen all 15 genera and 74 of the 101 lemur taxa recognized in this book—this to stimulate your interest and to give you something to shoot for. Some of you may already have seen more lemurs than Mittermeier, and we urge you to compile your list, send it to us, and later include it in what will be our eventual website for primate life-listing.

We wish you success and hope that you will join us in this new and exciting activity, and become another member of what will soon be a large community of primate-watchers around the world.

Fig. D.4: Ed Louis Jr. examining an indri (*Indri indri*), Anjanajatibe-Sud Special Reserve (photo by M. Mayor).

Russ Mittermeier's Lemur Life-List
(First Sightings through July, 2010)

Total: 72 species and 74 taxa

Scientific Name	Locality	Date*
Microcebus murinus	Berenty, gallery forest	August 20, 1984
Microcebus griseorufus	Berenty, spiny forest	November 20, 2003
Microcebus berthae	Analabe Forest, Menabe	November 21, 1985
Microcebus myoxinus	Tsingy Kely, Tsingy de Bemaraha National Park	November 16, 2003
Microcebus ravelobensis	Ampijoroa, Ankarafantsika National Park	November 20, 1997
Microcebus mamiratra	Ampasipohy, Lokobe National Park	September 28, 2006
Microcebus tavaratra	Ankarana National Park	December 9, 2004
Microcebus arnholdi	Nosy Mangabe	August 24, 1984
Microcebus lehilahytsara	Analamazaotra Special Reserve	August 18, 1984
Microcebus arnholdi	Joffreville, next to Montagne d'Ambre National Park	September 26, 2006
Microcebus rufus	Nosy Mangabe	August 24, 1984
Microcebus jollyae	Manombo Special Reserve	June 18, 2005
Microcebus lehilahytsara	Analamazaotra Special Reserve	August 18, 1984
Microcebus macarthurii	Nosy Mangabe Special Reserve	August 28, 1984
Microcebus mittermeieri	Anjanaharibe-Sud Special Reserve	January 24, 2003
Mirza coquereli	Analabe Forest, Menabe	November 21, 1985
Mirza zaza	Benavony Forest, 6 km from Ambanja	April 15, 2006
Allocebus trichotis	Analamazaotra Special Reserve	January 27, 2003
Cheirogaleus medius	Analabe Forest, Menabe	November 22, 1985
Cheirogaleus major	Montagne d'Ambre National Park	November 24, 1997
Cheirogaleus crossleyi	Analamazaotra Special Reserve	November 23, 1985
Phaner pallescens	Analabe Forest, Menabe	November 21, 1985
Phaner parienti	Benavony Forest, 6 km from Ambanja	April 15, 2006
Phaner electromontis	Montagne d'Ambre National Park	November 18, 1985
Lepilemur mustelinus	Analamazaotra Special Reserve	November 20, 1993

Scientific Name	Locality	Date*
Lepilemur milanoii	Daraina	April 18, 1995
Lepilemur ankaranensis	Ankarana Special Reserve	December 7, 2004
Lepilemur septentrionalis	Tsingy de Bemaraha National Park	August 20, 2005
Lepilemur tymerlachsonorum	Lokobe Strict Nature Reserve	June 25, 1991
Lepilemur mittermeieri	Ampasindava Peninsula	April 16, 2006
Lepilemur sahamalazensis	Sahamalaza	October 18, 2004
Lepilemur edwardsi	Ampijoroa, Ankarafantsika National Park	September 4, 1984
Lepilemur randrianasoloi	Tsingy de Bemaraha National Park	December 5, 2004
Lepilemur ruficaudatus	Analabe Forest, Menabe	November 22, 1985
Lepilemur hubbardorum	Zombitse-Vohibasia National Park	July 16, 2010
Lepilemur petteri	Beza-Mahafaly Special Reserve	September 7, 1984
Lepilemur leucopus	Berenty Private Reserve	August 20, 1984
Hapalemur griseus griseus	Analamazaotra Special Reserve	November 4, 1986
Hapalemur griseus ranomafanensis	Ranomafana National Park	July 27, 2001
Hapalemur meridionalis	Andohahela National Park	November 15, 1985
Hapalemur occidentalis	Benovony Forest, 6 km from Ambanja	April 15, 2006
Hapalemur alaotrensis	Andreba, Lac Alaotra	October 23, 2000
Hapalemur aureus	Ranomafana National Park	November 12, 1986
Prolemur simus	Ranomafana National Park	July 27, 2001
Lemur catta	Berenty	August 21, 1984
Eulemur fulvus	Ampijoroa, Ankarafantsika National Park	September 5, 1984
Eulemur rufus	Bay of Baly National Park	January 21, 2008
Eulemur rufifrons	Analabe Forest, Menabe	November 21, 1985
Eulemur albifrons	Nosy Mangabe Special Reserve	August 28, 1984
Eulemur sanfordi	Montagne d'Ambre National Park	November 18, 1985
Eulemur cinereiceps	Manombo Special Reserve	August 28, 1984
Eulemur collaris	Saint Luce Private Reserve	February 17, 1990

Scientific Name	Locality	Date*
Eulemur macaco	Nosy Komba	September 3, 1984
Eulemur flavifrons	Sahamalaza	October 18, 2004
Eulemur coronatus	Montagne d' Ambre National Park	November 19, 1985
Eulemur rubriventer	Ranomafana National Park	November 11, 1986
Eulemur mongoz	Ampijoroa, Ankarafantsika National Park	April 18, 2005
Varecia variegata editorum	Manombo Special Reserve	June 19, 2005
Varecia variegata subcincta	Nosy Mangabe Special Reserve	August 28, 1984
Varecia rubra	Masoala National Park	August 30, 1984
Avahi laniger	Analamazaotra Special Reserve	November 4, 1986
Avahi peyrierasi	Ranomafana National Park	November 10, 1985
Avahi occidentalis	Ampijoroa, Ankarafantsika National Park	September 4, 1984
Propithecus verreauxi	Berenty Special Reserve	August 21, 1984
Propithecus deckenii	Tsingy Kely, Tsingy de Bemaraha National Park	November 16, 2003
Propithecus coronatus	Katsepy	August 8, 1998
Propithecus coquereli	Ampijoroa, Ankarafantsika National Park	September 4, 1984
Propithecus tattersalli	Daraina	April 16, 1995
Propithecus diadema	Mantadia National Park	November 21, 1993
Propithecus edwardsi	Ranomafana National Park	November 11, 1986
Propithecus candidus	Anjanaharibe-Sud Special Reserve	January 25, 2003
Propithecus perrieri	Analamerana Special Reserve	November 25, 1997
Indri indri	Analamazaotra Special Reserve	August 18, 1984
Daubentonia madagascariensis	Nosy Mangabe Special Reserve	August 30, 1984

* The date given for each species indicates the first-ever time each was observed in the wild. Subsequent sightings are not listed.

Fig. D.5: Verreaux's sifaka (*Propithecus verreauxi*), Berenty Private Reserve (photo by R. A. Mittermeier).

References

Albignac, R. 1981a. Lemurine social and territorial organization in a north-western Malagasy Forest (restricted area of Ampijoroa). Pp.25–29 in: A. Chiarelli and R. Corrucini (eds.), *Primate Behavior and Sociobiology*. Springer Verlag, Berlin.

Albignac, R. 1981b. Variabilité dans l'organisation territoriale et l'écologie de *Avahi laniger* (lémurien nocturne de Madagascar). *Compte rendus de l'Académie des sciences de Paris* 292(3): 331–334.

Albignac, R. 1987. Status of the aye-aye in Madagascar. *Primate Conservation* (8): 44–45.

Albrecht, G. H., Jenkins, P. D. and Godfrey, L. R. 1990. Ecogeographic size variation among the living and subfossil prosimians of Madagascar. *American Journal of Primatology* 22(1):1–50.

Ali, J. R. and Huber. M. 2010. Mammalian biodiversity on Madagascar controlled by ocean currents. *Nature, London.* 20 January 2020. doi.10.1038/nature08706.

Ancrenaz, M., Lackman-Ancrenaz, I. and Mundy, N. 1994. Field observations of aye-ayes (*Daubentonia madagascariensis*) in Madagascar. *Folia Primatologica* 62(1–3): 22–36.

Andrews, J. 1989. Black lemur survey 1988: a survey of the distribution and habitat of black lemurs, *Lemur macaco*, in northwest Madagascar. Unpublished preliminary report.

Andrews, J. 1996. The ecology and conservation of the black lemur, *Eulemur macaco*. PhD thesis, Washington University, St. Louis, MO.

Andrews, J. 1998. Infanticide by a female black lemur, *Eulemur macaco*, in disturbed habitat on Nosy Be, north-western Madagascar. *Folia Primatologica* 69(suppl.1): 14–17.

Andrews, J. and Birkinshaw, C. 1998. A comparison between the daytime and night-time diet, activity and feeding height of the black lemur, *Eulemur macaco* (Primates: Lemuridae), in Lokobe Forest, Madagascar. *Folia Primatologica* 69(suppl.1): 175–182.

Andrews, J., Antilahimena, P. and Birkinshaw, C. R. 1998. Use of a day resting box by a wild sportive lemur, *Lepilemur dorsalis*, on Nosy Be, north-western Madagascar. *Folia Primatologica* 69(suppl.1): 18–21.

Andriaholinirina, V. N., Fausser, J.-L. and Rabarivola, J. C. 2003. Étude comparative de *Hapalemur simus* (Gray, 1870) de deux sites de la province autonome de Fianarantsoa, Madagascar: forêt dégradée d'Ambolomavo et forêt secondaire du Parc National de Ranomafana. *Lemur News* (8): 9–13.

Andriaholinirina, V. N., Rabarivola, C. and Rumpler, Y. 2004. Limites de la zone de répartition de *Propithecus diadema diadema* et *Propithecus diadema edwardsi*. *Lemur News* (9): 18–19.

Andriaholinirina, V. N., Rabarivola, C., Hauwy, M. and Rumpler, Y. 2005. Cytogenetic study of *Lepilemur microdon*. *Folia Primatologica* 76(4): 238–241.

Andriaholinirina, V. N., Fausser, J.-L., Roos, C., Zinner, D., Thalmann, U., Rabarivola, C., Ravoarimanana, I., Ganzhorn, J. U., Meier, B., Hilgartner, R., Walter, L., Zaramody, A., Langer, C. Hahn, T., Zimmermann, E., Radespiel, U., Craul, M., Tomiuk, J., Tattersall, I. and Rumpler, Y. 2006a. Molecular phylogeny and taxonomic revision of the sportive lemurs (*Lepilemur*, Primates). *BMC Evolutionary Biology* 6: 1–13.

Andriaholinirina, V. N., Rabarivola, C., Zaramody, A., Roos, C., Zinner, D., Fausser, J.-L., Hauwy, M., and Rumpler, Y. 2006b. Cytogenetic and molecular characterization of the newly described sportive lemur *Lepilemur jamesi* (Louis *et al.*, 2006). *Primate Report* (74): 25–33.

Andriamasimanana, M. 1994. Ecoethological study of free-ranging aye-ayes (*Daubentonia madagascariensis*) in Madagascar. *Folia Primatologica* 62(1–3): 37–45.

Andriamasimanana, R. H., Rabenandrasana, M. N., Raminoarisoa, T. S., Virgine, M. C., Ratelolahy, F. J. and Rakotonirainy, E. O. 2001. Effets de la fragmentation de la forêt humide sur les populations d'oiseaux et de lémuriens dans le corridor Mantadia-Zahamena. *Lemur News* (6): 18–22.

Andrianandrasana, L. H., Patel, E. R. and Wright, P. C. 2007. A comparison of scent overmarking in two species of wild rainforest sifakas: silky sifakas (*Propithecus candidus*) and Milne-Edwards' sifakas (*Propithecus edwardsi*). *Prosimian Congress Abstracts*, Ithala, South Africa. Abstract.

Andrianarivo, A. 1981. Etude comparée de l'organisaton sociale chez *Microcebus coquereli*. Unpublished dissertation, University of Madagascar, Antanananarivo.

Andrianjakarivelo, V. 2004. Exploration de la zone en dehors de la péninsule Sahamalaza pour l'évaluation rapide de la population d'*E. m. flavifrons*. Unpublished report, Wildlife Conservation Society (WCS), Antananarivo. 31pp.

Andriantompohavana, R., Zaonarivelo, J., Engberg, S., Randriamampionona, R., McGuire, S., Shore, G., Rakotonomenjanahary, R., Brenneman, R. and Louis, E. E. Jr. 2006. Mouse lemurs of northwestern Madagascar with a description of a new species at Lokobe Special Reserve. *Occasional Papers, Museum of Texas Tech University* (259): 1–24.

Andriantompohavana, R., Lei, R., Zaonarivelo, J. R., Engberg, S., Nalanirina, G., McGuire, S., Shore, G., Andrianasolo, J., Herrington, K., Brenneman, R. and Louis, E. E. Jr. 2007. Molecular phylogeny and taxonomic revision of the woolly lemurs, genus *Avahi* (Primates: Lemuriformes). *Museum of Texas Tech University Special Publications* (51): 1–60.

Andriatsarafara, R. 1988. Note sur les rythmes d'activité et sur le régime alimentaire de *Lemur mongoz* Linnaeus, 1766 à Ampijoroa. Pp.103–106 in: L. Rakotavao, V. Barre and J. Sayer (eds.), *L'Equilibre des Ecosystèmes Forestiers à Madagascar: Actes d'un Séminaire International*. IUCN, Gland, Switzerland, and Cambridge, UK.

Andrianstsiferana, R., Rarijaona, Y. and Randrianaivo, A. 1974. Observations sur la réproduction du Microcèbe (*Microcebus murinus* Miller, 1777) en captivité à Tananarive. *Mammalia* 38(2): 234–243.

Ankel-Simons, F. 1996. Deciduous dentition of the aye-aye, *Daubentonia madagascariensis*. *American Journal of Primatology* 39(2): 87–97.

Anthony, R. and Coupin, F. 1931. Tableau résumé d' une classification générique des primates fossiles et actuels. *Bulletin du Muséum national d'histoire naturelle de Paris* 3: 566–569.

Arbelot-Traqui, V. 1983. Etude ethoécologique de deux primates prosimiens: *Lemur coronatus* Gray et *Lemur fulvus sanfordi* Archbold. Contribution à l'étude des méchanismes d'isolement reproductif intervenant dans la spéciation. PhD thesis, University of Rennes, France.

Archie, E. A. and Digby, L. J. 1999. Juvenile dominance in *Eulemur macaco flavifrons*: the influence of sex and maternal rank. *Folia Primatologica* 70(5): 277–281.

Arnoud, J., Meier, B., Dugoujon, J. and Rumpler, Y. 1992. Study of the variability of erythrocyte enzymes in captive and wild populations of the black lemur (*Eulemur macaco macaco*). An indispensable preliminary in captive breeding programmes. *Primates* 33(1): 139–146.

Arrigo-Nelson, S. J. and Wright, P. C. 2004. Survey results from Ranomafana National Park: new evidence for the effects of habitat preference and disturbance on the distribution of *Hapalemur*. *Folia Primatologica* 75(5): 331–334.

Atsalis, S. A. 1998a. Feeding ecology and aspects of life history in *Microcebus rufus* (Family Cheirogaleidae). PhD dissertation, City University of New York, New York, NY.

Atsalis, S. A. 1998b. Seasonal fattening and changes in activity levels in the brown mouse lemur (*Microcebus rufus*) in Ranomafana National Park, Madagascar. *American Journal of Primatology* 45(2): 165. Abstract.

Atsalis, S. A. 1998c. Feeding ecology of the brown mouse lemur, *Microcebus rufus*. *Folia Primatologica* 69(suppl.1): 406–407. Abstract.

Atsalis, S. A. 1999a. Seasonal fluctuations in body fat and activity levels in a rain-forest species of mouse lemur, *Microcebus rufus*. *International Journal of Primatology* 20(6): 883–910.

Atsalis, S. A. 1999b. Diet of the brown mouse lemur (*Microcebus rufus*) in Ranomafana National Park, Madagascar. *International Journal of Primatology* 20(2): 193–229.

Atsalis, S. A. 2000. Spatial distribution and population composition of the brown mouse lemur (*Microcebus rufus*) in Ranomafana National Park, Madagascar, and its implications for social organization. *American Journal of Primatology* 51(1): 61–98.

Atsalis, S. A., Schmid, J. and Kappeler, P. M. 1996. Metrical comparisons of three species of mouse lemur. *Journal of Human Evolution* 31(1): 61–68.

Aujard, F. and Vasseur, F. 2001. Effect of ambient temperature on the body temperature rhythm of male gray mouse lemurs (*Microcebus murinus*). *International Journal of Primatology* 22(1): 43–56.

Ausilio, E. and Raveloarinoro, G. 1993. Statut et densités des espèces de lémuriens de la région d'Antsalova (ouest de Madagascar) (Forêts de l'Antsingy, de Tsimembo et de la région de Tsiandro). Unpublished report to UNESCO–Project 507/INT/40. Antananarivo.

Ausilio, E. and Raveloarinoro, G. 1998. Les lémuriens de la région de Bemaraha: Forêts de Tsimembo, de l'Antsingy et de la région de Tsiandro. *Lemur News* (3): 4-7.

Bachmann, L., Rumpler, Y., Ganzhorn, J. U. and Tomiuk, J. 2000. Genetic differentiation among natural populations of *Lepilemur ruficaudatus*. *International Journal of Primatology* 21(5): 853–864.

Balko, E. A. 1996. Intraspecific variation in the foraging ecology of *Varecia variegata variegata* at Ranomafana National Park, Madagascar. *American Journal of Physical Anthropology* 22(suppl.): 64. Abstract.

Balko, E. A. 1998. A behaviorally plastic response to forest composition and logging disturbance by *Varecia variegata variegata* in Ranomafana National Park, Madagascar. PhD thesis, State University of New York (SUNY) at Syracuse, New York.

Balko, E. A. and Underwood, H. B. 2005. Effects of forest structure and composition on food availability for *Varecia variegata* at Ranomafana National Park, Madagascar. *American Journal of Primatology* 66(1): 45–70.

Banks, M. 2005. Population dynamics of the critically endangered Perrier's sifaka (*Propithecus perrieri*) and sympatric species in the Analamera Special Reserve, northern Madagascar. Report to the Margot Marsh Biodiversity Foundation, Great Falls, VA.

Barthold, J., Fichtel, C. and Kappeler, P. M. 2009. What is it going to be? Pattern and potential function of natal coat change in sexually dichromatic redfronted lemurs (*Eulemur fulvus rufus*). *American Journal of Physical Anthropology* 138(1): 1–10.

Basilewsky, G. 1965. Keeping and breeding Madagascar lemurs in captivity. *International Zoo Yearbook* 5: 132–137.

Bauchot, R. and Stephan, H. 1966. Données nouvelles sur l'encéphalisation des insectivores et des prosimiens. *Mammalia* 30: 160–196.

Bayart, F. and Anthouard, M. 1992. Responses to a live snake by *Lemur macaco macaco* and *Lemur fulvus mayottensis* in captivity. *Folia Primatologica* 58(1): 41–46.

Bayart, F. and Simmen, B. 2005. Demography, range use, and behavior in black lemurs (*Eulemur macaco macaco*) at Ampasikely, northwest Madagascar. *American Journal of Primatology* 67(3): 299–312.

Beattie, J. C. and Feistner, A. T. C. 1998. Husbandry and breeding of the Alaotran gentle lemur *Hapalemur griseus alaotrensis* at Jersey Wildlife Preservation Trust. *International Zoo Yearbook* 36: 11–19.

Benadi, G., Fichtel, C. and Kappeler, P. M. 2008. Intergroup relations and home range use in Verreaux's sifakas, *Propithecus verreauxi*. *American Journal of Primatology* 70(10): 956–965.

Bennett, E. 1833. Characters of a new species of lemur (*Lemur rufifrons*). *Proceedings of the Zoological Society of London* (1833): 106.

Berg, W., Jolly, A., Rambeloarivony, H., Andriananome, V. and Rasamimanana, H. 2009. A scoring system for coat and tail condition in ringtailed lemurs, *Lemur catta*. *American Journal of Primatology* 71(3): 183–190.

Biebouw, K. 2009. Home range use and size in *Allocebus trichotis* in Analamazaotra Special Reserve, central eastern Madagascar. *International Journal of Primatology* 30(2): 367–386.

Biebouw, K., Bearder, S. K. and Nekaris, A. 2009. Tree hole utilization by the hairy-eared dwarf lemur (*Allocebus trichotis*) in Analamazaotra Special Reserve. *Folia Primatologica* 80(2): 89–103.

Birkinshaw, C. R. 1999a. The importance of the black lemur (*Eulemur macaco*) for seed dispersal in Lokobe Forest, Nosy Be. Pp.189–199 in: B. Rakotosamimanana, H. Rasamaninana, J. U. Ganzhorn, and S. M. Goodman (eds.), *New Directions in Lemur Studies*. Plenum Press, New York.

Birkinshaw, C. R. 1999b. Use of millipedes by black lemurs to anoint their bodies. *Folia Primatologica* 70(3): 170–171.

Birkinshaw, C. R. 2001. Fruit characteristics of species dispersed by the black lemur (*Eulemur macaco*) in the Lokobe Forest, Madagascar. *Biotropica* 33(3): 478–486.

Birkinshaw, C. R. and Colquhoun, I. C. 1998. Pollination of *Ravenala madagascariensis* and *Parkia madagascariensis* by *Eulemur macaco* in Madagascar. *Folia Primatologica* 69(5): 252–259.

Birkinshaw, C. R., Rabenantoandro, J., Randrianarivo, R. and Antilahimena, P. 2000. Observations on *Eulemur macaco macaco* and *Eulemur fulvus fulvus* in the Ramena River Valley, northwest Madagascar. *Lemur News* (5): 19.

Blanco, M. R. 2008. Reproductive schedules of female *Microcebus rufus* at Ranomafana National Park, Madagascar. *International Journal of Primatology* 29(2): 323–338.

Blanco, M. R., Godfrey, L. R., Rakotondratsima, M., Rahalinarivo, V., Samonds, K., Raharison, J.-L. and Irwin, M. 2009. Discovery of sympatric dwarf lemur species in the high-altitude rain forest of Tsinjoarivo, eastern Madagascar: implications for biogeography and conservation. *Folia Primatologica* 80(1): 1–17.

Blumenfeld-Jones, K., Randriamboavonjy, T. M., Williams, G., Mertl-Millhollen, A. S., Pinkus, S. and Rasamimanana, H. 2006. Tamarind recruitment and long-term stability in the Gallery Forest at Berenty, Madagascar. Pp.69–85 in: A. Jolly, R. W. Sussman, N. Koyama and H. Rasamimanana (eds.), *Ringtailed Lemur Biology: Lemur catta in Madagascar*. Springer, New York.

Bogart, M. H., Cooper, R. W. and Benirschke, K. 1977. Reproductive studies of black and ruffed lemurs *Lemur m. macaco* and *L. variegatus* ssp. *International Zoo Yearbook* 17: 177–182.

Bollen, A., Van Elsacker, L. and Ganzhorn, J. U. 2004. Relations between fruit and disperser assemblages in a Malagasy littoral forest: a community-level approach. *Journal of Tropical Ecology* 20(6): 599–612.

Bolwig, N. 1960. A comparative study of the behaviour of various lemurs. *Mémoires de l'Institut Scientifique de Madagascar* A 14: 205–217.

Bomford, E. 1976. In search of the aye-aye. *Wildlife* 18: 258–263.

Bomford, E. 1981. On the road to Nosy Mangabe. *International Wildlife* 11: 20–24.

Boskoff, K. J. 1977. Aspects of reproduction in ruffed lemurs (*Lemur variegatus*). *Folia Primatologica* 28(4): 241–250.

Boskoff, K. J. 1978. The oestrous cycle of the brown lemur, *Lemur fulvus*. *Journal of Reproduction and Fertility* 54: 313–318.

Bourlière, F., Petter-Rousseaux, A. and Petter, J.-J. 1961. Regular breeding in captivity of the lesser mouse lemur (*Microcebus murinus*). *International Zoo Yearbook* 3: 24–25.

Bradley, B., Stumpf, R. M. and Wright, P. C. 1997. Morphometrics of *Eulemur fulvus albocollaris* in Vevembe Forest, Madagascar. *American Journal of Physical Anthropology* 24(suppl.): 79–80. Abstract.

Bradt, H. 2007. *Madagascar Travel Guide*. 9th edition. Bradt Travel Guides Ltd., Chalfont St. Peter, UK and Globe Pequot Press, Guilford, CT.

Braune, P., Schmidt, S. and Zimmermann, E. 2005. Spacing and group coordination in a nocturnal primate, the golden brown mouse lemur (*Microcebus ravelobensis*): the role of olfactory and acoustic signals. *Behavioral Ecology and Sociobiology.* 58(6): 587–597.

Britt, A. 1997. Environmental influences on the behavioral ecology of the black-and-white ruffed lemur (*Varecia variegata variegata*). PhD thesis, University of Liverpool, UK.

Britt, A. 1998. Encouraging natural feeding behavior in captive-bred black-and-white ruffed lemurs (*Varecia variegata variegata*). *Zoo Biology* 17(5): 379–392.

Britt, A. 2000. Diet and feeding behavior of the black-and-white ruffed lemur (*Varecia variegata variegata*) in the Betampona Reserve, eastern Madagascar. *Folia Primatologica* 71(3): 133–141.

Britt, A. and Lambana, B. R. 2003. Can captive-bred *Varecia variegata variegata* adapt to a natural diet on release to the wild? *International Journal of Primatology* 24(5): 987–1005.

Britt, A., Axel, A. and Young, R. 1999. Brief surveys of two classified forests in Toamasina Province, eastern Madagasdcar. *Lemur News* (4): 25–27.

Britt, A., Welch, C. and Katz, A. 2001. The impact of *Cryptoprocta ferox* on the *Varecia variegata variegata* re-stocking project at Betampona. *Lemur News* (6): 35–37.

Britt, A., Randriamandratonirina, N. J., Glasscock, K. D. and Iambana, B. R. 2002. Diet and feeding behaviour of *Indri indri* in a low-altitude rain forest. *Folia Primatologica* 73(5): 225–239.

Britt, A., Iambana, B. R., Welch, C. R. and Katz, A. S. 2003. Restocking of *Varecia variegata variegata* in the Réserve Naturelle Intégrale de Betampona. Pp.1545–1551 in: S. M. Goodman and J. P. Benstead (eds.), *The Natural History of Madagascar*. The University of Chicago Press, Chicago.

Brockman, D. K. 1989. Management imperatives for *Varecia* in captivity. *Human Evolution* 4(2–3): 217–222.

Brockman, D. K. 1999. Reproductive behavior of female *Propithecus verreauxi* at Beza Mahafaly, Madagascar. *International Journal of Primatology* 20(3): 375–398.

Brockman, D. K. 2003. *Polyboroides radiatus* predation attempts on *Propithecus verreauxi*. *Folia Primatologica* 74(2): 71–74.

Brockman, D. K. and Whitten, P. L. 1996. Reproduction in free-ranging *Propithecus verreauxi*: estrus and the relationship between multiple partner matings and fertilization. *American Journal of Physical Anthropology* 100(1): 57–69.

Brockman, D. K., Willis, M. S. and Karesh, W. B. 1987a. Management and husbandry of ruffed lemurs, *Varecia variegata*, at the San Diego Zoo. I. Captive population, San Diego Zoo housing and diet. *Zoo Biology* 6(4): 341–347.

Brockman, D. K., Willis, M. S. and Karesh, W. B. 1987b. Management and husbandry of ruffed lemurs, *Varecia variegata*, at the San Diego Zoo. II. Reproduction, pregnancy, parturition, litter size, infant care, and reintroduction of hand-raised infants. *Zoo Biology* 6(4): 349–363.

Brockman, D. K., Willis, M. S. and Karesh, W. B. 1987c. Management and husbandry of ruffed lemurs, *Varecia variegata*, at the San Diego Zoo. III. Medical considerations and population management. *Zoo Biology* 7(3): 253–262.

Brockman, D. K., Whitten, P. L., Richard, A. F. and Schneider, A. 1998. Reproduction in free-ranging *Propithecus verreauxi*: the hormonal correlates of mating and aggression. *American Journal of Physical Anthropology* 105(2): 137–151.

Brockman, D. K., Whitten, P. L., Richard, A. F. and Benander, B. 2001. Birth season testosterone levels in male Verreaux's sifaka, *Propithecus verreauxi*: insights into socio-demographic factors mediating seasonal testicular function. *Behavioral Ecology and Sociobiology* 49(2–3): 117–127.

Brown, K. and Gurevitch, J. 2004. Long-term impacts on logging and forest diversity in Madagascar. *Proceedings of the National Academy of Sciences* 101(16): 6045–6049.

Buckley, G. A., Brochu, C. A., Krause, D. W. and Pol, D. 2000. A pug-nosed crocodyliform from the late Cretaceous of Madagascar. *Nature, London* 405: 941-944.

Budnitz, N. and Dainis, K. 1975. *Lemur catta*: ecology and behavior. Pp.219–235 in: I. Tattersall and R. W. Sussman, (eds.), *Lemur Biology*. Plenum Press, New York.

Buesching, C., Heistermann, M., Hodges, J. K. and Zimmermann, E. 1998. Multimodal oestrous advertisement in a small nocturnal prosimian, *Microcebus murinus*. *Folia Primatologica* 69(suppl.1): 295–308.

Buettner-Janusch, J. 1966. A note on the nutrition of Coquerel's sifaka, *Propithecus verreauxi coquereli*, in captivity. *International Zoo Yearbook* 6: 69.

Buettner-Janusch, J., Hamilton, A. E. and Bergeron, J. A. 1973. Chromosomes of Lemuriformes. I. A chromosome complement of *Lepilemur mustelinus* (I. Geoffroy, 1851). *American Journal of Physical Anthropology* 39(1): 1–5.

Burney, D. A. 2002. Sifaka predation by a large boa. *Folia Primatologica* 73(2–3): 144–145.

Burney, D. A. and Ramilisonina. 1998. The kilopilopitsofy, kidoky, and bokyboky: Accounts of strange animals from Belo-sur-mer, Madagascar, and the megafaunal "extinction window." *American Anthropologist* 100(4): 957–966.

Burney, D. A., Burney, L. P., Godfrey, L. R., Jungers, W. L., Goodman, S. M., Wright, H. T. and Jull, A. J. T. 2004. A chronology for late prehistoric Madagascar. *Journal of Human Evolution* 47(1–2): 25–63.

Butler, P. M., Stafford, D. K. and Ward, J. P. 1995. Relative efficiency of preferred and nonpreferred patterns of lateralized foraging in the gentle lemur (*Hapalemur griseus*). *American Journal of Primatology* 36(1): 71–77.

Campbell, J. L., Eisemann, J. H., Glander, K. E. and Crissey, S. D. 1999. Intake, digestibility, and passage of a commercially designed diet by two *Propithecus* species. *American Journal of Primatology* 48(3): 237–246.

Carrai, V. and Lunardini, A. 1996. Activity patterns and home range use of two groups of *Propithecus v. verreauxi* in the Kirindy Forest. *Primate Report* 46(1): 275–284.

Carrai, V., Borgognini-Tarli, S. M., Huffman, M. A. and Bardi, M. 2003. Increase in tannin consumption by sifaka (*Propithecus verreauxi verreauxi*) females during the birth season: a case for self-medication in prosimians? *Primates* 44(1): 61–66.

Carroll, J. B. and Beattie, J. C. 1993. Maintenance and breeding of the aye-aye *Daubentonia madagascariensis* at the Jersey Wildlife Preservation Trust. *Dodo, Journal of The Wildlife Preservation Trusts* 29: 45–54.

Carroll, J. B. and Haring, D. 1994a. Maintenance and breeding of the aye-aye *Daubentonia madagascariensis* at the Jersey Wildlife Preservation Trust. *Dodo, Journal of the Wildlife Preservation Trusts* 29: 45–54.

Carroll, J. B. and Haring, D. 1994b. Maintenance and breeding of aye-ayes (*Daubentonia madagascariensis*) in captivity: a review. *Folia Primatologica* 62(1–3): 54–62.

Catlett, K. K., Schwartz, G. T., Godfrey, L. R. and Jungers, W. L. 2010. "Life history space": a multivariate analysis of life history variation in extant and extinct Malagasy lemurs. *American Journal of Physical Anthropology*. In press.

CBSG. 2002. Evaluation et Plans de Gestion pour la Conservation (CAMP) de la Faune de Madagascar: Lémuriens, Autres Mammifères, Reptiles et Amphibiens, Poissons d'eau douce et Evaluation de la Viabilité des Populations et des Habitats des *Hypogeomys antimena* (Vositse). IUCN/ SSC Conservation Breeding Specialist Group (CBSG), Apple Valley, Minnesota.

Ceska, V., Hoffman, H.-U. and Winkelsträter, K.-H. 1992. *Lemuren im Zoo*. Verlag Paul Parey, Berlin.

Charles-Dominique, P. and Hladik, C. M. 1971. Le *Lepilemur* du sud de Madagascar: écologie, alimentation et vie sociale. *La Terre et la Vie* 25(1): 3–66.

Charles-Dominique, P. and Petter, J.-J. 1980. Ecology and social life of *Phaner furcifer*. Pp.75–96 in: P. Charles-Dominique, H. Cooper, A. Hladik, C. M. Hladik, E. Pagès, G. Pariente, A. Petter-Rousseaux, J.-J. Petter and A. Schilling (eds.), *Nocturnal Malagasy Primates: Ecology, Physiology and Behavior*. Academic Press, New York.

Charles-Dominique, P., Cooper, H. M., Hladik, A., Hladik, C. M., Pagès, E., Pariente, G. F., Petter-Rousseaux, A., Petter, J. J. and Schilling, A. (eds.). 1980. *Nocturnal Malagasy Primates*. Academic Press, New York.

Cherry, J. A., Izard, M. K. and Simons, E. L. 1987. Description of ultrasonic vocalizations of the mouse lemur (*Microcebus murinus*) and the fat-tailed dwarf lemur (*Cheirogaleus medius*). *American Journal of Primatology* 13 (2): 181–185.

Coffmann, B. S. 1990. Hand-rearing and reintroduction of a golden-crowned sifaka *Propithecus tattersalli* at the Duke University Primate Center. *International Zoo Yearbook* 29: 37–43.

Colas, S. 1999. Evidence for sex-biased behavioral maternal investment in the gray mouse lemur (*Microcebus murinus*). *International Journal of Primatology* 20(6): 911–926.

Colquhoun, I. C. 1993. The socioecology of *Eulemur macaco*: a preliminary report. Pp.13–26 in: P. M. Kappeler and J. U. Ganzhorn (eds.), *Lemur Social Systems and their Ecological Basis*. Plenum Press, New York.

Colquhoun, I. C. 1995. The socioecology of the black lemur: *Eulemur macaco*. PhD thesis, Washington University, St. Louis, MO.

Colquhoun, I. C. 1998a. Cathemeral behavior of *Eulemur macaco macaco* at Ambato Massif, Madagascar. *Folia Primatologica* 69(suppl.1): 22–34.

Colquhoun, I. C. 1998b. The lemur community of Ambato Massif: an example of the species richness of Madagascar's classified forests. *Lemur News* (3): 11–14.

Colquhoun, I. C. 2006. Predation and cathemerality: comparing the impact of predators on the activity patterns of lemurids and ceboids. *Folia Primatologica* 77(1–2): 143–165.

Conley, J. M. 1975. Notes on the activity pattern of *Lemur fulvus*. *Journal of Mammalogy* 56(3): 712–715.

Conservation International. 1999. Rapport préliminaire d'un Programme d'Inventaire Biologique Rapide (RAP): Corridor Mantadia-Zahamena. 7 novembre–10 décembre 1998, 18–24 janvier 1999. Conservation International, Washington, DC.

Conservation International. 2010. Lemurs poached for meat in Madagascar. *Traffic Bulletin* 22(3): 101.

Constable, I. D., Mittermeier, R A., Pollock, J. I., Ratsirarson, J. and Simons, H. 1985. Sightings of aye-ayes and red-ruffed lemurs on Nosy Mangabe and the Masoala Peninsula. *Primate Conservation* (5): 59–62.

Cooper, V. J. and Hosey, G. R. 2003. Sexual dichromatism and female preference in *Eulemur fulvus* subspecies. *International Journal of Primatology* 24(6): 1177–1188.

Corbin, G. D. and Schmid, J. 1995. Insect secretions determine habitat use patterns by a female lesser mouse lemur (*Microcebus murinus*). *American Journal of Primatology* 37(4): 317–324.

Cousins D. 2007. Albinism and leucism in primates. *International Zoo News* 54(3): 134–145.

Cranz, C., Ishak, B., Brun, B. and Rumpler, Y. 1986. Study of morphological and cytological parameters indicating oestrus in *Lemur fulvus mayottensis*. *Zoo Biology* 5(4): 379–386.

Craul, M., Zimmermann, E., Rasoloharijaona, S., Randrianambinina, B., and Radespiel, U. 2007. Unexpected species diversity of Malagasy primates (*Lepilemur* spp.) in the same biogeographic zone: a morphological and molecular approach with the description of two new species. *BMC Evolutionary Biology* 7: 83.

Craul, M., Radespiel, U., Rasolofoson, D. W., Rakotondratsimba, G., Rakotonirainy, O., Rasoloharijaona, S., Randrianambinina, B., Ratsimbazafy, J., Ratelolahy, F., Randrainamboavaonjy, T. and Rakotozafy, L. 2008. Large rivers do not always act as species barriers for *Lepilemur* sp. *Primates* 49(3): 211–218.

Crawford, G., Ichino, S., Jolly, A., Koyama, N., Ostpak, S., Rafanomiazantsoa, F., Rambeloarivony, H., Rasamimanana, H., Simmen, B., Soma, T., Tew, A., Andrianome, V. N., Andriafaneva, L. E. and Clarke, L. 2004. *Leucaena leucocephala*: A probable cause of alopecia in ring-tailed lemurs (*Lemur catta*). *Folia Primatologica* 75(suppl.1): 159. Abstract.

Crawford, G. C., Andriafaneva, L. E., Blumenfeld-Jones, K., Calaba, G., Clarke, L., Gray, L., Ichino, S., Jolly, A., Koyama, N., Mertl-Millhollen, A., Ostpak, S., Pride, R. E., Rasamimanana, H., Simmen, B., Soma, T., Tarnaud, L., Tew, A. and Williams, G. 2006. Bald lemur syndrome and the miracle tree: alopecia associated with *Leucaena leucocephala* at Berenty Reserve, Madagascar. Pp.332–342 in: A. Jolly, R. W. Sussman, N. Koyama and H. Rasamimanana (eds.), *Ringtailed Lemur Biology:* Lemur catta *in Madagascar*. Springer, New York.

Crovella, S. and Rumpler, Y. 1992. Confirmation of the specific status of *Hapalemur aureus* (Primates, Strepsirhini) by restriction genomic DNA banding patterns. *Human Evolution* 7(2): 63–67.

Crovella, S., Montagnon, D. and Rumpler, Y. 1993. Highly repeated DNA analysis and systematics of the Lemuridae, a family of Malagasy prosimians. *Primates* 34(1): 61–69.

Crovella, S. , Montagnon, D., Rakotosamimanana and Rumpler, Y. 1994. Molecular biology and systematics of an extinct lemur: *Pachylemur insignis*. *Primates* 35(4): 519–522.

Csermely, D. 1996. Antipredator behavior in lemurs: evidence of an extinct eagle on Madagascar or something else? *International Journal of Primatology* 17(3): 349–354.

Curtis, D. J. 1992. Substrate use in captive aye-ayes *Daubentonia madagascariensis*. *Dodo, Journal of The Wildlife Preservation Trusts* 28: 30–44.

Curtis, D. J. 2003. Diet and nutrition in wild mongoose lemurs (*Eulemur mongoz*) and their implications for the evolution of female dominance and small group size in lemurs. *American Journal of Physical Anthropology* 124(3): 234–247.

Curtis, D. J. and Feistner, A. T. C. 1994. Positional behavior in captive aye-ayes (*Daubentonia madagascariensis*). *Folia Primatologica* 62(1–3): 155–159.

Curtis, D. J. and Rasmussen, M. A. 2002. Cathemerality in lemurs. *Evolutionary Anthropology* 11(suppl.1): 83–86.

Curtis, D. J. and Rasmussen, M. A. 2006. The evolution of cathemerality in primates and other mammals: a comparative and chronoecological approach. *Folia Primatologica* 77(1–2): 178–193.

Curtis, D. J. and Zaramody, A. 1998. Group size, home range use, and seasonal variation in the ecology of *Eulemur mongoz*. *International Journal of Primatology* 19(5): 811–835.

Curtis, D. J. and Zaramody, A. 1999. Social structure and seasonal variation in the behaviour of *Eulemur mongoz*. *Folia Primatologica* 70(2): 79–96.

Curtis, D. J., Zaramody, A. and Rabetsimialona, O. D. 1995. Sighting of the western gentle lemur *Hapalemur griseus occidentalis* in north-west Madagascar. *Oryx* 29(3): 215–217.

Curtis, D. J., Velo, A., Raheliarisoa, E.-O., Zaramody, A. and Müller, P. 1998. Surveys on *Propithecus verreauxi deckeni*, a melanistic variant, and *P. v. coronatus* in northwest Madagascar. *Oryx* 32(2): 157–164.

Curtis, D. J., Zaramody, A. and Martin, R. D. 1999. Cathemerality in the mongoose lemur, *Eulemur mongoz*. *American Journal of Primatology* 47(4): 279–298.

Curtis, D. J., Zaramody, A., Green, D. I. and Pickard, A. R. 2000. Non-invasive monitoring of reproductive status in wild mongoose lemurs (*Eulemur mongoz*). *Reproduction, Fertility and Development* 12(1–2): 21–29.

Dagosto, M. 1995. Seasonal variation in positional behavior of Malagasy lemurs. *International Journal of Primatology* 16(5): 807–833.

Dague, C. and Petter, J.-J. 1988. Observations de *Lemur rubriventer* dans son milieu naturel. In: L. Rakotavao, V. Barre and J. Sayer (eds), *L'Equilibre des Ecosystèmes Forestiers à Madagascar: Actes d'un Séminairie International*. IUCN, Gland, Switzerland, and Cambridge, UK.

Dammhahn, M. and Kappeler, P. M. 2005. Social system of *Microcebus berthae*, the world's smallest primate. *International Journal of Primatology* 26(2): 407–435.

Dammhahn, M. and Kappeler, P. M. 2008a. Small-scale coexistence of two mouse lemur species (*Microcebus berthae* and *M. murinus*) within a homogeneous competitive environment. *Oecologia, Berlin* 157(3): 473–483.

Dammhahn, M. and Kappeler, P. M. 2008b. Comparative feeding ecology of sympatric *Microcebus berthae* and *M. murinus*. *International Journal of Primatology* 29(6): 1567–1589.

Dammhahn, M. and Kappeler, P. M. 2009. Females go where the food is. Does the socio-ecological model explain variation in social organization of solitary foragers? *Behavioral Ecology and Sociobiology* 63(6): 939–952.

Dausmann, K. H., Ganzhorn, J. U. and Heldmaier, G. 2000. Body temperature and metabolic rate of a hibernating primate in Madagascar: Preliminary results from a field study. Pp.41–47 in: G. Heldmaier and M. Klingenspor (eds.), *Life in the Cold: Eleventh International Hibernation Symposium*. Springer-Verlag, Berlin.

Dausmann, K. H., Glos, J., Ganzhorn, J. U. and Heldmaier, G. 2004. Hibernation in a tropical primate. *Nature, London* 429: 825–826.

D'Cruze, N., Sabel, J., Green, K., Dawson, J., Gardner, C., Robinson, J., Starkie, G., Vences, M. and Glaw, F. 2007. The first comprehensive survey of amphibians and reptiles at Montagne des Français, Madagascar. *Herpetological Conservation and Biology* 2(2): 87–99.

Del Pero, M., Crovella, S., Cervella, P., Ardito, G. and Rumpler, Y. 1995. Phylogenetic relationships among Malagasy lemurs as revealed by mitochondrial DNA sequence analysis. *Primates* 36(3): 431–440.

Delmore, K. E., Louis Jr., E. E. and Johnson, S. E. 2009. Morphological characterization of a brown lemur hybrid zone (*Eulemur rufifrons* × *E. cinereiceps*) in southeastern Madagascar. *American Journal of Primatology* 71(suppl.1): 43. Abstract.

Dew, J. L. and Wright, P. 1998. Frugivory and seed dispersal by four species of primates in Madagascar's eastern rain forest. *Biotropica* 30(3): 425–437.

Digby, L. J. 1999. Targeting aggression in blue-eyed black lemurs (*Eulemur macaco flavifrons*). *Primates* 40(4): 613–618.

Digby, L. J. and Kahlenberg, S. M. 2002. Female dominance in blue-eyed black lemurs (*Eulemur macaco flavifrons*). *Primates* 43(3): 191–199.

Djletati, R., Brun, B. and Rumpler, Y. 1997. Meiotic study of hybrids in the genus *Eulemur* and taxonomic considerations. *American Journal of Primatology* 42(3): 235–245.

Dolch, R., Hilgartner, R. D., Ndriamiary, J.-N. and Randriamahazo, H. 2004. The grandmother of all bamboo lemurs: evidence for the occurrence of *Hapalemur simus* in fragmented rain forest surrounding the Torotorofotsy marshes, Central Eastern Madagascar. *Lemur News* (9): 24–26.

Dolch, R., Fiely, J. L., Ndriamiary, J.-N., Rafalimandimby, J., Randriamampionona, R., Engberg, S. E. and Louis Jr., E. E. 2008. Confirmation of the greater bamboo lemur, *Prolemur simus*, north of the Torotorofotsy wetlands, eastern Madagascar. *Lemur News* (13): 14–17.

Donati, G. 2002. Activity rhythms and feeding behavior of *Eulemur fulvus collaris*. PhD dissertation, University of Pisa, Pisa. In Italian.

Donati, G. and Borgognini-Tarli, S. M. 2006. Influence of abiotic factors on cathemeral activity: the case of *Eulemur fulvus collaris* in the littoral forest of Madagascar. *Folia Primatologica* 77(1–2): 104–122.

Donati, G., Lunardini, A. and Kappeler, P. M. 1999. Cathemeral activity of red-fronted brown lemurs (*Eulemur fulvus rufus*) in the Kirindy/CFPF. Pp.119–137 in: B. Rakotosaminana, H. Rasamimanana, J. U. Ganzhorn and S. M. Goodman (eds.), *New Directions in Lemur Studies*. Kluwer Academic/ Plenum, New York.

Donati, G., Lunardini, A., Kappeler, P. M. and Tarli, S. 2001. Nocturnal activity in the cathemeral red-fronted lemur (*Eulemur fulvus rufus*), with observations during a lunar eclipse. *American Journal of Primatology* 53(2): 69–78.

Donati, G., Ramanamanjato, J. B., Ravoahangy, A. M. and Vincelette, M. 2007. Translocation as a conservation measure for an endangered species in the littoral forest of southeastern Madagascar: the case of *Eulemur collaris*. Pp.237–245 in: J. U. Ganzhorn, S. M. Goodman and M. Vincelette (eds.), *Biodiversity, Ecology and Conservation of Littoral Forest Ecosystems in Southeastern Madagascar, Tolagnaro (Fort Dauphin)*. Smithsonian Institution Press, Washington, DC.

Donati, G., Baldi, N., Morelli, V., Ganzhorn, J. U. and Borgognini-Tarli, S. M. 2009. Proximate and ultimate determinants of cathemeral activity in brown lemurs. *Animal Behaviour* 77(2): 317–325.

Drack, S., Ortmann, S., Bührmann, N., Schmid, J., Warren, R. D., Heldmaier, G. and Ganzhorn, J. U. 1999. Field metabolic rate and the cost of ranging of the red-tailed sportive lemur (*Lepilemur ruficaudatus*). Pp.83–91 in: B. Rakotosamimanana, H. Rasamimanana, J. U. Ganzhorn and S. M. Goodman (eds.). *New Directions in Lemur Studies*. Kluwer, London.

Dresser, M. E. and Hamilton, A. E. 1979. Chromosomes of Lemuriformes. V. A comparison of the karyotypes of *Cheirogaleus medius* and *Lemur fulvus fulvus*. *Cytogenetic and Cell Genetics* 24 (3): 160–167.

Dubois, C. and Izard, K. M. 1990. Social and sexual behaviours in captive aye-ayes (*Daubentonia madagascariensis*). *Journal of Psychology and Behavioral Sciences* 5: 1–10.

Duckworth, J. W. 1993. Feeding damage left in bamboos, probably by aye-ayes (*Daubentonia madagascariensis*). *International Journal of Primatology* 14(6): 927–931.

Duckworth, J. W., Evans, M. I., Hawkins, A. F. A., Safford, R. J. and Wilkinson, R. J. 1995. The lemurs of Marojejy Strict Reserve, Madagascar: a status overview with notes on ecology and threats. *International Journal of Primatology* 16(3): 545–559.

Dugmore, S. J., Bailey, K. and Evans, C. S. 1984. Discrimination by male ring-tailed lemurs (*Lemur catta*) between the scent marks of male and those of female conspecifics. *International Journal of Primatology* 5(3): 235–245.

Durrell, L. 1988. The role of zoos and captive breeding in lemur conservation. *Human Evolution* 4(2–3): 233–238.

Dutton, C. J., Junge, R. E. and Louis Jr., E. E. 2008. Biomedical evaluation of free-ranging red ruffed lemurs (*Varecia rubra*) within the Masoala National Park, Madagascar. *Journal of Zoo and Wildlife Medicine* 39(1): 76–85.

Eaglen, R. H. 1986. Morphometrics of the anterior dentition in strepsirhine primates. *American Journal of Physical Anthropology* 71(2): 185–201.

Eaglen, R. H. and Boskoff, K. J. 1978. The birth and early development of a captive sifaka, *Propithecus verreauxi coquereli*. *Folia Primatologica* 30(3): 206–219.

Eberle, M. and Kappeler, P. M. 2002. Mouse lemurs in space and time: a test of the socioecological model. *Behavioral Ecology and Sociobiology* 51(2): 131–139.

Eberle, M. and Kappeler, P. M. 2003. Cooperative breeding in grey mouse lemurs (*Microcebus murinus*). *Folia Primatologica* 74(5–6): 367–368.

Eberle, M. and Kappeler, P. M. 2004. Selected polyandry: female choice and intersexual conflict in a small nocturnal solitary primate (*Microcebus murinus*). *Behavioral Ecology and Sociobiology* 57(1): 91–100.

Eberle, M. and Kappeler, P. M. 2006. Family insurance: kin selection and cooperative breeding in a solitary primate (*Microcebus murinus*). *Behavioral Ecology and Sociobiology* 60(4): 582–288.

Eckhardt, R. B. 1969. A chromosome arm number index and its application to the phylogeny and classification of lemurs. *American Journal of Physical Anthropology* 31(1): 85–88.

Erhart, E. M. and Overdorff, D. J. 1998. Infanticide in *Propithecus diadema edwardsi*: an evaluation of the sexual selection hypothesis. *International Journal of Primatology* 19(1): 73–81.

Erhart, E. M. and Overdorff, D. J. 1999. Female coordination of group travel in wild *Propithecus* and *Eulemur*. *International Journal of Primatology* 20(6): 927–940.

Erhart, E. M. and Overdorff, D. J. 2008. Spatial memory during foraging in prosimian primates: *Propithecus edwardsi* and *Eulemur fulvus rufus*. *Folia Primatologica* 79(4): 185–196.

Erickson, C. J. 1991. Percussive foraging in the aye-aye, *Daubentonia madagascariensis*. *Animal Behaviour* 41(5): 793–801.

Erickson, C. J. 1994. Tap-scanning and extractive foraging in aye-ayes, *Daubentonia madagascariensis*. *Folia Primatologica* 62(1–3): 125–135.

Erickson, C. J. 1995. Feeding sites for extractive foraging by the aye-aye, *Daubentonia madagascariensis*. *American Journal of Primatology* 35(3): 235–240.

Erickson, C. J. 1998. Cues for prey location by aye-ayes (*Daubentonia madagascariensis*). *Folia Primatologica* 69(suppl. 1): 35–40.

Erickson, C. J., Nowicki, S., Dollar, L. and Goehring, N. 1998. Percussive foraging: stimuli for prey location by aye-ayes (*Daubentonia madagascariensis*). *International Journal of Primatology* 19(1): 111–122.

Erkert, H. G. and Cramer, B. 2006. Chronobiological background to cathemerality: circadian rhythms in *Eulemur fulvus albifrons* (Prosimii) and *Aotus azarai boliviensis* (Anthropoidea). *Folia Primatologica* 77(1–2): 87–103.

Erkert, H. G. and Kappeler, P. M. 2004. Arrived in the light: diet and seasonal activity patterns in wild Verreaux's sifakas (*Propithecus v. verreauxi*: Primates: Indriidae). *Behavioral Ecology and Sociobiology* 57(2): 174–186.

Evans, C. S. and Goy, R. W. 1968. Social behaviour and reproductive cycles in captive ring-tailed lemurs (*Lemur catta*). *Journal of Zoology, London* 156: 181–197.

Faulkner, A. L. and Lehman, S. M. 2006. Feeding patterns in a small-bodied nocturnal folivore (*Avahi laniger*) and the influence of leaf chemistry: a preliminary study. *Folia Primatologica* 77(3): 218–227.

Faure, M. and Guérin, C. 1990. *Hippopotamus laloumena* nov. sp., la troisième espèce d'hippopotame holocène de Madagascar. *Comptes rendus de l'Académie des sciences de Paris*, Série 11, 310: 1299–1305.

Fausser, J.-L., Rabarivola, C., Meier, B., Hahn, T. and Rumpler, Y. 2000. Genetic comparison between different populations of *Eulemur macaco flavifrons* in northwest Madagascar using RAPD markers. *American Journal of Primatology* 51(4): 249–255.

Fausser, J.-L., Prosper, P. and Rumpler, Y. 2002a. Relationships inside the genus *Hapalemur* based on mitochondrial DNA sequences. *Lemur News* (7): 25–26.

Fausser, J.-L., Prosper, P., Donati, G., Ramanamanjato, J.-B. and Rumpler, Y. 2002b. Phylogenetic relationships between *Hapalemur* species and subspecies based on mitochondrial DNA sequences. *BMC Evolutionary Biology* 2: 4.

Fausser, J.-L., Andriaholinirina, N., Rabarivola, C., and Rumpler, Y. 2004. Genetic comparison of two populations of *Hapalemur simus* inferred from D-loop mitochondrial DNA sequences. *Folia Primatologica* 75(1): 19–22.

Feistner, A. T. C. and Ashbourne, C. 1994. Infant development in a captive-bred aye-aye (*Daubentonia madagascariensis*) over the first year of life. *Folia Primatologica* 62(1–3): 74–92.

Feistner, A. T. C. and Carroll, J. B. 1993. Breeding aye-ayes: an aid to preserving biodiversity. *Biodiversity and Conservation* 2(3): 283–289.

Feistner, A. T. C. and Rakotoarinosy, M. 1993. Conservation of gentle lemur *Hapalemur griseus alaotrensis* at Lac Alaotra, Madagascar: Local knowledge. *Dodo, Journal of The Wildlife Preservation Trusts* 29: 54–65.

Feistner, A. T. C. and Schmid, J. 1999. Lemurs of the Réserve Naturelle Intégrale d'Andohahela, Madagascar. *Fieldiana Zoology* 94: 269–284.

Feistner, A. T. C. and Sterling, E. 1995. Body mass and sexual dimorphism in the aye-aye *Daubentonia madagascariensis*. *Dodo, Journal of the Wildlife Preservation Trusts* 31: 73–76.

Feistner, A. T. C. and Taylor, T. 1998. Sexual cycles and mating behaviour of captive aye-ayes, *Daubentonia madagascariensis*. *Folia Primatologica* 69(suppl. 1): 409.

Fenn, M., Randriamanalina, M. H. and Raharivololona, B. M. 1999. Inventaire biologique dans le sud malgache en vue d'une conservation pour l'écorégion de la forêt sèche de Madagascar: volet primatologie. *Lemur News* (4): 23–25.

Fichtel, C. 2004. Reciprocal recognition of sifaka (*Propithecus verreauxi verreauxi*) and redfronted lemur (*Eulemur fulvus rufus*) alarm calls. *Animal Cognition* 7(1): 45–52.

Fichtel, C. 2007. Avoiding predators at night: antipredator strategies in red-tailed sportive lemurs (*Lepilemur ruficaudatus*). *American Journal of Primatology* 69(6): 611–624.

Fichtel, C. 2008. Ontogeny of conspecific and heterospecific alarm call recognition in wild Verreaux's sifakas (*Propithecus v. verreauxi*). *American Journal of Primatology* 70(2): 127–135.

Fichtel, C. and Hammerschmidt, K. 2002. Responses of redfronted lemurs to experimentally modified alarm calls. Evidence for urgency-based changes in call structure. *Ethology* 108(9): 763–777.

Fichtel, C. and Kappeler, P. M. 2002. Anti-predator behavior of group-living Malagasy primates: mixed evidence for a referential alarm call system. *Behavioral Ecology and Sociobiology* 51(3): 262–275.

Fichtel, C. and Van Schaik, C. P. 2006. Semantic differences in sifaka (*Propithecus verreauxi*) alarm calls: a reflection of genetic or cultural variants? *Ethology* 112(9): 839.

Fietz, J. 1998. Body mass in wild *Microcebus murinus* over the dry season. *Folia Primatologica* 69(suppl. 1): 183–190.

Fietz, J. 1999a. Demography and floating males in a population of *Cheirogaleus medius*. Pp.159–172 in: B. Rakotosamimanana, H. Rasamimanana, J. U. Ganzhorn and S. M. Goodman (eds.), *New Directions in Lemur Studies*. Kluwer Academic/Plenum, New York.

Fietz, J. 1999b. Monogamy as a rule rather than an exception in nocturnal lemurs: The case of the fat-tailed dwarf lemur, *Cheirogaleus medius*. *Ethology* 105(3): 259–272.

Fietz, J. 1999c. Mating system of *Microcebus murinus*. *American Journal of Primatology* 48(2): 127–133.

Fietz, J. 2003. Primates: *Cheirogaleus*, dwarf lemurs or fat-tailed lemurs. Pp.1307–1309 in: S. M. Goodman and J. P. Benstead (eds.), *The Natural History of Madagascar*. The University of Chicago Press, Chicago.

Fietz, J. and Dausmann, K. H. 2003. Costs and potential benefits of parental care in the nocturnal fat-tailed dwarf lemur (*Cheirogaleus medius*). *Folia Primatologica* 74(5–6): 246–258.

Fietz, J. and Ganzhorn, J. U. 1999. Feeding ecology of a hibernating primate *Cheirogaleus medius*: Or how do they get so fat? *Oecologia, Berlin* 121(2): 157–164.

Fietz, J., Zischler, H., Schwiegk, C., Tomiuk, J., Dausmann, K. H. and Ganzhorn, J. U. 2000. High rates of extra-pair young in the pair-living fat-tailed dwarf lemur *Cheirogaleus medius*. *Behavioral Ecology and Sociobiology* 49(1): 8–17.

Filhol, H. 1895. Observations concernant les mammifères contemporains des *Aepyornis* à Madagascar. *Bulletin du Muséum national d'histoire naturelle, Paris* 1: 12–14.

de Flacourt, E. [1658] 1991. *Histoire de la grande île Madagascar*. Réédition facsimile. A.R.S. Terres Créoles, La Réunion.

Fleagle, J. G. 1999. *Primate Adaptation and Evolution*. 2nd edition. Academic Press, San Diego.

Foerg, R. 1982a. Reproductive behavior in *Varecia variegata*. *Folia Primatologica* 38(1–2): 108–121.

Foerg, R. 1982b. Reproduction in *Cheirogaleus medius*. *Folia Primatologica* 39(1–2): 49–62.

Foerg, R. and Hoffmann, R. 1982. Seasonal and daily activity changes in captive *Cheirogaleus medius*. *Folia Primatologica* 38(3–4): 259–268.

Forsyth-Major, C. I. 1894a. On *Megaladapis madagascariensis*, an extinct giant lemuroid from Madagascar: with remarks on the associated fauna, and on its geological age. *Philosophical Transactions of the Royal Society of London* 185:15–38.

Forsyth Major, C. I. 1894b. Über die Malagassischen Lemuriden–Gattungen *Microcebus*, *Opolemur*, und *Chirogale*. *Novitates Zoologicae* 1: 1–39.

Forsyth Major, C. I. 1896. Preliminary notice on fossil monkeys from Madagascar. *Geological Magazine* 3: 433–436.

Forsyth Major, C. I. 1897. On the general results of a zoological expedition to Madagascar in 1894–96. *Proceedings of the Zoological Society of London* (1896): 971–978.

Forsyth Major, C. I. 1900a. Extinct Mammalia from Madagascar. I. *Megaladapis insignis*, sp. n.

Philosophical Transactions of the Royal Society of London 193: 47–50.

Forsyth Major, C. I. 1900b. A summary of our present knowledge of extinct primates from Madagascar. *Geological Magazine* 7: 492–499.

Forsyth Major, C. I. 1901. On *Lemur mongoz* and *Lemur rubriventer*. *Proceedings of the Zoological Society of London* (1901): 248–268.

Fowler, S. V., Chapman, P., Checkley, D., Hurd, S., McHale, M., Ramangason, G.-S., Randriamasy, J. E., Stewart, P., Walters, R. and Wilson, J. M. 1989. Survey and management proposals for a tropical deciduous forest reserve at Ankarana in northern Madagascar. *Biological Conservation* 47: 297–313.

Fredsted, T., Pertoldi, C., Olesen, J. M., Eberle, M. and Kappeler, P. M. 2004. Microgeographic heterogeneity in spatial distribution and mtDNA variability of gray mouse lemurs (*Microcebus murinus*, Primates: Cheirogaleidae). *Behavioral Ecology and Sociobiology* 56(4): 393–403.

Fredsted, T., Schierup, M. H. , Groeneveld, L. F. and Kappeler, P. M. 2007. Genetic structure, lack of sex-biased dispersal and behavioral flexibility in the pair-living fat-tailed dwarf lemur, *Cheirogaleus medius*. *Behavioral Ecology and Sociobiology* 61(6): 943–954.

Freed, B. Z. 1996. Co-occurrence among crowned lemurs (*Lemur coronatus*) and Sanford's lemur (*Lemur fulvus sanfordi*) of Madagascar. PhD thesis, Washington University, St. Louis, MO.

Gachot-Neveu, H., Petit, M. and Roeder, J. J. 1999. Paternity determination in two groups of *Eulemur fulvus mayottensis*: implication for understanding mating strategies. *International Journal of Primatology* 20(1): 107–119.

Ganzhorn, J. U. 1985. Habitat separation in semifree-ranging *Lemur catta* and *Lemur fulvus*. *Folia Primatologica* 45(2): 76–88.

Ganzhorn, J. U. 1986. Feeding behavior of *Lemur catta* and *Lemur fulvus*. *International Journal of Primatology* 7(1): 17–30.

Ganzhorn, J. U. 1987a. Soil consumption of two groups of semi-free-ranging lemurs (*Lemur catta* and *Lemur fulvus*). *Ethology* 74(2): 146–154.

Ganzhorn, J. U. 1987b. A possible role of plantations for primate conservation in Madagascar. *American Journal of Primatology* 12(2): 205–215.

Ganzhorn, J. U. 1988. Food partitioning among Malagasy primates. *Oecologia, Berlin* 75(3): 436–450.

Ganzhorn, J. U. 1989. Niche separation of seven lemur species in the eastern rainforest of Madagascar. *Oecologia, Berlin* 79(2): 279–286.

Ganzhorn, J. U. 1993. Flexibility and constraints of *Lepilemur* ecology. Pp.153–165 in: P. M. Kappeler and J. U. Ganzhorn (eds.), *Lemur Social Systems and their Ecological Basis*. Plenum Press, New York.

Ganzhorn, J. U. 1994. Les lémuriens. Pp.70–72 in: S. Goodman and O. Langrand (eds.), *Recherches pour le Développement*, Série Sciences Biologiques, Centre d'Information et de Documentation Scientifique et Technique, Antananarivo, no. spécial: 1–106.

Ganzhorn, J. U. 1995. Low-level forest disturbance effects on primary production, leaf chemistry, and lemur populations. *Ecology* 76(7): 2084–2096.

Ganzhorn, J. U. 1998a. Nested patterns of species composition and their implications for lemur biogeography in Madagascar. *Folia Primatologica* 69(suppl. 1): 332–341.

Ganzhorn, J. U. 1998b. Progress report on the QMM faunal studies in the littoral forest of southeast Madagascar. *Lemur News* (3): 22–23.

Ganzhorn, J. U. 2002. Distribution of a folivorous lemur in relation to seasonally varying food resources: integrating quantitative and qualitative aspects of food characteristics. *Oecologia, Berlin* 131(3): 427–435.

Ganzhorn, J. U. and Abraham, J. P. 1991. Possible role of plantations for lemur conservation in Madagascar: food for folivorous species. *Folia Primatologica* 56(3): 171–176.

Ganzhorn, J. U. and Kappeler, P. M. 1996. Lemurs of the Kirindy Forest. Pp.257–274 in: J. U. Ganzhorn and J.-P. Sorg (eds.), *Ecology and Economy of a Dry Tropical Forest in Madagascar. Primate Report* 46 (1).

Ganzhorn, J. U. and Rabesoa, J. 1986a. The aye-aye (*Daubentonia madagascariensis*) found in eastern rain forest of Madagascar. *Folia Primatologica* 46(3): 125–126.

Ganzhorn, J. U. and Rabesoa, J. 1986b. Sightings of aye-aye in the eastern rain forest of Madagascar. *Primate Conservation* (7): 45.

Ganzhorn, J. U. and Randriamanalina, M. H. 2004. Les lémuriens de la forêt de Mikea. Pp.87–93 in: A. Raselimanana and S. M. Goodman (eds.), *Inventaire Floristique et Faunistique de la Forêt de Mikea: Paysage Écologique et Diversité Biologique d'une Préoccupation Majeure pour la Conservation. Vol. 21.*, Ministère de l'Education Nationale et de la Recherche Scientifique, Antananarivo.

Ganzhorn, J. U. and Schmid, J. 1998. Different population dynamics of *Microcebus murinus* in primary and secondary deciduous dry forests of Madagascar. *International Journal of Primatology* 19(5): 785–796.

Ganzhorn, J. U., Abraham, J. P. and Razanahoera-Rakotomalala, M. 1985. Some aspects of the natural history and food selection of *Avahi laniger*. *Primates* 26(4): 452–463.

Ganzhorn, J. U., Langrand, O., Wright, P. C., O'Connor, S., Rakotosamimanana, B., Feistner, A. T. C. and Rumpler, Y. (1996/1997). The status of lemur conservation in Madagascar. *Primate Conservation* (17): 70–86.

Ganzhorn, J. U., Malcomber, S., Andrianantoanina, O. and Goodman, S. M. 1997. Habitat characteristics and lemur species richness in Madagascar. *Biotropica* 29(3): 331.

Ganzhorn, J. U., Fietz, J., Rakotovao, E., Schwab, D. and Zinner, D. 1999. Lemurs and the regeneration of dry deciduous forest in Madagascar. *Conservation Biology* 13(4): 794.

Ganzhorn, J., Pietsch, T. Fietz, J., Gross, S. and Steiner, N. 2004. Selection of food and ranging behaviour in a sexually monomorphic folivorous lemur: *Lepilemur ruficaudatus*. *Journal of Zoology, London* 263: 393–399.

Ganzhorn, J. U., Goodman, S. M. and Vincelette, M. (eds.). 2007. *Biodiversity, Ecology, and Conservation of Littoral Ecosystems in the Region of Tolagnaro (Fort Dauphin), Southeastern Madagascar*. Smithsonian Institution Press, Washington, DC.

Garbutt, N. 2001. Brief observations of hairy-eared dwarf lemur (*Allocebus trichotis*) in Analamazaotra Special Reserve, eastern Madagascar. *Lemur News* (6): 37.

Garbutt, N. 2002/2003. With a crown of gold. *Africa Geographic* 59–67.

Garbutt, N. 2007. *Mammals of Madagascar: A Complete Guide*. A. and C. Black, London.

Garcia, G. and Goodman, S. M. 2003. Hunting of protected animals in the Parc National d'Ankarafantsika, north-western Madagascar. *Oryx* 37(1): 115–118.

Garrison, L. K. and White, F. J. 1993. Group formation and behavioural changes with release to free-ranging in red ruffed lemurs, *Varecia variegata rubra. Animal Welfare* 2(2): 219–233.

Gauthier, C.-A., Godfrin, K. and Santini-Palka, M. 1998. Maintenance and captive breeding of endangered species at the Paris Zoological Park: the case of the greater bamboo lemur (*Hapalemur simus*). *Folia Primatologica* 69(1): 43. Abstract.

Geissman, T. and Mutschler, T. 2006. Diurnal distribution of loud calls in sympatric wild indris (*Indri indri*) and ruffed lemurs (*Varecia variegata*): implications for call functions. *Primates* 47(4): 393–396.

Génin, F. 2003. Female dominance in competition for gum trees in the grey mouse lemur *Microcebus murinus. Revue d'Ecologie* 58: 397–410.

Génin, F. 2008. Life in unpredictable environments: first investigation of the natural history of *Microcebus griseorufus. International Journal of Primatology* 29(2): 303–334.

Gerlach, J. and Canning, L. 1998. Taxonomy of Indian Ocean giant tortoises (*Dipsochelys*). *Chelonian Conservation and Biology* 3(1): 3–19.

Gerson, J. S. 1999. Size in *Eulemur fulvus rufus* from western Madagascar: sexual dimorphism and ecogeographic variation. *American Journal of Physical Anthropology* 28(suppl.): 134. Abstract.

Giacoma, C., Sorrentino, V., Rabarivola, C. and Gamba, M. 2010. Sex differences in the song of *Indri indri. International Journal of Primatology.* DOI 10.1007/s10764-010-9412-8.

Gilbert, M. and Tingay, R. E. 2001. Predation of a fat-tailed dwarf lemur *Cheirogaleus medius* by a Madagascar Harrier-hawk (*Polyboroides radiatus*): an incidental observation. *Lemur News* (6): 6.

Glander, K. E. 1994a. Aye-aye weight and gestation. *American Journal of Physical Anthropology* 18(suppl.): 94. Abstract.

Glander, K. E. 1994b. Morphometrics and growth in captive aye-ayes (*Daubentonia madagascariensis*). *Folia Primatologica* 62(1–3): 108–114.

Glander, K. E. and Powzyk, J. A. 1998. Morphometrics of wild *Indri indri* and *Propithecus diadema diadema. Folia Primatologica* 69(suppl. 1): 399. Abstract.

Glander, K. E., Freed, B. Z. and Ganzhorn, J. U. 1985. Meat eating and predation in captive-born semi free-ranging *Lemur fulvus* and caged *Lemur macaco. Zoo Biology* 4(4): 361–365.

Glander, K. E., Wright, P. C., Seigler, D. S. and Randrianasolo, B. 1989. Consumption of a cyanogenic bamboo by a newly discovered species of bamboo lemur. *American Journal of Primatology* 19(1): 119–124.

Glander, K. E., Wright, P. C., Daniels, P. S. and Merenlander, A. M. 1992. Morphometrics and testicle size of rain forest lemur species from southeastern Madagascar. *Journal of Human Evolution* 22(1): 1–17.

Glatston, A. R. 1981. The husbandry, breeding and hand-rearing of the lesser mouse lemur *Microcebus murinus* at Rotterdam Zoo. *International Zoo Yearbook* 21: 131–137.

Glatston, A. R. 2001. Relevance of studbook data to the successful captive management of grey mouse lemurs. *International Journal of Primatology* 22(1): 57–69.

Glaw, F. and Vences, M. 2007. *Field Guide to the Amphibians and Reptiles of Madagascar.* 3rd edition. Vences and Glaw Verlag, Köln.

Glessner, K. D. G. and Britt, A. 2005. Population density and home range size of *Indri indri* in a protected low altitude rain forest. *International Journal of Primatology* 26(4): 855–872.

Gligor, M., Ganzhorn, J. U., Rakotondravony, D., Ramilijaona, O. R., Razafimahatratra, E., Zischler, H. and Hapke, A. 2009. Hybridization between mouse lemurs in an ecological transition zone in southern Madagascar. *Molecular Ecology* 18(3): 520–533.

Godfrey, L. R. 2004. Developing a conservation strategy for *Microcebus griseorufus* and *Microcebus murinus* (Primates, Cheirogaleidae) at the Beza-Mahafaly Special Reserve, southwestern Madagascar. Unpublished report to the Margot Marsh Biodiversity Foundation, Great Falls, VA.

Godfrey, L.R. and Irwin., M. T. 2007. The evolution of extinction risk: past and present anthropogenic impacts on the primate communities of Madagascar. *Folia Primatologica* 78(5-6): 405–419.

Godfrey, L. R. and Jungers, W. L. 2002. Quaternary fossil lemurs. Pp.97–121 in W. C. Hartwig (ed.), *The Primate Fossil Record*. Cambridge University Press, Cambridge, UK.

Godfrey, L. R. and Jungers, W. L. 2003a. The extinct sloth lemurs of Madagascar. *Evolutionary Anthropology* 12(6): 252–263.

Godfrey, L. R. and Jungers, W. L. 2003b. Subfossil lemurs. Pp.1247–1252 in: S. M. Goodman and J. P. Benstead (eds.), *The Natural History of Madagascar*. The University of Chicago Press, Chicago.

Godfrey, L. R. and Vuillaume-Randriamanatena, M. 1986. *Hapalemur simus*: endangered lemur once widespread. *Primate Conservation* (7): 92–96.

Godfrey, L. R., Simons, E. L., Chatrath, P. S. and Rakotosamimanana, B. 1990. A new fossil lemur (*Babakotia*, Primates) from northern Madagascar. *Comptes rendus de l'Académie des sciences de Paris* 310(1): 81–87.

Godfrey, L. R., Lyon, S. K. and Sutherland, M. R. 1993. Sexual dimorphism in large-bodied primates: the case of the subfossil lemurs. *American Journal of Physical Anthropology* 90(3): 315–334.

Godfrey, L.R., Wilson, J. M., Simons, E. L., Stewart, P. D. and Vuillaume-Randriamanantena, M. 1996. Ankarana: window to Madagascar's past? *Lemur News* (2)2: 16–17.

Godfrey, L. R., Jungers, W. L., Wunderlich, R. E. and Richmond, B. G. 1997. Reappraisal of the postcranium of *Hadropithecus* (Primates, Indroidea). *American Journal of Physical Anthropology* 103(4): 529–556.

Godfrey, L. R., Jungers, W. L., Simons, E. L,, Chatrath, P. S. and Rakotosaminana, B. 1999. Past and present distributions of lemurs in Madagascar. Pp.19–53 in: B. Rakotosamimanana, H. Rasimimanana, J. U. Ganzhorn and S. M. Goodman (eds.), *New Directions in Lemur Studies*. Kluwer Academic/Plenum Publishers, New York.

Godfrey, L. R., Semprebon, G. M., Jungers, W. L., Sutherland, M. R., Simons, E. L. and Solounias, N. 2004a. Dental use wear in extinct lemurs: evidence of diet and niche differentiation. *Journal of Human Evolution* 47(3): 145–169.

Godfrey, L. R., Simons, E. L., Jungers, W. L., Deblieux, D. D. and Chatrath, P. S. 2004b. New discovery of subfossil *Hapalemur simus*, the greater bamboo lemur, in western Madagascar. *Lemur News* (9): 9–11.

Godfrey, L. R., Semprebon, G. M., Schwartz, G. T., Burney, D. A., Jungers, W. L., Flanagan, E. K., Cuozzo, F. P. and King, S. J. 2005. New insights into old lemurs: the trophic adaptations of the Archaeolemuridae. *International Journal of Primatology* 26(4): 825–854.

Godfrey, L. R., Schwartz, G. T., Samonds, K. E., Jungers, W. L. and Catlett, K. K. 2006a. The secrets of lemur teeth. *Evolutionary Anthropology* 15(4): 142–154.

Godfrey, L. R., Jungers, W. L., Burney, D. A., Vasey, N., Ramilisonina, Wheeler, W., Lemelin, P., Shapiro, L., Schwartz, G., King, S., Ramarolahy, M., Raharivony, L. and Randria, G. 2006b. New discoveries of skeletal elements of *Hadropithecus stenognatus* from Andrahomena Cave, southeastern Madagascar. *Journal of Human Evolution* 51(4): 395–410.

Godinot, M. 2006. Lemuriform origins as viewed from the fossil record. *Folia Primatologica* 77(6): 446–464.

Goix, E. 1993. L' utilisation de la main chez le aye-aye en captivité (*Daubentonia madagascariensis*) (prosimiens, daubentoniidés). *Mammalia* 57(2): 177–188.

Golden, C. D. 2005. Eaten to endangerment: mammal hunting and the bushmeat trade in Madagascar's Makira Forest. Undergraduate thesis, Harvard University, Cambridge, MA.

Golden, C. D. 2009. Bushmeat hunting and use in the Makira Forest, north-eastern Madagascar: a conservation and livelihoods issue. *Oryx* 43(3): 386–392.

Gommery, D., Tombomiadana, S., Valentin, F., Ramanivosoa, B., Bezoma, R. 2004. Nouvelle découverte dans le Nord-Ouest de Madagascar et répartition géographique des espèces du genre *Palaeopropithecus*. *Annales de Paléontologie* 90(4): 279–286.

Gommery, D., Ramanivosoa, B., Tombomiadana-Raveloson, S., Randrianantenaina, H. and Kerloc'h, P. 2009. Une nouvelle espèce de lémurien géant subfossile du nord-ouest de Madagascar (*Palaeopropithecus kelyus*, Primates). *Comptes Rendus Palevol* 8(5): 471–480.

Goodman, S. M. 1999. A floral and faunal inventory of the Réserve Naturelle Intégrale d'Andohahela, Madagascar: with reference to elevational variation. *Fieldiana: Zoology, new series* 94. Field Museum Natural History, Chicago.

Goodman, S. M. 2003. Predation on lemurs. Pp. 1221–1228 in: S. Goodman and J. P. Benstead (eds.), *The Natural History of Madagascar*. The University of Chicago Press, Chicago.

Goodman, S. M. and Benstead, J. P. (eds.). 2003. *The Natural History of Madagascar*. University of Chicago Press, Chicago.

Goodman, S. M. and Benstead, J. P. 2005. Updated estimates of biotic diversity and endemism for Madagascar. *Oryx* 39(1): 73–77.

Goodman, S. M. and Ganzhorn, J. U. 2004a. Elevational ranges of lemurs in the humid forests of Madagascar. *International Journal of Primatology* 25(2): 331–350.

Goodman, S. M. and Ganzhorn, J. U. 2004b. Biogeography of lemurs in the humid forests of Madagascar: the role of elevational distribution and rivers. *Journal of Biogeography* 31(1): 47–55.

Goodman, S. M. and Hawkins, A. F. A. 2008. Les oiseaux. Pp.383–434 in S. M. Goodman (ed.), *Paysages Naturels et Biodiversité de Madagascar*. Muséum National d'Histoire Naturelle, Paris.

Goodman, S. M. and Langrand, O. 1996a. Food remains found in a nest of the Madagascar buzzard (*Buteo brachypterus*) in the Vohibasia Forest. *Working Group on Birds in the Madagascar Region Newsletter* 6(2): 13–14.

Goodman, S. M. and Langrand, O. 1996b. A high mountain population of the ring-tailed lemur (*Lemur catta*) on the Andringitra Massif, Madagascar. *Oryx* 30(4): 259–268.

Goodman, S. M. and Rakotondravony, D. 1996. The Holocene distribution of *Hypogeomys* (Rodentia: Muridae: Nesomyinae) on Madagascar. *Biogéographie de Madagascar* (1996): 283–293.

Goodman, S. M. and Rakotondravony, D. 1998. Les lémuriens. Pp.213–222 in: J. Ratsirarson and S. M. Goodman (eds.), *Inventaire Biologique de la Forêt Littorale de Tampolo (Fenoarivo Atsinanana)*. Volume 14 in Recherches Pour le Développement, Série Sciences Biologiques, Centre d'Information et de Documentation Scientifique et Technique, Antananarivo.

Goodman, S. M. and Raselimanana, A. P. 2002. The occurrence of *Allocebus trichotis* in the Parc National de Marojejy. *Lemur News* (7): 21–22.

Goodman, S. M. and Raselimanana, A. 2003. Hunting of wild animals by Sakalava of the Menabe region: A field report from Kirindy-Mitea. *Lemur News* (8): 4–6.

Goodman, S. M. and Rasolonandrasana, B. P. N. 2001. Elevational zonation of birds, insectivores, rodents, and primates on the slopes of the Andringitra Massif, Madagascar. *Journal of Natural History* 35: 285–305.

Goodman, S. M. and Schütz, H. 1999. Observations of lemurs in the forest east of Tsinjoarivo, Ambatolampy. *Lemur News* (4): 14–16.

Goodman, S. M. and Schütz, H. 2000. The lemurs of the northeastern slopes of the Réserve Spéciale de Manongarivo. *Lemur News* (5): 30–33.

Goodman, S. M. and Soarimalala, V. 2002. Les petits mammifères de la Réserve Spéciale de Manongarivo, Madagascar. Pp.383–401 in: L. Gautier and S. Goodman (eds.), *Inventaire Floristique et Faunistique de la Réserve Spéciale de Manongarivo, Madagascar*. Boissiera 59.

Goodman, S. M. and Wilmé, L. 2003. *Nouveaux résultats d'inventaires biologiques faisant référence à l'altitude dans la région des massifs montagneux de Marojejy et d'Anjanaharibe-Sud*, Recherches pour le Développement, Série Sciences Biologiques ed., Vol. 19, Centre d'Information et de Documentation Scientifique et Technique, Antananarivo.

Goodman, S. M., Langrand, O. and Raxworthy, C. J. 1993a. Food habits of the Madagascar Long-eared Owl *Asio madagascariensis* in two habitats in southern Madagascar. *Ostrich* 64: 79–85.

Goodman, S. M., Langrand, O. and Raxworthy, C. J. 1993b. The food habits of the Barn Owl *Tyto alba* at three sites in Madagascar. *Ostrich* 64: 160–171.

Goodman, S. M., O'Connor, S. and Langrand, O. 1993c. A review of predation on lemurs: implications for the evolution of social behavior in small, nocturnal primates. Pp.51–66 in: P. M. Kappeler and J. U. Ganzhorn (eds.), *Lemur Social Systems and Their Ecological Basis*. Plenum Press, New York.

Goodman, S. M., Langrand, O. and Rasolonandrasana, B. P. N. 1997. The food habits of *Cryptoprocta ferox* in the high mountain zone of the Andringitra Massif, Madagascar (Carnivora, Viverridae). *Mammalia* 61: 185–192.

Goodman, S. M., de Roland, L.A. R. and Thorstrom, R. 1998. Predation on the eastern woolly lemur (*Avahi laniger*) and other vertebrates by Henst's goshawk (*Accipiter henstii*). *Lemur News* (3): 14–15.

Goodman, S. M., Razafindratsia, V., Schütz, V. and Ratsimbazafy, R. 2001. Les lémuriens. Pp.231–243 in: S. M. Goodman and V. Razafindratsia (eds.), *Inventaire Biologique du Parc National de Ranomafana et du Couloir Forestier qui le Relie au Parc National d'Andringitra, Vol. 17*. Centre d'Information et de Documentation Scientifique et Technique, Antananarivo.

Goodman, S. M., Raherilalao, M. J., Rakotomalala, D., Rakotondravony, D., Raselimanana, A. P., Razakarivony, H. V., and Soarimalala, V. 2002. Inventaire des vertébrés du Parc National de Tsimanampetsotsa (Toliara (= Tuléar)). *Akon'ny Ala* 28: 1–36.

Goodman, S. M., Goodman, S. M., Ganzhorn, J. U. and Rakotondravony, D. 2003a. Introduction to the mammals. Pp.1159–1186 in: S. M. Goodman and J. P. Benstead (eds.), *The Natural History of*

Madagascar. The University of Chicago Press, Chicago.

Goodman, S. M., Kerridge, F. J. and Ralisoamalala, R. C. 2003b. A note on the diet of *Fossa fossana* (Carnivora) in the central eastern humid forests of Madagascar. *Mammalia* 67: 595–597.

Goodman, S. M., Soarimalala, V. R. L., and Ganzhorn, J. U. 2004. La chasse aux animaux sauvages dans la forêt de Mikea. Pp. 95–100 in: A. P. Raselimanana, and S. M. Goodman (eds.), *Inventaire Floristique et Faunistique de la Forêt de Mikea: Paysage Écologique et Diversité Biologique d'une Préoccupation Majeure pour la Conservation. Vol. 21.*, Ministère de l'Education Nationale et de la Recherche Scientifique, Antananarivo.

Goodwin, H. A. and Holloway C. W. 1972. IUCN *Red Data Book Volume 1 - Mammalia* [Ring-bound]. International Union for Conservation of Nature and Natural Resources (IUCN), Morges, Switzerland.

Gould, L. 1990. The social development of free-ranging infant *Lemur catta* at Berenty Reserve, Madagascar. *International Journal of Primatology* 11(4): 297–318.

Gould, L. 1992. Alloparental care in free-ranging *Lemur catta* at Berenty Reserve, Madagascar. *Folia Primatologica* 58(2): 72–83

Gould, L. 1996a. Vigilance behavior during the birth and lactation season in naturally occurring ring-tailed lemurs (*Lemur catta*) at the Beza-Mahafaly Reserve, Madagascar. *American Journal of Primatology* 39(1): 63–78.

Gould, L. 1996b. Male-female affiliative relationships in naturally occuring ringtailed lemurs (*Lemur catta*) at the Beza-Mahafaly Reserve, Madagascar. *American Journal of Primatology* 39(1): 63–78.

Gould, L. 1997a. Affiliative relationships between adult males and immature group members in naturally occurring ringtailed lemurs (*Lemur catta*). *American Journal of Physical Anthropology* 103(2): 163–171.

Gould, L. 1997b. Intermale affiliative behavior in ringtailed lemurs (*Lemur catta*) at the Beza-Mahafaly Reserve, Madagascar. *Primates* 38(1): 15–30.

Gould, L. and Overdorff, D. J. 2002. Adult male scent-marking in *Lemur catta* and *Eulemur fulvus rufus*. *International Journal of Primatology* 23(3): 575–586.

Gould, L., Sussman, R. W., and Sauther, M. L. 1999. Natural disasters and primate populations: the effects of a 2-year drought on a naturally occurring population of ring-tailed lemurs (*Lemur catta*) in southwestern Madagascar. *International Journal of Primatology* 20(1): 69–84.

Gould, L., Sussman, R. W. and Sauther, M. L. 2003. Demographic and life-history patterns in a population of ring-tailed lemurs (*Lemur catta*) at Beza Mahafaly Reserve, Madagascar: a 15-year perspective. *American Journal of Physical Anthropology* 120(2): 182–194.

Gould, L. R., Jungers, W. L. and Schwartz, G. T. 2007. *Ecology and Extinction of Madagascar's Subfossil Lemurs.* Springer, New York.

Grandidier, A. 1867. Description d'une nouvelle espèce de Chirogale découverte sur la côte ouest de Madagascar. *Annals of Science and Nature (Zoology)* 8: 294.

Grandidier, A. 1868. Sur les découvertes zoologiques faites rècemment à Madagascar. *Annals of Science and Nature (Zoology)* 10: 375–378.

Grandidier, A. 1871. Observations sur les Propithèques de Madagascar. Extrait d'une lettre adressée à M. Milne Edwards. *Comptes rendus de l'Académie des sciences de Paris* 72: 231–232.

Grandidier, G. 1899a. Description d'ossements de lémuriens disparus. *Bulletin du Muséum national d'histoire naturelle, Paris* 5: 272–276.

Grandidier, G. 1899b. Description d'ossements de lémuriens disparus. *Bulletin du Muséum national d'histoire naturelle, Paris* 5: 344-348.

Grandidier, G. 1905. Recherches sur les lémuriens disparus et en particulier ceux qui vivaient à Madagascar. *Nouvelles archives du Muséum national d'histoire naturelle, Paris* 7: 1–142.

Grandidier, G. 1929. Une variété de *Cheiromys madagascariensis* actuel et un nouveau *Cheiromys* subfossile. *Bulletin de l'Académie* (nouvelle série) 11: 101–107.

Grassi, C. 1998. Forest composition and bamboo distribution: influences on the distribution of *Hapalemur* species. *American Journal of Physical Anthropology* 26(suppl.): 100. Abstract.

Grassi, C. 2001. The behavioral ecology of *Hapalemur griseus griseus*: the influences of microhabitat and population density on this small-bodied prosimian folivore. PhD dissertation, University of Texas, Austin, TX.

Grassi, C. 2002. Sex differences in feeding, height, and space use in *Hapalemur griseus*. *International Journal of Primatology* 23(3): 677–693.

Grassi, C. 2006. Variability in habitat, diet and social structure of *Hapalemur griseus* in Ranomafana National Park, Madagascar. *American Journal of Physical Anthropology* 131(1): 50–63.

Gray, J. E. 1842. Descriptions of some new genera and fifty unrecorded species of Mammalia. *Annals and Magazine of Natural History* 10: 255–267.

Gray, J. E. 1863. Revision of the species of lemuroid animals, with the description of some new species. *Proceedings of the Zoological Society of London* (1863): 129–152.

Gray, J. E. 1870. *Catalogue of Monkeys, Lemurs, and Fruit-eating Bats in the Collections of the British Museum*. British Museum, London. 137pp.

Gray, J. E. 1871a. On *Hapalemur simus*, a new species lately living in the gardens of the society. *Proceedings of the Zoological Society of London* (1871): 828–831.

Gray, J. E. 1871b. On a new species of lemur from Madagascar, and on the changes of *Lemur macaco* Linn. *Annals and Magazine of Natural History* 7: 339–340.

Gray, J. E. 1872. On the varieties of *Indris* and *Propithecus*. *Annals and Magazine of Natural History* 10: 474.

Gray, J. E. 1873. Notes on *Propithecus*, *Indris* and other lemurs (Lemurina) in the British Museum. *Proceedings of the Zoological Society of London* (1873): 846–860.

Green, K. M. and Sussman, R. W. 1990. Deforestation history of the eastern rain forests of Madagascar from satellite images. *Science* 248: 212–215.

Grieser, B. 1992. Infant development and parental care in two species of sifakas. *Primates* 33(3): 305–314.

Groeneveld, L. F., Weisrock, D. W., Rasoloarison, R. M., Yoder, A. D. and Kappeler, P. M. 2009. Species delimitation in lemurs: multiple genetic loci reveal low levels of species diversity in the genus *Cheirogaleus*. *BMC Evolutionary Biology* 9: 30.

Groeneveld, L. F., Blanco, M. B., Raharison, J.-L., Rahalinarivo, V., Rasoloarison, R. M., Kappeler, P. M., Godfrey, L. R. and Irwin, M. T. 2010. MtDNA and nDNA corroborate existence of sympatric dwarf lemur species at Tsinjoraivo, eastern Madagascar. *Molecular Phylogenetics and Evolution*. In press. doi:10.1016/j.ympev.2010.03.004.

Groves, C. P. 1974. Taxonomy and phylogeny of prosimians. Pp.449–473 in: R. D. Martin, G. A. Doyle, and A. C. Walker (eds.), *Prosimian Biology*. Duckworth, London.

Groves, C. P. 1978. A note on nomenclature and taxonomy in the Lemuridae. *Mammalia* 42(1): 131–132.

Groves, C. P. 1989. *A Theory of Human and Primate Evolution*. Oxford University Press, New York.

Groves, C. P. 2000. The genus *Cheirogaleus* : unrecognized diversity in dwarf lemurs. *International Journal of Primatology* 21(6): 943–962.

Groves, C. P. 2001. *Primate Taxonomy*. Smithsonian Institution Press, Washington, DC.

Groves, C. P. 2004. The what, why and how of primate taxonomy. *International Journal of Primatology* 25(5): 1105–1126.

Groves, C. P. 2006. Red-fronted lemurs are not the same as red lemurs. *Australian Primatology* 18(1): 23.

Groves, C. P. and Eaglen, R. H. 1988. Systematics of the Lemuridae (Primates, Strepsirhini). *Journal of Human Evolution* 17(5): 513–538.

Groves, C. P. and Helgen, K. M. 2007. Craniodental characters in the taxonomy of *Propithecus*. *International Journal of Primatology* 28(6): 1363–1383.

Groves, C. P. and Tattersall, I. 1991. Geographical variation in the fork-marked lemur *Phaner furcifer* (Primates, Cheirogaleidae). *Folia Primatologica* 56(1): 39–49.

Guillaumet, J.-L. 1984. The vegetation: An extraordinary diversity. Pp.27-54 in: A. Jolly, P. Oberlé and R. Albignac (eds.), *Key Environments: Madagascar*. Pergamon Press, Oxford.

Günther, A. 1875. Notes on some mammals from Madagascar. *Proceedings of the Zoological Society of London* (1875): 78–80.

Hafen, T., Neveu, H., Rumpler, Y., Wilden, I. and Zimmermann, E. 1998. Acoustically dimorphic advertisement calls separate morphologically and genetically homogeneous populations of the grey mouse lemur (*Microcebus murinus*). *Folia Primatologica* 69(suppl.1): 342–356.

Hamrick, M. W., Simons E. L. and Jungers W. L. 2000. New wrist bones of the Malagasy giant subfossil lemurs. *Journal of Human Evolution* 38(5): 635–650.

Hapke, A., Eberle, M. and Zischler, H. 2003a. Isolation of new microsatellite markers and application in four species of mouse lemurs (*Microcebus* spp.). *Molecular Ecology Notes* 3(2): 205.

Hapke, A., Schülke, O. and Zischler, H. 2003b. Microsatellite markers for paternity testing in fork-marked lemurs (*Phaner furcifer*). *Molecular Ecology Notes* 3(3): 438.

Hapke, A., Fietz, J., Nash, S. D., Rakotondravony, D., Rakotosamimanana, B., Ramanamanjato, J.-B., Randria, G. F. N., and Zischler, H. 2005. Biogeography of dwarf lemurs: genetic evidence for unexpected patterns in southeastern Madagascar. *International Journal of Primatology* 26(4): 873–901.

Harcourt, C. 1987. Brief trap/retrap study of the brown mouse lemur (*Microcebus rufus*). *Folia Primatologica* 49(3–4): 209–211.

Harcourt, C. 1988. *Avahi laniger*: a study in activity. *Primate Eye* (35): 9. Abstract.

Harcourt, C. 1991. Diet and behaviour of a nocturnal lemur, *Avahi laniger*, in the wild. *Journal of Zoology, London* 223(4): 667–674.

Harcourt, C. and Thornback, J. 1990. *Lemurs of Madagascar and the Comoros. The IUCN Red Data Book*. IUCN, Gland, Switzerland and Cambridge, UK.

Haring, D. M. 1989. Natural history and captive management of Verreaux's sifaka *Propithecus verreauxi*. *International Zoo Yearbook* 27(1): 125–134.

Haring, D. and Davis, K. 1998. Management of the grey gentle or eastern lesser bamboo lemur *Hapalemur griseus griseus* at Duke University Primate Center, Durham. *International Zoo Yearbook* 36: 20–34.

Haring, D. M., Hess, W. R., Coffman, B. S., Simons, E. L. and Owens, T. M. 1994. Natural history and captive management of the aye-aye *Daubentonia madagascariensis* at the Duke University Primate Center, Durham. *International Zoo Yearbook* 33: 201–219.

Harper, F. 1945. *Extinct and Vanishing Mammals of the Old World*. American Committee on International Wildlife Protection, Washington, DC.

Harper, G., Steininger, M. K., Tucker, C. J., Juhn, D. and Hawkins, F. 2007. Fifty years of deforestation and forest fragmentation in Madagascar. *Environmental Conservation* 34(4): 1–9.

Harrington, J. E. 1975. Field observations of social behavior of *Lemur fulvus fulvus* E. Geoffroy 1812. Pp.259–279 in: I. Tattersall and R. W. Sussman (eds.), *Lemur Biology*. Plenum Press, New York.

Harrington, J. E. 1977. Discrimination between males and females by scent in *Lemur fulvus*. *Animal Behaviour* 25(1): 147–151.

Harrington, J. E. 1978a. Development of behaviour in *Lemur macaco* in the first nineteen weeks. *Folia Primatologica* 29(2): 107–128.

Harrington, J. E. 1978b. Diurnal behavior of *Lemur mongoz* at Ampijoroa, Madagascar. *Folia Primatologica* 29(2): 291–302.

Harste, L. V., Wright, P. C. and Jernvall, J. 1997. *Microcebus rufus* feeding behaviour in the south-eastern rain forest of Madagascar. *Primate Eye* (62): 6–7. Abstract.

Hawkins, A. F. A. 1999. The primates of Isalo National Park, Madagascar. *Lemur News* (4): 10–14.

Hawkins, A. F. A. and Goodman S. M. 2003. Introduction to the birds. Pp.1019–1044 in: S. M. Goodman and J. P. Benstead (eds.), *The Natural History of Madagascar*. The University of Chicago Press, Chicago.

Hawkins, A. F. A., Chapman, P., Ganzhorn, J. U., Bloxam, Q. M., Barlow, S. C. and Tonge, S. J. 1990. Vertebrate conservation in Ankarana Special Reserve, northern Madagascar. *Biological Conservation* 54: 83–110.

Hawkins, A. F. A., Durbin, J. C. and Reid, D. B. 1998. The primates of the Baly Bay area, north-western Madagascar. *Folia Primatologica* 69(6): 337–345.

Hayes, R. A., Morelli, T. L. and Wright, P. C. 2004. Anogenital gland secretions of *Lemur catta* and *Propithecus verreauxi coquereli*: a preliminary chemical examination. *American Journal of Primatology* 63(2): 49–62.

Hearn, G. W., Berghaier, R. W. and George, D. D. 1996. Evidence for social enhancement of reproduction in two *Eulemur* species. *Zoo Biology* 15(1): 1–12.

Heckman, K. L., Rasoazanabary, E., Machlin, E., Godfrey, L. R. and Yoder, A. D. 2006. Incongruence between genetic and morphological diversity in *Microcebus griseorufus* at Beza Mahafaly. *BMC Evolutionary Biology* 6: 98. doi 10.1186/1471-2148/6/98.

Hekkala, E. R. and Rakotondratsima, M. 1999. Report on preliminary surveys for distribution and population genetic structure of the red-ruffed lemur (*Varecia variegata rubra*) in the Antainambalana/Andranofotsy River basin of Madagascar: An assessment of forest remnants as corridors for conservation. Report to Wildlife Conservation Society (WCS), Antananarivo.

Hekkala, E., Rakotondratsima, M., and Vasey, N. 2007. Habitat and distribution of the ruffed lemur (*Varecia*) north of the Bay of Antongil in northeastern Madagascar. *Primate Conservation* (22): 89–95.

Hemingway, C. A. 1995. Feeding and reproductive strategies of the Milne-Edwards' sifaka, *Propithecus diadema edwardsi*. PhD thesis, Duke University, Durham, NC.

Hemingway, C. A. 1996. Morphology and phenology of seeds and whole fruit eaten by Milne-Edwards' sifaka, *Propithecus diadema edwardsi*, in Ranomafana National Park, Madagascar. *International Journal of Primatology* 17(5): 637–659.

Hemingway, C. A. 1998. Selectivity and variability in the diet of Milne-Edwards' sifakas (*Propithecus diadema edwardsi*): implications for folivory and seed-eating. *International Journal of Primatology* 19(2): 355–377.

Hemingway, C. A. 1999. Time budgets and foraging in a Malagasy primate: do sex differences reflect reproduction condition and female dominance? *Behavioral Ecology and Sociobiology* 45(3–4): 311–322.

Hick, U. 1976. Hand-rearing a ring-tailed lemur *Lemur catta* and a crowned lemur *Lemur mongoz coronatus* at Cologne Zoo. *International Zoo Yearbook* 16: 187–189.

Hilgartner, R, Zinner, D, and Kappeler, P. M. 2008. Life history traits and parental care in *Lepilemur ruficaudatus*. *American Journal of Primatology* 70(1): 2–11.

Hill, W. C. O. 1953. *Primates: Comparative Anatomy and Taxonomy. I. Strepsirhini*. The University Press, Edinburgh, UK.

Hladik, C. M. and Charles-Dominique, P. 1974. The behavior and ecology of the sportive lemur (*Lepilemur mustelinus*) in relation to its dietary peculiartities. Pp.23–37 in: R. D. Martin, G. A. Doyle and A. C. Walker (eds.), *Prosimian Biology*. Duckworth, London.

Hladik, C. M., Charles-Dominique, P. and Petter, J.-J. 1980. Feeding strategies of five nocturnal prosimians in the dry forest of the west coast of Madagascar. Pp.41–73 in: P. Charles-Dominique, H. M. Cooper, A. Hladik, C. M. Hladik, E. Pagès, G. F. Pariente, A. Petter-Rousseaux, J.-J. Petter and A. Schilling (eds.), *Nocturnal Malagasy Primates: Ecology, Physiology and Behavior*. Academic Press, New York.

Hladik, C. M., Pinte, M. and Simmen, B. 1998. Les densités de population des prosimians nocturnes du sud de Madagascar varient-elles à long terme dans les rèserves forestières accessibles au public? *Revue d'écologie* 53(2): 181–185.

Hood, L. C. 2005. Infanticide among ringtailed lemurs (*Lemur catta*) at Berenty Reserve, Madagascar. *American Journal of Primatology* 33(1): 65–69.

Hood, L. C. and Jolly, A. 1995. Troop fission in female *Lemur catta* at Berenty Reserve, Madagascar. *International Journal of Primatology* 16(6): 997–1015.

Horvath, J. E., Weisrock, D. W., Embry, S. L, Fiorentino, I., Balhoff, J. P., Kappeler, P. M., Wray, G. A., Willard, H. F. and Yoder, A. D. 2008. Development and application of a phylogenomic toolkit: resolving the evolutionary history of Madagascar's lemurs. *Genome Research* 18(3): 489–499.

Hosey, G. R., Jacques, M. and Pitts, A. 1997. Drinking from tails: social learning of a novel behaviour in a group of ring-tailed lemurs (*Lemur catta*). *Primates* 38(4): 415–422.

Howarth, C. J., Wilson, J. M., Adamson, A. P., Wilson, M. E. and Boase, M. J. 1986. Population ecology of the ring-tailed lemur, *Lemur catta*, and the white sifaka, *Propithecus verreauxi verreauxi*, at Berenty, Madagascar, 1981. *Folia Primatologica* 47(1): 39–48.

Humbert, H. 1927. La destruction d'une flore insulaire par le feu. Principaux aspects de la végétation à Madagascar. *Mémoires de l'Académie Malgache* 5: 1–78.

Humbert, H. and Cours Darne, G. 1965. Carte internationale du tapis végétal et des conditions écologiques. 3 coupures au 1/1,000,000 de Madagascar. *Travaux de la Section Scientifique et Technique, Institut Français de Pondichéry*, hors sér., 3 maps.

Ichino, S. and Koyama, N. 2006. Social changes in a wild population of ringtailed lemurs (*Lemur catta*) at Berenty, Madagascar. Pp. 234–244 in: A. Jolly, R. W. Sussman, N. Koyama and H. Rasamimanana (eds.), *Ringtailed Lemur Biology:* Lemur catta *in Madagascar*. Springer, New York.

Irwin, M. T. 2006. Ecological Impacts of Forest Fragmentation on Diademed Sifakas (*Propithecus diadema*) at Tsinjoarivo, Eastern Madagascar: Implications for Conservation in Fragmented Landscapes. PhD dissertation, Stony Brook University, NY.

Irwin, M. T. 2007. Living in forest fragments reduces group cohesion in diademed sifakas (*Propithecus diadema*) in eastern Madagascar by reducing food patch size. *American Journal of Primatology* 69(4): 434–447.

Irwin, M. T. 2008a. Feeding ecology of *Propithecus diadema* in forest fragments and continuous forest. *International Journal of Primatology* 29(1): 95–115.

Irwin, M. T. 2008b. Diademed sifaka (*Propithecus diadema*) ranging and habitat use in continuous and fragmented forest: higher density but lower viability in fragments? *Biotropica* 40(2): 231–240.

Irwin, M. T. 2008b. Ecological impacts of forest fragmentation on diademed sifakas (*Propithecus diadema*) at Tsinjoarivo, eastern Madagascar. *Lemur News* (13): 45.

Irwin, M. T. and Ravelomanantsoa, H. V. 2004. Illegal rum production threatens health of lemur populations at Tsinjoarivo, eastern central Madagascar: brief report and request for information. *Lemur News* (9): 16–17.

Irwin, M. T., Smith, T. M. and Wright, P. C. 2000. Census of three eastern rain forest sites north of Ranomafana National Park: preliminary results and implications for lemur conservation. *Lemur News* (5): 20–22.

Irwin, M. T., Samonds, K. and Raharison, J.-L. 2001. A biological inventory of the lemur community of Réserve Spéciale de Kalambatritra, south-central Madagascar. *Lemur News* (6): 24–28.

Irwin, M. T., Samonds, K. E., Raharison, J.-L. and Wright, P. C. 2004. Lemur latrines: observations of latrine behavior in wild primates and possible ecological significance. *Journal of Mammalogy* 85(3): 420–427.

Irwin, M. T, Johnson, S. E., and Wright, P. C. 2005. The state of lemur conservation in southeastern Madagascar: population and habitat assessments for diurnal lemurs using surveys, satellite imagery and GIS. *Oryx* 39(2): 1–15.

Irwin, M. T., Raharison, J. L. and Wright, P. C. 2009. Spatial and temporal variability in predation on rainforest primates: do forest fragmentation and predation act synergistically? *Animal Conservation* 12: 220–230.

Ishak, B., Warter, S., Dutrillaux, B. and Rumpler, Y. 1992. Chromosomal rearrangements and speciation of sportive lemurs (*Lepilemur* species). *Folia Primatologica* 58(3): 121–130.

ISIS. 2009. International Species Information System (ISIS). Website: <http://www.isis.org>. Accessed: 20 December 2009.

IUCN. 1994. *IUCN Red List Categories*. IUCN – The World Conservation Union, Species Survival Commission (SSC), Cambridge, UK and Gland, Switzerland.

IUCN. 2001. *IUCN Red List Categories and Criteria. Version 3.1*. IUCN – The World Conservation Union, Species Survival Commission (SSC), Cambridge, UK and Gland, Switzerland.

IUCN. 2008. *2008 IUCN Red List of Threatened Species*. International Union for Conservation of Nature (IUCN), Species Survival Commission (SSC), Cambridge, UK, and Gland, Switzerland. Website: <http://www.iucnredlist.org>.

Iwano, T. 1989. Some observations of two kinds of Lemuridae (*Varecia variegata variegata* and *Lemur fulvus albifrons*) in the reserve of Nosy Mangabe. *Primates* 30(2): 241–248.

Iwano, T. 1991. The usage of the digits of a captive aye-aye (*Daubentonia madagascariensis*). *African Study Monographs* 12(2): 87–98.

Iwano, T. and Iwakawa, C. 1988. Feeding behavior of the aye-aye (*Daubentonia madagascariensis*) on nuts of ramy (*Canarium madagascariensis*). *Folia Primatologica* 50(1–2): 136–142.

Iwano, T., Randalana, R. and Rakotoarisoa, G. 1991. Ecology of the aye-aye (*Daubentonia madagascariensis*), I. Distribution. Pp.41–42 in: A. Ehara, T. Kimura, O. Takenaka and M. Iwamoto (eds.), *Primatology Today*. Elsevier, Amsterdam.

Izard, M. K., Coffman, B, Katz, A. and Simons, E. 1993. Reproduction in the collared lemur (*Eulemur fulvus collaris*). *American Journal of Primatology* 30(4): 320. Abstract.

Izard, M. K., Savage, C. and Simons, E. 1994. Reproduction in Sanford's lemur (*Eulemur fulvus sanfordi*). *American Journal of Primatology* 33(3): 217. Abstract.

Jeannoda, V., Rakotonirina, O., Randrianarivo, H., Rakoto, D., Wright, P. and Hladik, C-M. 2003. Le principe toxique du bamboo consommé par *Hapalemur aureus* n'est pas neutralisé par la terre ingérée. *Revue d'ecologie: La Terre et la Vie* 58(1): 151–154.

Jenkins, P. D. 1987. *Catalogue of the Primates in the British Museum (Natural History) and Elsewhere in the British Isles. Part IV: Suborder Strepsirhini, including the Subfossil Madagascan Lemurs and the Family Tarsiidae*. British Museum (Natural History), London.

Jenkins, P. D. and Albrecht, G. H. 1991. Sexual dimorphism and sex ratios in Madagascan prosimians. *American Journal of Primatology* 24(1): 1–14.

Jenkins, P. D. and Carleton, M. 2005. Charles Immanuel Forsyth Major's expedition to Madagascar, 1894 to 1896: beginnings of modern systematic study of the island's mammalian fauna. *Journal of Natural History* 39(20): 1779–1818.

Johnson, S. E. 2002. Ecology and speciation in brown lemurs: White-collared lemurs (*Eulemur albocollaris*) and hybrids (*Eulemur albocollaris* × *Eulemur fulvus rufus*) in southeastern Madagascar. PhD thesis, University of Texas, Austin.

Johnson, S. E. 2006. Evolutionary divergence in the brown lemur species complex. Pp.187–210 in: L. Gould and M. L. Sauther (eds.), *Lemurs: Ecology and Adaptation*. Springer, New York.

Johnson, S. E. and Overdorff, D. J. 1999. Census of brown lemurs (*Eulemur fulvus* spp.) in southeastern Madagascar: methods testing and conservation implications. *American Journal of Primatology* 47(1): 51–60.

Johnson, S. and Wyner, Y. 2000. Notes on the biogeography of *Eulemur fulvus albocollaris*. *Lemur News* (5): 25–28.

Johnson, S. E., Gordon, A. D., Stumpf, R. M., Overdorff, D. J. and Wright, P. C. 2005. Morphological variation in populations of *Eulemur albocollaris* and *E. fulvus rufus*. *International Journal of Primatology* 26(6): 1399–1416.

Johnson, S. E., Lei, R., Martin, S. K., Irwin, M. T. and Louis Jr., E. E. 2008. Does *Eulemur cinereiceps* exist? Preliminary evidence from genetics and ground surveys in southeastern Madagascar. *American Journal of Primatology* 70(4): 372–385.

Johnson, S. E., Ratsimbazafy, J., Stevens, N., Andriamaharoa, H., Martin S. and Ralainasolo, F. 2009. Gray-headed lemur *Eulemur cinereiceps* (Milne-Edwards and Grandidier, 1880). Pp.15-17 in: R. A. Mittermeier *et al.* (eds.), *Primates in Peril: The World's 25 Most Endangered Primates 2008-2010*. IUCN/SSC Primate Specialist Group, International Primatological Society (IPS), and Conservation International, Arlington, VA.

Jolly, A. 1966. *Lemur Behavior*. The University of Chicago Press, Chicago.

Jolly, A. 1972. Troop continuity and troop spacing in *Propithecus verreauxi* and *Lemur catta* at Berenty (Madagascar). *Folia Primatologica* 17(5): 335–362.

Jolly, A. 1977. Population, espace vital et composition des groupes chez le maki (*Lemur catta*) et le sifaka (*Propithecus verreauxi*) à Berenty, Republique Malagasy. *Bulletin de l'Académie malgache* 53(1–2): 126–139.

Jolly, A. 1998. Pair-bonding, female aggression and the evolution of lemur societies. *Folia Primatologica* 69(suppl.1): 1–13.

Jolly, A. 2003. *Lemur catta*, ring-tailed lemur, *maky*. Pp. 1329–1331 in: S. M. Goodman and J. P. Benstead (eds.), *The Natural History of Madagascar*. The University of Chicago Press, Chicago.

Jolly, A. 2004. *Lords and Lemurs; Mad Scientists, Kings with Spears and the Survival of Diversity in Madagascar*. Houghton Mifflin Co., Boston, MT.

Jolly, A. 2009a. Coat condition of ringtailed lemurs, *Lemur catta*, at Berenty Reserve, Madagascar: I. Differences by age, sex, density and tourism, 1996–2006. *American Journal of Primatology* 71(3): 191–198.

Jolly, A. 2009b. Coat condition of ringtailed lemurs, *Lemur catta*, at Berenty Reserve, Madagascar: II. Coat and tail alopecia associated with *Leucaena leucocephala*, 2001–2006. *American Journal of Primatology* 71(3): 199–205.

Jolly, A. and Pride, E. 1999. Troop histories and range inertia of *Lemur catta* at Berenty, Madagascar: a 33-year perspective. *International Journal of Primatology* 20(3): 359–373.

Jolly, A. and Oliver, W. L. R. 1985. Predatory behavior in captive *Lemur* spp. *Zoo Biology* 4(2): 139–145.

Jolly, A., Oliver, W. L. R. and O'Connor, S. M. 1982a. Population and troop ranges of *Lemur catta* and *Lemur fulvus* at Berenty, Madagascar: 1980 census. *Folia Primatologica* 39(1–2): 115–123.

Jolly, A., Gustafson, H., Oliver, W. L. R. and O'Connor, S. M. 1982b. *Propithecus verreauxi* population and ranging at Berenty, Madagascar, 1975 and 1980. *Folia Primatologica* 39(1–2): 124–144.

Jolly, A., Albignac, R. and Petter, J.-J. 1984. The lemurs. Pp.183–203 in: A. Jolly, P. Oberlé and R. Albignac (eds.), *Key Environments: Madagascar*. Pergamon Press, Oxford.

Jolly, A., Caless, S., Cavigelli, S., Gould, L., Pereira, M. E., Pitts, A., Pride, R. E., Rabenandrasana, H. D., Walker, J. D. and Zafison, T. 2000. Infant killing, wounding and predation in *Eulemur* and *Lemur. International Journal of Primatology* 21(1): 21–40.

Jolly, A., Dobson, A., Rasamimanana, H. M., Walker, J., O'Connor, S., Solberg, M. and Perel, V. 2002. Demography of *Lemur catta* at Berenty Reserve, Madagascar: Effects of troop size, habitat and rainfall. *International Journal of Primatology* 23(2): 327–353.

Jolly, A., Sussman, R. W., Koyama N., Rasamimanana H. (eds.). 2006a. *Ringtailed Lemur Biology: Lemur catta in Madagascar*. Springer, New York.

Jolly, A., Koyama, N., Rasamimanana, H., Crowley, H. and Williams, G. 2006b. Berenty Reserve: a research site in southern Madagascar. Pp.32–42 in: A. Jolly, R. W. Sussman, N. Koyama and H. Rasamimanana H. (eds.), *Ringtailed Lemur Biology: Lemur catta in Madagascar*. Springer, New York.

Jolly, C. J. 1970. *Hadropithecus*: a lemuroid small-object feeder. *Man* 5(4): 619–626.

Jones, K. D. 1983. Inter-troop transfer of *Lemur catta* males at Berenty, Madagascar. *Folia Primatologica* 40(1–2): 145–160.

Jouffroy, F. K. 1963. Contribution à la connaissance du genre *Archaeolemur* Filhol, 1895. *Annales de paléontologie* 49: 129–155.

Junge, R. E. and Louis, E. E. 2005a. Preliminary biomedical evaluation of wild ruffed lemurs (*Varecia variegata* and *V. rubra*). *American Journal of Primatology* 66(1): 85–94.

Junge, R. E. and Louis, E. E. 2005b. Biomedical evaluation of two sympatric lemur species (*Propithecus verreauxi deckeni* and *Eulemur fulvus rufus*) in Tsiombikibo Classified Forest, Madagascar. *Journal of Zoo and Wildlife Medicine* 36(4): 581–589.

Junge, R. E. and Louis, E. E. 2007. Biomedical evaluation of black lemurs (*Eulemur macaco macaco*) in Lokobe Reserve, Madagascar. *Journal of Zoo and Wildlife Medicine* 38(1): 67–76.

Jungers, W. L. 1980. Adaptive diversity in subfossil Malagasy prosimians. *Zeitschrift für Morphologie und Anthropologie* 71: 177–186.

Jungers, W. L. and Rumpler, Y. 1976. Craniometric corroboration of the specific status of *Lepilemur septentrionalis*, an endemic lemur from the north of Madagascar. *Journal of Human Evolution* 5(4): 317–321.

Jungers, W. L., Godfrey, L. R., Simons, E. L., Chatrath, P. S. and Rakotosamimanana, B. 1991. Phylogenetic and functional affinities of *Babakotia* (Primates), a fossil lemur from northern Madagascar. *Proceedings of the National Academy of Science* 88: 9082–9086.

Jungers, W. L., Godfrey, L. R., Simons, E. L. and Chatrath, P. S. 1995. Subfossil *Indri indri* from the Ankarana Massif of northern Madagascar. *American Journal of Physical Anthropology* 97(4): 357–366.

Jungers, W. L., Godfrey, L. R., Simons, E. L. and Chatrath, P. S. 1997. Phalangeal curvature and positional behavior in extinct sloth lemurs (Primates, Palaeopropithecidae). *Proceedings of the National Academy of Sciences of the USA* 94(22): 11998–12001.

Jungers, W. L, Godfrey, L. R., Simons, E. L., Wunderlich, R. E., Richmond, B. G. and Chatrath, P. S. 2002. Ecomorphology and behavior of giant extinct lemurs from Madagascar. Pp.371–411 in: J. M. Placing, R. F. Kay, W. L. Jungers and C. P. van Schaik (eds.), *Reconstructing Behavior in the Primate Fossil Record.* Kluwer Academic/Plenum Publishers, New York.

Jungers, W. L., Lemelin, P., Godfrey, L. R., Wunderlich, R. E., Burney, D. A., Simons, E. L., Chatrath, P. S., James H. F. and Randria G. F. N. 2005. The hands and feet of *Archaeolemur*: metrical affinities and their functional significance. *Journal of Human Evolution* 49(1): 36–55.

Kappeler, P. M. 1987. Reproduction in the crowned lemur (*Lemur coronatus*) in captivity. *American Journal of Primatology* 12(4): 497–503.

Kappeler, P. M. 1988. A preliminary study of olfactory behavior of captive *Lemur coronatus* during the breeding season. *International Journal of Primatology* 9(2): 135–146.

Kappeler, P. M. 1989. Agonistic and grooming behavior of captive crowned lemurs (*Lemur coronatus*) during the breeding season. *Human Evolution* 4(2–3): 207–215.

Kappeler, P. M. 1990a. Female dominance in *Lemur catta*: More than just feeding priority. *Folia Primatologica* 55(2): 92–95.

Kappeler, P. M. 1990b. The evolution of sexual size dimorphism in prosimian primates. *American Journal of Primatology* 21(3): 201–204.

Kappeler, P. M. 1990c. Social status and scent-marking behaviour in *Lemur catta*. *Animal Behaviour* 40(4): 774–776.

Kappeler, P. M. 1991. Patterns of sexual dimorphism in body weight among prosimian primates. *Folia Primatologica* 57(3): 132–146.

Kappeler, P. M. 1993. Variation in social structure: the effects of sex and kinship on social interactions in three lemur species. *Ethology* 93(2): 125–145.

Kappeler, P. M. 1997. Intrasexual selection in *Mirza coquereli*: evidence for scramble competition in a solitary primate. *Behavioral Ecology and Sociobiology* 41(2): 115–127.

Kappeler, P. M. 1998. To whom it may concern: the transmission and function of chemical signals in *Lemur catta*. *Behavioural Ecology and Sociobiology* 42(6): 411–421.

Kappeler, P. M. 2000. Lemur origins: rafting by groups of hibernators? *Folia Primatologica* 71(6): 422–425.

Kappeler, P. M. 2003. *Mirza coquereli*, Coquerel's dwarf lemur. Pp.1316–1318 in: S. M. Goodman and J. P. Benstead (eds.), *The Natural History of Madagascar*. The University of Chicago Press, Chicago.

Kappeler, P. M. and Erkert, H. G. 2003. On the move around the clock: correlates and determinants of cathemeral activity in wild red-fronted lemurs (*Eulemur fulvus rufus*). *Behavioral Ecology and Sociobiology* 54(4): 359–369.

Kappeler, P. M and Ganzhorn, J. 1993. The evolution of primate communities and societies in Madagascar. *Evolutionary Anthropology* 2(5): 159–171.

Kappeler, P. M. and Port, M. 2008. Mutual tolerance or reproductive competition? Patterns of reproductive skew among male redfronted lemurs (*Eulemur fulvus rufus*). *Behavioral Ecology and Sociobiology* 62(9): 1477–1488.

Kappeler, P. M. and Rasoloarison, R. M. 2003. *Microcebus*, mouse lemurs, *tsidy*. Pp.1310–1315 in S. M. Goodman and J. P. Benstead (eds.), *The Natural History of Madagascar*. The University of Chicago Press, Chicago.

Kappeler. P. M. and Schaeffler, L. 2008. The lemur syndrome unresolved: extreme male reproductive skew in sifakas (*Propithecus verreauxi*), a sexually monomorphic primate with female dominance. *Behavioral Ecology and Sociobiology* 62(6): 1007–1015.

Kappeler, P. M., Rasoloaraison, R. M., Razafimanantsoa, L., Walter, L. and Roos, C. 2005. Morphology, behaviour and molecular evolution of giant mouse lemurs (*Mirza* spp.) Gray, 1870, with description of a new species. *Primate Report* 71: 3–26.

Karanth, K. P., Delefosse, T., Rakotosaminanana, B., Parsons, T. J. and Yoder, A. D. 2005. Ancient DNA from giant extinct lemurs confirms single origin of Malagasy primates. *Proceedings of the National Academy of Sciences* 102(14): 5090–5095.

Karpanty, S. M. 2006. Direct and indirect impacts of raptor predation on lemurs in southeastern Madagascar. *International Journal of Primatology* 27(1): 239–261.

Karpanty, S. M. and Goodman, S. M. 1999. Diet of the Madagascar harrier-hawk, *Polyboroides radiatus*, in southeastern Madagascar. *Journal of Raptor Research* 33: 313–316.

Karpanty, S. M. and Grella, R. 2001. Lemur responses to diurnal raptor calls in Ranomafana National Park, Madagascar. *Folia Primatologica* 72(2): 100–103.

Katz, A. S. and Welch, C. R. 2003. Parc Ivoloina. Pp.1555–1559 in: S. M. Goodman and J. P. Benstead (eds.), *The Natural History of Madagascar*. The University of Chicago Press, Chicago.

Kaudern, W. 1915. Säugetiere aus Madagaskar. *Arkiv für Zoologie* 9 (18): 1–101.

Kaufman, R. 1991. Female dominance in semifree-ranging black-and-white ruffed lemurs, *Varecia variegata variegata*. *Folia Primatologica* 7(1): 39–41.

Kaufman, R. 1996. The nature and frequency of agonism in free-ranging and semi-free-ranging brown lemurs, *Eulemur fulvus*. *Primates* 37(4): 335–350.

Kay, R. F., Sussman, R. W. and Tattersall, I. 1978. Dietary and dental variations in the genus *Lemur*, with comments concerning dietary-dental correlations among Malagasy primates. *American Journal of Physical Anthropology* 49(1): 119–127.

Kay, R. F., Ross, C. and Williams, B. A. 1997. Anthropoid origins. *Science* 275: 797–804.

Keith-Lucas, T., White, F. J., Keith-Lucas, L. and Vick, L. G. 1999. Changes in behavior in free-ranging *Lemur catta* following release in a natural habitat. *American Journal of Primatology* 47(1): 1–14.

Kelley, E. and Mayor, M. I. 2002. Preliminary study of the silky sifaka (*Propithecus diadema candidus*) in northeast Madagascar. *Lemur News* (7): 16–18.

Kerridge, F. J. 2005. Environmental enrichment to address behavioral differences between wild and captive black-and-white ruffed lemurs (*Varecia variegata*). *American Journal of Primatology* 66(1): 71–84.

Kobbe, S. and Dausmann, K. 2009. Hibernation in Malagasy mouse lemurs as a strategy to counter environmental challenge. *Naturwissenschaften* 96: 1221–1227.

Koenders, L. 1989. An eco-ethological comparison of *Lemur fulvus* and *Lemur macaco*. *Human Evolution* 4(2–3): 187–193.

Koenders, L., Rumpler, Y., Ratsirarson, J. and Peyriéras, A. 1985a. *Lemur macaco flavifrons* (Gray, 1867): a rediscovered subspecies of primate. *Folia Primatologica* 44(3–4): 210–215.

Koenders, L., Rumpler, Y. and Ropartz, P. 1985b. Differences in male-female interaction between *Lemur fulvus* and *L. macaco. Primates* 26: 195–201.

Koenig, P. 2005. Découverte d'une dépouille de aye-aye (*Daubentonia madagascariensis*) dans le nord-ouest de Madagascar. *Lemur News* (10): 6–7.

Kollman, M. 1910. Note sur les genres *Chirogale* et *Microcebus. Bulletin du Muséum d'histoire naturelle, Paris* 16(6): 301–304.

Koury, M. 1996. Effect of the mating season on the affiliative behavior of juvenile red-fronted brown lemurs (*Eulemur fulvus rufus*). PhD dissertation, Duke University, Durham, NC.

Koyama, N. 1988. Mating behavior of ring-tailed lemurs (*Lemur catta*) at Berenty, Madagascar. *Primates* 29(2): 163. Abstract.

Koyama, N., Nakamichi, M., Oda, R., Miyamoto, N. and Takahata, Y. 2001. A ten-year summary of reproductive parameters for ring-tailed lemurs at Berenty, Madagascar. *Primates* 42(1): 1–14.

Koyama, N., Nakamichi, N., Ichino, S. and Takahata, Y. 2002. Population and social dynamics changes in ring-tailed lemur troops at Berenty, Madagascar, between 1989–1999. *Primates* 43(4): 291–314.

Koyama, N., Soma, T., Ichino, S. and Takahata, Y. 2006. Home ranges of ringtailed lemur troops and the density of large trees at Berenty Reserve, Madagascar. Pp.86–101 in: A. Jolly, R. W. Sussman, N. Koyama and H. Rasamimanana H. (eds.), *Ringtailed Lemur Biology:* Lemur Catta *in Madagascar.* Springer, New York.

Koyama, N., Aimi, M., Kawamoto ,Y., Hirai, H., Go, Y., Ichino, S. and Takahata, Y. 2008. Body mass of wild ring-tailed lemurs in Berenty Reserve, Madagascar, with reference to tick infestation: a preliminary analysis. *Primates* 49(1): 9–15.

Krakauer, E., Lemelin, P. and Schmitt, D. 2002. Hand and body position during locomotor behavior in the aye-aye (*Daubentonia madagascariensis*). *American Journal of Primatology* 57(3): 105–118.

Kraus, C., Heistermann, M. and Kappeler, P. M. 1999. Physiological suppression of sexual function of subordinate males: a subtle form of intrasexual competition among male sifakas (*Propithecus verreauxi*)? *Physiology and Behavior* 66(5): 855–861.

Krause, D. W., Hartman, J. H. and Wells, N. A. 1997. Late Cretaceous vertebrates from Madagascar: implications for biotic change in deep time. Pp.3–43 in S. M. Goodman and B. D. Patterson (eds.), *Natural Change and Human Impact in Madagascar.* Smithsonian Institution Press, Washington, DC.

Krause, D. W., O'Connor, P. M., Rasoamiaramanana, A. H., Buckley, G. A., Burney, D., Carrano, M. T., Chatrath, P. S., Flynn, J. J., Forster, C. A, Godfrey, L. R., Jungers, W. L., Rogers, R. R., Samonds, K. E., Simons, E. L. and Wyss, A. R. 2006. The importance of keeping the island's vertebrate fossils in the public domain. *Madagascar Conservation and Development* 1(1): 43–47.

Kremen, C. 1998. Madagascar creates its largest protected area on the Masoala Peninsula. *Lemur News* (3): 1–3.

Kubzdela, K. S., Richard, A. F. and Pereira, M. E. 1992. Social relations in semi free-ranging sifakas (*P. v. coquereli*) and the question of female dominance. *American Journal of Primatology* 28(2): 139–145.

Kuhn, H. 1972. Die Geschichte der Säugetiere Madagaskars. *Zeitschrift des Kölner Zoo* 15(1): 28–42.

Lahann, P. 2007. Feeding ecology and seed dispersal of sympatric cheirogaleid lemurs (*Microcebus murinus, Cheirogaleus medius, Cheirogaleus major*) in the littoral rainforest of south-east Madagascar. *Journal of Zoology, London* 271: 88–98.

Lahann, P., Schmid, J. and Ganzhorn, J. U. 2006. Geographic variation in life history traits of *Microcebus murinus* in Madagascar. *International Journal of Primatology* 27(4): 983–999.

Lamberton, C. 1934a. Contribution à la connaissance de la faune subfossile de Madagascar. Lémuriens et Ratites. L'*Archaeoindris fontoynontii* Stand. *Mémoires de l'Académie malgache* 17: 9–39.

Lamberton, C. 1934b. Contribution à la connaissance de la faune subfossile de Madagascar. Lémuriens et Ratites. *Chiromys robustus* sp. nov. Lamb. *Mémoires de l'Académie malgache* 17: 40–46.

Lamberton, C. 1936a. Sur un nouveau genre de lémuriens fossiles Malgaches: le *Prohapalemur* (*P. gallienii*). *Bulletin du Muséum national d'histoire naturelle, Paris* 8(5): 367–369.

Lamberton, C. 1936b. Nouveaux lémuriens fossiles du groupe des Propithèques et l'intérêt de leur découverte. *Bulletin du Muséum national d'histoire naturelle, Paris* 8(5): 370–373.

Lamberton, C. 1938. Contribution à la connaissance de la faune subfossile de Madagascar. Note III: Les Hadropithèques. *Bulletin de l'Académie Malgache* (nouvelle série) 20: 127–170.

Langrand, O. 1990. *Guide to the Birds of Madagascar*. Yale University Press, New Haven.

Langrand, O. and Goodman, S. M. 1996. Notes on the diet of the Madagascar long-eared owl (*Asio madagascariensis*) in the Special Reserve of Ambohitantely. *Working Group on Birds in the Madagascar Region Newsletter* 6(2): 9–10.

Langrand, O. and Rasolonandrasana, B. P. N. 1997. The food habits of *Cryptoprocta ferox* in the high mountain zone of the Andringitra Massif, Madagascar (Carnivora, Viverridae). *Mammalia* 61: 185–192.

Laura, C. 1994. Infanticide among ring-tailed lemurs (*Lemur catta*) at Berenty Reserve, Madagascar. *American Journal of Primatology* 33(1): 65–69.

Lavauden, L. 1931. Un nouveau propithèque de Madagascar (*P. perrieri*, sp. nov.). *Comptes rendus de l'Académie des sciences de Paris* 193(1): 77–79.

Lawler, R. R. 2006. Sifaka positional behavior: ontogenetic and quantitative genetic approaches. *American Journal of Physical Anthropology* 131: 261–271.

Lawler, R. R. 2008. Morphological integration and natural selection in the postcranium of wild Verreaux's sifaka (*Propithecus verreauxi verreauxi*). *American Journal of Physical Anthropology* 136(2): 204–213.

Lawler, R. R., Richard, A. F. and Riley, M. A. 2001. Characterization and screening of microsatellite loci in a wild lemur population (*Propithecus verreauxi verreauxi*). *American Journal of Primatology* 55(4): 253–259.

Lawler, R. R., Richard, A. F. and Riley, M. A. 2003. Genetic population structure of the white sifaka (*Propithecus verreauxi verreauxi*) at Beza Mahafaly Special Reserve, southwest Madagascar (1992–2001). *Molecular Ecology* 12(9): 2307.

Lawler, R R., Richard, A. F. and Riley, M. A. 2005. Intrasexual selection in Verreaux's sifaka (*Propithecus verreauxi verreauxi*). *Journal of Human Evolution* 48(3): 259–277.

Leclercq, B. and Santini-Palka, M. 1995. Comparative study of the feeding behaviour of two folivorous lemur species (*Hapalemur simus* and *Hapalemur griseus*) at the Zoological Park of Paris. *Folia Primatologica* 64(1–2): 84. Abstract.

Lehman, S. M. 2005. Conservation biology of Malagasy strepsirhines: a phylogenetic approach. *American Journal of Physical Anthropology* 130(2): 238–253.

Lehman, S. M. and Mayor, M. I. 2004. Dietary patterns in Perrier's sifakas (*Propithecus diadema perrieri*): a preliminary study. *American Journal of Primatology* 62(2): 115–122.

Lehman, S. M. and Wright, P. C. 2000. Preliminary study of the conservation status of lemur communities in the Betsakandrika region of eastern Madagascar. *Lemur News* (5): 23–25.

Lehman, S. M., Mayor, M. I. and Wright, P. C. 2005a. Ecogeographic size variation in sifakas: a test of the resource seasonality and resource quality hypotheses. *American Journal of Physical Anthropology* 126(3): 318–328.

Lehman, S. M., Rajaonson, A. and Day, S. 2005b. Composition of the lemur community in the Vohibola III Classified Forest, SE Madagascar. *Lemur News* (10): 16.

Lehman, S. M., Rajaonson, A. and Day, S. 2005c. Edge effects and their influence on lemur density and distribution in southeast Madagscar. *American Journal of Physical Anthropology* 129(2): 232–241.

Lehman, S. M., Rajaonson, A. and Day, S. 2006a. Lemur responses to edge effects in the Vohibola III Classified Forest, Madagascar. *American Journal of Physical Anthropology* 129(2): 232–241.

Lehman, S. M., Ratsimbazafy, J., Rajaonson, A. and Day, S. 2006b. Decline of *Propithecus diadema edwardsi* and *Varecia variegata variegata* (Primates: Lemuridae) in south-east Madagascar. *Oryx* 40(1): 108–111.

Lei, R., Engberg, S. E., Andriantompohavana, R., McGuire, S., Mittermeier, R. A., Zaonarivelo, J., Brenneman, R., and Louis Jr., E. E. 2008. Nocturnal lemur diversity at Masoala National Park. *Museum of Texas Tech University Special Publications* 53: 1–41.

Leigh, S. R. and Terranova, C. J. 1998. Comparative perspectives on bimaturism, ontogeny, and dimorphism in lemurid primates. *International Journal of Primatology* 19(4): 723–749.

Lemelin, P. and Schmitt, D. 2004. Seasonal variation in body mass and locomotor kinetics of the fat-tailed dwarf lemur (*Cheirogaleus medius*). *Journal of Morphology* 260(1): 65–71.

Lernould, J.-M. 2002. Un programme international de recherche et de conservation pour le lémur aux yeux turquoise (*Eulemur macaco flavifrons*). *Lemur News* (7): 30–33.

Lernould, J.-M. 2006. AEECL zoos involved in the discovery of four new lemur species. *EAZA News* (55): 14–15.

Lesson, R. P. 1840. *Especes des Mammifères Bimanes et Quadrumanes*. Paris.

Lewis, R. J. 2004. Male–female relationships in sifaka (*Propithecus verreauxi verreauxi*): power, conflict and cooperation. PhD thesis, Duke University, Durham, NC.

Lewis, R. J. 2008. Social influences on group membership in *Propithecus verreauxi verreauxi*. *International Journal of Primatology* 29(5): 1249–1270.

Lewis, R. J. and Kappeler, P. M. 2005a. Seasonality, body condition, and timing of reproduction in *Propithecus verreauxi verreauxi* in the Kirindy Forest. *American Journal of Primatology* 67(3): 347–364.

Lewis, R. J. and Kappeler, P. M. 2005b. Are Kirindy sifaka capital or income breeders? It depends. *American Journal of Primatology* 67(3): 365–369.

Lewis, R. J., Razafindrasamba, S. M. and Tolojanahary, J. P. 2003. Observed infanticide in a seasonal breeding prosimian (*Propithecus verreauxi verreauxi*) in Kirindy Forest, Madagascar. *Folia Primatologica* 74(2): 101–103.

Lhota, S., Junek, T., Bartos, L. and Kubena, A. A. 2008. Specialized use of two fingers in free-ranging aye-ayes (*Daubentonia madagascariensis*). *American Journal of Primatology* 70(8): 786–795.

Lhota, S., Junek, T. and Bartos, L. 2009. Patterns and laterality of hand use in free-ranging aye-ayes (*Daubentonia madagascariensis*) and a comparison with captive studies. *Ethology* 27(3): 419–428.

Lindsay, N. B. D. 1977. Notes on the taxonomic status and breeding of the ruffed lemur *Lemur* (*Varecia*) *variegatus*. *Dodo, Journal of the Wildlife Preservation Trusts* 14: 65–69.

Lindsay, N. B. D. and Simons, H. J. 1986. Notes on *Varecia* in the northern limits of its range. *Dodo, Journal of the Wildlife Preservation Trusts* 23: 29–34.

Lorenz von Liburnau, L. 1899. Über eienen fossilen Anthropoid en von Madagaskar. *Anzeiger der kaiserlichen Akademie der Wissenschaften in Wien* 37: 8–9.

Lorenz von Liburnau, L. 1902. Über *Hadropithecus stenognathus* Lz. Nebst bemerkungen zu einigen anderen ausgestorbenen Primaten von Madagaskar. *Denkschriften kaiserlichen Akademie der Wissenschaften in Wien* 72: 243–254.

Lorenz von Liburnau, L. 1905. *Megaladapis edwardsi* Grandidier. *Denkschriften kaiserlichen Akademie der Wissenschaften in Wien* 77: 451–490.

Louis Jr., E. E., Ratsimbazafy, J. H., Razakamaharauo, V. R., Pierson, D. J., Barber, R. C. and Brennemen, R. A. 2005. Conservation genetics of black-and-white ruffed lemurs, *Varecia variegata*, from southeastern Madagascar. *Animal Conservation* 8: 105–111.

Louis Jr, E. E., Coles, M. S., Andriantompohavana, R., Sommer, J. A, Engberg, S. E., Zaonarivelo, J., Mayor, M. I. and Brenneman, R. A. 2006a. Revision of the mouse lemurs (*Microcebus*) of eastern Madagascar. *International Journal of Primatology* 27(2): 347–389.

Louis Jr., E. E., Engberg, S. E., Lei, R., Geng, H., Sommer, J. A., Randriamampionona, R., Randriamanana, J., Zaonarivelo, J., Andriantompohavana, R., Randria, G., Prosper, Ramaromilanto, B., Rakotoarisoa, G., Rooney, A., and Brenneman, R. A. 2006b. Molecular and morphological analyses of the sportive lemurs (family Megaladapidae: genus *Lepilemur*) reveals 11 previously unrecognized species. *Museum of Texas Tech University, Special Publication* (49): 1–49.

Louis Jr., E. E., Engberg, S. E., McGuire, S., McCormick, M., Randriamampionona, R., Ranaivoarisoa, J., Bailey, C., Mittermeier, R. A. and Lei, R. 2008. Revision of the mouse lemurs, *Microcebus* (Primates, Lemuriformes), of northern and northwestern Madagascar with descriptions of two new species at Montagne d'Ambre National Park and Antafondro Classified Forest. *Primate Conservation* (23): 19–38.

Mace. G. M. and Lande, R. 1991. Assessing extinction threats: toward a re-evaluation of IUCN threatened species categories. *Conservation Biology* 5: 148-157.

Macedonia, J. M. 1986. Individuality in a contact call of the ringtailed lemur (*Lemur catta*). *American Journal of Primatology* 11(2): 163–19.

Macedonia, J. M. 1987. Effects of housing differences upon activity budgets in captive sifakas (*Propithecus verreauxi*). *Zoo Biology* 6(1): 55–67.

Macedonia, J. M. 1990. What is communicated in the anti-predator calls of lemurs: evidence from playback experiments with ringtailed and ruffed lemurs. *Ethology* 86(3): 177–190.

Macedonia, J. M. 1993. The vocal repertoire of the ringtailed lemur (*Lemur catta*). *Folia Primatologica* 61(4): 186–217.

Macedonia, J. M. and Polak, J. F. 1989. Visual assessment of avian threat in semi-captive ringtailed lemurs (*Lemur catta*). *Behaviour* 111(1–4): 291–304.

Macedonia, J. M. and Stanger, K. F. 1994. Phylogeny of the Lemuridae revisited: evidence from communication signals. *Folia Primatologica* 63(1): 1–43.

Macedonia, J. M. and Taylor, L. L. 1985. Subspecific difference in a loud call of the ruffed lemur (*Varecia variegata*). *American Journal of Primatology* 9(4): 295–304.

Macedonia, J. M. and Yount, P. L. 1991. Auditory assessment of avian predator threat in semi-captive ringtailed lemurs (*Lemur catta*). *Primates* 32(2): 169–182.

Mack, D. and Mittermeier, R. A. (eds.). 1984. *The International Primate Trade, Vol. 1: Legislation, Trade and Captive Breeding*. TRAFFIC (USA), Washington, DC.

MacPhee, R. D. E. 1994. Morphology, adaptations and relationships of *Plesiorycteropus* and a diagnosis of a new order of eutherian mammals. *Bulletin of the American Museum of Natural History* 220: 1–214.

MacPhee, R. D. E. and Raholimavo, E. M. 1988. Modified subfossil aye-aye incisors from southwestern Madagascar: Species allocation and paleoecological significance. *Folia Primatologica* 51(2-3): 126–142.

Markolf, M., Kappeler, P. M. and Rasoloarison, R. 2008a. Distribution and conservation status of *Mirza zaza*. *Lemur News* (13): 37–40.

Markolf, M., Roos, C., and Kappeler, P. M. 2008b. Genetic and demographic consequences of a rapid reduction in population size in a solitary lemur (*Mirza coquereli*). *The Open Conservation Biology Journal* 2: 21–29.

Martin, R. D. 1972a. A preliminary field study of the lesser mouse lemur (*Microcebus murinus* J. F. Miller 1777). *Zeitschrift für Tierpsychologie* 9(suppl.): 43–89.

Martin, R. D. 1972b. Adaptive radiation and behaviour of the Malagasy lemurs. *Philosophical Transactions of the Royal Society* 264: 295–352.

Martin, R. D. 1973. A review of the behaviour and ecology of the lesser mouse lemur (*Microcebus murinus* J. F. Miller 1777). Pp.1–68 in: R. P. Michael and J. H. Crook (eds.), *Comparative Ecology and Behaviour of Primates*. Academic Press, London.

Martin, R. D. 1993. Primate origins: plugging the gaps. *Nature, London* 363: 223–234.

Martin, R. D. 2000. Origins, diversity and relationships of lemurs. *International Journal of Primatology* 21(6): 1021–1049.

Martin, R. D., Soligo, C. and Tavaré, S. 2007. Primate origins: implications of a Cretaceous ancestry. *Folia Primatologica* 78(5–6): 277–296.

Mason, A. M., Wolfe, L. D. and Johnson, J. C. 1995. Hand preference in the sifaka (*Propithecus verreauxi coquereli*) during feeding in captivity. *Primates* 36(2): 275–280.

Mass, V., Heistermann, M., and Kappeler, P. M. 2009. Mate guarding as a male reproductive tactic in verreaux's sifakas (*Propithecus verreauxi*). *International Journal of Primatology* 30(3): 389–409.

Mast, R. B., Rodriguez, J. V. and Mittermeier, R. A. 1993. The Colombian cotton-top tamarin in the wild. Pp.3-43 in: N. K. Clapp (ed.), *A Primate Model for the Study of Colitis and Colonic Carcinoma: the Cotton-Top Tamarin:* Saguinus oedipus. CRC Press, Boca Raton.

Masters, J. C., Lovegrove, B. G. and de Wit, M. J. 2006a. Eyes wide shut: can hypometabolism really explain the primate colonization of Madagascar? *Journal of Biogeography* 34(1): 21–37.

Masters, J. C., de Wit, M. J. and Asher, R. J. 2006b. Reconciling the origins of Africa, India and Madagascar with vertebrate dispersal scenarios. *Folia Primatologica* 77(6): 399–418.

Mayor, M. I. and Lehman, S. M. 1999. Conservation of Perrier's sifaka (*Propithecus diadema perrieri*) in Analamerana Special Reserve, Madagascar. *Lemur News* (4): 21–23.

Mayor, M. I., Sommer, J. A., Houck, M. L., Zaonarivelo, J. R., Wright, P. C., Ingram, C., Engel, S. R. and Louis E. E., Jr. 2004. Specific status of *Propithecus* spp. *International Journal of Primatology* 25(4): 875–900.

McCall, R. A. 1997. Implications of recent geological investigations of the Mozambique Channel for the mammalian colonization of Madagascar. *Proceedings of the Royal Society of London B* 264: 663–665.

MEFT, USAID and CI. 2009. *Evolution de la couverture de forêts naturelles à Madagascar, 1990–2000–2005.* Ministère de l'Environnement, de Forêts et du Tourisme (MEFT), Antananarivo, United States Agency for International Development (USAID), Washington, DC, and Conservation International, Arlington, VA.

Meier, B. 1987. Preliminary report of a field study on *Lemur rubriventer* and *Hapalemur simus* (nov. species) in Ranomafana–Ifanadiana 312 Faritany Fianarantsoa, Madagascar, July 1986 – January 1987. Report to Ministry of Scientific Research, Antananarivo.

Meier, B., and Albignac, R. 1989. Hairy-eared dwarf lemur rediscovered (*Allocebus trichotis*). *Primate Conservation* (10): 30.

Meier, B. and Albignac, R. 1991. Rediscovery of *Allocebus trichotis* Guenther 1875 (Primates) in northeast Madagascar. *Folia Primatologica* 56(1): 57–63.

Meier, B. and Rumpler, Y. 1987. Preliminary survey of *Hapalemur simus* and of a new species of *Hapalemur* in eastern Betsileo, Madagascar. *Primate Conservation* (8): 40–43.

Meier, B., Albignac, R., Peyriéras, A., Rumpler, Y. and Wright, P. C. 1987. A new species of *Hapalemur* (Primates) from south east Madagascar. *Folia Primatologica* 48(3–4): 211–215.

Méndes-Cárdenas, M., Randrianambinina, B., Rabesandratana, A., Rasoloharijaona, S. and Zimmermann, E. 2008. Geographic variation in loud calls of sportive lemurs (*Lepilemur* spp.) and their implications for conservation. *American Journal of Primatology* 7(9): 828–838.

Merenlender, A., Kremen, C., Rakotondratsima, M. and Weiss, A.1998. Monitoring impacts of natural resource extraction on lemurs of the Masoala Peninsula, Madagascar. *Ecology and Society* 2(2): 5.

Mertl-Millhollen, A. S. 1976. Olfactory and visual cues in social interactions of *Lemur catta*. *Folia Primatologica* 26(2): 151–161.

Mertl-Millhollen, A. S. 1977. Habituation to territorial scent marks in the field by *Lemur catta*. *Behavioral and Neural Ecology* 21(4): 500–507.

Mertl-Millhollen, A. S. 1979. Olfactory demarcation of territorial boundaries by a primate— *Propithecus verreauxi*. *Folia Primatologica* 32(1–2): 35–42.

Mertl-Millhollen, A. S. 1988. Olfactory demarcation of territorial but not home range boundaries by *Lemur catta*. *Folia Primatologica* 50(3–4): 175–187.

Mertl-Millhollen, A. S. 2000. Tradition in *Lemur catta* behavior at Berenty Reserve, Madagascar. *International Journal of Primatology* 21(2): 287–298.

Mertl-Millhollen, A. S. 2006. Scent-marking as resource defense by female *Lemur catta*. *American Journal of Primatology* 68(6): 605–621.

Mertl-Milhollen, A. S., Gustafson, H. L., Budnitz, N., Dainis, K. and Jolly, A. 1979. Population and territory stability of the *Lemur catta* at Berenty, Madagascar. *Folia Primatologica* 31(1–2): 106–122.

Mertl-Milhollen, A. S., Moret, E. S., Felantsoa, D., Rasamimanana, H., Blumenfeld-Jones, K. C. and Jollly, A. 2003. Ring-tailed lemur home ranges correlate with food abundance and nutritional content at a time of environmental stress. *International Journal of Primatology* 24(5): 969–985.

Meyers, D. 1988. Behavioral ecology of *Lemur fulvus rufus* in rain forest in Madagascar. *American Journal of Physical Anthropology* 75(2): 250. Abstract.

Meyers, D. 1993. The effects of resource seasonality on the behavior and reproduction of the golden-crowned sifaka (*Propithecus tattersalli*, Simons, 1988) in three Malagasy forests. PhD dissertation, Duke University, Durham, NC.

Meyers, D. 1996. Update on the endangered sifaka of the north. *Lemur News* (2): 13–14.

Meyers, D. and Ratsirarson, J. 1988. Survey of the rare *Propithecus diadema* subspecies in Madagascar. Report to World Wildlife Fund (WWF). Project number 6384, Antananarivo.

Meyers, D. and Ratsirarson, J. 1989. Distribution and conservation of two endangered sifakas in northern Madagascar. *Primate Conservation* (10): 82–87.

Meyers, D. M. and Wright, P. C. 1993. Resource tracking: Food availability and *Propithecus* seasonal reproduction. Pp.179–192 in: P. M. Kappeler and J. U. Ganzhorn (eds.), *Lemur Social Systems and Their Ecological Basis*. Plenum Press, New York.

Meyers, D., Rabarivola, C. and Rumpler, Y. 1989. Distribution and conservation of Sclater's lemur: Implications of a morphological cline. *Primate Conservation* (10): 77–80.

Meyer, L., Gallo, T. and Schultz, S. 1999. Female dominance in captive red ruffed lemurs, *Varecia variegata rubra* (Primates, Lemuridae). *Folia Primatologica* 70(6): 358–361.

Milliken, G. W., Ward, J. P. and Erickson, C. J. 1991. Independent digit control in foraging by the aye-aye (*Daubentonia madagascariensis*). *Folia Primatologica* 56(4): 219–224.

Milliken, G. W., Ferra, G., Kraiter, K. S. and Ross, C. L. 2005. Reach and posture hand preferences during arboreal feeding in sifakas (*Propithecus* sp.): a test of the postural origins theory of behavioral lateralization. *Journal of Comparative Psychology* 119(4): 430–439.

Milne-Edwards, A. 1871. L'ordre des lémuriens. *Revue Scientifique* (1871): 222–227.

Milne-Edwards, A. and Grandidier, A. 1875. *L'Histoire Politique, Physique et Naturelle de Madagascar: Histoire Naturelle des Mammifères*, Paris, Impr. nationale.

Mittermeier, R. A. 1987. Effects of hunting on rain forest primates. Pp.109–146. in C. W. Marsh and R. A. Mittermeier (eds.), *Primate Conservation in the Tropical Rain Forest*. Alan R. Liss, New York.

Mittermeier, R. A. and Coimbra-Filho, A. F. 1977. Primate conservation in Brazilian Amazonia. Pp.117–166 in H.S.H. Prince Rainier III of Monaco and G. H. Bourne (eds.), *Primate Conservation*. Academic Press, New York.

Mittermeier, R. A., Konstant, W. R., Nicoll, M. E. and Langrand, O. 1992. *Lemurs of Madagascar: An Action Plan for their Conservation, 1993–1999*. IUCN/SSC Primate Specialist Group, Gland, Switzerland.

Mittermeier, R. A., Tattersall, I., Konstant, W. R., Meyers, D., and Mast, R. 1994. *Lemurs of Madagascar*. Conservation International, Washington, DC.

Mittermeier, R. A., Robles, G. P. and Mittermeier, C. G. (eds.). 1997. *Megadiversity: Earth's Biologically Wealthiest Nations*. Cemex, Mexico City, Mexico.

Mittermeier, R. A., Myers, N., Robles, G. P. and Mittermeier, C. G. (eds.). 1999. *Hotspots: Earth's Biologically Richest and Most Endangered Terrestrial Ecoregions*. Cemex, Mexico City, Mexico.

Mittermeier, R. A., Konstant, W. R. and Rylands, A. B. 2003. Lemur conservation. Pp.1538–1543 in: S. M. Goodman and J. P. Benstead (eds.), *The Natural History of Madagascar*. The University of Chicago Press, Chicago.

Mittermeier, R. A., Robles, G. P., Hoffmann, M., Pilgrim, J., Brooks, T., Mittermeier, C. G., Lamoreux, J. and Fonseca, G. A. B. (eds.). 2004. *Hotspots Revisited: Earth's Biologically Richest and Most Endangered Terrestrial Ecoregions*. Cemex, Mexico City, Mexico.

Mittermeier, R. A., Konstant, W. R., Hawkins, F., Louis Jr., E. E., Langrand, O., Ratsimbazafy, J., Rasoloarison, R., Ganzhorn, J. U., Rajaobelina, S., Tattersall, I. and Meyers, D. M. 2006. *Lemurs of Madagascar,* 2nd edition. Conservation International, Washington, DC.

Mittermeier, R. A., Ratsimbazafy, J., Rylands, A. B., Williamson, E., Oates, J. F., Mbora, D., Ganzhorn, J. U., Rodríguez-Luna, E., Palacios, E., Heymann, E., Kierulff, M. C. M., Yongcheng, L., Supriatna, J., Roos, C., Walker, S. and Aguiar, J. (eds.). 2007. Primates in peril: the world's 25 most endangered primates, 2006–2008. *Primate Conservation* (22): 1–40.

Mittermeier, R. A., Louis, E. E., Richardson, M., Konstant, W. R., Langrand, O., Hawkins, F., Ratsimbazafy, J., Rasoloarison, R., Ganzhorn, J. U., Rajaobelina, S. and Schwitzer, C. 2008a. *Lemurs of Madagascar Pocket Identification Guide: Diurnal and Cathemeral Lemurs*. Conservation International, Arlington, VA.

Mittermeier, R. A., Louis, E. E., Richardson, M., Konstant, W. R., Langrand, O., Hawkins, F., Ratsimbazafy, J., Rasoloarison, R., Ganzhorn, J. U., Rajaobelina, S. and Schwitzer, C. 2008b. *Lemurs of Madagascar Pocket Identification Guide: Nocturnal Lemurs*. Conservation International, Arlington, VA.

Mittermeier, R. A., Ganzhorn, J. U., Konstant, W. R., Glander, K., Tattersall, I., Groves, C. P., Rylands, A. B., Hapke, A., Ratsimbazafy, J., Mayor, M. I., Louis Jr., E. E., Rumpler, Y., Schwitzer, C. and Rasoloarison, R. M. 2008c. Lemur diversity in Madagascar. *International Journal of Primatology* 29(6): 1607–1656.

Mivart, S. G. 1873. On *Lepilemur* and *Cheirogaleus* and on the zoological rank of the Lemuroidea. *Proceedings of the Zoological Society of London* (1873): 484–510.

Mizuta, T. 2002. Predation by *Eulemur fulvus fulvus* on a nestling of *Terpsiphone mutata* (Aves: Monarchidae) in dry forest in north-western Madagascar. *Folia Primatologica* 73(4): 217–219.

Montagnon, D., Crovella, S. and Rumpler, Y. 1993. Comparison of highly repeated DNA sequences in some Lemuridae and taxonomic implications. *Cytogenetic and Cell Genetics* 63(2): 131–134.

Montagnon, D., Ravaoarimanana, B., Rakotosamimanana, B. and Rumpler, Y. 2001. Ancient DNA from *Megaladapis edwardsi* (Malagasy subfossil): preliminary results using partial cytochrome b sequence. *Folia Primatologica* 72(1): 30–32.

Morland, H. S. 1989. Infant survival and parental care in ruffed lemurs (*Varecia variegata*) in the wild. *American Journal of Primatology* 18(2): 157. Abstract.

Morland, H. S. 1990. Parental behavior and infant development in ruffed lemurs (*Varecia variegata*) in a northeast Madagascar rain forest. *American Journal of Primatology* 20(4): 253–265.

Morland, H. S. 1991a. Social organization and ecology of black-and-white ruffed lemurs (*Varecia variegata variegata*) in lowland rain forest, Nosy Mangabe, Madagascar. PhD thesis, Yale University, New Haven, CT.

Morland, H. S. 1991b. Preliminary report on the social organization of ruffed lemurs (*Varecia variegata variegata*) in a northeast Madagascar rain forest. *Folia Primatologica* 56(3): 157–161.

Morland, H. S. 1993. Reproductive activity of ruffed lemurs (*Varecia variegata variegata*) in a Madagascar rain forest. *American Journal of Physical Anthropology* 91(1): 71–82.

Muehlenbein, M. P., Schwartz, M. and Richard, A. F. 2003. Parasitologic analysis of the sifaka (*Propithecus verreauxi verreauxi*) at Beza Mahafaly, Madagascar. *Journal of Zoo and Wildlife Medicine* 34(3): 274–277.

Muldoon, K. M., de Blieux, D. D., Simons, E. L. and Chatrath, P. S. 2009a. The subfossil occurrence and paleoecological significance of small mammals at Ankilitelo Cave, southwestern Madagascar. *Journal of Mammalogy* 90: 1111–1131.

Muldoon, K. M., Godfrey, L. R., Jungers, W. L. and Chipman, J. W. 2009b. Geographic patterning in subfossil primate community dynamics in Madagascar. *American Journal of Physical Anthropology* Suppl.48: 270. Abstract.

Mueller, A. E. 1988. A preliminary report on the social organization of *Cheirogaleus medius* (Cheirogaleidae: Primates) in north-west Madagascar. *Folia Primatologica* 69(3): 160–166.

Mueller, A. E. 1999a. Social organization of the fat-tailed dwarf lemur (*Cheirogaleus medius*) in northwestern Madagascar. Pp.139–157 in: B. Rakotosamimanana, H. Rasamimanana, J. U. Ganzhorn and S. M. Goodman (eds.), *New Directions in Lemur Studies*. Kluwer Academic/Plenum, New York.

Mueller, A. E. 1999b. Aspects of social life in the fat-tailed dwarf lemur (*Cheirogaleus medius*): inferences from body weights and trapping data. *American Journal of Primatology* 49(3): 265–280.

Mueller, A. E. and Thalmann, U. 2002. Biology of the fat-tailed dwarf lemur (*Cheirogaleus medius* E. Geoffroy 1812): new results from the field. *Evolutionary Anthropology* 11(suppl.1): 79–82.

Mueller, P., Velo, A., Raheliarisoa, E.-O., Zaramody, A. and Curtis, D. J. 2000. Surveys of five sympatric lemurs at Anjamena, north-west Madagascar. *African Journal of Ecology* 38: 248–257.

Mutschler, T. 1999. Folivory in a small-bodied lemur: the nutrition of the Alaotran gentle lemur (*Hapalemur griseus alaotrensis*). Pp.221–239 in: B. Rakotosamimanana, H. Rasamimanana, J. U. Ganzhorn and S. M. Goodman (eds.), *New Directions in Lemur Studies*. Kluwer Academic/Plenum Publishers, New York.

Mutschler, T. 2000. Taxonomic distinctiveness of *Hapalemur* and phylogenetic relationships within the genus: evidence from vocal communication. PhD thesis, Washington University, St. Louis, MO.

Mutschler, T. 2002. Alaotran gentle lemur: some aspects of its behavioral ecology. *Evolutionary Anthropology* 11(suppl.1): 101–104.

Mutschler, T. and Feistner, A. T. C. 1995. Conservation status and distribution of the Alaotran gentle lemur *Hapalemur griseus alaotrensis*. *Oryx* 29(4): 267–274.

Mutschler, T. and Feistner, A. T. C. 1998. New information on the distribution and conservation status of the Alaotran gentle lemur, *Hapalemur griseus alaotrensis*. *Folia Primatologica* 69(suppl. 1): 400–401. Abstract.

Mutschler, T. and Tan, C. L. 2003. *Hapalemur*, bamboo or gentle lemurs. Pp. 1324–1329 in: S. M. Goodman and J. P. Benstead (eds.), *The Natural History of Madagascar*. The University of Chicago Press, Chicago.

Mutschler, T. and Thalmann, U. 1994. Sighting of *Avahi* (woolly lemur) in western Madagascar. *Primate Conservation* (11): 15–17.

Mutschler, T., Feistner, A. T. C. and Nievergelt, C. M. 1998. Preliminary field data on group size, diet and activity in the Alaotran gentle lemur, *Hapalemur griseus alaotrensis*. *Folia Primatologica* 69(5): 325–330.

Mutschler, T., Nievergelt, C. M. and Feistner, A. T. C. 2000. Social organization of the Alaotran gentle lemur *(Hapalemur griseus alaotrensis)*. *American Journal of Primatology* 50(1): 9–24.

Mutschler, T., Randrianarisoa, A. J. and Feistner, A. T. C. 2001. Population status of the Alaotran gentle lemur *Hapalemur griseus alaotrensis*. *Oryx* 35(2): 152–157.

Mzilikazi, N., Lovegrove, B. G. and Masters J. C. 2004. No evidence for torpor in a small African mainland primate: the lesser bushbaby, *Galago moholi*. *Biological Papers of the University of Alaska* 27: 29–40.

Nakamichi, M. and Koyama, N. 1997. Social relationships among ring-tailed lemurs (*Lemur catta*) in two free-ranging troops at Berenty Reserve, Madagascar. *International Journal of Primatology* 18(1): 73–93.

Nakamichi, M. and Koyama, N. 2000. Intra-troop affiliative relationships of females with newborn infants in wild ring-tailed lemurs (*Lemur catta*). *American Journal of Primatology* 50(3): 187–203.

Nakamichi, M., Koyama, N. and Jolly, A. 1996. Maternal responses to dead and dying infants in wild troops of ring-tailed lemurs at the Berenty Reserve, Madagascar. *International Journal of Primatology* 17(4): 505–523.

Nakamichi, M., Rakototiana, M. L. O. and Koyama, N. 1997. Effects of spatial proximity and alliances on dominance relations among female ring-tailed lemurs (*Lemur catta*) at the Berenty Reserve, Madagascar. *Primates* 38(3): 331–340.

Nakamura, M. 2004. Predation by *Eulemur fulvus fulvus* on eggs of *Ploceus sakalava sakalava* (Aves: Ploceidae) in Ankarafantsika, Madagascar. *Folia Primatologica* 75(6): 376–378.

Napier, J. P. and Walker, A. C. 1967. Vertical clinging and leaping: a newly recognized category of locomotor behaviour of primates. *Folia Primatologica* 6(3): 204–219.

Nash, L. T. 1998. Vertical clingers and sleepers: seasonal influences on the activities and substrate use of *Lepilemur leucopus* at Beza Mahafaly Special Reserve, Madagascar. *Folia Primatologica* 69(suppl. 1): 204–217.

Neveu, H., Hafen, T., Zimmermann, E. and Rumpler, Y. 1998. Comparison of the genetic diversity of wild and captive groups of *Microcebus murinus* using the random amplified polymorphic DNA method. *Folia Primatologica* 69(suppl. 1): 127–135.

Nicoll, M. E. and Langrand, O. 1989. *Madagascar: Revue de la Conservation et des Aires Protégées*. World Wide Fund for Nature (WWF), Gland, Switzerland.

Nievergelt, C. M., Mutschler, T. and Feistner, A. T. C. 1998. Group encounters and territoriality in wild Alaotran gentle lemurs (*Hapalemur griseus alaotrensis*). *American Journal of Primatology* 46(3): 251–258.

Nievergelt, C. M., Mutschler, T., Feistner, A. T. C. and Woodruff, D. S. 2002a. Social system of the

Alaotran gentle lemur (*Hapalemur griseus alaotrensis*): genetic characterization of group composition and mating system. *American Journal of Primatology* 57(4): 157–176.

Nievergelt, C. M., Pastorini, J. and Woodruff, D. S. 2002b. Genetic variability and phylogeography in the wild Alaotran gentle lemur population. *Evolutionary Anthropology* 11(suppl.1): 175–179.

Nilsson, L. A., Rabakonandrianina, E., Pettersson, B. and Gruenmeier, R. 1993. Lemur pollination in the Malagasy rain forest liana *Strongylodon craveniae* (Leguminosae). *Evolutionary Trends in Plants* 7(2): 49–56.

Noble, S. J., Chesser, R. K. and Ryder, O. A. 1990. Inbreeding effects in captive populations of ruffed lemurs. *Human Evolution* 5(3): 283–291.

Norcross, J. L., Newman, J. D. and Cofrancesco, L. M. 1999. Context and sex differences exist in the acoustic structure of phee calls by newly-paired common marmosets (*Callithrix jacchus*). *American Journal of Primatology* 49(2): 165–181.

Norscia, I. 2008. Pilot survey of *Avahi* population (woolly lemurs) in littoral forest fragments of southeast Madagascar. *Primates* 49(1): 85–88.

Norscia, I. and Palagi, E. 2008. Berenty 2006: census of *Propithecus verreauxi* and possible evidence of population stress. *International Journal of Primatology* 29(4): 1099–1115.

Norscia, I., Carrai, V., Ceccanti, V. and Borgognini-Tarli, S. M. 2005. Termite soil eating in Kirindy sifakas (Madagascar): proposing a new proximate factor. *Folia Primatologica* 76(2): 119–122.

Nunn, C. L. 2000. Maternal recognition of infant calls in ring-tailed lemurs. *Folia Primatologica* 71(3): 142–146.

Nunn, C. L. and Pereira, M. E. 2000. Group histories and offspring sex ratios in ringtailed lemurs (*Lemur catta*). *Behavioural Ecology and Sociobiology* 48(1): 18–28.

O'Connor, S. M. 1987. The effect of human impact on vegetation and the consequences to primates in two riverine forests, southern Madagascar. PhD thesis, University of Cambridge, Cambridge, UK.

O'Connor, S. M., Pidgeon, M. and Randria, Z. 1986. Conservation program for the Andohahela Reserve, Madagascar. *Primate Conservation* (7): 48–52.

O'Connor, S. M., Pidgeon, M. and Randria, Z. 1987. Un programme de conservation pour la Réserve d'Andohahela. Pp.31–36 in: R. Mittermeier, L. Rakotovao, V. Randrianasolo, E. Sterling and D. Devitre (eds.), *Priorités en Matière de Conservation des Espèces à Madagascar. Occasional Papers of the IUCN Species Survival Commission (SSC)*, No. 2. Gland, Switzerland.

Oda, R. 1996a. Predation on a chameleon by a ring-tailed lemur (*Lemur catta*) in the Berenty Reserve, Madagascar. *Folia Primatologica* 67(1): 40–43.

Oda, R. 1996b. Effects of contextual and social variables on contact call production in free-ranging ringtailed lemurs (*Lemur catta*). *International Journal of Primatology* 17(2): 191–205.

Oda, R. 1998. The responses of Verreaux's sifakas to anti-predator alarm calls given by sympatric ring-tailed lemurs. *Folia Primatologica* 69(6): 357–360.

Oda, R. 1999. Scent marking and contact call production in ring-tailed lemurs (*Lemur catta*). *Folia Primatologica* 70 (2): 121–124.

Oda, R. and Masataka, N. 1996. Interspecific responses of ringtailed lemurs to playback of antipredator alarm calls given by Verreaux's sifakas. *Ethology* 106(6): 441–453.

Oliver, W. and O' Connor, S. 1980. Circadian distribution of *Indri indri* group vocalizations: a short period sampling at two study sites near Perinet, eastern Madagascar. *Dodo, Journal of the Wildlife Preservation Trusts* 17: 19–27.

Olivieri, G., Craul, M. and Radespiel, U. 2005. Inventaire des lémuriens dans 15 fragments de forêt de la province de Mahajanga. *Lemur News* (10): 11-16.

Olivieri, G., Zimmermann, E., Randrianambinina, B., Rassoloharijaona, S., Rakotondravony, D., Guschanski, K., and Radespiel, U. 2007a. The ever-increasing diversity in mouse lemurs: three new species in north and northwestern Madagascar. *Molecular Phylogenetics and Evolution* 43(1): 309–327.

Olivieri, G. L., Schwitzer, C., Schwitzer, N., Craul, M. and Randriatahina, G. H. 2007b. *Lepilemur sahamalazensis* Andriaholinirina *et al.*, 2006. Pp.6-7, 23 in: R. A. Mittermeier *et al.* (eds.), Primates in peril: The world's 25 most endangered primates, 2006-2008. *Primate Conservation* (22): 1-40.

Ortmann, S., Heldmaier, G., Schmid, J. and Ganzhorn, J. U. 1997. Spontaneous daily torpor in Malagasy mouse lemurs. *Naturwissenschafften* 84 (4): 28–32.

Ossi, K. and Kamilar, J. M. 2006. Environmental and phylogenetic correlates of *Eulemur* behavior and ecology (Primates: Lemuridae). *Behavioral Ecology and Sociobiology* 61(1): 53–64.

Ostner, J. 2002. Social thermoregulation in redfronted lemurs (*Eulemur fulvus rufus*). *Folia Primatologica* 73(4): 175–180.

Ostner, J. and Kappeler, P. M. 1999. Central males instead of multiple pairs in red-fronted lemurs, *Eulemur fulvus rufus* (Primates, Lemuridae) *Animal Behaviour* 58(5): 1069–1078.

Ostner, J., Kappeler, P. M. and Heistermann, M. 2008. Androgen and glucocorticoid levels reflect seasonally occurring social challenges in male redfronted lemurs (*Eulemur fulvus rufus*). *Behavioral Ecology and Sociobiology* 62(4): 627–638.

Overdorff, D. J. 1988. Preliminary report on the activity cycle and diet of the red-bellied lemur (*Lemur rubriventer*) in Madagascar. *American Journal of Primatology* 16(2): 143–153.

Overdorff, D. J. 1991. Ecological correlates of social structure in two prosimian primates: *Eulemur fulvus rufus* and *Eulemur rubriventer* in Madagascar. Unpublished PhD thesis, Duke University, Durham, North Carolina.

Overdorff, D. J. 1992. Differential patterns in flower feeding by *Eulemur fulvus rufus* and *Eulemur rubriventer* in Madagascar. *American Journal of Primatology* 28(3): 191–203.

Overdorff, D. J. 1993. Similarities, differences and seasonal patterns in the diets of *Eulemur rubriventer* and *Eulemur fulvus rufus* in the Ranomafana National Park, Madagascar. *International Journal of Primatology* 14(5): 721–753.

Overdorff, D. J. 1996a. Ecological correlates to activity and habitat use of two prosimian primates: *Eulemur rubriventer* and *Eulemur fulvus rufus* in Madagascar. *American Journal of Primatology* 40(4): 327–342.

Overdorff, D. J. 1996b. Ecological correlates to social structure in two lemur species in Madagascar. *American Journal of Physical Anthropology* 100(4): 487–506.

Overdorff, D. J. 1998. Are *Eulemur* species pairbonded? Social organization and mating strategies of *Eulemur fulvus rufus* in Madagascar. *American Journal of Physical Anthropology* 105(2): 153–166.

Overdorff, D. J. and Johnson, S. 2003. *Eulemur*, true lemurs. Pp.1320–1324 in: S. M. Goodman and J. P. Benstead (eds.), *The Natural History of Madagascar*. The University of Chicago Press, Chicago.

Overdorff, D. J. and Rasmussen, M. A. 1995. Determination of night-time activity in "diurnal" lemurs. Pp.61–74 in: L. Alterman, G. A. Doyle and M. K. Izard (eds.), *Creatures of the Dark: The Nocturnal Prosimians*. Plenum Press, New York.

Overdorff, D. J. and Strait, S. G. 1995. Life-history and predation in *Eulemur rubriventer* in Madagascar. *American Journal of Physical Anthropology* 20(suppl.): 164–165. Abstract.

Overdorff, D. J. and Strait, S. G. 1998. Seed handling by three prosimian primates in southeastern Madagascar: implications for seed dispersal. *American Journal of Primatology* 45(1): 69–82.

Overdorff, D. J., Strait, S. G. and Telo, A. 1997. Seasonal variation in activity and diet in a small-bodied folivorous primate, *Hapalemur griseus*, in southeastern Madagascar. *American Journal of Primatology* 43(3): 211–223.

Overdorff, D. J., Merenlender, A. M., Talata, P., Telo, A. and Forward, Z. 1999. Life history of *Eulemur fulvus rufus* from 1988–1997: Implications for ecological stress in southeastern Madagascar. *American Journal of Physical Anthropology* 108(3): 295–310.

Overdorff, D. J., Erhart, E. M. and Mutschler, T. 2005. Does female dominance facilitate breeding priority in black-and-white ruffed lemurs (*Varecia variegata*) in southeastern Madagascar? *American Journal of Primatology* 66(1): 7–22.

Owen, R. 1863. Monograph on the Aye-aye (*Chiromys madagascariensis*, Cuvier). London.

Owen, R. 1866. On the aye-aye (*Chiromys*, Cuvier; *Chiromys madagascariensis*, Desm.; *Sciurus madagascariensis*, Gmel., Sonnerat; *Lemur psilodactylus*, Schreber, Shaw). *Transactions of the Zoological Society of London* 5: 33–101.

Oxnard, C. E. 1981. The uniqueness of *Daubentonia*. *American Journal of Physical Anthropology* 54(1): 1–21.

Pagès, E. 1978. Home range, behaviour and tactile communication in a nocturnal Malagasy lemur *Microcebus coquereli*. Pp.171–177 in: D. J. Chivers and K. A. Joysey (eds), *Recent Advances in Primatology, Vol. 3*. Academic Press, London.

Pagès, E. 1980. Ethoecology of *Microcebus coquereli* during the dry season. Pp.97–116 in: P. Charles-Dominique, H. M. Cooper, A. Hladik, C. M. Hladik, E. Pagès, G. F. Pariente, A. Petter-Rousseaux, J.-J. Petter and A. Schilling (eds.), *Nocturnal Malagasy Primates: Ecology, Physiology and Behavior*. Academic Press, New York.

Pagès, E. 1983. Identification, characterization et role du jeu social chez un prosimien nocturne, *Microcebus coquereli*. *Biology of Behavior* 8: 319–343.

Pagès, E. and Petter-Rousseaux, A. 1980. Annual variations in the circadian activity rhythms of five sympatric species of nocturnal prosimians in captivity. Pp.153–167 in: P. Charles-Dominique, H. M. Cooper, A. Hladik, C. M. Hladik, G. F. Pariente, A. Petter-Rousseaux, A. Schilling, and J. J. Petter (eds.), *Nocturnal Malagasy Primates*. Academic Press, New York.

Pagès-Feuillade, E. 1988. Modalités de l'occupation de l'espace et relations interindividualles chez un prosimian nocturne malgache (*Microcebus murinus*). *Folia Primatologica* 50(3–4): 204–220.

Palagi, E. and Norscia, I. 2009. Multimodal signaling in wild *Lemur catta*. Economic design and territorial function of urine marking. *American Journal of Physical Anthropology* 139(2): 182–192.

Palagi, E., Gregorace, A. and Borgognini-Tarli, S. M. 2002. Development of olfactory behavior in captive ring-tailed lemurs (*Lemur catta*). *International Journal of Primatology* 23(3): 587–599.

Palagi, E., Telara, S. and Borgognini-Tarli, S. M. 2003. Sniffing behavior in *Lemur catta* : seasonality, sex, and rank. *International Journal of Primatology* 24(2): 335–350.

Palagi, E., Telara, S. and Borgognini-Tarli, S. M. 2004. Reproductive strategies in *Lemur catta*: balance among sending, receiving and countermarking scent signals. *International Journal of Primatology* 25(5): 1019–1031.

Palagi, E., Paoli, T. and Borgognini-Tarli, S. M. 2005a. Aggression and reconciliation in two captive groups of *Lemur catta*. *International Journal of Primatology* 26(2): 279–294.

Palagi, E., Dapporto, L. and Borgognini-Tarli, S. 2005b. The neglected scent: on the marking function of urine in *Lemur catta*. *Behavioural Ecology and Sociobiology* 58(5): 437–445.

Palagi, E., Antonacci, D. and Norscia, I. 2008. Peacemaking on treetops: first evidence of reconciliation from a wild prosimian (*Propithecus verreauxi*). *Animal Behavior* 76(3): 737–747

Parga, J. A. 2003. Copulatory plug displacement evidences sperm competition in *Lemur catta*. *International Journal of Primatology* 24(4): 889–899.

Pariente, G. 1974. Influence of light on the activity rhythms of two Malagasy lemurs: *Phaner furcifer* and *Lepilemur mustelinus leucopus*. Pp.183-198 in: R. D. Martin, G. A. Doyle and A. C. Walker (eds.), *Prosimian Biology*. Duckworth, London.

Pariente, G. 1975. Light and activity rhythm of *Phaner furcifer* (nocturnal Malagasy prosimian) in its natural environment. *Journal of Physiology* 70(5): 637–647.

Pastorini, J. 2000. Molecular systematics of lemurs. PhD dissertation, Universität Zürich, Zürich.

Pastorini, J., Zaramody, A., Scheffrahn, W., Clark, M., Waters, M. and Curtis, D. J. 1998. Body measurements from wild mongoose lemurs at Anjamena. XVIIth Congress of the International Primatological Society, Poster Abstracts, Antananarivo, Madagascar.

Pastorini, J., Forstner, M. R. J. and Martin, R. D. 1999. Molecular phylogenetics of Lemuridae. *Primatology and Anthropology into the Third Millenium. Centenary Congress of the Anthropological Institute and Museum in Zurich*. University of Zurich, Irchel, Switzerland.

Pastorini, J., Forstner, M. R. J. and Martin, R. D. 2000. Relationships among brown lemurs (*Eulemur fulvus*) based on mitochondrial DNA sequences. *Molecular Phylogenetics and Evolution* 16(3): 418–429.

Pastorini, J., Martin, R. D., Ehresmann, P., Zimmermann, E. and Forstner, M. R. J. 2001a. Molecular phylogeny of the lemur family Cheirogaleidae (Primates) based on mitochondrial DNA sequences. *Molecular Phylogenetics and Evolution* 19(1): 45–56.

Pastorini, J., Forstner, M. R. J. and Martin, R. D. 2001b. Phylogenetic history of sifakas (*Propithecus*: Lemuriformes) derived from mtDNA sequences. *American Journal of Primatology* 53(1): 1–17.

Pastorini, J., Forstner, M. R. J. and Martin, R. D. 2002a. Phylogenetic relationships of gentle lemurs (*Hapalemur*). *Evolutionary Anthropology* 1(suppl.): 150–154.

Pastorini, J., Forstner, M. R. J. and Martin, R. D. 2002b. Phylogenetic relationships among Lemuridae (Primates): evidence from mtDNA. *Journal of Human Evolution* 43(4): 463–478.

Pastorini, J., Thalmann, U., and Martin, R. D. 2003. A molecular approach to comparative phylogeography of extant Malagasy lemurs. *Proceedings of the National Academy of Sciences* 100: 5879–5884.

Pastorini, J., Zaramody, A., Curtis, D. J., Nievergelt, C. M. and Mundy, N. 2009. Genetic analysis of hybridization and introgression between wild mongoose and brown lemurs. *BMC Evolutionary Biology* 9: 32

Patel, E. R. 2002. Behavioral ecology and communication in wild silky sifakas. Unpublished report to the Margot Marsh Biodiversity Foundation, Great Falls, VA.

Patel, E. R. 2005. Silky sifaka (*Propithecus candidus*) predation by a fossa (*Cryptoprocta ferox*). *Lemur News* (10): 25–27.

Patel, E. R. 2006. Activity budget, ranging, and group size in silky sifakas (*Propithecus candidus*). *Lemur News* (11): 42–45.

Patel, E. R. 2006a. Scent-marking in wild silky sifakas (*Propithecus candidus*) in Madagascar: sex differences and seasonal effects in usage and response across multiple scent-mark types. *International Journal of Primatology* 27(1): Abstract #496.

Patel, E. R. 2006b. Activity budget, ranging, and group size in silky sifakas (*Propithecus candidus*). *Lemur News* (11): 42–45.

Patel, E. R. 2007a. Non-maternal infant care in wild silky sifakas (*Propithecus candidus*). *Lemur News* 12: 39–42.

Patel, E. R. 2007b. Logging of rare rosewood and palisandre (*Dalbergia* spp.) within Marojejy National Park, Madagascar. *Madagascar Conservation and Development* 2: 11–16.

Patel, E. R. 2009a. Silky sifaka, *Propithecus candidus*, Grandidier 1871. Pp.23–26 in: R. A. Mittermeier *et al.* (eds.), *Primates in Peril: The World's 25 Most Endangered Primates 2008–2010*. IUCN/SSC Primate Specialist Group (PSG), International Primatological Society (IPS), and Conservation International (CI), Arlington, VA.

Patel, E. R. 2009b. A tragedy with villains: severe resurgence of selective rosewood logging in Marojejy National Park leads to temporary park closure. *Lemur News* (14): 1–6.

Patel, E. R. and Andrianandrasana, L.H. 2008. Low elevation silky sifakas (*Propithecus candidus*) in the Makira Conservation Site at Andaparaty-Rabeson: Ranging, demography, and possible sympatry with red ruffed lemurs (*Varecia rubra*). *Lemur News* (13): 18–22.

Patel, E. R. and Girard-Buttoz, C. 2008. Non-nutritive tree gouging in wild Milne-Edwards' sifakas (*Propithecus edwardsi*): description and potential communicative functions. *Primate Eye* (96): Abstract #283.

Patel, E. R., Coke, C. S., Ritchie, A. and Santorelli, C. 2003a. Assessing production specificity of free ranging silky sifaka (*Propithecus diadema candidus*) "antipredator" vocalizations: weak evidence for "aerial predator" but not "terrestrial predator" calls. *American Journal of Primatology* 60(Suppl.1): 71–72. Abstract.

Patel, E. R., Coke, C. S., Richie, A. and Santorelli, C. 2003b. Alloparental care (including allonursing) in free ranging silky sifakas (*Propithecus diadema candidus*) in primary northeastern montane rain forest in Madagascar. *American Journal of Primatology* 60(suppl.1): 71. Abstract.

Patel, E. R., Marshall, J. J . and Parathian, H. 2005a. Silky sifaka (*Propithecus candidus*) conservation education in northeastern Madagascar. *Laboratory Primate Newsletter* 44(3): 8–11.

Patel, E. R., Anderson, J. D. and Owren, M. J. 2005b. Sex differences in the acoustic structure of an alarm vocalization in a monomorphic primate: wild silky sifakas (*Propithecus candidus*) of Northeastern Madagascar. *American Journal of Primatology* 66(Suppl.1): 46-47. Abstract.

Patel, E. R., Anderson, J. D., Irwin, M. T. and Owren, M. J. 2005c. Quantifying the vocal repertoire of wild adult diademed sifakas (*Propithecus diadema diadema*) in Madagascar. *American Journal of Primatology* 66(1): 48. Abstract.

Patel, E. R., Anderson, J. D., and Owren, M. J. 2006. Exploring the function of "Zzuss" alarm vocalizations in wild silky sifakas (*Propithecus candidus*): moderate evidence for individual distinctiveness. *International Journal of Primatology* 27(suppl.1): Abstract #504.

Pereira, M. E. 1991. Asynchrony within estrous synchrony among ringtailed lemurs (Primates: Lemuridae). *Physiology and Behavior* 49(1): 47–52.

Pereira, M. E. and Kappeler, P. M. 1997. Divergent systems of agonistic behaviour in lemurid primates. *Behaviour* 134(3–4): 225–274.

Pereira, M. E. and McGlynn, C. A. 1999. Special relationships instead of female dominance for redfronted lemurs, *Eulemur fulvus rufus*. *American Journal of Primatology* 43(3): 239–258.

Pereira, M. E. and Weiss, M. L. 1991. Female mate choice, male migration, and the threat of infanticide in ring-tailed lemurs. *Behavioral Ecology and Sociobiology* 28(2): 141–152.

Pereira, M. E., Klepper, A. and Simons, E. L. 1987. Tactics of care for young infants by forest-living ruffed lemurs *Varecia variegata variegata*: ground nests, parking and biparental guarding. *American Journal of Primatology* 13(2): 219–244.

Pereiera, M. E., Seeligson, M. L. and Macedonia, J. M. 1988. The behavioral repertoire of the black-and-white ruffed lemur, *Varecia variegata variegata*. *Folia Primatologica* 51(1): 1–32.

Pereira, M. E., Kaufman, R., Kappeler, P. M. and Overdorff, D. J. 1990. Female dominance does not characterize all the Lemuridae. *Folia Primatologica* 55(2): 96–103.

Perez, V. R., Burney, D. A., Godfrey, L. R. and Nowak-Kemp, M. 2003. Butchered sloth lemurs. *Evolutionary Anthropology* 12(6): 260.

Perez, V. R., Godfrey, L. R., Nowak-Kemp, M., Burney, D. A., Ratsimbazafy, J. and Vasey, N. 2005. Evidence of early butchery of giant lemurs in Madagascar. *Journal of Human Evolution* 49(6): 722–742.

Perret, M. 1982. Influence du groupement social sur la reproduction de la female de *Microcebus murinus* (Miller, 1777). *Zeitschrift für Tierpsychologie* 60: 47–65.

Perret, M. 1992. Environmental and social determinants of sexual function in the male lesser mouse lemur (*Microcebus murinus*). *Folia Primatologica* 59(1): 1–25.

Perret, M. 1998. Energetic advantage of nest-sharing in a solitary primate, the lesser mouse lemur (*Microcebus murinus*). *Journal of Mammalogy* 79(4): 1093–1102.

Perret, M. and Aujard, F. 2001. Regulation by photoperiod of seasonal changes in body mass and reproductive function in gray mouse lemurs (*Microcebus murinus*): differential responses by sex. *International Journal of Primatology* 22(1): 5–24.

Perry, J. M., Izard, M. K. and Fail, P. A. 1992. Observations on reproduction, hormones, copulatory behavior, and neonatal mortality in captive *Lemur mongoz* (mongoose lemur). *Zoo Biology* 11(2): 81–97.

Peters, W. C. H. 1852. *Naturwissenschaftliche Reise nach Mossambique*. Georg Reimer Verlag, Berlin.

Petter, A. and Petter, J.-J. 1971. Part 3.1 Infraorder Lemuriformes. Pp.1–10 in: J. Meeter and H. Setzer (eds.), *The Mammals of Africa: An Identification Manual*. Smithsonian Institution Press, Washington, DC.

Petter, J.-J. 1962a. Recherches sur l'écologie et l'éthologique des lémuriens malgaches. *Mémoires Muséum National de Histoire Naturelle, Paris* (A) 27: 1–146.

Petter. J.-J. 1962b. Ecological and behavioral studies of Madagascar lemurs in the field. *Annals of the New York Academy of Sciences* 102: 267–281.

Petter, J.-J. 1977. The aye-aye. Pp.37–57 in: Prince Rainier of Monaco and G. H. Bourne (eds.), *Primate Conservation*. Academic Press, New York.

Petter, J.-J. 1978. Ecological and physiological adaptations of five sympatric nocturnal lemurs to seasonal variations in food production. Pp.211–223 in: D. J. Chivers and J. Herbert (eds.), *Recent Advances in Primatology*, Vol. 1. Academic Press, New York.

Petter, J.-J. and Andriatsarafara, F. 1987. Conservation status and distribution of lemurs in the west and northwest of Madagascar. *Primate Conservation* (8): 169–171.

Petter, J.-J. and Petter, A. 1967. The aye-aye of Madagascar. Pp.195–205 in: S. A. Altmann (ed.), *Social Communication Among Primates*. The University of Chicago Press, Chicago.

Petter, J.-J. and Petter-Rousseaux, A. 1956. A propos du lémurien malgache *Cheirogaleus trichotis*. *Mammalia* 20(1): 46–48.

Petter, J.-J. and Petter-Rousseaux, A. 1960. Remarques sur la systématique du genre *Lepilemur*. *Mammalia* 24(1): 76–86.

Petter, J.-J. and Petter-Rousseaux, A. 1979. Classification of the prosimians. Pp.359–409 in: G. A. Doyle and R. D. Martin (eds.), *The Study of Prosimian Behavior*. Academic Press, London.

Petter, J.-J. and Peyriéras, A. 1970a. Observations éco-éthologiques sur les lémuriens malgaches du genre *Hapalemur*. *La Terre et la Vie* 24: 356–382.

Petter, J.-J. and Peyriéras, A. 1970b. Nouvelle contibution à l'étude d'un lémurien Malgache, le aye-aye (*Daubentonia madagascariensis* E. Geoffroy). *Mammalia* 34(2): 167–193.

Petter, J.-J. and Peyriéras, A. 1972. Melanization in the genus Propithecus Malagasy lemur. *Journal of Human Evolution* 1: 379–388.

Petter, J.-J. and Peyriéras, A. 1975. Preliminary notes on the behavior and ecology of *Hapalemur griseus*. Pp.281–286 in: I. Tattersall and R. W. Sussman (eds.), *Lemur Biology*. Plenum Press, New York.

Petter, J.-J. and van der Sloot, J.-H. 2000. *Lemurs of Madagascar and the Comoros*. (CD-ROM). Expert Center for Taxonomic Identification, Amsterdam.

Petter, J.-J., Schilling, A. and Pariente, G. 1971. Observations éco-éthologiques sur deux lémuriens malgaches nocturnes: *Phaner furcifer* et *Microcebus coquereli*. *La Terre et la Vie* 25: 287–327.

Petter, J.-J., Schilling, A. and Pariente, G. 1975. Observations on the behavior and ecology of *Phaner furcifer*. Pp.209–218 in: I. Tattersall and R. W. Sussman (eds.), *Lemur Biology*. Plenum Press, New York.

Petter, J.-J., Albignac, R. and Rumpler, Y. 1977. *Mammifères Lémuriens (Primates, Prosimiens)*. *Faune de Madagascar* 44: 1–513. ORSTOM/CNRS, Paris.

Petter-Rousseaux, A. 1962. Recherches sur la biologie de la reproduction des primates inférieurs. *Mammalia* 26 (suppl. 1): 1–88.

Petter-Rousseaux, A. 1964. Reproductive physiology and behavior of the Lemuroidea. Pp. 91–132 in: J. Buettner-Janusch (ed.), *Evolutionary and Genetic Biology of Primates*. Academic Press, New York.

Petter-Rousseaux, A. 1980. Seasonal activity rhythms, reproduction and body weight variations in five sympatric nocturnal prosimians, in simulated light and climatic conditions. Pp.137-152 in: P. Charles-Dominique, H. M. Cooper, A. Hladik, C. M. Hladik, E. Pagès, G. F. Pariente, A. Petter-Rousseaux and A. Schilling (eds.), *Nocturnal Malagasy Primates: Ecology, Physiology, and Behavior*. Academic Press, New York.

Petter-Rousseaux, A. and Bourlière, F. 1965. Persistence des phénomèns d' ovogénèse chez l' adulte de *Daubentonia madagascariensis* (Prosimii, Lemuriformes). *Folia Primatologica* 3: 2 41–244.

Petter-Rousseaux, A. and Petter, J.-J. 1967. Contribution à la systématique des Cheirogaleinae (lémuriens malgaches). *Allocebus*, gen. nov., pour *Cheirogaleus trichotis* Gunther 1875. *Mammalia* 31(4): 574–582.

Pinkus, S., Smith, J. N. M. and Jolly, A. 2006. Feeding competition between introduced *Eulemur fulvus* and native *Lemur catta* during the birth season at Berenty Reserve, southern Madagascar. Pp.119–140 in: A. Jolly, R. W. Sussman, N. Koyama and H. Rasamimanana (eds.), *Ringtailed Lemur Biology: Lemur catta in Madagascar*. Springer, New York

Pitts, A. 1995. Predation by *Eulemur fulvus rufus* on an infant *Lemur catta* at Berenty, Madagascar. *Folia Primatologica* 65(3): 169–171.

Pochron, S. T. and Wright, P. C. 2003. Variability in adult group composition of a prosimian primate. *Behavioral Ecology and Sociobiology* 54(3): 285–293.

Pochron, S. T. and Wright, P. C. 2005. Testes size and body weight in the Milne-Edwards' sifaka (*Propithecus edwardsi*) of Ranomafana National Park, Madagascar, relative to other strepsirhine primates. *Folia Primatologica* 76(1): 37–41.

Pochron, S. T., Wright, P. C., Schaentzler, E., Ippolito, M., Rakotonirina, G., Ratsimbazafy, R. and Rakotosoa, R. 2002. Effect of season and age on the gonadosomatic index of Milne-Edwards' sifakas (*Propithecus diadema edwardsi*) in Ranomafana National Park, Madagascar. *International Journal of Primatology* 23(2): 355–364.

Pochron, S. T., Fitzgerald, J., Gilbert, C. C., Lawrence, D., Grgas, M., Rakotonirina, G., Ratsimbazafy, G., Rakotosoa, R. and Wright, P. C. 2003. Patterns of female dominance in *Propithecus diadema edwardsi* of Ranomafana National Park, Madagascar. *American Journal of Primatology* 61(4): 173–185.

Pochron, S. T., Tucker, W. T. and Wright, P. C. 2004. Demography, life history, and social structure in *Propithecus diadema edwardsi* from 1986–2000 in Ranomafana National Park, Madagascar. *American Journal of Primatology* 125(1): 61–72.

Pochron, S. T., Morelli, T. L., Terranova, P., Scirbona, J., Cohen, J., Kunapareddy, G., Rakotonirina, G., Ratsimbazafy, R., Rakotosoa, R. and Wright, P. C. 2005a. Patterns of male scent-marking in *Propithecus edwardsi* of Ranomafana National Park, Madagascar. *American Journal of Primatology* 65(2): 103–115.

Pochron, S. T., Morelli, T. L., Scirbona, J. and Wright, P. C. 2005b. Sex differences in scent marking in *Propithecus edwardsi* of Ranomafana National Park, Madagascar. *American Journal of Primatology* 66(2): 97–110.

Pocock, R. I. 1917. The lemurs of the *Hapalemur* group. *Annals and Magazine of Natural History* 19: 343–352.

Pollock. J. I. 1975a. The social behaviour and ecology of *Indri indri*. PhD dissertation, University of London, London, UK.

Pollock, J. I. 1975b. Field observations on *Indri indri*: a preliminary report. Pp.287–311 in: I. Tattersall and R. W. Sussman (eds.), *Lemur Biology*. Plenum Press, New York.

Pollock, J. I. 1977. The ecology and sociology of feeding in *Indri indri*. Pp.37–69 in: T. H. Clutton-Brock (ed.), *Primate Ecology: Studies of Feeding and Ranging Behaviour in Lemurs, Monkeys and Apes*. Academic Press, London.

Pollock, J. I. 1979a. Female dominance in *Indri indri*. *Folia Primatologica* 31(1–2): 143–164.

Pollock, J. I.. 1979b. Spatial distribution and ranging behavior in lemurs. Pp.359–409 in: G. A. Doyle and R. D. Martin (eds.), *The Study of Prosimian Behavior*. Academic Press, New York.

Pollock, J. I. 1984. Preliminary report on a mission to Madagascar by Dr. J. Pollock in August and September 1984. Unpublished report to WWF–US Primate Program, Washington, DC.

Pollock, J. I. 1986a. The song of the indri (*Indri indri*: Primates: Lemuroidea): natural history, form, and function. *International Journal of Primatology* 7(3): 225–264.

Pollock, J. I. 1986b. A note on the ecology and behavior of *Hapalemur griseus*. *Primate Conservation* (7): 97–100.

Pollock, J. I., Constable, I. D., Mittermeier, R. A., Ratsirarson, J. and Simons, H. 1985. A note on the diet and feeding behavior of the aye-aye *Daubentonia madagascariensis*. *International Journal of Primatology* 6(4): 435–447.

Polowinsky, S. and Schwitzer, C. 2009. Nutritional ecology of the blue-eyed black lemur (*Eulemur flavifrons*): integrating *in situ* and *ex situ* research to assist the conservation of a Critically Endangered species. In: M. Clauss, A. Fidgett, G. Janssens, J. M. Hatt, T. Huisman, J. Hummel, J. Nijboer and A. Plowman (eds.), *Zoo Animal Nutrition IV*. Filander Verlag, Fuerth, Germany.

Poorman, P. A. 1983. The banded chromosomes of Coquerel's sifaka, *Propithecus verreauxi coquereli* (Primates, Indriidae). *International Journal of Primatology* 4(4): 419–425.

Poorman-Allen, P. A. and Izard, M. 1990. Chromosome banding patterns of the aye-aye, *Daubentonia madagascariensis* (Primates, Daubentoniidae). *International Journal of Primatology* 11(5): 401–410.

Port, M, Clough, D. and Kappeler, P. M. 2009. Market effects offset the reciprocation of grooming in free-ranging red-fronted lemurs (*Eulemur fulvus rufus*). *Animal Behaviour* 77(1): 29–36.

Porter, L. M. 1998. Influences on the distribution of *Lepilemur microdon* in the Ranomafana National Park, Madagascar. *Folia Primatologica* 69(3): 172–176.

Porton, I. 1993. The North American captive breeding program for lemurs. *Lemur News* 1(1): 9.

Powzyk, J. A. 1996. A comparison of feeding strategies between the sympatric *Indri indri* and *Propithecus diadema diadema* in primary rain forest. *American Journal of Physical Anthropology* 22(suppl.): 190. Abstract.

Powzyk, J. A. 1997. The socio-ecology of two sympatric indrids, *Propithecus diadema diadema* and *Indri indri*: a comparison of feeding strategies and their possible repercussions on species-specific behaviors. PhD thesis, Duke University, Durham, NC.

Powzyk, J. A. and Mowry, C. B. 2003. Dietary and feeding differences between sympatric *Propithecus diadema diadema* and *Indri indri*. *International Journal of Primatology* 24(6): 1143–1162.

Powzyk, J. and Thalmann, U. 2003. *Indri indri*, indri. Pp.1342–1345 in: S. M. Goodman and J. P. Benstead (eds.), *The Natural History of Madagascar*. The University of Chicago Press, Chicago.

Prescott, J. 1980. Breeding the brown lemur *Lemur macaco fulvus* at the Quebec Zoo. *International Zoo Yearbook* 20: 215–218.

Price, E. C. and Feistner, A. T. C. 1994. Responses of captive aye-ayes (*Daubentonia madagascariensis*) to the scent of conspecifics: a preliminary investigation. *Folia Primatologica* 62(1–3): 170–174.

Pride, R. E. 2005. Optimal group size and seasonal stress in ring-tailed lemurs (*Lemur catta*). *Behavioural Ecology* 16(3): 550–560.

Pride, R. E., Felantsoa, D, Randriamboavonjy, R. and Randriambelona, R. 2006. Resource defense in *Lemur catta*: the importance of group size. Pp. 208–232 in: A. Jolly, R. W. Sussman, N. Koyama and H. Rasamimanana (eds.), *Ringtailed Lemur Biology:* Lemur catta *in Madagascar*. Springer, New York.

Projet ZICOMA 1999. Les zones d'importance pour la conservation des oiseaux à Madagascar. Projet ZICOMA, Antananarivo, Madagascar.

Purvis, A. 1995. A composite estimate of primate phylogeny. *Philosophical Transactions of the Royal Society of London* B348: 405–421.

Quansah, N. 1988. *Manongarivo Special Reserve. Expedition Report*. Madagascar Environmental Research Group, Conservation Foundation, London, UK.

Queslin, E. and Patel, E. R. 2008. A preliminary study of wild silky sifaka (*Propithecus candidus*) diet, feeding ecology, and habitat use in Marojejy National Park, Madagascar. XXII Congress of the International Primatological Society. *Primate Eye* (96): Abstract #143.

Quinn, A. and Wilson, D. 2004. *Daubentonia madagascariensis. Mammalian Species* (740): 6pp. American Society of Mammalogists.

Rabarivola, C., Meyers, D. and Rumpler, Y. 1991. Distribution and morphological characters of intermediate forms between the black lemur (*Eulemur macaco macaco*) and the Sclater's lemur (*E. m. flavifrons*). *Primates* 32(2): 269–273.

Rabarivola, C., Meier, B., Langer, C., Scheffrahn, W. and Rumpler, Y. 1996. Population genetics of *Eulemur macaco macaco* (Primates: Lemuridae) on the islands of Nosy-Be and Nosy-Komba and the peninsula of Ambato (Madagascar). *Primates* 37(2): 215–225.

Rabarivola, C., Meier, B., Langer, C., Bayart, F., Ludes, B. and Rumpler, Y. 1998. Comparison of genetic variability in wild insular and mainland populations of *Eulemur macaco* : implications for conservation strategy. *Folia Primatologica* 69(suppl. 1): 136–146.

Rabarivola, C., Andriaholinirina, N. and Rumpler, Y. 2004. Cytogenetic arguments in favour of the specific status of *Lepilemur microdon. Folia Primatologica* 75(suppl.1): 320–321. Abstract.

Rabarivola, C., Zaramody, A., Fausser, J., Andriaholinirina, N., Roos, C., Zinner, D., Marcel, H. and Rumpler, Y. 2006. Cytogenetic and molecular characteristics of a new species of sportive lemur from northern Madagascar. *Lemur News* (11): 45–49.

Rabarivola, C., Prosper, P., Zaramody, A., Andriaholinirina, N. and Hauwy, M. 2007. Cytogenetics and taxonomy of the genus *Hapalemur. Lemur News* (12): 46–49.

Rabinowitz, P. D. and Woods, S. 2006. The Africa-Madagascar connection and mammalian migrations. *Journal of African Earth Sciences* 44: 270–276.

Radespiel, U. 2000. Sociality in the gray mouse lemur *(Microcebus murinus*) in northwestern Madagascar. *American Journal of Primatology* 51(1): 21–40.

Radespiel, U. and Zimmermann, E. 2001a. Female dominance in captive gray mouse lemurs (*Microcebus murinus*). *American Journal of Primatology* 54(4): 181–192.

Radespiel, U. and Zimmermann, E. 2001b. Dynamics of estrous synchrony in captive gray mouse lemurs (*Microcebus murinus*). *International Journal of Primatology* 22(1): 71–90.

Radespiel, U., Cepok, S., Zietemann, V. and Zimmermann, E. 1998. Sex-specific usage patterns of sleeping sites in grey mouse lemurs (*Microcebus murinus*) in northwestern Madagascar. *American Journal of Primatology* 46(1): 77–84.

Radespiel, U., Ehresmann, P. and Zimmermann, E. 2001. Contest versus scramble competition for males: the composition and spatial structure of a population of grey mouse lemurs (*Microcebus murinus*) in north-west Madagascar. *Primates* 42(3): 207–220.

Radespiel, U., Ehresmann, P. and Zimmermann, E. 2003. Species-specific usage of sleeping sites in two sympatric mouse lemur species (*Microcebus murinus* and *M. ravelobensis*) in northwestern Madagascar. *American Journal of Primatology* 59(4): 139–151.

Radespiel, U., Reimann, W., Rahelinirina, M., and Zimmermann, E. 2006. Feeding ecology of sympatric mouse lemur species in northwestern Madagascar. *International Journal of Primatology* 27(1): 311–321.

Radespiel, U., Olivieri, G., Rasolofoson, D. W., Rakotondratsimba, G., Rakotonirainy, O., Rasoloharijaona, S. Randrianambinina, B., Ratsimbazafy, J. H., Ratelolohy, F., Randriamboavonjy, T., Rasolofoharivelo, T., Craul, M., Rakotozafy, L. and Randrianarison, R. 2008. Exceptional diversity of mouse lemurs (*Microcebus* spp.) in the Makira region with the description of one new species. *American Journal of Primatology* 70(11): 1033–1046.

Rahajanirina, L. P. and Dollar, L. 2004. Confirmation of aye-aye (*Daubentonia madagascariensis*) in the Tsingy de Bemaraha National Park. *Lemur News* (9): 11–12.

Raharivololona, B. M. and Ganzhorn, J. U. 2009. Gastrointestinal parasite infection of the gray mouse lemur (*Microcebus murinus*) in the littoral forest of Mandena, Madagascar: effects of forest fragmentation and degradation. *Madagascar Conservation and Development* 4: 103–112.

Raharivololona, B. M. and Ranaivosoa, V. 2000. Suivi écologique des lémuriens diurnes dans le Parc National d'Andohahela à Tolagnaro. *Lemur News* (5): 8–11.

Raharivololona B. M., Rakotondravao and Ganzhorn, J. U. 2007. Gastrointestinal parasites of small mammals in the littoral forest of Mandena. In: *Biodiversity, Ecology and Conservation of littoral Forest Ecosystems in Southeastern Madagascar, Tolagnaro (Fort Dauphin)*, J. U. Ganzhorn, S. M. Goodman and M. Vincelette (eds.), pp.247–258. Smithsonian Institution Press, Washington, DC.

Rakotoarison, N. 1995a. First sighting and capture of the hairy-eared dwarf lemur (*Allocebus trichotis*) in the Strict Nature Reserve of Zahamena. Report to Conservation International, Washington, DC.

Rakotoarison, N. 1995b. Rapport sur l'inventaire des mammifères dans la Réserve Naturelle Intégrale No. 3 de Zahamena. Conservation International-Madagascar, Antananarivo.

Rakotoarison, N. 1998. Recent discoveries of the hairy-eared dwarf lemur (*Allocebus trichotis*). *Lemur News* (3): 21.

Rakotoarison, N., Mutschler, T. and Thalmann, U. 1993. Lemurs in Bemaraha (World Heritage Landscape, western Madagascar). *Oryx* 27(1): 35–40.

Rakotoarison, N., Zimmermann, H. and Zimmermann, E. 1997. First discovery of the hairy-eared dwarf lemur (*Allocebus trichotis*) in a highland rain forest of eastern Madagascar. *Folia Primatologica* 68(2): 86–94.

Rakotondratsima, M. and Kremen, C. 2001. Suivi écologique de deux espèces de lémuriens diurnes *Varecia variegata rubra* et *Eulemur fulvus albifrons* dans la presqu'île de Masoala (1993–1998). *Lemur News* (6): 31–35.

Rakotondravony, D. and Razafindramahatra, L. V. 2004. Contribution à l'étude des populations de *Hapalemur aureus* dans le couloir forestier Ranomafana-Andringitra. *Lemur News* (9): 28–32.

Rakotondravony, D., Goodman, S. M. and Soarimalala, V. 1998. Predation on *Hapalemur griseus griseus* by *Boa manditra* (Boidae) in the littoral forest of eastern Madagascar. *Folia Primatologica* 69(6): 405–408.

Rakotosamimanana, B., Ralaiarison, R. R., Ralisoamalala, R., Rasolofoharivelo, T., Raharimanantsoa, V., Randrianarison, R., Rakotondratsimba, J., Rasolofoson, D., Rakotonirainy, E. and Randriamboavonjy, T. 2004. Comment et pourquoi les lémuriens diurnes disparaissent peu à peu dans les forêts d'Ambato et de Moramanga (région de Moramanga) Madagascar? *Lemur News* (9): 19–24.

Ralainasolo, F. B. 2004. Influence des effets anthropiques sur la dynamique de population de *Hapalemur griseus alaotrensis* ou «Bandro» dans son habitat naturel. *Lemur News* (9): 32–35.

Ralainasolo, F. B., Ratsimbazafy, H. J., Jeannoda, V. H. and Letsara, R. 2005. Etude comportementale et nutritionnelle de *Varecia variegata editorum* dans la forêt de Manombo. *Lemur News* (10): 22–25.

Ralisoamalala, R. C. 1996. Rôle de *Eulemur fulvus rufus* (Audebert, 1799) et de *Propithecus verreauxi verreauxi* (A. Grandidier, 1867) dans la dissémination des graines. Pp.285–293 in: J. U. Ganzhorn and J.-P. Sorg (eds.), *Ecology and Economy of a Tropical Dry Forest in Madagascar*. *Primate Report* 46.

Ramaromilanto, B., Lei, R. H., Engberg, S. E., Johnson, S. E., Sitzmann, B.D. and Louis, E. E. Jr. 2009. Sportive lemur diversity at Mananara-Nord Biosphere Reserve, Madagascar. *Occasional Papers of the Museum of Texas Tech University* (286): 1-22.

Ramsay, N. F. and Giller, P. S. 1996. Scent-marking in ring-tailed lemurs: responses to the introduction of "foreign" scent in the home range. *Primates* 37(1): 13–23.

Rand, A. L. 1935. On the habits of some Madagascar mammals. *Journal of Mammalogy* 16: 89–104.

Randrianambinina, B., Rakotondravony, D., Radespiel, U. and Zimmermann, E. 2003a. Diverging annual rhythms of closely related nocturnal primates: a comparison of golden brown and brown mouse lemurs. *Folia Primatologica* 74(4): 214–215. Abstract.

Randrainambinina, B., Rakotondravony, D., Radespiel, U. and Zimmermann, E. 2003b. Seasonal changes in general activity, body mass and reproduction of two small nocturnal primates: a comparison of the golden brown mouse lemur (*Microcebus ravelobensis*) in northwestern Madagascar and the brown mouse lemur (*Microcebus rufus*) in eastern Madagascar. *Primates* 44(4): 321–331.

Randrianambinina, B., Rasoloharijaona, S., Rakotosamimanana, B. and Zimmermann, E. 2003c. Inventaire des communautés lémuriennes dans la Réserve Spéciale de Bora au nord-ouest et la Forêt dominiale Mahilaka-Maromandia au nord de Madagascar. *Lemur News* (8): 15–18.

Randrianambinina, B., Mbotizafy, S., Rasoloharijaona, S., Ravoahangimalala, R. O. and Zimmermann, E. 2007. Seasonality in reproduction of *Lepilemur edwardsi*. *International Journal of Primatology* 28(4): 783–790.

Randrianarisoa, P. M., Rasamison, A. and Rakotozafy, L. 1999. Les lémuriens de la région de Daraina: forêt d'Analamazava, forêt de Bekaraoka et forêt de Sahaka. *Lemur News* (4): 19–21.

Randrianarisoa, P. M., Rasamison, A. and Rakotozafy, L. 2000. Inventaire biologique dans la Réserve Spéciale de Bemarivo: Volet primatologie. *Lemur News* (5): 16–19.

Randrianarisoa, M. A., Rasamison, A. and Rakotozafy, L. 2001a. Notes sur la faune lémurien dans la Réserve Spéciale d'Ambohijanahary. *Lemur News* (6): 5.

Randrianarisoa, M. A., Rasamison, A., Rakotozafy, L. and Totovalahy, A. 2001b. Inventaire des lémuriens dans la Réserve Spéciale de Kasijy. *Lemur News* (6): 7–8.

Randriatahina, G. H., and Rabarivola, J. C. 2004. Inventaire des lémuriens dans la partie nord-ouest de Madagascar et distribution d'*Eulemur macaco flavifrons*. *Lemur News* (9): 7–9.

Randriatahina, G. H. and Roeder, J. J. In press. Group size, group composition and group stabiliity in a wild population of blue-eyed lemurs (*Eulemur macaco flavifrons*) at Ankarafa, Sahamalaza National Park. In: J. C. Masters, M. Gamba and F. Guenin (eds.), *Leaping Ahead: Advances in Prosimian Biology*. Springer, New York.

Raps, S. and White, F. J. 1995. Female social dominance in semi-free-ranging ruffed lemurs (*Varecia variegata*). *Folia Primatologica* 65(3): 163–168.

Rasamimanana, H. 1999. Influence of social organization patterns on food intake of *Lemur catta* in the Berenty Reserve. Pp.173–188 in: B. Rakotosamimanana, H. Rasamimanana, J. U. Ganzhorn and S. M. Goodman (eds.), *New Directions in Lemur Studies*. Kluwer Academic/Plenum Publishers, New York,

Rasaminanana, H. R. and Rafidinarivo, E. 1993. Feeding behavior of *Lemur catta* females in relation to their physiological state. Pp.123–133 in: P. M. Kappeler and J. U. Ganzhorn (eds.), *Lemur Social Systems and their Ecological Basis*. Plenum Press, New York.

Rasamimanana, H., Andrianome, V. N., Rambeloarivony, H. and Pasquet, P. 2006. Male and female ringtailed lemurs' energetic strategy does not explain female dominance. Pp.271–295 in: A. Jolly, R. W. Sussman, N. Koyama and H. Rasamimanana (eds.), *Ringtailed Lemur Biology*: Lemur catta *in Madagascar*. Springer, New York.

Rasamison, A. A., Rakotozafy, L., and Raokotomanga, B. 2005. Inventaire des lémuriens dans la Réserve Spéciale de Maningoza. *Lemur News* (10): 20–22.

Rasmussen, D. T. 1985. A comparative study of breeding seasonality and litter size in eleven taxa of captive lemurs (*Lemur* and *Varecia*). *International Journal of Primatology* 6(5): 501–517.

Rasmussen, M. A. 1999. Ecological influences on the activity cycle in two cathemeral primates: the mongoose lemur (*Eulemur mongoz*) and the common brown lemur (*Eulemur fulvus fulvus*). PhD thesis, Duke University, Durham, NC.

Rasoarimanana, J. 2005. Suivi des lémuriens diurnes dans le Parc National d'Andohahela. *Lemur News* (10): 27–29.

Rasoazanabary, E. 2001. Stratégie adaptive des mêles chez *Microcebus murinus* pendant la saison sèche dans le forêt de Kirindy, Morondava. Mémoire D. E. A., Université d'Antananarivo, Antananarivo.

Rasoazanabary, E. 2004. A preliminary study of mouse lemurs in the Beza Mahafaly Special Reserve, southwest Madagascar. *Lemur News* (9): 4–7.

Rasoazanabary, E. 2006. Male and female activity patterns in *Microcebus murinus* during the dry season at Kirindy Forest, western Madagascar. *International Journal of Primatology* 27(2): 437–464.

Rasoloarison, V. and Paquier, F. 2003. Tsingy de Bemaraha. Pp.1507–1512 in: S. M. Goodman and J. P. Benstead (eds.), *The Natural History of Madagascar*. The University of Chicago Press, Chicago.

Rasoloarison, R. M., Rasolonandrasana, B. P. N., Ganzhorn, J. U. and Goodman, S. M. 1995. Predation on vertebrates in the Kirindy Forest, western Madagascar. *Ecotropica* 1: 59–65.

Rasoloarison, R. M., Goodman, S. M. and Ganzhorn, J. U. 2000. Taxonomic revision of mouse lemurs (*Microcebus*) in the western portions of Madagascar. *International Journal of Primatology* 21(6): 963–1019.

Rasolofoson, D., Rakotondratsimba, G., Rakotoirainy, O., Rasolofoharivelo, T., Rakotozafy, L., Ratsimbazafy, J., Ratelolahy, F., Andriamaholy, V., and Sarovy, A. 2007a. Le bloc forestier de Makira charnière de Lémuriens. *Lemurs News* (12): 49–53.

Rasolofoson, D., Rakotondratsimba, G., Rakotonirainy, O., Rakotozafy, L. M. A., Ratsimbazafy, J. H., Rabetafika, L. and Randrianarison R. M. 2007b. Influence of human pressure on lemur groups on the Makira Plateau, Maroantsetra, Madagascar. *Madagascar Conservation and Development* 2: 21–27.

Rasoloharijoana, S., Rakotosamimanana, B. and Zimmermann, E. 2000. Infanticide by a male Milne-Edwards' sportive lemur (*Lepilemur edwardsi*) in Ampijoroa, NW-Madagascar. *International Journal of Primatology* 21(1): 41–45.

Rasoloharijaona, S., Rakotosamimanana, B., Randrianambanina, B. and Zimmermann, E. 2003. Pair-specific usage of sleeping sites and their implications for social organization in a nocturnal Malagasy primate, the Milne-Edwards' sportive lemur (*Lepilemur edwardsi*). *American Journal of Physical Anthropology* 122(3): 251–258.

Rasoloharijaona, S., Randrianambinina, B., Rakotosamiminana, B. and Zimmermann, E. 2005. Inventaires des lémuriens dans la forêt d'Andranovelona / Madirovalo (nord oust de Madagascar), les "savoka" de Manehoko, la Réserve de Lokobe, la Réserve Spéciale de l'Ankarana, et la Réserve Spéciale d'Analamerana, au nord de Madagascar. *Lemur News* (10): 8–11.

Rasoloharijaona, S., Randrianambinina, B. and Zimmermann, E. 2007. Sleeping site ecology in a rain-forest dwelling nocturnal lemur (*Lepilemur mustelinus*): implications for sociality and conservation. *American Journal of Primatology* 70(3): 247–253.

Ratsimbazafy, J. H. 2002. Responses of black-and-white ruffed lemurs (*Varecia variegata variegata*) to disturbance in Manombo forest Madagascar. PhD thesis, State University of New York at Stony Brook, NY.

Ratsimbazafy, J. H., Ramarosandratana, H. V. and Zaonarivelo, R. J. 2002. How do black-and-white ruffed lemurs still survive in a highly disturbed habitat? *Lemur News* (7): 7–10.

Ratsirarson, J. 2003. Réserve Spéciale de Beza Mahafaly. Pp.1520–1525 in: S. M. Goodman and J. P. Benstead (eds.), *The Natural History of Madagascar*. The University of Chicago Press, Chicago.

Ratsirarson, J. and Ranaivonasy, J. 2002. Ecologie des lémuriens dans la forêt littorale de Tampolo. *Lemur News* (7): 26–30.

Ratsirarson, J. and Rumpler, Y. 1988. Contribution à l'étude comparée de l'éco-éthologie de deux espèces de lémuriens, *Lepilemur mustelinus* (I. Geoffroy 1850), et *Lepilemur septentrionalis* (Rumpler and Albignac 1975) Pp. 100–102 in: L. Rakotovao, V. Barre and J. Sayer (eds.), *L'Equilibre des Ecosystèmes Forestiers à Madagascar, Actes d'un Séminaire International*. IUCN, Gland, Switzerland and Cambridge, UK.

Ratsirarson, J., Anderson, J., Warter, S. and Rumpler, Y. 1987. Notes on the distribution of *Lepilemur septentrionalis* and *L. mustelinus* in northern Madagascar. *Primates* 28(1): 119–122.

Ravaoarimanana, B., Fausser, J.-L. and Rumpler, Y. 2001. Genetic comparison of wild populations of *Lepilemur septentrionalis* and *Lepilemur dorsalis* using RAPD markers. *Primates* 42(3): 221–231.

Ravaoarimanana, I. 2001. Apport de la biologie moléculaire à la taxonomie et à l'étude de la spéciation des *Lepilemur septentrionalis*. Complémentarité des techniques morphologiques, cytogénétiques et moléculaires. Thèse de Doctorat de l'Université Louis Pasteur, Strasbourg.

Ravaoarimanana, I. B., Tiedemann, R., Montagnon, D. and Rumpler, Y. 2004. Molecular and cytogenetic evidence for cryptic speciation within a rare endemic Malagasy lemur, the northern sportive lemur (*Lepilemur septentrionalis*). *Molecular Phylogenetics and Evolution* 31(2): 440–448.

Ravaorimanana, I., Zaramody, A., Rabarivola, C. and Rumpler, Y. 2009. Northern sportive lemur *Lepilemur septentrionalis* Rumpler and Albignac, 1975. In: Primates in Peril: the world's 25 most endangered primates 2008-2010, R. A. Mittermeier *et al.* (eds.), *Primate Conservation* (24): 11, 36–37.

Ravosa, M. J., Meyers, D. M. and Glander, K. E. 1993. Relative growth of the limbs and trunk in sifakas: heterochronic, ecological and functional considerations. *American Journal of Physical Anthropology* 92(4): 499–520.

Raxworthy, C. J. 2003. Introduction to the Reptiles. Pp.934–949 in: S. M. Goodman and J. P. Benstead (eds.), *The Natural History of Madagascar*. University of Chicago Press. Chicago.

Raxworthy, C. J. and Rakotondraparany, F. 1988. Mammals report. In: Manongarivo Special Reserve (Madagascar), 1987/88 Expedition Report. Madagascar Environmental Research Group, UK.

Razafindraibe, H., Montagnon, D. and Rumpler, Y. 1997. Phylogenetic relationships among Indriidae (Primates, Strepsirhini) inferred from highly repeated DNA band patterns. *Comptes rendus de l'Academie des sciences de Paris* 320(6): 469–475.

Razafindraibe, H., Montagnon, D., Ravoarimanana, B. and Rumpler, Y. 2000. Interspecific nucleotide sequence differences in the cytochrome B gene of Indriidae (Primates, Strepsirhini). *Primates* 41(2): 149–197.

Razafindramahatra, L. V. 2004. Etudes des comportements des groupes de *Hapalemur griseus alaotrensis* dans un parc villageois du Lac Alaotra. *Lemur News* (9): 44. Thesis abstract.

Razanahoera-Rakotomalala, M. 1981. Les adaptations alimentaires comparées de deux lémuriens folivores sympatriques: *Avahi* Jordan, 1834–*Lepilemur* I. Geoffroy, 1851. PhD thesis, University of Madagascar, Antananarivo.

Rendall, D. 1993. Does female social precedence characterize captive aye-ayes (*Daubentonia madagascariensis*)? *International Journal of Primatology* 14(1): 125–130.

Rendall, D., Owren M. J ., Weerts, E. and Hienz, R. D. 2004. Sex differences in the acoustic structure of vowel-like grunt vocalizations in baboons and their perceptual discrimination by baboon listeners. *Journal of the Acoustical Society of America* 115(1): 411–421.

Rendigs, A., Radespiel, U., Wrogemann, D. and Zimmermann, E. 2003. Relationship between microhabitat structure and distribution of mouse lemurs (*Microcebus* spp.) in northwestern Madagascar. *International Journal of Primatology* 24(1): 47–64.

Richard, A. F. 1973. The Social Organization and Ecology of *Propithecus verreauxi*. PhD thesis, London University, UK.

Richard, A. F. 1974a. Patterns of mating in *Propithecus verreauxi verreauxi*. Pp.49–74 in: R. D. Martin, G. A. Doyle and A. C. Walker (eds.), *Prosimian Biology*. Duckworth, London.

Richard, A. F. 1974b. Intra-specific variation in the social organization and ecology of *Propithecus verreauxi*. *Folia Primatologica* 22(2–3): 178–207.

Richard, A. F. 1976. Preliminary observations on the birth and development of *Propithecus verreauxi* to the age of six months. *Primates* 17(3): 357–366.

Richard, A. 1977. The feeding behavior of *Propithecus verreauxi*. Pp.71–96 in: T. H. Clutton-Brock (ed.), *Primate Ecology: Studies of Feeding and Ranging Behavior in Lemurs, Monkeys and Apes*. Academic Press, London.

Richard, A. F. 1978a. Variability in the feeding behavior of a Malagasy prosimian, *Propithecus verreauxi*: Lemuriformes. Pp.519–533 in: G. G. Montgomery (ed.), *The Ecology of Arboreal Folivores*.

Smithsonian Institution Press, Washington, DC.

Richard, A. F. 1978b. *Behavioral Variation: Case Study of a Malagasy Lemur*. Associated University Press, New Jersey.

Richard, A. F. 1985. Social boundaries in a Malagasy prosimian, the sifaka (*Propithecus verreauxi*). *International Journal of Primatology* 6(6): 553–568.

Richard, A. F. 1987. Malagasy prosimians: female dominance. Pp.25–33 in: B. B. Smuts, D. L. Cheney, R. M. Seyfarth, R. W. Wrangham and T. T. Struhsaker (eds.), *Primate Societies*. University of Chicago Press, Chicago.

Richard, A. F. 2003. *Propithecus*, sifakas. Pp.1345–1348 in: S. M. Goodman and J. P. Benstead (eds.), *The Natural History of Madagascar*. The Chicago University Press, Chicago.

Richard, A. F. and Nicoll, M. E. 1987. Female social dominance and basal metabolism in a Malagasy primate, *Propithecus verreauxi*. *American Journal of Primatology* 12(3): 309–314.

Richard, A. F., Rakotomanga, P. and Schwartz, M. 1991. Demography of *Propithecus verreauxi* at Beza Mahafaly, Madagascar: sex ratio, survival, and fertility, 1984–1988. *American Journal of Physical Anthropology* 84(3): 307–322.

Richard, A. F., Rakotomanga, P. and Schwartz, M. 1993. Dispersal by *Propithecus verreauxi* at Beza Mahafaly, Madagascar: 1984–1991. *American Journal of Primatology* 30(1): 1–20.

Richard, A. F., Dewar, R. E., Schwartz, M. and Ratsirarson, J. 2000. Mass change, environmental variability and female fertility in wild *Propithecus verreauxi*. *Journal of Human Evolution* 39(4): 381–391.

Richard, A. F., Dewar, R. E., Schwartz, M. and Ratsirarson, J. 2002. Life in the slow lane? Demography and life histories of male and female sifaka (*Propithecus verreauxi verreuaxi*). *Journal of Zoology, London* 256: 421–436.

Rigamonti, M. M. 1993. Home range and diet in red ruffed lemurs (*Varecia varigata rubra*) on the Masoala Peninsula, Madagascar. Pp.25–39 in: P. M. Kappeler and J. U. Ganzhorn (eds.), *Lemur Social Systems and their Ecological Basis*. Plenum Press, New York.

Rigamonti, M. M. 1996. Red ruffed lemur (*Varecia variegata rubra*): a rare species from the Masoala rain forests. *Lemur News* (2): 9–11.

Rigamonti, M. M., Spiezio, C., Poli, M. D. and Fazio, F. 2005. Laterality of manual function in foraging and positional behavior in wild indri (*Indri indri*). *American Journal of Primatology* 65(1): 27–38.

Ritchie, A. and Patel, E. R. 2006. The existence and potential function of "totem-tree" scent-marking in silky sifakas (*Propithecus candidus*). *International Journal of Primatology* 27(1): Abstract #361.

Roeder, J.-J. and Fornasieri, I. 1995. Does agonistic dominance imply feeding priority in lemurs? A study in *Eulemur fulvus mayottensis*. *International Journal of Primatology* 16(4): 629–642.

Roeder, J.-J., Fornasieri, I. and Gosset, D. 2001. Conflict and postconflict behaviour in two lemur species with different social organizations (*Eulemur fulvus* and *Eulemur macaco*): a study on captive groups. *Aggressive Behavior* 28(1): 62–74.

Roeder, J.-J., Duval, L. and Gosset, D. 2002. Aggressive and neutral interventions in conflicts in captive groups of brown lemurs (*Eulemur fulvus fulvus*). *American Journal of Physical Anthropology* 118(3): 253–258.

Rolland, N. and Roeder, J.-J. 2000. Do ringtailed lemurs (*Lemur catta*) reconcile in the hour post-conflict?: a pilot study. *Primates* 41(2): 223–228.

Roos, C. and Kappeler, P. M. 2006. Distribution and conservation status of two newly described cheirogaleid species, *Mirza zaza* and *Microcebus lehilahytsara*. *Primate Conservation* (21): 51–54.

Roos, C., Schmitz, J. and Zischler, H. 2004. Primate jumping genes elucidate strepsirrhine phylogeny. *Proceedings of the National Academy of Sciences* 101: 10560–10564.

Rosenthal, M. 1972. A note on the fat-tailed dwarf lemur *Cheirogaleus medius*. *International Zoo Yearbook* 12: 169.

Rübel, A. and Bauert, M. 2009. Masoala–The eye of the forest massively threatened by illegal lumbering. *Lemur News* (14): 6–7.

Rumpler, Y. 1975. The significance of chromosomal studies in the systematics of the Malagasy lemurs. Pp.25–40, in: I. Tattersall and R. W. Sussman (eds.), *Lemur Biology*. Plenum Press, New York.

Rumpler, Y. 2000. What cytogenetic studies may tell us about species diversity and speciation of lemurs. *International Journal of Primatology* 21(5): 865–881.

Rumpler, Y. 2004. Complementary approaches of cytogenetics and molecular biology to the taxonomy and study of speciation processes in lemurs. *Evolutionary Anthropology* 13(2): 67–78.

Rumpler, Y. and Albignac, R. 1973a. Cytogenetic study of the endemic Malagasy lemur: *Hapalemur*, I. Geoffroy, 1851. *Journal of Human Evolution* 2(4): 267–270.

Rumpler, Y. and Albignac, R. 1973b. Cytogenetic study of the endemic Malagasy lemurs subfamily Cheirogaleinae Gregory 1915. *American Journal of Physical Anthropology* 38(2): 261–264.

Rumpler, Y. and Albignac, R. 1975. Intraspecific chromosome variability in a lemur from the north of Madagascar: *Lepilemur septentrionalis*, species nova. *American Journal of Physical Anthropology* 42(3): 425–429.

Rumpler, Y. and Albignac, R. 1978. Chromosomal evolution in Malagasy lemurs. III. Chromosome banding studies in the genus *Hapalemur* and the species *Lemur catta*. *Cytogenetics and Cell Genetics* 21(4): 201–211.

Rumpler, Y., Couturier, J., Warter, S. and Dutrillaux, B. 1983. Chromosomal evolution in Malagasy lemurs. VII. Phylogenetic relationships between *Propithecus*, *Avahi* (Indriidae), *Microcebus* (Cheirogaleidae), and *Lemur* (Lemuridae). *Cytogenetic and Cell Genetics* 36(3): 542–546.

Rumpler, Y., Ishak, B., Warter, S. and Dutrillaux, B. 1985. Chromosomal evolution in Malagasy lemurs. VIII. Chromosomal banding studies on *Lepilemur ruficaudatus*, *L. leucopus*, and *L. septentrionalis*. *Cytogenetic and Cell Genetics* 39(3): 194–199.

Rumpler, Y., Ishak, B., Dutrillaux, B., Warter, S. and Ratsirarson, J. 1986. Chromosomal evolution in Malagasy lemurs. IX. Chromosomal banding studies on *Lepilemur mustelinus*, *L. dorsalis*, and *L. edwardsi*. *Cytogenetic and Cell Genetics* 42(3): 164–168.

Rumpler, Y., Warter, S., Ishak, B. and Dutrillaux, B. 1988a. Chromosomal variation in Malagasy lemurs. X. Chromosome banding studies of *Propithecus diadema edwardsi* and *Indri indri* and phylogenetic relationships between all the species of the Indriidae. *American Journal of Primatology* 16(1): 63–71.

Rumpler, Y., Warter, S., Petter, J.-J., Albignac, R. and Dutrillaux, B. 1988b. Chromosomal evolution of Malagasy lemurs. XI. Phylogenetic position of *Daubentonia madagascariensis*. *Folia Primatologica* 50(1–2): 124–129.

Rumpler, Y., Warter, S., Ishak, B. and Dutrillaux, B. 1989. Chromosomal evolution in primates. *Human Evolution* 4(2–3): 157–170.

Rumpler, Y., Warter, S., Rabarivola, C., Petter, J.-J. and Dutrillaux, B. 1990. Chromosomal evolution in Malagasy lemurs: XII. Chromosomal banding study of *Avahi laniger occidentalis* (syn: *Lichanotus laniger occidentalis*) and cytogenetic data in favor of its classification in a species apart—*Avahi occidentalis*. *American Journal of Primatology* 21(4): 307–316.

Rumpler, Y., Warter, S., Hauwy, M., Meier, B., Peyriéras, A., Albignac, R., Petter, J.-J. and Dutrillaux, B. 1995. Cytogenetic study of *Allocebus trichotis*, a Malagasy prosimian. *American Journal of Primatology* 36(3): 239–244.

Rumpler, Y., Lernould, J.-M., Nogge, G. and Ceska, V. 1996. A project to create a reserve for *Eulemur macaco flavifrons* in the north-west of Madagascar. *Folia Primatologica* 67(2): 87. Abstract.

Rumpler, Y., Ganzhorn, J. U. Tomiuk, J., Leipoldt, M. and Warter, S. 1998. A cytogenetic study of *Microcebus myoxinus*. *Folia Primatologica* 69(5): 307–311.

Rumpler, Y., Ravaoarimanana, B., Hauwy, M. and Warter, S. 2001. Cytogenetic arguments in favour of taxonomic revision of *Lepilemur septentrionalis* species. *Folia Primatologica* 72(6): 308–315.

Rumpler, Y., Prosper, P., Hauwy, M., Rabarivola, C., Rakotoarisoa, G. and Dutrillaux, B. 2002. Chromosomal evolution of the *Hapalemur griseus* subspecies (Malagasy prosimian), including a new chromosomal polymorphic cytotype. *Chromosome Research* 10: 145–153.

Rumpler, Y., Andriaholinirina, Warter, S., Hauwy, M. and Rabarivola, C. 2004. Phylogenetic history of the sifakas (*Propithecus*: Lemuriformes) derived from cytogenetic studies. *Chromosome Research* 12(5): 453–463.

Rumpler, Y., Warter, S., Hauwy, M., Randrianasolo, V. and Dutrillaux, B. 2005. Cytogenetic study of *Hapalemur aureus*. *American Journal of Physical Anthropology* 86(1): 81–84.

Ruperti, F. S. 2007. Population Density and Habitat Preferences of the Sahamalaza Sportive Lemur (*Lepilemur sahamalazensis*) at the Ankarafa Research Site, NW Madagascar. MSc dissertation, Oxford Brookes University, Oxford, UK.

Russell, R. J. 1977. The behavior, ecology, and environmental physiology of a nocturnal primate, *Lepilemur mustelinus* (Strepsirhini, Lemuriformes, Lepilemuridae). PhD thesis, Duke University, Durham, NC.

Russell, R. J. 1980. The environmental physiology and ecology of *Lepilemur ruficaudatus* (= *L. leucopus*) in arid southern Madagascar. *American Journal of Physical Anthropology* 52: 272–274.

Russell, R. J. and McGeorge, L. 1977. Distribution of *Phaner* (Primates, Lemuriformes, Cheirogaleidae, Phanerinae) in southern Madagascar. *Journal of Biogeography* 4(2): 169–170.

Sabel, J., Green, K., Dawson, J., Robinson, J., Gardner, C., Starkie, G. and D'Cruze, N. 2009. The conservation status of mammals and avifauna in the Montagne des Français massif, *Madagascar. Madagascar Conservation and Development* 4(1): 44–51.

Safford, R. J. and Duckworth, J. W. (eds.) (1989). A wildlife survey of Marojejy Nature Reserve, Madagascar. *International Council for Bird Preservation Study Report* 40: 1–184.

Safford, R. J., Durbin, J. C., and Duckworth, J. W. 1989. Cambridge Madagascar Rain forest Expedition 1988 to RNI No. 12–Marojejy. Unpublished report.

Saint-Pie, J. 1970. Birth and rearing of a brown lemur x red-bellied lemur hybrid *Lemur fulvus* × *L. rubriventer* and breeding of grey gentle lemur *Hapalemur griseus* at Asson Zoo. *International Zoo Yearbook* 10: 71–72.

Santini-Palka, M.-E. 1994. Feeding behaviour and activity patterns of two Malagasy bamboo lemurs, *Hapalemur simus* and *Hapalemur griseus*, in captivity. *Folia Primatologica* 63(1): 44–49.

Santos, L. R., Barnes, J. L. and Nahajan, N. 2005. Expectations about numerical events in four lemur species (*Eulemur fulvus*, *Eulemur mongoz*, *Lemur catta* and *Varecia rubra*). *Animal Cognition* 8(4): 253–262.

Sarikaya, Z. and Kappeler, P. M. 1997. Nest building behavior of Coquerel's dwarf lemur (*Mirza coquereli*). *Primate Report* 47: 3–9.

Sauther, M. L. 1989. Antipredator behavior in troops of free-ranging *Lemur catta* at Beza Mahafaly Special Reserve, Madagascar. *International Journal of Primatology* 10(6): 595–606.

Sauther, M. L. 1991. Reproductive behavior of free-ranging *Lemur catta* at Beza Mahafaly Special Reserve, Madagascar. *Americal Journal of Physical Anthropology* 84(4): 463–477.

Sauther, M. L. 1993. Resource competition in wild populations of ringtailed lemurs (*Lemur catta*): Implications of female dominance. Pp.135–152 in: P. M. Kappeler and J. U. Ganzhorn (eds.), *Lemur Social Systems and their Ecological Basis*. Plenum Press, New York.

Sauther, M. 1998. Interplay of phenology and reproduction in ring-tailed lemurs: implications for ring-tailed lemur conservation. *Folia Primatologica* 69(suppl.1): 309–320.

Sauther, M. L. and Cuozzo, F. P. 2008. Somatic variation in living, wild ring-tailed lemurs (*Lemur catta*). *Folia Primatologica* 79(2): 55–78.

Sauther, M. L., Sussman, R. W. and Gould, L. 1999. The socioecology of the ringtailed lemur: Thirty-five years of research. *Evolutionary Anthropology* 8(4): 120–132.

Sauther, M. L., Cuozzo, F. P. and Sussman, R. W. 2001. Analysis of dentition of a living wild population of ring-tailed lemurs (*Lemur catta*) from Beza Mahafaly, Madagascar. *American Journal of Physical Anthropology* 114(3): 215–223.

Sauther, M. L., Sussman, R. W. and Cuozzo, F. 2002. Dental and general health in a population of wild ring-tailed lemurs: a life history approach. *American Journal of Physical Anthropology* 117(2): 122–132.

Schaaf, C. D. and Stuart, M. D. 1983. Reproduction of the mongoose lemur (*Lemur mongoz*) in captivity. *Zoo Biology* 2(1): 23–38.

Schad, J., Ganzhorn J. U. and Sommer, S. 2005. Parasite burden and constitution of Major Histocompatibility Complex in the Malagasy mouse lemur, *Microcebus murinus*. *Evolution* 59(2): 439–450.

Scheffrahn, W., Rabarivola, C. and Rumpler, Y. 1998. Field studies of population genetics in *Eulemur*: a discussion of their potential importance in conservation. *Folia Primatologica* 69(suppl. 1): 147–151.

Scheffrahn, W., Fausser, L. and Rabarivola, C. 2000. Genetic variation in prosimian species. *International Journal of Primatology* 21(5): 883–887.

Schilling, A. 1980. Seasonal variation and the fecal marking of *Cheirogaleus medius* in simulated climatic conditions. Pp.181–190 in: P. Charles-Dominique, H. M. Cooper, A. Hladik, C. M. Hladik, E. Pagès, G. F. Pariente, A. Petter-Rousseaux, J.-J. Petter and A. Schilling (eds.), *Nocturnal Malagasy Primates: Ecology, Physiology and Behavior*. Academic Press, New York.

Schmid, J. 1998. Tree holes used for resting by gray mouse lemurs (*Microcebus murinus*) in Madagascar: insulation capacities and energetic consequences. *International Journal of Primatology* 19(5): 797–809.

Schmid, J. 1999. Sex-specific differences in activity patterns and fattening in the gray mouse lemur (*Microcebus murinus*) in Madagascar. *Journal of Mammalogy* 80(3): 749–757.

Schmid, J. 2000. Daily torpor in the gray mouse lemur (*Microcebus murinus*) in Madagascar: energetic consequences and biological significance. *Oecologia, Berlin* 123(2):175–183.

Schmid, J. 2001. Daily torpor in free-ranging gray mouse lemurs (*Microcebus murinus*) in Madagascar. *International Journal of Primatology* 22(6): 1021–1031.

Schmid, J. and Alonso, L. E. (eds.). 2005. Une Evaluation Biologique Rapide du Corridor Mantadia-Zahamena, Madagascar. A rapid biological Assessment of the Mantadia-Zahamena Corridor, Madagascar. *RAP Bulletin of Biological Assessment* 32: 1–151.

Schmid, J. and Ganzhorn, J. U. 1996. Resting metabolic rates of *Lepilemur ruficaudatus*. *American Journal of Primatology* 38(2): 169–174.

Schmid, J. and Ganzhorn, J. U. 2009. Optional strategies for reduced metabolism in gray mouse lemurs. *Naturwissenschaften* 96(6): 737–741.

Schmid, J. and Kappeler, P. M. 1994. Sympatric mouse lemurs (*Microcebus* spp.) in western Madagascar. *Folia Primatologica* 63(3): 162–170.

Schmid, J. and Kappeler, P. M. 1998. Fluctuating sexual dimorphism and differential hibernation by sex in a primate, the gray mouse lemur (*Microcebus murinus*). *Behavioral Ecology and Sociobiology* 43: 125–132.

Schmid, J. and Smolker, R. 1998. Lemurs of the Réserve Spéciale d'Anjanaharibe-Sud, Madagascar. *Fieldiana Zoology* 90: 227–240.

Schmid, J., Ruf, T. and Heldmaier, G. 2000. Metabolism and temperature regulation during daily torpor in the smallest primate, the pygmy mouse lemur (*Microcebus myoxinus*) in Madagascar. *Journal of Comparative Physiology* B 170(1): 59–68.

Scholz, F. and Kappeler, P. M. 2004. Effects of seasonal water scarcity on the ranging behavior of *Eulemur fulvus rufus*. *International Journal of Primatology* 25(3): 599–613.

Schülke, O. 2001. Social anti-predator behaviour in a nocturnal lemur. *Folia Primatologica* 72(6): 332–334.

Schülke, O. 2003a. *Phaner furcifer*, fork-marked lemur, *Vakihandry*, *Tanta*. Pp.1318–1320 in: S. M. Goodman and J. P. Benstead (eds.), *The Natural History of Madagascar*. The University of Chicago Press, Chicago.

Schülke, O. 2003b. To breed or not to breed–food competition and other factors involved in female breeding decisions in the pair-living nocturnal fork-marked lemur (*Phaner furcifer*). *Behavioral Ecology and Sociobiology* 55(1): 11–21.

Schülke, O. 2005. Evolution of pair-living in *Phaner furcifer*. *International Journal of Primatology* 26(4): 903–919.

Schülke, O. and Kappeler, P. M. 2003. So near and yet so far: territorial pairs, but low cohesion between pair partners in a nocturnal lemur, *Phaner furcifer*. *Animal Behaviour* 65(2): 331–343.

Schülke, O. and Ostner, J. 2001. Predation on *Lepilemur* by a Harrier Hawk and implications for sleeping site quality. *Lemur News* (6): 5.

Schülke, O. and Ostner, J. 2005. Big times for dwarfs: social organization, sexual selection, and cooperation in the Cheirogaleidae. *Evolutionary Anthropology* 14(5): 170–185.

Schülke, O. and Ostner, J. 2007. Physiological ecology of cheirogaleid primates: variation in hibernation and torpor. *Acta Ethologica* 10(1): 13–21.

Schülke, O., Hilgartner, R. and Zinner, D. 2002. Das nächtliche Leben zweier wenig bekannter Lemurenarten Westmadagaskars. *Zeitschrift des Kölner Zoo* 45(4): 179–194.

Schülke, O., Kappeler, P. M. and Zischler, H. 2004. Small testes size despite high extra-pair paternity in the pair-living nocturnal primate *Phaner furcifer*. *Behavoural Ecology and Sociobiology* 55(3): 293–301.

Schütz, H., and Goodman, S. 1998. Photographic evidence of *Allocebus trichotis* in the Réserve Spéciale d'Anjanaharibe-Sud. *Lemur News* (3): 21–22.

Schwab, D. 2000a. Erratum. *American Journal of Primatology* 51(3): 216.

Schwab, D. 2000b. A preliminary study of spatial distribution and mating system of pygmy mouse lemurs (*Microcebus* cf. *myoxinus*). *American Journal of Primatology* 51(1): 41–60.

Schwab, D. and Ganzhorn, J. U. 2004. Distribution, population structure and habitat use of *Microcebus berthae* compared to those of other sympatric cheirogaleids. *International Journal of Primatology* 25(2): 307–330.

Schwartz, G. T., Mahoney, P., Godfrey, L. R., Cuozzo, F. P., Jungers, W. L. and Randria, G. F. N. 2005. Dental development in *Megaladapis edwardsi* (Primates, Lemuriformes): implications for understanding life history variation in subfossil lemurs. *Journal of Human Evolution* 49(6): 702–721.

Schwartz, J. H. and Tattersall, I. 1985. Evolutionary relationships of living lemurs and lorises (Mammalia, Primates) and their potential affinities with European Eocene Adapidae. *Anthropological Papers of the American Museum of Natural History* 60: 1–100.

Schwarz, E. 1931. A revision of the genera and species of Madagascar Lemuridae. *Proceedings of the Zoological Society of London* (1931): 399–428.

Schwarz, E. 1936. A propos du "*Lemur macaco* " Linnaeus. *Mammalia* 1: 25–26.

Schwitzer, C. 2003. Energy intake and obesity in captive lemurs (Primates, Lemuridae). Dissertation, Universität zu Köln, Köln. Schüling Verlag, Münster.

Schwitzer, C. and Kaumanns, W. 2001a. Body weights of ruffed lemurs (*Varecia variegata*) in European zoos with reference to the problem of obesity. *Zoo Biology* 20(4): 261–9.

Schwitzer, C. and Kaumanns, W. 2001b. European Regional Studbook. 2000 for the ruffed lemur (*Varecia variegata*). Zoologischer Garten Köln, Köln. 131pp.

Schwitzer, C. and Kaumanns, W. 2005. Blue-eyed black lemur (*Eulemur macaco flavifrons* Gray 1867): Perspectives for *in situ*- and *ex situ*-research and conservation activities. *Proceedings of the 2004 WAZA Conference*. EAZA Executive Office, Amsterdam.

Schwitzer, C. and Lork, A. 2004. Projet Sahamalaza–Iles Radama: Ein internationales schutzprojekt für den Sclater's Maki (*Eulemur macaco flavifrons* Gray, 1867). *Zeitschrift des Kölner Zoo* 4 (2): 75–84.

Schwitzer, C., Arnoult, O. and Rakotosamimanana, B. 2006. An international conservation and research programme for Perrier's sifaka (*Propithecus perrieri* Lavauden, 1931) in northern Madagascar. *Lemur News* 11: 12–14.

Schwitzer, C., Moisson, O., Randriatahina, G. H., Volampeno, S., Schwitzer, N. and Rabarivola, C. J. 2009. Sclater's black lemur, blue-eyed black lemur *Eulemur flavifrons* (Gray, 1867). Pp.18–22 in: R.

A. Mittermeier *et al.* (eds.), *Primates in Peril: The World's 25 Most Endangered Primates 2008-2010*. IUCN/SSC Primate Specialist Group, International Primatological Society (IPS), and Conservation International, Arlington, VA.

Schwitzer, N. Randriatahina, G. H., Kaumanns, W., Hoffmeister, D. and Schwitzer, C. 2007a. Habitat utilization of blue-eyed black lemurs, *Eulemur macaco flavifrons* (Gray, 1867), in primary and altered forest fragments. *Primate Conservation* (22): 79–87.

Schwitzer, N., Kaumanns, W., Seitz, P.. and Schwitzer, C. 2007b. Cathemeral activity patternss of the blue-eyed black lemur *Eulemur macaco flavifrons* in intact and degraded forest fragments. *Endangered Species Research* 3: 239–247.

Scotese, C. R. 2000. *PALEOMAP Project: Earth History*. Department of Geology, University of Texas, Arlington. TX.

Seddon, N., Tobias, J., Yount, J. W., Ramanampamonjy, J. R., Butchart, S. and Randrianizahana, H. 2000. Conservation issues and priorities in the Mikea Forest of south-west Madagascar. *Oryx* 34(4): 287–304.

Shapiro, L. J., Seiffert, C. V. M., Godfrey, L. R., Jungers, W. L., Simons, E. L. and Randria, G.F.N. 2005. Morphometric analysis of lumbar vertebrae in extinct Malagasy strepsirrhines. *American Journal of Physical Anthropology* 128(4): 823–839.

Shedd, D. H. and Macedonia, J. M. 1991. Metachromism and its phylogenetic implications for the genus *Eulemur* (Prosimii: Lemuridae). *Folia Primatolgica* 57(4): 221–231.

Simmen, B., Hladik, A. and Ramasiarasoa, P. 2003. Food intake and dietary overlap in native *Lemur catta* and *Propithecus verreauxi* and introduced *Eulemur fulvus* at Berenty, southern Madagascar. *International Journal of Primatology* 24(5): 949–969.

Simmen, B., Sauther, M. L., Soma, T., Rasamimanana, H., Sussman, R. W., Jolly, A., Tarnaud, L. and Hladik, A. 2006a. Plant species fed on by *Lemur catta* in Gallery Forests of the southern domain of Madagascar. Pp.55–68 in: A. Jolly, R. W. Sussman, N. Koyama and H. Rasamimanana (eds.), *Ringtailed Lemur Biology:* Lemur catta *in Madagascar*. Springer, New York.

Simmen, B., Peronny, S., Jeanson, M., Hladik, A. and Marez, A. 2006b. Diet quality and taste perception of plant secondary metabolites by Lemur catta. Pp.160–183 in: A. Jolly, R. W. Sussman, N. Koyama and H. Rasamimanana (eds.), *Ringtailed Lemur Biology:* Lemur catta *in Madagascar.* Springer, New York.

Simmen, B., Bayart, F., Marez, A. and Hladik, A. 2007. Diet, nutritional ecology, and birth season of *Eulemur macaco* in an anthropogenic forest in Madagascar. *International Journal of Primatology* 28(6): 1253–1266.

Simon, N. 1966. *Red Data Book. Volume 1: Mammalia*. International Union for the Conservation of Nature and Natural Resources (IUCN), Morges, Switzerland.

Simons, E. L. 1988. A new species of *Propithecus* (Primates) from northeast Madagascar. *Folia Primatologica* 50(1–2): 143–151.

Simons, E. L. 1993. Discovery of the western aye-aye. *Lemur News* (1): 6.

Simons, E. L. 1994. The giant aye-aye *Daubentonia robusta*. *Folia Primatologica* 62(1–3): 14–21.

Simons, E. L. and Meyers, D. 2001. Folklore and beliefs about the aye-aye (*Daubentonia madagascariensis*). *Lemur News* (6): 11–16.

Simons, E. L. and Rumpler, Y. 1988. *Eulemur*: new generic name for species of *Lemur* other than *Lemur catta*. *Comptes rendus de l'Academie des sciences de Paris, serie 3* 307(9): 547–551.

Simons, E. L., Godfrey, L. R., Jungers, W. L., Chatrath, P. S. and Rakotosamimanana, B. 1992. A new giant subfossil lemur, *Babakotia*, and the evolution of the sloth lemurs. *Folia Primatologica* 58(4): 197–203.

Simons, E. L., Godfrey, L. R., Jungers, W. L., Chatrath, P. S. and Ravaoarisoa, J. 1995. A new species of *Mesopropithecus* (Primates, Palaeopropithecidae) from northern Madagascar. *International Journal of Primatology* 15(5): 653–682.

Simons, E. L., Simons, V. F. H., Chatrath, P. S., Muldoon, K. M., Oliphant, M., Pistole, N. and Savvas, C. 2004. Research on subfossils in southwestern Madagascar and Ankilitelo Cave. *Lemur News* (9): 12–16.

Simons, H. J. 1984. Report on a survey expedition to Natural Reserve No. 3 of Zahamena. Unpublished report.

Simons, H. J. and Lindsay, N. B. D. 1987. Survey work on ruffed lemurs (*Varecia variegata*) and other primates in the northeastern rain forests of Madagascar. *Primate Conservation* (8): 88–91.

Simpson, G. G. 1940. Mammals and land bridges. *Journal of the Washington Academy of Sciences* 30: 137–163.

Simpson, G. G. 1952. Probabilities of dispersal in geologic time. *Bulletin of the American Museum of Natural History* 99: 164-176.

Smith, A. P., Horning, N. and Moore, D. 1997. Regional biodiversity planning and lemur conservation with GIS in western Madagascar. *Conservation Biology* 11(2): 498–512.

Smith, R. J. and Jungers, W. L. 1997. Body mass in comparative primatology. *Journal of Human Evolution* 32(6): 523–559.

Soligo, C. 2005. Anatomy of the hand and arm in *Daubentonia madagascariensis*: a functional and phylogenetic outlook. *Folia Primatologica* 76(5): 262–300.

Soligo, C. and Martin, R. D. 2006. Adaptive origins of primates revisited. *Journal of Human Evolution* 50(4): 414–430.

Soligo, C., Will, O., Tavaré, S., Marshal, C. R. and Martin, R. D. 2007. New light on the dates of primate origins and divergence. Pp.29–49 in M. J. Ravosa, and M. Dagosto (eds.), *Primate Origins: Adaptations and Evolution*. Springer, New York.

Soma, T. 2006. Tradition and novelty: *Lemur catta* feeding strategy on introduced tree species at Berenty Reserve. Pp.141–159 in: A. Jolly, R. W. Sussman, N. Koyama and H. Rasamimanana (eds.), *Ringtailed Lemur Biology: Lemur Catta in Madagascar*. Springer, New York.

Sommerfeld, R., Bauert, M., Hillmann, E. and Stauffacher, M. 2005. Feeding enrichment by self-operated food boxes for white-fronted lemurs (*Eulemur fuluvs albifrons*) in the Masoala exhibit of the Zurich Zoo. *Zoo Biology* 25(2): 145–154.

Standing, H. F. 1903. Rapport sur des ossements sub-fossiles provenant d'Ampasambazimba. *Bulletin de l'Académie malgache* 2: 227–235.

Standing, H. F. 1905. Rapport sur des ossements sub-fossiles provenant d'Ampasambazimba. *Bulletin de l'Académie malgache* 4: 95–100.

Standing, H. F. 1908. On recently discovered subfossil primates from Madagascar. *Transactions of the Zoological Society of London* 18: 59–216.

Standing, H. F. 1909. Subfossiles provenant des fouilles d'Ampasambazimba. *Bulletin de l'Académie malgache* 6: 9–11.

Stanger, K. F. and Macedonia, J. M. 1994. Vocalizations of aye-ayes (*Daubentonia madagascariensis*) in captivity. *Folia Primatologica* 62(1–3): 160–169.

Stanger, K. F., Coffman, B. and Izard, M. 1995. Reproduction in Coquerel's dwarf lemur (*Mirza coquereli*). *American Journal of Primatology* 36(3): 223–237.

Stanger-Hall, K. F. 1997. Phylogenetic affinities among the extant Malagasy lemurs (Lemuriformes) based on morphology and behavior. *Journal of Mammalian Evolution* 4(3): 163–194.

Stankiewicz, J., Thiart, C., Masters, J. C. and de Wit, M. J. 2005. Did lemurs have sweepstake tickets? An exploration of Simpson's model for the colonization of Madagascar by mammals. *Journal of Biogeography* 33: 221–235.

Sterling, E. J. 1992. Timing of reproduction in aye-ayes in Madagascar (abstract). *American Journal of Primatology* 27(1): 59–60. Abstract.

Sterling, E. J. 1993a. Patterns of range use and social organization in aye-ayes (*Daubentonia madagascariensis*) on Nosy Mangabe. Pp.1–10 in: P. M. Kappeler and J. U. Ganzhorn (eds.), *Lemur Social Systems and Their Ecological Basis*. Plenum Press, New York.

Sterling, E. J. 1993b. Behavioral ecology of the aye-aye (*Daubentonia madagascariensis*) on Nosy Mangabe, Madagascar. PhD thesis, Yale University, New Haven, CT.

Sterling, E. J. 1994a. Taxonomy and distribution of *Daubentonia*: a historical perspective. *Folia Primatologica* 62(1–3): 8–13.

Sterling, E. J. 1994b. Aye-ayes: specialists on structurally defended resources. *Folia Primatologica* 62(1–3): 142–152.

Sterling, E. J. 1994c. Evidence for nonseasonal reproduction in wild aye-ayes (*Daubentonia madagascariensis*). *Folia Primatologica* 62(1–3): 46–53.

Sterling, E. J. 1998. Preliminary report on a survey for *Daubentonia madagascariensis* and other primate species in the west of Madagascar, June–August 1994. *Lemur News* (3): 7–8.

Sterling, E. J. 2003. *Daubentonia madagascariensis*, aye-aye, *aye-aye*. Pp.1348–1351 in: S. M. Goodman and J. P. Benstead (eds.), *The Natural History of Madagascar*. The University of Chicago Press, Chicago.

Sterling, E. J. and McFadden, K. 2000. Rapid census of lemur populations in Parc National de Marojejy, Madagascar. *Fieldiana Zoology* 90: 227–240.

Sterling, E. J. and Povinelli, D. J. 1999. Tool use, aye-ayes, and sensorimotor intelligence. *Folia Primatologica* 70(1): 8–16.

Sterling, E. J. and Rakotoarison, N. 1998. Rapid assessment of richness and density of primate species on the Masoala peninsula, eastern Madagascar. *Folia Primatologica* 69(suppl. 1): 109–116.

Sterling, E. J. and Ramaroson, M. G. 1996. Rapid assessment of the primate fauna of the eastern slopes of the Réserve Naturelle Intégrale d'Andringitra, Madagascar. Pp. 293–305 in: S. M. Goodman (ed.), *A Floral and Faunal Inventory of the Eastern Slopes of the Réserve Naturelle Intégrale d'Andringitra, Madagascar: with Reference to Elevational Variation. Fieldiana Zoology, new series* 85: 293–305.

Sterling, E. J. and Richard, A. F. 1995. Social organization in the aye-aye (*Daubentonia madagascariensis*) and the perceived distinctiveness of nocturnal primates. Pp.439–451 in: L. Alterman, G. A. Doyle and M. K. Izard (eds.), *Creatures of the Dark: The Nocturnal Prosimians*. Plenum Press, New York.

Sterling, E. J., Dierenfeld, E. S., Ashbourne, C. J. and Feistner, A.T. C. 1994. Dietary intake, food composition and nutrient intake in wild and captive populations of *Daubentonia madagascariensis*. *Folia Primatologica* 62(1–3): 115–124.

Stevens, N. and Heesy, C. 2006. Malagasy primate origins: phylogenies, fossils and biogeographic reconstructions. *Folia Primatologica* 77(6): 419–433.

Stuenes, S. 1989. Taxonomy, habits and relationships of the sub-fossil Madagascan hippopotamuses *Hippopotamus lemerlei* and *H. madagascariensis*. *Journal of Vertebrate Paleontology* 9: 241–268.

Sussman, R. W. 1974. Ecological distinctions in sympatric species of *Lemur*. Pp.75–108 in: R. D. Martin, G. A. Doyle and A. C. Walker (eds.), *Prosimian Biology*. Duckworth, London.

Sussman, R. W. 1975. A preliminary study of the behavior and ecology of *Lemur fulvus rufus* Audebert 1800. Pp.237–258 in: I. Tattersall and R. W. Sussman (eds.), *Lemur Biology*. Plenum Press, New York.

Sussman, R. W. 1977. Distribution of Malagasy lemurs. Part 2: *Lemur catta* and *Lemur fulvus* in southern and western Madagascar. *Annals of the New York Academy of Sciences* 293: 170–183.

Sussman, R. W. 1991. Demography and social organization of free-ranging *Lemur catta* in the Beza Mahafaly Reserve, Madagascar. *American Journal of Physical Anthropology* 84(1): 43–58.

Sussman, R. W. 1992. Male life history and intergroup mobility among ringtailed lemurs (*Lemur catta*). *International Journal of Primatology* 13(4): 395–410.

Sussman, R. W. 2002. Adaptive array of lemurs of Madagascar revisited. *Evolutionary Anthropology* 11(suppl.1): 75–78.

Sussman, R. W. 2003. Social behavior and aggression among ringtailed lemurs. *Folia Primatologica* 74(3): 168–172.

Sussman, R. W. and Richard, A. 1986. Lemur conservation in Madagascar: the status of lemurs in the south. *Primate Conservation* (7): 85–92.

Sussman, R. W. and Tattersall, I. 1976. Cycles of activity, group composition and diet of *Lemur mongoz* Linnaeus 1766 in Madagascar. *Folia Primatologica* 26(4): 270–283.

Sussman, R. W., Richard, A. F. and Ravelojaona, G. 1985. Madagascar: current projects and problems in conservation. *Primate Conservation* (5): 53–58.

Sussman, R. W., Richard, A. F. and Rakotamanga, P. 1987. La conservation des lémuriens à Madagascar: leur statut dans le sud. Pp. 75–81 in: Mittermeier, R. A., Rakotovao, L. H., Randrianasolo, V., Sterling, E. J. and Devitre, D. (eds.), *Priorités en Matière de Conservation des Espèces à Madagascar*. *Occasional Papers of the IUCN Species Survival Commission (SSC)*, No. 2. Gland, Switzerland.

Sussman, R. W., Green, G. M., Porton, I., Andrianasolondraibe, O. L. and Ratsirarson, J. 2003. A survey of habitat of *Lemur catta* in southwestern and southern Madagascar. *Primate Conservation* (19): 32–57.

Takahata, Y., Koyama, N., Ichino, S., Miyamoto, N. and Nakamichi, M. 2006. Influence of group size on reproductive success of female ringtailed lemurs: distinguishing between IGFC and PFC hypotheses. *Primates* 47(4): 383–387.

Takahata, Y., Koyama, N., Ichino, S., Miyamoto, N., Nakamichi, M. and Soma, T. 2008. The relationship between female rank and reproductive parameters of the ringtailed lemur: a preliminary analyses. *Primates* 49(2): 135–138.

Tan, C. L. 1999. Group composition, home range size, and diet in three sympatric bamboo lemur species (genus *Hapalemur*) in Ranomafana National Park, Madagascar. *International Journal of Primatology* 20(4): 547–566.

Tan, C. L. 2000. Behavior and ecology of three sympatric bamboo lemur species (genus *Hapalemur*) in Ranomafana National Park, Madagascar. PhD thesis, State University of New York, Stony Brook, NY.

Tanaka, M. 2007. Habitat use and social structure of a brown lemur hybrid population in the Berenty Reserve, Madagascar. *American Journal of Primatology* 69(10): 1189–1194.

Tarnaud, L. 2004. Ontogeny of feeding behavior of *Eulemur fulvus* in the dry forest of Mayotte. *International Journal of Primatology* 25(4): 803–824.

Tarnaud, L. 2006. Cathemerality in the Mayotte brown lemur (*Eulemur fulvus*): seasonality and food quality. *Folia Primatologica* 77(1–2): 166–177.

Tarnaud, L. and Simmen, B. 2002. A major increase in the population of brown lemurs on Mayotte since the decline reported in 1987. *Oryx* 36(3): 297–300.

Tattersall, I. 1971. Revision of the subfossil Indriinae. *Folia Primatologica* 16: 257–269.

Tattersall, I. 1973a. Cranial anatomy of the Archaeolemurinae (Lemuroidea, Primates). *Anthropological Papers of the American Museum of Natural History* (52): 1–110.

Tattersall, I. 1973b. Subfossil lemuroids and the 'adaptive radiation' of the Malagasy lemurs. *Transactions of the New York Academy of Sci*ence 35: 314–324.

Tattersall, I. 1976a. Group structure and activity rhythm in *Lemur mongoz* (Primates, Lemuriformes) on Anjouan and Mohéli Islands, Comoro Archipelago. *Anthropological Papers of the American Museum of Natural History* 53(2): 367–380.

Tattersall, I. 1976b. Note sur la distribution et sur la situation actuelle de lémuriens des Comores. *Mammalia* 40(3): 519–521.

Tattersall, I. 1977a. Distribution of the Malagasy lemurs, Part 1: The lemurs of northern Madagascar. *Annals of the New York Academy of Sciences* 293: 160–169.

Tattersall, I. 1977b. The lemurs of the Comoro Islands. *Oryx* 13(5): 445–448.

Tattersall, I. 1977c. Behavioral variation in *Lemur mongoz* (= *Lemur m. mongoz*). Pp.127–132 in: D. J. Chivers and K. A. Joysey (eds.), *Recent Advances in Primatology*. Academic Press, London.

Tattersall, I. 1977d. Ecology and behavior of *Lemur fulvus mayottensis* (Primates, Lemuriformes). *Anthropological Papers of the American Museum of Natural History* 54(4): 423–482.

Tattersall, I. 1977e. Patterns of activity in the Mayotte lemur, *Lemur fulvus mayottensis*. *Journal of Mammalogy* 60(2): 314–323.

Tattersall, I. 1982. *The Primates of Madagascar*. Columbia University Press, New York.

Tattersall, I. 1983. Status of the Comoro lemurs: a reappraisal. *IUCN/SSC Primate Specialist Group Newsletter* (3): 24–26.

Tattersall, I. 1986. Notes on the distribution and taxonomic status of some species of *Propithecus* in Madagascar. *Folia Primatologica* 46(1): 51–63.

Tattersall, I. 1987. Cathemeral activity in primates: a definition. *Folia Primatologica* 49(3): 200–202.

Tattersall, I. 1998. Lemurs of the Comoro Archipelago: status of *Eulemur mongoz* on Mohéli and Anjouan, and of *Eulemur fulvus* on Mayotte. *Lemur News* (3): 15–17.

Tattersall, I. 2007. Madagascar's lemurs: cryptic diversity or taxonomic inflation? *Evolutionary Anthropology* 16: 12–23.

Tattersall, I. and Schwartz, J. H. 1974. Craniodental morphology and the systematics of the Malagasy lemurs (Primates, Prosimii). *Anthropological Papers of the American Nuseum of Natural History* 52(3): 141–192.

Tattersall, I. and Schwartz, J. H. 1991. Phylogeny and nomenclature in the Lemur-group of Malagasy strepsirhine primates. *Anthropological Papers of the American Museum of Natural History* 69: 1–18.

Tattersall, I. and Sussman, R. W. 1975. Observations on the ecology and behavior of the mongoose lemur *Lemur mongoz mongoz* Linnaeus (Primates, Lemuriformes) at Ampijoroa, Madagascar. *Anthropological Papers of the American Nuseum of Natural History* 52(4): 195–216.

Tattersall, I. and Sussman, R. W. 1998. "Little brown lemurs" of northern Madagascar. *Folia Primatologica* 69(suppl. 1): 379–388.

Tavaré, S., Marshall, C. R., Will, O., Soligo, C. and Martin, R. D. 2002. Using the fossil record to estimate the age of the last common ancestor of extant primates. *Nature, London* 416: 726–729

Taylor, L. and Sussman, R. W. 1985. A preliminary study of kinship and social organization in a semi-free-ranging group of *Lemur catta*. *International Journal of Primatology* 6(6): 601–614.

Taylor, T. D. and Feistner, A. T. C. 1996. Infant rearing in captive *Hapalemur griseus alaotrensis*: singleton versus twins. *Folia Primatologica* 67(1): 44–51.

Teelen, S. 1996. Tourism in the Kirindy Forest, Western Madagascar. MSc thesis, Durrell Institute of Conservation and Ecology, University of Kent, Canterbury, UK.

Terranova, C. J. 1996. Variation in the leaping of lemurs. *American Journal of Primatology* 40(2): 145–165.

Terranova, C. J. and Coffman, B. S. 1997. Body weights of wild and captive lemurs. *Zoo Biology* 16(1): 17–30.

Thalmann, U. 2001. Food resource characteristics in two nocturnal lemurs with different social behavior: *Avahi occidentalis* and *Lepilemur edwardsi*. *International Journal of Primatology* 22(2): 287–324.

Thalmann, U. 2002. Contrasts between two nocturnal leaf-eating lemurs. *Evolutionary Anthropology* 11(suppl. 1): 105–107.

Thalmann, U. 2003. *Avahi*, woolly lemurs, *avahy*, *fotsy-fe*, *ampongy*, *tsarafangitra*, *dadintsifaky*. Pp.1340–1342 in: S. M. Goodman and J. P. Benstead (eds.), *The Natural History of Madagascar*. The University of Chicago Press, Chicago.

Thalmann, U. and Ganzhorn, J. U. 2003. *Lepilemur*, sportive lemur. Pp.1336–1340 in: S. M. Goodman and J. P, Benstead (eds.), *The Natural History of Madagascar*. The University of Chicago Press, Chicago.

Thalmann, U. and Geissmann, T. 2000. Distribution and geographic variation in the western woolly lemur (*Avahi occidentalis*) with description of a new species (*A. unicolor*). *International Journal of Primatology* 21(6): 915–941.

Thalmann, U. and Geissmann, T. 2005. New species of woolly lemur *Avahi* (Primates: Lemuriformes) in Bemaraha (central western Madagascar). *American Journal of Primatology* 67(3): 371–376.

Thalmann, U. and Geissmann, T. 2006. Conservation assessment of the recently described John Cleese's woolly lemur, *Avahi cleesei* (Lemuriformes, Indirdae). *Primate Conservation* (21): 45–49.

Thalmann, U. and Rakotoarison, N. 1994. Distribution of lemurs in central western Madagascar, with a regional distribution hypothesis. *Folia Primatologica* 63: 156–161.

Thalmann, U., Geissmann, T., Simona, A. and Mutschler, T. 1993. The indris of Anjanaharibe-Sud, northeastern Madagascar. *International Journal of Primatology* 14(3): 357–381.

Thalmann, U., Muller, A. E. , Kerloc'h, P. and Zaramody, A. 1999. A visit to the Strict Nature Reserve Tsingy de Namoroka (NW Madagascar). *Lemur News* (4): 16–19.

Thalmann, U., Kümmerli, R. and Zaramody, A. 2002. Why *Propithecus verreauxi deckeni* and *P. v. coronatus* are valid taxa–quantitative and qualitative arguments. *Lemur News* (7): 11–16.

Tilden, C. D. 1990. A study of locomotor behavior in a captive colony of red-bellied lemurs (*Eulemur rubriventer*). *American Journal of Primatology* 22(2): 87–100.

Tokiniaina, H., Bailey, C. A., Shore, G. D., Delmore, K. E., Johnson, S. E., Louis Jr., E.E. and Brenneman, R. A. 2009. Characterization of 18 microsatellite marker loci in the white-collared lemur (*Eulemur cinereiceps*). *Conservation Genetics* 10(5): 1459–1462.

Tombomiadana, S. and Rakotodravony, R. 2000. Inventaire des lémuriens de la Réserve Spéciale de Marotandrano. *Lemur News* (5): 35–36.

Tomiuk, J., Bachmann, L., Leipoldt, M., Ganzhorn, J. U., Ries, R., Weis, M. and Loeschcke, V. 1997. Genetic diversity of *Lepilemur mustelinus ruficaudatus*, a nocturnal lemur of Madagascar. *Conservation Biology* 11 (2): 491–497.

Tomiuk, J., Bachmann, L., Leipoldt, M., Atsalis, S., Kappeler, P. M., Schmid, J. and Ganzhorn, J. U. 1998. The impact of genetics on the conservation of Malagasy lemur species. *Folia Primatologica* 69(suppl.1): 121–126.

Traber, S. Y. and Müller, A. E. 2006. A note on the activity cycle of captive white-fronted lemurs (*Eulemur fulvus albifrons*). *Folia Primatologica* 77(1–2): 139–142.

Trillmich, J., Fichtel, C. and Kappeler, P. M. 2004. Coordination of group movements in wild Verreaux's sifakas (*Propithecus verreauxi*). *Behaviour* 141(9): 1103–1120.

Turvey, T. (ed.). 2009. *Holocene Extinctions*. Oxford University Press, Oxford.

Van Horn, R. N. 1975. Primate breeding season: photoperiodic regulation in captive *Lemur catta*. *Folia Primatologica* 24(2–3): 203–220.

Vargas, A. Jiménez, I., Palomares, F. and Palacios, M. J. 2002. Distribution, status, and conservation needs of the golden-crowned sifaka (*Propithecus tattersalli*). *Biological Conservation* 108(3): 325–334.

Vasey, N. 1996. Clinging to life: *Varecia variegata rubra* and the Masoala coastal forests. *Lemur News* (2): 7–9.

Vasey, N. 1997a. Community ecology and behavior of *Varecia variegata rubra* and *Lemur fulvus albifrons* on the Masoala Peninsula, Madagascar. PhD thesis, Washington University, St. Louis, MO.

Vasey, N. 1997b. How many red ruffed lemurs are left? *International Journal of Primatology* 18(2): 207–216.

Vasey, N. 1997c. The cooperative breeding system of *Varecia variegata. American Journal of Physical Anthropology* 24 (suppl.): 232. Abstract.

Vasey, N. 1999. Positional behavior of *Varecia variegate rubra* and *Lemur fulvus albifrons. American Journal of Physical Anthropology* 24(suppl.): 270. Abstract.

Vasey, N. 2000a. Niche separation in *Varecia variegata rubra* and *Eulemur fulvus albifrons*: I. Interspecific patterns. *American Journal of Physical Anthropology* 112: 411–431.

Vasey, N. 2000b. Plant species composition of diet in two sympatric lemurs: *Varecia variegata rubra* and *Eulemur fulvus albifrons. American Journal of Physical Anthropology* 30(suppl.): 309–310. Abstract.

Vasey, N. 2002. Niche separation in *Varecia variegata rubra* and *Eulemur fulvus albifrons*: II. Intraspecific patterns. *American Journal of Physical Anthropology* 118: 169–183.

Vasey, N. 2003. *Varecia*, ruffed lemurs. Pp. 1332–1336 in: S. M. Goodman and J. P. Benstead (eds.), *The Natural History of Madagascar*. The University of Chicago Press, Chicago.

Vasey, N. 2004. Circadian rhythms in diet and habitat use in red ruffed lemurs (*Varecia rubra*) and white-fronted brown lemurs (*Eulemur fulvus albifrons*). *American Journal of Physical Anthropology* 124(4): 353–363.

Vasey, N. 2005a. New developments in the behavioral ecology and conservation of ruffed lemurs (*Varecia*). *American Journal of Primatology* 66(1): 1–6.

Vasey, N. 2005b. Activity budgets and activity rhythms in red ruffed lemurs (*Varecia rubra*) on the Masoala Peninsula, Madagascar: seasonality and reproductive energetics. *American Journal of Primatology* 66(1): 23–44.

Vasey, N. 2006. Impact of seasonality and reproduction on social structure, ranging patterns, and fission-fusion social organization in red ruffed lemurs. Pp.275–304 in: L. Gould and M. Sauther (eds.), *Lemurs: Ecology and Adaptation*. Springer, New York.

Vasey, N. 2007. The breeding system of wild red ruffed lemurs (*Varecia rubra*): a preliminary report. *Primates* 48(1): 41–54.

Vasey, N. and Tattersall, I. 2002. Do ruffed lemurs form a hybrid zone? Distribution and discovery of *Varecia*, with systematic and conservation implications. *American Museum Novitates* (3376): 1–26.

Ventura, M., Boniotto, M., Cardone, M.F., Fulizio, L., Archidiacono, N., Rocchi, M. and Crovella, S. 2001. Characterization of a highly repeated DNA sequence family in five species of the genus *Eulemur. Gene* 275(2): 305–310.

Vick, L. G. and Conley, J. M. 1976. An ethogram for *Lemur fulvus. Primates* 17(2): 125–144.

Vick, L. G. and Pereira, M. E. 1989. Episodic targeting aggression and the history of *Lemur* social groups. *Behavioral Ecology and Sociobiology* 25(1): 3–12.

Vick, L. G., Pereira, M. E., Izard, M. K. and Taub, D. M. 1989. Seasonal changes in body weight and testicular volume in male *Lemur catta. American Journal of Primatology* 18(2): 167. Abstract.

Vuillaume-Randriamanantena, M. 1988. The taxonomic attributions of giant sub-fossil lemur bones from Ampasambazimba: *Archaeoindris* and *Lemuridotherium. Journal of Human Evolution* 17(4): 379–391.

Vuillaume-Randriamanantena, M. 1990. *Palaeopropithecus ingens* Grandidier, 1899 synonyme de *Thaumastolemur grandidieri* Filhol, 1895. *Comptes rendus de l'Académie des sciences de Paris* 310(9): 1307–1313.

Vuillaume-Randriamanantena, M., Godfrey, L. R. and Sutherland, M. R. 1985. Revision of *Hapalemur* (*Prohapalemur*) *gallieni* (Standing 1905). *Folia Primatologica* 45(2): 89–116.

Vuillaume-Randriamanantena, M., Godfrey, L. R., Jungers, W. L. and Simons, E. L. 1992. Morphology, taxonomy and distribution of *Megaladapis*: giant subfossil lemur from Madagascar. *Comptes rendus de l'Académie des sciences de Paris* 315(13): 1835–1842.

Waeber, P. O. and Hemelrijk, C. K. 2003. Female dominance and social structure in Alaotran gentle lemurs. *Behaviour* 140(10): 1235–1246.

Walker, A. C. 1967. Locomotor adaptation in recent and fossil Madagascan lemurs. PhD thesis, University of London, London, UK.

Walker, A. C., Ryan, T. M., Silcox, M. T., Simons, E. L. and Spoor, F. 2008. The semicircular canal system and locomotion: the case of extinct lemuroids and lorisoids. *Evolutionary Anthropology* 17(3): 135–145.

Ward, S. C. and Sussman, R. W. 1979. Correlates between locomotor anatomy and behavior in two sympatric species of *Lemur*. *American Journal of Physical Anthropology* 50(4): 575–590.

Warren, R. D. 1997. Habitat use and support preference of two free-ranging saltatory lemurs (*Lepilemur edwardsi* and *Avahi occidentalis*). *Jounal of Zoology, London* 241(2): 325–341.

Warren, R. D. and Crompton, R. H. 1997a. A comparative study of the ranging behavior, activity rhythms and sociality of *Lepilemur edwardsi* (Primates, Lepilemuridae) and *Avahi occidentalis* (Primates, Indriidae) at Ampijoroa, Madagascar. *Journal of Zoology, London* 243(2): 397–415.

Warren, R. D. and Crompton, R. H. 1997b. Locomotor ecology of *Lepilemur edwardsi* and *Avahi occidentalis*. *American Journal of Physical Anthropology* 104(4): 471–486.

Warter, S. and Tattersall, I. 1994. Update on the article "Cytogenetic study of a new species of *Hapalemur griseus.*" *Folia Primatologica* 63(3): 170.

Warter, S., Randrianasolo, G., Dutrillaux, B. and Rumpler, Y. 1987. Cytogenetic study of a new subspecies of *Hapalemur griseus*. *Folia Primatologica* 48(1): 50–55.

Warter, S., Hauwy, M., Dutrillaux, B. and Rumpler, Y. 2005. Application of molecular cytogenetics for chromosomal evolution of the Lemuriformes (prosimians). *Cytogenetic and Genome Research* 108: 197–203.

Weidt, A., Hagenah, N., Randrianambinina, B., Radespiel, U. and Zimmermann, E. 2004. Social organization of the golden brown mouse lemur (*Microcebus ravelobensis*). *American Journal of Physical Anthropology* 123(1): 40–51.

Weisrock, D. W., Rasoloarison, R. M., Fiorentino, I., Ralison, J. M., Goodman, S. M., Kappeler, P. M. and Yoder, A. D. Delimiting species without nuclear monophyly in Madagascar's mouse lemurs. *PLoS One* 5(3): e9883. doi:10.1371/journal.pone.0009883.

White, F. J. 1989. Diet, ranging behavior and social organization of the black-and-white ruffed lemur, *Varecia variegata variegata*, in southeastern Madagascar. *American Journal of Physical Anthropology* 78(2): 323. Abstract.

White, F. J. 1991. Social organization, feeding ecology, and reproductive strategy of ruffed lemurs, *Varecia variegata*. Pp.81–84 in: A. Ehara, T. Kimura, O. Takenaka and M. Iwamoto (eds.), *Primatology Today* (eds.). Elsevier, Amsterdam.

White, F. J., Burton, A., Buchholz, S. and Glander, K. 1992. Social organization of free-ranging ruffed lemurs, *Varecia variegata variegata*: mother–adult daughter relationship. *American Journal of Primatology* 28(4): 281–287.

White, F. J., Overdorff, D. J., Balko, E. and Wright, P. C. 1995. Distribution of ruffed lemurs (*Varecia variegata*) in Ranomafana National Park, Madagascar. *Folia Primatologica* 64(3): 124–131.

Wilme, L. and Callmander, M. W. 2006. Relic populations of primates: sifakas. *Lemur News* (11): 24–31.

Wilson, J. M. 1995. *Lemurs of the Lost World: Exploring the Forests and Crocodile Caves of Madagascar*. 2nd edition. Impact Books, London.

Wilson, J. M., Stewart, P. D. and Fowler, S. V. 1988. Ankarana—a rediscovered nature reserve in northern Madagascar. *Oryx* 22(3): 163–171.

Wilson, J. M., Stewart, P. D., Ramangason, G.-S., Denning, A. M. and Hutchings, M. S. 1989. Ecology and conservation of the crowned lemur, *Lemur coronatus*, at Ankarana, N. Madagascar, with notes on Sanford's lemur, other sympatrics and subfossil lemurs. *Folia Primatologica* 52(1–2): 1–26.

Wilson, J. M., Godfrey, L. R., Simons, E. L., Stewart, P. D. and Vuillaume-Randriamanantena, M. 1995. Past and present lemur fauna at Ankarana, north Madagascar. *Primate Conservation* (16): 47–52.

Wilson, W. A. 1975. Discriminative conditioning of vocalizations in *Lemur catta*. *Animal Behaviour* 23: 432–436.

Wimmer, B., Tautz, D. and Kappeler, P. M. 2002. The genetic population structure of the grey mouse lemur, *Microcebus murinus*, a basal primate from Madagascar. *Behavioral Ecology and Sociobiology* 52: 166–175.

Winn, R. M. 1989. The aye-ayes, *Daubentonia madagascariensis*, at the Paris Zoological Garden: maintenance and preliminary behavioural observations. *Folia Primatologica* 52(3–4): 109–123.

Winn, R. M. 1994a. Development of behaviour in a young aye-aye (*Daubentonia madagascariensis*) in captivity. *Folia Primatologica* 62(1–3): 93–107.

Winn, R. M. 1994b. Preliminary study of the sexual behaviour of three aye-ayes (*Daubentonia madagascariensis*) in captivity. *Folia Primatologica* 62(1–3): 63–73.

World Bank, USAID, Coopération Suisse, UNESCO, UNDP and WWF. 1988. National Environmental Action Plan – Document de synthèse générale et propositions d'orientations. Report E 0021, Government of Madagascar, Antananarivo.

Wright, P. C. 1986. Diet, ranging behavior and activity pattern of the gentle lemur (*Hapalemur griseus*) in Madagascar. *American Journal of Physical Anthropology* 69(2): 283.

Wright, P. C. 1987. Diet and ranging patterns of *Propithecus diadema edwardsi*. *American Journal of Physical Anthropology* 72(2): 271. Abstract.

Wright, P. C. 1988. Social behavior of *Propithecus diadema edwardsi* in Madagascar. *American Journal of Physical Anthropology* 75(1–4): 269. Abstract.

Wright, P. C. 1989. Comparative ecology of three sympatric bamboo lemurs in Madagascar. *American Journal of Physical Anthropology* 78(2): 327. Abstract.

Wright, P. C. 1990. Patterns of paternal care in primates. *International Journal of Primatology* 11: 89–102.

Wright, P. C. 1992. Primate ecology, rain forest conservation, and economic development: building a national park in Madagascar. *Evolutionary Anthropology* 1(1): 25–33.

Wright, P. C. 1995. Demography and life history of free-ranging *Propithecus diadema edwardsi* in

Ranomafana National Park, Madagascar. *International Journal of Primatology* 16(5): 835–854.

Wright, P. C. 1998. Impact of predation on the behaviour of *Propithecus diadema edwardsi* in the rain forest of Madagascar. *Behaviour* 135(4): 483–512.

Wright, P. C. 1999. Lemur traits and Madagascar ecology: coping with an island environment. *Yearbook of Physical Anthropology* 42: 31–72.

Wright, P. C. and Martin, L. B. 1995. Predation, pollination and torpor in two nocturnal prosimians: *Cheirogaleus major* and *Microcebus rufus* in the rain forest of Madagascar. Pp.45–60 in: L. Alterman, G. A. Doyle and M. K. Izard (eds.), *Creatures of the Dark: The Nocturnal Prosimians*. Plenum Press, New York.

Wright, P. C. and Porter, A. 2004. Investigation into new primate species in Kalambatritra Reserve and Midongy du Sud National Park rain forests in south central Madagascar. Report to Conservation International, Washington, DC.

Wright, P. C., Daniels, P. S., Meyers, D. M., Overdorff, D. J. and Rabesoa, J. 1987. A census and study of *Hapalemur* and *Propithecus* in southeastern Madagascar. *Primate Conservation* (8): 84–87.

Wright, P. C., Heckscher, S. K. and Dunham, A. E. 1997. Predation on Milne-Edwards' sifaka (*Propithecus diadema edwardsi*) by the fossa (*Cryptoprocta ferox*) in the rain forest of southeastern Madagascar. *Folia Primatologica* 68(1): 34–43.

Wright, P. C., Johnson, S. E., Irwin, M. T., Jacobs, R., Schlicting, P., Lehman, S., Louis, E. E. Jr., Arrigo-Nelson, S. J., Raharison, J.-L., Rafaliarison, R., Razafindratsita, V., Ratsimbazafy, J., Ratelolahy, F. J., Dolch, R. and Tan, C. 2008. The crisis of the critically endangered greater bamboo lemur (*Prolemur simus*). *Primate Conservation* (23): 5–17.

Wright, P. C., Larney, E., Louis Jr. E. E., Dolch, R. and Rafaliarison, R. R. 2009. Greater bamboo lemur *Prolemur simus* (Gray, 1871). Pp.11-14 in: R. A. Mittermeier *et al.* (eds.), *Primates in Peril: The World's 25 Most Endangered Primates 2008-2010*. IUCN/SSC Primate Specialist Group, International Primatological Society (IPS), and Conservation International, Arlington, VA.

Wrogemann, D. and Glatston, A. 2001. Mouse lemur biology in breeding colonies: introduction. *Biomedical and Life Sciences* 22(1): 1–3.

Wrogemann, D. and Zimmermann, E. 2001. Aspects of reproduction in the eastern rufous mouse lemur (*Microcebus rufus*) and their implications for captive management. *Zoo Biology* 20(3): 157–167.

Wrogemann, D., Radespiel, U. and Zimmermann, E. 2001. Comparison of reproductive characteristics and changes in body weight between captive populations of rufous and gray mouse lemurs. *International Journal of Primatology* 22(1): 91–108.

Wunderlich, R. E., Simons, E. L. and Jungers, W. L. 1996. New pedal remains of *Megaladapis* and their functional significance. *American Journal of Physical Anthropology* 100: 115–139.

Wyner, Y. M., Amato, G. and Desalle, R. 1999a. Captive breeding, reintroduction, and the conservation genetics of black and white ruffed lemurs, *Varecia variegata variegata*. *Molecular Ecology* 8(12 suppl.): 107–115.

Wyner, Y. M., Absher, R., Amato, G., Sterling, E., Stumpf, R., Rumpler, Y. and DeSalle, R. 1999b. Species concepts and the determination of historic gene flow patterns in the *Eulemur fulvus* (brown lemur) complex. *Biological Journal of the Linnean Society* 66(1): 39–56.

Wyner, Y. M., DeSalle, R. and Absher, R. 2000. Phylogeny and character behavior in the family Lemuridae. *Molecular Phylogenetics and Evolution* 15(1): 124–134.

Wyner, Y. M., Johnson, S. E., Stumpf, R. M. and DeSalle, R. 2002. Genetic assessment of a white-collared × red-fronted lemur hybrid zone at Andringitra, Madagascar. *American Journal of Primatology* 57(2): 51–66.

Yamashita, N. 1996. Seasonality and site specificity of mechanical dietary patterns in two Malagasy lemur families (Lemuridae and Indriidae). *International Journal of Primatology* 17(3): 355–387.

Yamashita, N. 2002. Diets of two lemur species in different microhabitats in Beza Mahafaly Special Reserve, Madagascar. *International Journal of Primatology* 23(5): 1025–1051.

Yamashita, N., Vinyard, C. and Tan, C. 2008. Food mechanical properties in three sympatric species of *Hapalemur* in Ranomafana National Park, Madagascar. *American Journal of Physical Anthropology* 139(3): 368–381.

Yoder, A. D. 1994. Relative position of the Cheirogaleidae in strepsirhine phylogeny: a comparison of morphological and molecular methods and results. *American Journal of Physical Anthropology* 94(1): 25–46.

Yoder, A. D. 1996. Pilot study to determine the status of *Allocebus trichotis* in Madagascar. *Lemur News* (2): 14–15.

Yoder, A. D. 2001. Ancient DNA from *Megaladapis edwardsi*. *Folia Primatologica* 72(6): 342–344.

Yoder, A. D. and Irwin, J. A. 1999. Phylogeny of the Lemuridae: effects of character and taxon sampling on resolution of species relationships within *Eulemur*. *Cladistics* 15(3): 351.

Yoder, A. D. and Nowak, M. D. 2006. Has vicariance or dispersal been the predominant biogeographic force in Madagascar? Only time will tell. *Annual Review of Ecology and Systematics* 37: 405–431.

Yoder, A. D. and Yang, Z. 2004. Divergence dates for Malagasy lemurs estimated from multiple gene loci: geological and evolutionary context. *Molecular Ecology* 13(4): 757–773.

Yoder, A. D., Cartmill, M., Ruvolo, M., Smith, K. and Vilgalys, R. 1996. Ancient single origin for Malagasy lemurs. *Proceedings of the National Academy of Sciences* 93: 5122–5126.

Yoder, A. D., Irwin, J. A., Goodman, S. M. and Rakotoarisoa, S. V. 1999a. *Lemur catta* from the Andringitra Massif are *Lemur catta*. *Lemur News* (4): 32–33.

Yoder, A.D., Rakotosamimanana, B. and Parsons, T. J. 1999b. Ancient DNA in subfossil lemurs. Pp.1-17 in: B. Rakotosamimanana, H. Rasamimanana, J. U. Ganzhorn and S. M. Goodman (eds.), *New Directions In Lemur Studies*. Kluwer/Plenum, New York.

Yoder, A. D., Irwin, J. A., Goodman, S. M. and Rakotoarisoa, S. V. 2000a. Genetic tests of the taxonomic status of the ring-tailed lemur (*Lemur catta*) from the high mountain zone of the Andringitra Massif, Madagascar. *Journal of Zoology, London* 252: 1–9.

Yoder, A. D., Rasoloarison, R. M., Goodman, S. M., Irwin, J. A., Atsalis, S., Ravosa, M. J. and Ganzhorn, J. U. 2000b. Remarkable species diversity in Malagasy mouse lemurs (Primates, *Microcebus*). *Proceedings of the National Academy of Sciences* 97(21): 11325–11330.

Yoder, A. D., Burns, M. M. and Genin, F. 2002. Molecular evidence of reproductive isolation in sympatric sibling species of mouse lemurs. *International Journal of Primatology* 23(6): 1335–1343.

Zapfe, H. von. 1963. Lebensbild von *Megaladapis edwardsi* (Grandidier). *Folia Primatologica* 1(3–4): 178–187.

Zaramody, A. and Pastorini, J. 2001. Indications for hybridization between red-fronted lemurs (*Eulemur fulvus rufus*) and mongoose lemurs (*E. mongoz*) in northwest Madagascar. *Lemur News* (6): 28–31.

Zaramody, A., Andriaholinirina, N., Rousset, D. and Rabarivola, C. 2005. Nouvelle répartition respective de *Lepilemur microdon* et *L. mustelinus*, et de *L. ruficaudatus* et *L. edwardsi*. *Lemur News* (10): 19–20.

Zaramody, A., Fausser, J.-L., Roos, C., Zinner, D., Andriaholinirina, N., Rabarivola, C., Norscia, I., Tattersall, I. and Rumpler, Y. 2006. Molecular phylogeny and taxonomic revision of the eastern woolly lemurs (*Avahi laniger*). *Primate Report* 74: 9–23.

Zeeve, S. and Porton, I. 1997. Zoo-based conservation of Malagasy prosimians. Pp.83-95 in: J. Wallis (ed.), *Primate Conservation: The Role of Zoological Parks*. American Society of Primatologists, Norman, OK.

ZICOMA. 1999. *Les Zones d'Importance pour la Conservation des Oiseaux à Madagascar*. Antananarivo, Madagascar.

Zimmermann, E. 1998. Waldgeister der Tropen-die nachtaktiven Lemuren Madagaskars. *Biologie in unserer Zeit* 5: 294–303.

Zimmermann, E. and Hafen, T. G. 2001. Colony specificity in a social call of mouse lemurs (*Microcebus* spp.). *American Journal of Primatology* 54(3): 129–141.

Zimmermann, E. and Lerch, C. 1993. The complex acoustic design of an advertisement call in male mouse lemurs (*Microcebus murinus*, Prosimii, Primates) and sources of variation. *Ethology* 93(3): 211–224.

Zimmermann, E., Ehresmann, P., Zietemann, V., Radespiel, U., Randrianambinina, B. and Rakotoarsioan, N. 1997. A new primate species in north-western Madagascar: the golden-brown mouse lemur (*Microcebus ravelobensis*). *Primate Eye* (63): 26–27. Abstract.

Zimmermann, E., Cepok, S., Rakotoarison, N., Zietemann, V. and Radespiel, U. 1998. Sympatric mouse lemurs in north-west Madagascar: A new rufous mouse lemur species (*Microcebus ravelobensis*). *Folia Primatologica* 69(2): 106–114.

Zimmermann, E., Vorobieva, E., Wrogemann, D. and Hafen, T. 2000. Use of vocal fingerprinting for specific discrimination of gray (*Microcebus murinus*) and rufous mouse lemurs (*Microcebus rufus*). *International Journal of Primatology* 21(5): 837–852.

Zinner, D., Ostner, J., Dill, A., Razafimanantsoa, L. and Rasoloarison, R. 2001. Results of a reconnaissance expedition in the western dry forests between Morondava and Morombe. *Lemur News* (6): 16–18.

Zinner, D., Hilgartner, R. D., Kappeler, P. M., Pietsch, T., and Ganzhorn, J. U. 2003. Social organization of *Lepilemur ruficaudatus*. *International Journal of Primatology* 24(4): 869–888.

Zinner, D., Roos, C. Fausser, J-L., Groves, C. and Rumpler, Y. 2007. Disputed taxonomy classification of sportive lemurs (*Lepilemur*) in NW Madagascar. *Lemur News* (12): 53–56.

YOUR PERSONAL LEMUR LIFE-LIST

Scientific Name	Locality	Date
Microcebus murinus		
Microcebus griseorufus		
Microcebus berthae		
Microcebus myoxinus		
Microcebus ravelobensis		
Microcebus bongolavensis		
Microcebus danfossi		
Microcebus margotmarshae		
Microcebus sambiranensis		
Microcebus mamiratra		
Microcebus tavaratra		
Microcebus arnholdi		
Microcebus rufus		
Microcebus jollyae		
Microcebus lehilahytsara		
Microcebus simmonsi		
Microcebus macarthurii		
Microcebus mittermeieri		
Mirza coquereli		
Mirza zaza		
Allocebus trichotis		
Cheirogaleus medius		
Cheirogaleus sibreei		
Cheirogaleus major		

Scientific Name	Locality	Date
Cheirogaleus crossleyi		
Cheirogaleus minusculus		
Phaner furcifer		
Phaner pallescens		
Phaner parienti		
Phaner electromontis		
Lepilemur mustelinus		
Lepilemur betsileo		
Lepilemur microdon		
Lepilemur jamesorum		
Lepilemur wrightae		
Lepilemur fleuretae		
Lepilemur hollandorum		
Lepilemur seali		
Lepilemur scottorum		
Lepilemur milanoii		
Lepilemur ankaranensis		
Lepilemur septentrionalis		
Lepilemur dorsalis		
Lepilemur tymerlachsonorum		
Lepilemur mittermeieri		
Lepilemur sahamalazensis		
Lepilemur grewcockorum		
Lepilemur otto		
Lepilemur edwardsi		
Lepilemur aeeclis		
Lepilemur ahmansonorum		

Scientific Name	Locality	Date
Lepilemur petteri		
Lepilemur randrianasoloi		
Lepilemur ruficaudatus		
Lepilemur hubbardorum		
Lepilemur leucopus		
Hapalemur griseus gilberti		
Hapalemur griseus griseus		
Hapalemur griseus ranomafanensis		
Hapalemur meridionalis		
Hapalemur occidentalis		
Hapalemur alaotrensis		
Hapalemur aureus		
Prolemur simus		
Lemur catta		
Eulemur fulvus		
Eulemur rufus		
Eulemur rufifrons		
Eulemur albifrons		
Eulemur sanfordi		
Eulemur cinereiceps		
Eulemur collaris		
Eulemur macaco		
Eulemur flavifrons		
Eulemur coronatus		
Eulemur rubriventer		
Eulemur mongoz		

Scientific Name	Locality	Date
Varecia variegata variegata		
Varecia variegata editorum		
Varecia variegata subcincta		
Varecia rubra		
Avahi laniger		
Avahi mooreorum		
Avahi peyrierasi		
Avahi betsileo		
Avahi ramanantsoavanai		
Avahi meridionalis		
Avahi occidentalis		
Avahi cleesei		
Avahi unicolor		
Propithecus verreauxi		
Propithecus deckenii		
Propithecus coronatus		
Propithecus coquereli		
Propithecus tattersalli		
Propithecus diadema		
Propithecus edwardsi		
Propithecus candidus		
Propithecus perrieri		
Indri indri		
Daubentonia madagascariensis		

* The date given for each species indicates the first-ever time each was observed in the wild. Subsequent sightings are not listed.

NOTES

NOTES

NOTES

REQUESTS FOR INFORMATION

As indicated in the "How to Use This Field Guide" section, we would welcome hearing from you if you see lemurs in unusual places or in unusual circumstances. If you think you have seen something of scientific value, please contact one of us at the addresses below. You may have made an observation worthy of publication in *Lemur News*, the newsletter of the IUCN/SSC Primate Specialist Group's Madagascar Section, or another primatological journal. Of particular interest are the following kinds of data:

1. Lemur sightings outside the geographical ranges given in this book (please provide place names and GPS coordinates where possible).

2. Photographs or videotape of the animal(s) sighted to assist us in confirming identifications.

3. Cases in which lemurs have been kept as pets, or captured or shot for food. This would include situations in which lemurs or lemur body parts (skins, meat, skulls, etc.) are being sold in markets or shops, or are being kept in private homes (again, photographs would be helpful).

4. Sites not mentioned in this book where lemurs are especially abundant or where observation conditions are particularly good. We would like to add such sites to future editions of this guide.

5. Any other information that you think might be useful in improving our knowledge of lemur biology and conservation.

Please write to:

Russell A. Mittermeier, President, Conservation International, 2011 Crystal Drive, Suite 500, Arlington, VA 22202, USA
E-mail: r.mittermeier@conservation.org

Edward E. Louis Jr., Henry Doorly Zoo, 3701 South 10th Street, Omaha, NB 68107–2200, USA
E-mail: edlo@omahazoo.com

Matthew Richardson, c/o Conservation International, 2011 Crystal Drive, Arlington, VA 22202, USA
E-mail: livingprimates@hotmail.com

Christoph Schwitzer, Head of Research, Bristol Conservation and Science Foundation, Bristol Zoo Gardens, Clifton, Bristol BS8 3HA, UK
E-mail: cschwitzer@bristolzoo.org.uk

Olivier Langrand, Executive Vice-President for Conservation International, 2011 Crystal Drive, Arlington, VA 22202, USA
E-mail: o.langrand@conservation.org

Frank Hawkins, Vice President, Africa and Madagascar Division, Conservation International, 2011 Crystal Drive, Arlington, VA 22202, USA
E-mail: f.hawkins@conservation.org

Serge Rajaobelina, President, Fanamby, LOT IIK 40 Ankadivato, Antananarivo 101, Madagascar
E-mail: s.rajaobelina@fanamby.org.mg

Jonah Ratsimbazafy, Training and Conservation Coordinator, Durrell Madagascar Programme, B. P. 8511, Antananarivo 101, Madagascar
E-mail: jonah.ratsimbazafy@durrell.org

Rodin Rasoloarison, Laboratoire de Palaeontologie, Université d'Antananarivo, B. P. 906, Antananarivo 101, Madagascar
E-mail: rmrasoloarison@yahoo.fr

Christian Roos, Primate Genetics Laboratory, German Primate Center, Kellnerweg 4, 37077 Göttingen, Germany
E-mail: croos@dpz.eu

Peter M. Kappeler, Department of Sociobiology/Anthropology, University of Göttingen, Kellnerweg 6, D–37077, Göttingen, Germany
E-mail: pkappel@gwde.de

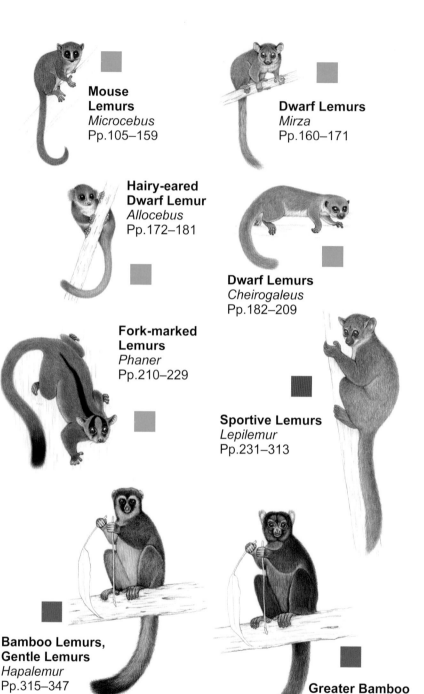

Cheirogaleidae

Lepilemuridae

Lemuridae

Indriidae

**Mouse
Lemurs**
Microcebus
Pp.105–159

Dwarf Lemurs
Mirza
Pp.160–171

**Hairy-eared
Dwarf Lemur**
Allocebus
Pp.172–181

Dwarf Lemurs
Cheirogaleus
Pp.182–209

**Fork-marked
Lemurs**
Phaner
Pp.210–229

Sportive Lemurs
Lepilemur
Pp.231–313

**Bamboo Lemurs,
Gentle Lemurs**
Hapalemur
Pp.315–347

**Greater Bamboo
Lemur**
Prolemur
Pp.348–357